MEDALLION EDITION · AMERICA READS

PURPOSE in Literature

MEDALLION EDITION · AMERICA READS

PURPOSE in Literature
Edmund J. Farrell
Ruth S. Cohen
L. Jane Christensen
H. Keith Wright

LITERATURE and LIFE
Helen McDonnell
Ruth S. Cohen
Thomas Gage
Alan L. Madsen

ARRANGEMENT in Literature
Edmund J. Farrell
Ouida H. Clapp
James L. Pierce
Raymond J. Rodrigues

QUESTION and FORM in Literature
James E. Miller, Jr.
Roseann Dueñas Gonzalez
Nancy C. Millett

UNITED STATES in Literature
James E. Miller, Jr.
Carlota Cárdenas de Dwyer
Robert Hayden
Russell J. Hogan
Kerry M. Wood

ENGLAND in Literature
Helen McDonnell
Neil E. Nakadate
John Pfordresher
Thomas E. Shoemate

MEDALLION EDITION • AMERICA READS

PURPOSE in Literature

Edmund J. Farrell

Ruth S. Cohen

L. Jane Christensen

H. Keith Wright

Scott, Foresman and Company

Editorial Offices: Glenview, Illinois

Regional Sales Offices: Palo Alto, California •
Tucker, Georgia • Glenview, Illinois •
Oakland, New Jersey • Dallas, Texas

EDMUND J. FARRELL Professor, English Education, University of Texas, Austin. Formerly Associate Executive Director for the National Council of Teachers of English, Supervisor of Secondary English, University of California, Berkeley, Chairman of English, James Lick High School, San Jose, California. Past President of both the Central California Council of Teachers of English and the California Association of Teachers of English.

RUTH S. COHEN Free-lance writer and editor of books for young people. Author on the *Signal* Program, Scott, Foresman and Company. Editor-Compiler of *Craft of Detection, The Life Force, Present Imperfect, Edges of Reality,* and *The Fractured Image,* collections of shorter long fiction selections.

L. JANE CHRISTENSEN Chairman of the Language Arts Department at Everitt Junior High School in Jefferson County, Colorado. Consultant for workshops and seminars on the teaching of composition and humanities. Formerly member of the National Council of Teachers of English Commission on the English Curriculum, the Committee to Review Affiliate Publications, and the Committee for Publication of *Your Reading,* a junior-high booklist.

H. KEITH WRIGHT Manager of Special Programs for the Yakima Public Schools in Yakima, Washington. Formerly teacher of English at Central Washington State College, Ellensburg, and Western Washington State College, Bellingham. Formerly member of the Board of Directors of the Secondary Section of both the National Council of Teachers of English and the Washington State Council of Teachers of English.

ISBN: 0-673-12930-6

Copyright © 1982, 1979
Scott, Foresman and Company, Glenview, Illinois.
All Rights Reserved.
Printed in the United States of America.

345678910-RRW-9089888786858483

Contents

Unit **1**

Encounters

2	**Say It with Flowers** by Toshio Mori
10	**Speed Adjustments** by John Ciardi
12	**The Circuit** by Francisco Jiménez
17	Notes and Comments: *The Story Behind the Story* by Francisco Jiménez
18	**The Sidewalk Racer** by Lillian Morrison
19	**The Birdman** by Mari Sandoz
24	**I'll Give You Law** by Molly Picon
29	**old age sticks** by E. E. Cummings
30	**Mirror of Ice** by Gary Wright
38	**The Gift** by John Steinbeck

Unit Review/Tests

60	Review
60	Test I, **Stolen Day** by Sherwood Anderson
65	Test II, Composition

Unit 2

Insights

	68	**A Man Who Had No Eyes** by MacKinlay Kantor
	72	**Last Cover** by Paul Annixter
	80	**The Fox and the Grapes** by Marianne Moore
	81	**A Time of Greatness** by Dorothy Johnson
	94	**Two Songs** by Uvavnuk
	96	**Let Me Hear You Whisper** by Paul Zindel
	109	Notes and Comments: *If Dolphins Could Talk, What Would They Say?*
	110	**A Haircut** by I. S. Nakata
	114	**Win or Lose** by Brian Glanville
Unit Review/Tests	**122**	Review
	122	Test I, **The Conjurer's Revenge** by Stephen Leacock
	125	Test II, Composition

Unit 3

The Outsider

	128	**The Baroque Marble** by E. A. Proulx
	138	**I'm Nobody** by Emily Dickinson
	139	Notes and Comments: *Too Modern for Her Time*
	140	**Nancy** by Elizabeth Enright
	153	**Hunger** by Richard Wright
	157	**A Loud Sneer for Our Feathered Friends** by Ruth McKenney
	163	**Sarah Cynthia Sylvia Stout Would Not Take the Garbage Out** by Shel Silverstein

	166	**Moving Camp Too Far** by Nila Northsun
	167	Notes and Comments: *Between Two Cultures*
	168	**Beauty Is Truth** by Anna Guest
	175	**in the inner city** by Lucille Clifton
	176	**My True Name** by Laurence Yep
	186	**Identity** by Julio Noboa, Jr.
Unit Review/Tests	188	Review
	188	Test I, **The Nomad Harvesters** by Marie de L. Welch
	189	Test II, Composition

Unit 4

Heroes

	192	**Where the Girl Saved Her Brother** by Strange Owl
	196	**Caught in a Grip of Stone** by Jack Markowitz
	206	Notes and Comments: *The Carnegie Hero Fund*
	207	from **Harriet Tubman** by Ann Petry
	216	**The Campers at Kitty Hawk** by John Dos Passos
	224	**Being Somebody** by Francene Sabin
	233	**The Pharmacist's Mate** by Budd Schulberg
	260	Notes and Comments: *Emergency at Sea* by George Weller
	262	**The Old Demon** by Pearl S. Buck
Unit Review/Tests	272	Review
	272	Test I, **Nobody's Better Off Dead** by Quentin Reynolds
	275	Test II, Composition

Unit 5

The Adventures of Ulysses

278   *Introduction*

280-353   **The Adventures of Ulysses** by Bernard Evslin

280   Ships and Men

281   The Ciconians

284   Notes and Comments: *Uncovering the Real Troy*

285   The Lotus-Eaters

287   The Cyclops's Cave

293   Keeper of the Winds

298   Circe

308   Map: *The Voyages of Ulysses*

310   *Glossary of Proper Names*

312   The Land of the Dead

317   The Sirens

319   Scylla and Charybdis

321   The Cattle of the Sun

325   Calypso

332   Notes and Comments: *English Borrowings from Greek*

333   Ino's Veil

335   Nausicaa

342   The Return

Unit Review/Tests   357   Review

357   Test I, **An Ancient Gesture** by Edna St. Vincent Millay

359   Test II, Composition: **Penelope** by Dorothy Parker

Unit 6

Yesterday, Today, Tomorrow

362   **The Hundredth Dove** by Jane Yolen

366   **Jabberwocky** by Lewis Carroll

367   Notes and Comments: *Glossary of Jabberwocky Terms*

368   **Rikki-tikki-tavi** by Rudyard Kipling

380   **Macavity: The Mystery Cat** by T. S. Eliot

382   **The Storyteller** by H. H. Munro

388   **Where the Sidewalk Ends** by Shel Silverstein

389   Notes and Comments: *You're Imagining Things*

390   **Get That Straight** by Sabine Ulibarri

396   **Virtuoso** by Herbert Goldstone

402   **The Fallen Angel** by Evan Hunter

413   **The Monsters Are Due on Maple Street** by Rod Serling

427   Notes and Comments: *Questions Put to a Playwright*

Unit Review/Tests   428   Review

428   Test I, **Key Item** by Isaac Asimov

431   Test II, Composition

Unit 7

Poetry

Section 1	434	**Kidnap Poem** by Nikki Giovanni
	435	**The Hunter** by Ogden Nash
	436	**To a Dead Goldfish** by O. B. Hardison, Jr.
	437	**Business** by Victor Hernández Cruz
	438	**The Contraption** by May Swenson
	440	**The Demon of the Gibbet** by Fitz-James O'Brien
	442	**The Builders** by Sara Henderson Hay
	444	Notes and Comments: *It Doesn't Have to Rhyme*
	445	**Visits** by Vern Rutsala
Section 2	447	**who knows if the moon's** by E. E. Cummings
	448	**Words** by Pauli Murray
	449	**Under the Mistletoe** by Countee Cullen
	450	**I Know That Feeling** by Simon Ortiz
	451	**Portrait** by Carolyn Rodgers
	452	**Street Window** by Carl Sandburg
	454	**The Forecast** by Dan Jaffe
	456	Notes and Comments: *It Says a Lot in a Little*
	457	**Apparently with No Surprise** by Emily Dickinson
Section 3	458	**The Pasture** by Robert Frost
	459	**The Chipmunk's Day** by Randall Jarrell
	460	**Woodpeckers in Summer Frolic** by David Nava Monreal
	461	**Rain** by Ross Parmenter
	462	**Song of the Sky Loom** (Tewa Indian)
	463	**after any sunset** by Mary Celinia Bruce
Unit Review/Tests	464	Review
	464	Test I, **Farewell** by Liz Sohappy Bahe
	465	Test II, Composition

Unit 8

Affinities

468   **A Few Notes About the Arabian Oryx**
by Paul Darcy Boles

480   **Mama Is a Sunrise** by Evelyn Tooley Hunt

481   **While I Slept** by Robert Francis

482   **My Father and the Hippopotamus** by Leon Hugo

490   **The River Took My Sister** by Shirley Crawford

491   **Who Am I?** by Felice Holman

492   **Gentleman of Río en Medio** by Juan A. A. Sedillo

496   **I Am Through** by Nguyen Trai

497   **A Time To Talk** by Robert Frost

498   **Teacher, Teacher** by Ellison Carroll

526   Notes and Comments: *Able Though Disabled*

Unit Review/Tests   527   Review

527   Test I, **The Hummingbird That Lived Through Winter**
by William Saroyan

530   Test II, Composition

Handbook
of
Literary
Terms

531

532 from **National Velvet** by Enid Bagnold

534 **What Could It Be?** by William Cole

535 from **The Wind** by Robert Louis Stevenson

536 from **The Apprentice** by Dorothy Canfield Fisher

538 **Foreign Student** by Barbara B. Robinson

540 from **Roll of Thunder, Hear My Cry** by Mildred Taylor

542 **Washed in Silver** by James Stephens

543 **The Rich Man** by Franklin P. Adams

544 **Broken Sky** by Carl Sandburg

544 **Metaphor** by Eve Merriam

546 **Take Over, Bos'n** by Oscar Schisgall

550 **Minnie Morse** by Kaye Starbird

551 **Beetle Bemused** by R. P. Lister

552 from **The Wreck of the Hesperus**
by Henry Wadsworth Longfellow

552 **The White Seal's Lullaby** by Rudyard Kipling

553 **Trees and Evening Sky** by N. Scott Momaday

555 **Simile: Willow and Ginkgo** by Eve Merriam

559 **For an Old Man** by Floris Clark McLaren

560 from **To a Small Boy Standing on My Shoes While
I Am Wearing Them** by Ogden Nash

561 Pronunciation Key

562 Glossary

590 Index of Extensions (Reading, Speaking, Writing)

590 Index of Vocabulary Exercises

590 Index of Authors and Titles

PURPOSE in Literature

Meet people face to face with

the threat of sudden death,

the loss of something always desired,

the choice between honesty and dishonesty,

the surprise of new-found riches.

Meet people whose lives are affected by these

and other **ENCOUNTERS**

1

"Why don't you do as you're told?"
the boss asked, and the others wondered
how long the new clerk could keep his job
if he didn't play by the rules.

Say It with Flowers

Toshio Mori

He was a weird one to come to the shop and ask Mr. Sasaki[1] for a job, but at the time I kept my mouth shut. There was something about this young man's appearance which I could not altogether harmonize with a job as a clerk in a flower shop. I was a delivery boy for Mr. Sasaki then. I had seen clerks come and go, and although they were of various sorts of temperaments and conducts, all of them had the technique of waiting on the customers or acquired one eventually. You could never tell about a new one, however, and to be on the safe side I said nothing and watched our boss readily take on this young man. Anyhow we were glad to have an extra hand because the busy season was coming around.

Mr. Sasaki undoubtedly remembered last year's rush when Tommy, Mr. Sasaki and I had to do everything and had our hands tied behind our backs from having so many things to do at one time. He wanted to be ready this time. "Another clerk and we'll be all set for any kind of business," he used to tell us. When Teruo[2] came around looking for a job, he got it, and Morning Glory Flower Shop was all set for the year as far as our boss was concerned.

When Teruo reported for work the following morning Mr. Sasaki left him in Tommy's hands. Tommy had been our number one clerk for a long time.

"Tommy, teach him all you can," Mr. Sasaki said. "Teruo's going to be with us from now on."

"Sure," Tommy said.

"Tommy's a good florist. You watch and listen to him," the boss told the young man.

"Say It with Flowers" from *Yokohama, California* by Toshio Mori. Copyright 1949 by The Caxton Printers, Ltd. Reprinted by permission.

Toshio Mori (tō shē ō môr ē).

1. *Sasaki* (sä sä kē).

2. *Teruo* (te rü ō).

"All right, Mr. Sasaki," the young man said. He turned to us and said, "My name is Teruo." We shook hands.

We got to know one another pretty well after that. He was a quiet fellow with very little words for anybody, but his smile disarmed a person. We soon learned that he knew nothing about the florist business. He could identify a rose when he saw one, and gardenias and carnations too; but other flowers and materials were new to him.

"You fellows teach me something about this business and I'll be grateful. I want to start from the bottom," Teruo said.

Tommy and I nodded. We were pretty sure by then he was all right. Tommy eagerly went about showing Teruo the florist game. Every morning for several days Tommy repeated the prices of the flowers for him. He told Teruo what to do on telephone orders; how to keep the greens fresh; how to make bouquets, corsages, and sprays. "You need a little more time to learn how to make big funeral pieces," Tommy said. "That'll come later."

In a couple of weeks Teruo was just as good a clerk as we had had in a long time. He was curious almost to a fault, and was a glutton for work. It was about this time our boss decided to move ahead his yearly business trip to Seattle. Undoubtedly he was satisfied with Teruo, and he knew we could get along without him for a while. He went off and left Tommy in full charge.

During Mr. Sasaki's absence I was often in the shop helping Tommy and Teruo with the customers and the orders. One day Teruo learned that I once worked in the nursery and had experience in flower-growing.

"How do you tell when a flower is fresh or old?" he asked me. "I can't tell one from the other. All I do is follow your instructions

and sell the ones you tell me to sell first, but I can't tell one from the other."

I laughed. "You don't need to know that, Teruo," I told him. "When the customers ask you whether the flowers are fresh, say yes firmly. 'Our flowers are always fresh, madam.' "

Teruo picked up a vase of carnations. "These flowers came in four or five days ago, didn't they?" he asked me.

"You're right. Five days ago," I said.

"How long will they keep if a customer bought them today?" Teruo asked.

"I guess in this weather they'll hold a day or two," I said.

"Then they're old," Teruo almost gasped. "Why, we have fresh ones that last a week or so in the shop."

"Sure, Teruo. And why should you worry about that?" Tommy said. "You talk right to the customers and they'll believe you. 'Our flowers are always fresh? You bet they are! Just came in a little while ago from the market.' "

Teruo looked at us calmly. "That's a hard thing to say when you know it isn't true."

"You've got to get it over with sooner or later," I told him. "Everybody has to do it. You too, unless you want to lose your job."

"I don't think I can say it convincingly again," Teruo said. "I must've said yes forty times already when I didn't know any better. It'll be harder next time."

"You've said it forty times already so why can't you say yes forty million times more? What's the difference? Remember, Teruo, it's your business to live," Tommy said.

"I don't like it," Teruo said.

"Do we like it? Do you think we're any different from you?" Tommy asked Teruo. "You're just a green kid. You don't know any better so I don't get sore, but you got to play the game when you're in it. You understand, don't you?"

Teruo nodded. For a moment he stood and looked curiously at us for the first time, and then went away to water the potted plants.

In the ensuing weeks we watched Teruo develop into a slick salesclerk but for one thing. If a customer forgot to ask about the condition of the flowers Teruo did splendidly. But if someone should mention about the freshness of the flowers he wilted right in front of the customers. Sometimes he would splutter. He would stand gaping speechless on other occasions without a comeback. Sometimes, looking embarrassedly at us, he would take the customers to the fresh flowers in the rear and complete the sales.

"Don't do that any more, Teruo," Tommy warned him one afternoon after watching him repeatedly sell the fresh ones. "You know we got plenty of the old stuff in the front. We can't throw all that stuff away. First thing you know the boss'll start losing money and we'll all be thrown out."

"I wish I could sell like you," Teruo said. "Whenever they ask me, 'Is this fresh?' 'How long will it keep?' I lose all sense about selling the stuff, and begin to think of the difference between the fresh and the old stuff. Then the trouble begins."

"Remember, the boss has to run the shop so he can keep it going," Tommy told him. "When he returns next week you better not let him see you touch the fresh flowers in the rear."

On the day Mr. Sasaki came back to the shop we saw something unusual. For the first time I watched Teruo sell some old stuff to a customer. I heard the man plainly ask him if the flowers would keep good, and very clearly I heard Teruo reply, "Yes, sir. These flowers'll keep good." I looked at Tommy,

and he winked back. When Teruo came back to make it into a bouquet he looked as if he had a snail in his mouth. Mr. Sasaki came back to the rear and watched him make the bouquet. When Teruo went up front to complete the sale Mr. Sasaki looked at Tommy and nodded approvingly.

When I went out to the truck to make my last delivery for the day Teruo followed me. "Gee, I feel rotten," he said to me. "Those flowers I sold to the people, they won't last longer than tomorrow. I feel lousy. I'm lousy. The people'll get to know my word pretty soon."

"Forget it," I said. "Quit worrying. What's the matter with you?"

"I'm lousy," he said, and went back to the store.

Then one early morning the inevitable happened. While Teruo was selling the fresh flowers in the back to a customer Mr. Sasaki came in quietly and watched the transaction. The boss didn't say anything at the time. All day Teruo looked sick. He didn't know whether to explain to the boss or shut up.

While Teruo was out to lunch Mr. Sasaki called us aside. "How long has this been going on?" he asked us. He was pretty sore.

"He's been doing it off and on. We told him to quit it," Tommy said. "He says he feels rotten selling old flowers."

"Old flowers!" snorted Mr. Sasaki. "I'll tell him plenty when he comes back. Old flowers! Maybe you can call them old at the wholesale market but they're not old in a flower shop."

"He feels guilty fooling the customers," Tommy explained.

The boss laughed impatiently. "That's no reason for a businessman."

When Teruo came back he knew what was up. He looked at us for a moment and then went about cleaning the stems of the old flowers.

"Teruo," Mr. Sasaki called.

Teruo approached us as if steeled for an attack.

"You've been selling fresh flowers and leaving the old ones go to waste. I can't afford that, Teruo," Mr. Sasaki said. "Why don't you do as you're told? We all sell the flowers in the front. I tell you they're not old in a flower shop. Why can't you sell them?"

"I don't like it, Mr. Sasaki," Teruo said. "When the people ask me if they're fresh I hate to answer. I feel rotten after selling the old ones."

"Look here, Teruo," Mr. Sasaki said. "I don't want to fire you. You're a good boy, and I know you need a job, but you've got to be a good clerk here or you're going out. Do you get me?"

"I get you," Teruo said.

In the morning we were all at the shop early. I had an eight o'clock delivery, and the others had to rush with a big funeral order. Teruo was there early. "Hello," he greeted us cheerfully as we came in. He was unusually high-spirited, and I couldn't account for it. He was there before us and had already filled out the eight o'clock package for me. He was almost through with the funeral frame, padding it with wet moss and covering all over with brake fern, when Tommy came in. When Mr. Sasaki arrived, Teruo waved his hand and cheerfully went about gathering the flowers for the funeral piece. As he flitted here and there he seemed as if he had forgotten our presence, even the boss. He looked at each vase, sized up the flowers, and then cocked his head at the next one. He did this with great deliberation, as if he were the boss and the last word in the shop. That was all right, but when a cus-

tomer soon came in, he swiftly attended him as if he owned all the flowers in the world. When the man asked Teruo if he was getting fresh flowers Teruo without batting an eye escorted the customer into the rear and eventually showed and sold the fresh ones. He did it with so much grace, dignity and swiftness that we stood around like his stooges. However, Mr. Sasaki went on with his work as if nothing had happened.

Along toward noon Teruo attended his second customer. He fairly ran to greet an old lady who wanted a cheap bouquet around fifty cents for a dinner table. This time he not only went back to the rear for the fresh ones but added three or four extras. To make it more irritating for the boss, who was watching every move, Teruo used an extra lot of maidenhair because the old lady was appreciative of his art of making bouquets. Tommy and I watched the boss fuming inside of his office.

When the old lady went out of the shop Mr. Sasaki came out furious. "You're a blockhead. You have no business sense. What are you doing here?" he said to Teruo. "Are you crazy?"

Teruo looked cheerful. "I'm not crazy, Mr. Sasaki," he said. "And I'm not dumb. I just like to do it that way, that's all."

The boss turned to Tommy and me. "That boy's a sap," he said. "He's got no head."

Teruo laughed and walked off to the front with a broom. Mr. Sasaki shook his head. "What's the matter with him? I can't understand him," he said.

While the boss was out to lunch Teruo went on a mad spree. He waited on three customers at one time, ignoring our presence. It was amazing how he did it. He hurriedly took one customer's order and had

him write a birthday greeting for it; jumped to the second customer's side and persuaded her to buy Columbia roses because they were the freshest of the lot. She wanted them delivered so he jotted it down on the sales book, and leaped to the third customer.

"I want to buy that orchid in the window," she stated without deliberation.

"Do you have to have orchid, madam?" Teruo asked the lady.

"No," she said. "But I want something nice for tonight's ball, and I think the orchid will match my dress. Why do you ask?"

"If I were you I wouldn't buy that orchid," he told her. "It won't keep. I could sell it to you and make a profit but I don't want to do that and spoil your evening. Come to the back, madam, and I'll show you some of the nicest gardenias in the market today. We call them Belmont and they're fresh today."

He came to the rear with the lady. We watched him pick out three of the biggest gardenias and make them into a corsage. When the lady went out with her package a little boy about eleven years old came in and wanted a twenty-five-cent bouquet for his mother's birthday. Teruo waited on the boy. He was out in the front, and we saw him pick out a dozen of the two-dollar-a-dozen roses and give them to the kid.

Tommy nudged me. "If he was the boss he couldn't do those things," he said.

"In the first place," I said, "I don't think he could be a boss."

"What do you think?" Tommy said. "Is he crazy? Is he trying to get himself fired?"

"I don't know," I said.

When Mr. Sasaki returned, Teruo was waiting on another customer, a young lady.

"Did Teruo eat yet?" Mr. Sasaki asked Tommy.

"No, he won't go. He says he's not hungry today," Tommy said.

We watched Teruo talking to the young lady. The boss shook his head. Then it came. Teruo came back to the rear and picked out a dozen of the very fresh white roses and took them out to the lady.

"Aren't they lovely?" we heard her exclaim.

We watched him come back, take down a box, place several maidenhairs and asparagus, place the roses neatly inside, sprinkle a few drops, and then give it to her. We watched him thank her, and we noticed her smile and thanks. The girl walked out.

Mr. Sasaki ran excitedly to the front. "Teruo! She forgot to pay!"

Teruo stopped the boss on the way out. "Wait, Mr. Sasaki," he said. "I gave it to her."

"What!" the boss cried indignantly.

"She came in just to look around and see the flowers. She likes pretty roses. Don't you think she's wonderful?"

"What's the matter with you?" the boss said. "Are you crazy? What did she buy?"

"Nothing, I tell you," Teruo said. "I gave

it to her because she admired it, and she's pretty enough to deserve beautiful things, and I liked her."

"You're fired! Get out!" Mr. Sasaki spluttered. "Don't come back to the store again."

"And I gave her fresh ones too," Teruo said.

Mr. Sasaki rolled out several bills from his pocketbook. "Here's your wages for this week. Now, get out," he said.

"I don't want it," Teruo said. "You keep it and buy some more flowers."

"Here, take it. Get out," Mr. Sasaki said.

Teruo took the bills and rang up the cash register. "All right, I'll go now. I feel fine. I'm happy. Thanks to you." He waved his hand to Mr. Sasaki. "No hard feelings."

On the way out Teruo remembered our presence. He looked back. "Good-bye. Good luck," he said cheerfully to Tommy and me.

He walked out of the shop with his shoulders straight, head high, and whistling. He did not come back to see us again. □□

Discussion

1. (a) How does Teruo behave when he is first hired as a clerk? (b) What predicament does he face after he learns more about the flower-selling business? (c) From this point on, how do his sales techniques change?

2. (a) What are Mr. Sasaki's reactions when he sees Teruo becoming less and less dependable as a clerk? (b) Do you think these reactions are justified? Why or why not?

3. (a) Trace the changes in attitude of Tommy and the delivery boy toward Teruo. (b) Near the end of the story the delivery boy says about Teruo, "I don't think he could be a boss." What do you think he means to suggest by this statement? (c) Tommy wonders if Teruo is crazy. "Is he trying to get himself fired?" Tommy asks. What has Teruo done to provoke Tommy's question?

4. (a) Do you think Teruo was trying to get himself fired? Explain. (b) How did you react to the manner in which Teruo departed? (c) Would you say

that this story has a happy ending? Why or why not?

Extension • Writing

Teruo has applied for a trainee's job as an elevator-safety inspector. Tommy—as a former co-worker—is asked for a reference as to Teruo's character and qualifications. Write a letter explaining why you, as Tommy, would or would not recommend Teruo for the job.

Vocabulary

These aids can help you understand words you don't know:

CONTEXT: the setting the word appears in; other words or ideas in the sentence, paragraph, or selection.

STRUCTURE: the arrangement and meaning of parts of words (root words and affixes).

PRONUNCIATION: Use the dictionary when you need help with pronunciation.

DICTIONARY: If the meaning can't be determined by using context or structure clues, consult the dictionary.

Throughout this book you will find exercises showing you how to use these aids. The following exercise deals with context.

Vocabulary · Context

Does the word *wound* rhyme with *sound* or *tuned?* Does it mean "injury" or is it a form of the verb "wind"? How could you be sure that the meaning and pronunciation you've given *wound* are correct?

He inflicted the *wound* upon himself when he *wound* the toy.

Which of the italicized words in the sentence above means "injury"? What is the meaning of the other italicized word? Which context clues helped you determine the correct meaning and pronunciation in each case?

When a word has more than one definition or pronunciation, the context in which it appears usually indicates which definition or pronunciation is intended. The context in which an unfamiliar word appears also provides clues to its meaning.

Conrad is a *pusillanimous* boy.

Does the sentence above give you enough clues to the meaning of the italicized word?

Unlike Karl, who is brave, Conrad is *pusillanimous*.

Is Conrad probably fat, cowardly, or near-sighted? Which two words in the sentence are the best clues to its meaning? Could you figure out its pronunciation without a dictionary?

Sometimes the context in which a word appears reveals an unfamiliar word.

My sister and I have had a few *spats* in the last week.

What are *spats*?

There was a picture in the old book of a gentleman wearing *spats*.

What clue to a new meaning of *spats* is given in the above sentence?

In three of the four sentences below you should be able to figure out the meaning of the italicized word from context clues. Read each sentence and complete the statement that follows. In which sentence is there no helpful clue?

1. The clerks were of various kinds of temperaments and *con-*ducts, but all of them had the technique or method of waiting on customers.

Conduct means either "way of acting" or "guide or lead." Which meaning is intended in the sentence above?

2. He was soon as good a clerk as we had had in a long time, and he was a *glutton* for work.

Glutton means: **(a)** person who works very slowly; **(b)** person who never seems to have enough of something; **(c)** person who is not honest in business.

3. He stood waiting as if *steeled* for attack.

Steeled means: **(a)** eager; **(b)** strengthened; **(c)** no helpful clue.

4. He cheerfully offered the customer his arm and *escorted* her into the rear where he showed her the fresh flowers.

Escorted means: **(a)** went with; **(b)** locked; **(c)** chased.

Toshio Mori 1910 ·

Toshio Mori has been writing seriously ever since he gave up a career in professional baseball as a young man. He has written four novels and has published a collection of short stories entitled *Yokohama, California*, about life in Oakland and San Leandro during the 1920s and '30s.

Have you ever encountered a two-speed person like John?

Speed Adjustments

John Ciardi

A man stopped by and he wanted to know
Why my son John had become so slow.

I looked out the window and there was John
Running so fast he had been and gone
5 Before I saw him. "Look at him go!"
I said to the man. "Do you call *that* slow?"

"He seems to be fast when he wants to be,"
The man said. "He appears to be
One of those two-speed boys. You know—
10 Sometimes fast, and sometimes slow,
He can run a mile in nothing flat.
He can run right out from under his hat
When there's nowhere, really, to go. And yet
That very same boy that's as fast as a jet
15 Will take all day—and sometimes two—
To get to school. I'm sure that you
Send him to school. But yesterday
He didn't arrive. And all he would say
Was, yes, he started at half-past eight
20 But it took so long he got there late."

"How late?" said I.
                    Said the man, "A day."

"I see," said I, "and I think I can say
He won't be late again. He needs
A little adjustment of his speeds,
25 And I'm sure I know the place to adjust."

"Well, then," said he, "that's that, and I must
Be on my way."
                "Thank you," said I.
"If you see John as you go by
Would you be so good as to send him in?

30 There is never a better time to begin
A speed adjustment than right away."

"Agreed, and I will," said the man.
        "Good day."
And just a few minutes after that
In came John and down he sat:
35 "You wanted to see me, I understand?"
"I did and I do. But you'll have to stand—
At least at first—for what I need.
I'm going to have to adjust your speed.
And when I'm through adjusting it,
40 I think you won't much care to sit.
Do you know what I mean?"
                        "Oh, oh," said he,
"I'm afraid I do. Is it going to be
Terribly long before you're through?"

"Why, not at all," said I. "Like you,
45 I can be speedy sometimes, too."

And soon after that his speed was adjusted.
And also the seat of his pants was dusted.
It was busy work, but it didn't take long,
Though I double-checked as I went along
50 Just to make sure there was nothing wrong.
And whatever *was* wrong, I set it straight,
For since that time he hasn't been late.

Scott, Foresman and Company Staff

Discussion

1. When is John fast and when is he slow?

2. How does his father adjust his speed?

3. Do you think his father's method is the best one? Explain.

John Ciardi

The truant officer didn't really come by to check on John Ciardi's son. Instead, Ciardi says that he began this poem ". . . as a joke about him, and probably to remind him that he is fast about what he likes to do and slow about what I want him to do, and that I intend to speed him up a bit about what I want him to do."

The Boston-born poet serves as a contributing editor for *Saturday Review*. He is a nationally popular lecturer on poets and poetry.

It was that time of year.
Everything was neatly packed—again.

The Circuit

Francisco Jiménez

It was that time of year again. Ito, the strawberry sharecropper, did not smile. It was natural. The peak of the strawberry season was over and the last few days the workers, most of them *braceros*,[1] were not picking as many boxes as they had during the months of June and July.

As the last days of August disappeared, so did the number of braceros. Sunday, only one—the best picker—came to work. I liked him. Sometimes we talked during our half-hour lunch break. That is how I found out he was from Jalisco,[2] the same state in Mexico

my family was from. That Sunday was the last time I saw him.

When the sun had tired and sunk behind the mountains, Ito signaled us that it was time to go home. *"Ya esora,"*[3] he yelled in his broken Spanish. Those were the words I

"The Circuit" by Francisco Jiménez from *The Arizona Quarterly*, Autumn 1973. Copyright © 1973 by The Arizona Quarterly. Reprinted by permission.

Francisco Jiménez (frän sēs′kō hē mā′nes).

1. *braceros* (brä sä′rōs), Mexicans allowed to enter the United States to do farm work.
2. *Jalisco* (hä lēs′kō).
3. *Ya esora* (yä äs ô′rä), a contraction of *ya es la hora*, which means "Now it's time."

waited for twelve hours a day, everyday, seven days a week, week after week. And the thought of not hearing them again saddened me.

As we drove home Papa did not say a word. With both hands on the wheel, he stared at the dirt road. My older brother, Roberto, was also silent. He leaned his head back and closed his eyes. Once in a while he cleared from his throat the dust that blew in from outside.

Yes, it was that time of year. When I opened the front door to the shack, I stopped. Everything we owned was neatly packed in cardboard boxes. Suddenly I felt even more the weight of hours, days, weeks, and months of work. I sat down on a box. The thought of having to move to Fresno and knowing what was in store for me there brought tears to my eyes.

That night I could not sleep. I lay in bed thinking about how much I hated this move.

A little before five o'clock in the morning, Papa woke everyone up. A few minutes later, the yelling and screaming of my little brothers and sisters, for whom the move was a great adventure, broke the silence of dawn. Shortly, the barking of the dogs accompanied them.

While we packed the breakfast dishes, Papa went outside to start the "Carcanchita." That was the name Papa gave his old '38 black Plymouth. He bought it in a used-car lot in Santa Rosa in the winter of 1949. Papa was very proud of his car. *"Mi Carcanchita,"*[4] my little jalopy, he called it. He had a right to be proud of it. He spent a lot of time looking at other cars before buying this one. When he finally chose the "Carcanchita," he checked it thoroughly before driving it out of the car lot. He examined every inch of the car. He listened to the motor, tilting his head from side to side like a parrot, trying to detect any noises that spelled car trouble. After being satisfied with the looks and sounds of the car, Papa then insisted on knowing who the original owner was. He never did find out from the car salesman. But he bought the car anyway. Papa figured the original owner must have been an important man because behind the rear seat of the car he found a blue necktie.

Papa parked the car out in front and left the motor running. *"Listo"*[5] (ready), he yelled. Without saying a word, Roberto and I began to carry the boxes out to the car. Roberto carried the two big boxes and I carried the two smaller ones. Papa then threw the mattress on top of the car roof and tied it with ropes to the front and rear bumpers.

Everything was packed except Mama's pot. It was an old large galvanized pot she had picked up at an army surplus store in Santa Maria the year I was born. The pot was full of dents and nicks, and the more dents and nicks it had, the more Mama liked it. *"Mi olla"*[6] (my pot), she used to say proudly.

I held the front door open as Mama carefully carried out her pot by both handles, making sure not to spill the cooked beans. When she got to the car, Papa reached out to help her with it. Roberto opened the rear car door and Papa gently placed it on the floor behind the front seat. All of us then climbed in. Papa sighed, wiped the sweat off his forehead with his sleeve, and said wearily: *"Es todo"*[7] (that's it).

As we drove away, I felt a lump in my throat. I turned around and looked at our little shack for the last time.

At sunset we drove into a labor camp near Fresno. Since Papa did not speak English, Mama asked the camp foreman if he needed any more workers. "We don't need no more," said the foreman, scratching his head. "Check with Sullivan down the road. Can't miss him. He lives in a big white house with a fence around it."

When we got there, Mama walked up to the house. She went through a white gate, past a row of rose bushes, up the stairs to the front door. She rang the doorbell. The porch light went on and a tall husky man came out. They exchanged a few words. After the man went in, Mama clasped her hands and hurried back to the car. "We have work! Mr. Sullivan said we can stay there the whole season," she said gasping and pointing to an old garage near the stables.

The garage was worn out by the years. It had no windows. The walls, eaten by termites, strained to support the roof full of holes. The loose dirt floor, populated by earthworms, looked like a gray road map.

That night, by the light of a kerosene lamp, we unpacked and cleaned our new home. Roberto swept away the loose dirt,

4. *Mi Carcanchita* (mē kär′kän chē′tä).
5. *Listo* (lēs′tō).
6. *Mi olla* (mē ô′yä).
7. *Es todo* (äs tō′dō).

leaving the hard ground. Papa plugged the holes in the walls with old newspapers and tin can tops. Mama fed my little brothers and sisters. Papa and Roberto then brought in the mattress and placed it on the far corner of the garage. "Mama, you and the little ones sleep on the mattress. Roberto, Panchito, and I will sleep outside under the trees," Papa said.

Early next morning Mr. Sullivan showed us where his crop was, and after breakfast, Papa, Roberto, and I headed for the vineyard to pick.

Around nine o'clock the temperature had risen to almost one hundred degrees. I was completely soaked in sweat and my mouth felt as if I had been chewing on a handkerchief. I walked over to the end of the row, picked up the jug of water we had brought, and began drinking. "Don't drink too much; you'll get sick," Roberto shouted. No sooner had he said that than I felt sick to my stomach. I dropped to my knees and let the jug roll off my hands. I remained motionless with my eyes glued on the hot sandy ground. All I could hear was the drone of insects. Slowly I began to recover. I poured water over my face and neck and watched the black mud run down my arms and hit the ground.

I still felt a little dizzy when we took a break to eat lunch. It was past two o'clock and we sat underneath a large walnut tree that was on the side of the road. While we ate, Papa jotted down the number of boxes we had picked. Roberto drew designs on the ground with a stick. Suddenly I noticed Papa's face turn pale as he looked down the road. "Here comes the school bus," he whispered loudly in alarm. Instinctively, Roberto and I ran and hid in the vineyards. We did not want to get in trouble for not going to school. The yellow bus stopped in front of Mr. Sullivan's house. Two neatly dressed boys about my age got off. They carried books under their arms. After they crossed the street, the bus drove away. Roberto and I came out from hiding and joined Papa. *"Tienen que tener cuidado"*[8] (you have to be careful), he warned us.

After lunch we went back to work. The sun kept beating down. The buzzing insects, the wet sweat, and the hot dry dust made the afternoon seem to last forever. Finally the mountains around the valley reached out and swallowed the sun. Within an hour it was too dark to continue picking. The vines blanketed the grapes, making it difficult to see the bunches. *"Vámonos,"*[9] said Papa, signaling to us that it was time to quit work. Papa then took out a pencil and began to figure out how much we had earned our first day. He wrote down numbers, crossed some out, wrote down some more. *"Quince"*[10] (fifteen dollars), he murmured.

When we arrived home, we took a cold shower underneath a waterhose. We then sat down to eat dinner around some wooden crates that served as a table. Mama had cooked a special meal for us. We had rice and tortillas with *carne con chile*, my favorite dish.

The next morning I could hardly move. My body ached all over. I felt little control over my arms and legs. This feeling went on every morning for days until my muscles finally got used to the work.

It was Monday, the first week of November. The grape season was over and I could now go to school. I woke up early that morning and lay in bed, looking at the stars and savoring the thought of not going to

8. *Tienen que tener cuidado* (tyā′nen kā tā nār′ kwē dä′dō).
9. *Vámonos* (bvä′mō nōs), "Let's go."
10. *Quince* (kēn′se).

work and of starting sixth grade for the first time that year. Since I could not sleep, I decided to get up and join Papa and Roberto at breakfast. I sat at the table across from Roberto, but I kept my head down. I did not want to look up and face him. I knew he was sad. He was not going to school today. He was not going tomorrow, or next week, or next month. He would not go until the cotton season was over, and that was sometime in February. I rubbed my hands together and watched the dry, acid-stained skin fall to the floor in little rolls.

When Papa and Roberto left for work, I felt relief. I walked to the top of a small grade next to the shack and watched the "Carcanchita" disappear in the distance in a cloud of dust.

Two hours later, around eight o'clock, I stood by the side of the road waiting for school bus number twenty. When it arrived I climbed in. No one noticed me. Everyone was busy either talking or yelling. I sat in an empty seat in the back.

When the bus stopped in front of the school, I felt very nervous. I looked out the bus window and saw boys and girls carrying books under their arms. I felt empty. I put my hands in my pants pockets and walked to the principal's office. When I entered I heard a woman's voice say: "May I help you?" I was startled. I had not heard English for months. For a few seconds I remained speechless. I looked at the lady who waited for an answer. My first instinct was to answer her in Spanish, but I held back. Finally, after struggling for English words I managed to tell her that I wanted to enroll in the sixth grade. After answering many questions, I was led to the classroom.

Mr. Lema, the sixth-grade teacher, greeted me and assigned me a desk. He then introduced me to the class. I was so nervous and scared at that moment when everyone's eyes were on me that I wished I were with Papa and Roberto picking cotton. After taking roll, Mr. Lema gave the class the assignment for the first hour. "The first thing we have to do this morning is finish reading the story we began yesterday," he said enthusiastically. He walked up to me, handed me an English book, and asked me to read. "We are on page 125," he said politely. When I heard this, I felt my blood rush to my head; I felt dizzy. "Would you like to read?" he asked hesitantly. I opened the book to page 125. My mouth was dry. My eyes began to water. I could not begin. "You can read later," Mr. Lema said understandingly.

For the rest of the reading period I kept getting angrier and angrier with myself. I should have read, I thought to myself.

During recess I went into the restroom and opened my English book to page 125. I began to read in a low voice, pretending I was in class. There were many words I did not know. I closed the book and headed back to the classroom.

Mr. Lema was sitting at his desk correcting papers. When I entered he looked up at me and smiled. I felt better. I walked up to him and asked if he could help me with the new words. "Gladly," he said.

The rest of the month I spent my lunch hours working on English with Mr. Lema, my best friend at school.

One Friday during lunch hour Mr. Lema asked me to take a walk with him to the music room. "Do you like music?" he asked me as we entered the building.

"Yes, I like Mexican *corridos*,"[11] I answered. He then picked up a trumpet, blew on it and handed it to me. The sound gave

---

11. *corridos* (kôr rē′dōs), Mexican folk ballads, usually telling of the adventures of a hero.

me goose bumps. I knew that sound. I had heard it in many Mexican corridos. "How would you like to learn how to play it?" he asked. He must have read my face because before I could answer, he added: "I'll teach you how to play it during our lunch hours."

That day I could hardly wait to get home to tell Papa and Mama the great news. As I got off the bus, my little brothers and sisters ran up to meet me. They were yelling and screaming. I thought they were happy to see me, but when I opened the door to our shack, I saw that everything we owned was neatly packed in cardboard boxes. □□

Discussion

1. (**a**) Describe the *setting*—the time, the place, and the general environment—of this selection. (**b**) How does the setting influence the way the family lives? (**c**) Explain how the setting helps to determine what happens in the story.

2. To portray a setting vividly an author often appeals to the reader's senses of sight, hearing, touch, taste, and smell. Find at least three descriptive phrases or sentences in the story that appeal to one of these senses.

3. Find evidence in the story that indicates the concern and respect shown each other by various family members.

4. What are some of the narrator's personal reactions to his life and work?

5. (**a**) What specific occurrences make the narrator feel uncomfortable and self-conscious on the first day of school? (**b**) Do you think there are other problems that might cause him to feel uncomfortable? Explain.

6. Describe Mr. Lema.

7. (**a**) What situation does the narrator face at the end of the story? (**b**) How do you think he will respond to it?

---

notes and comments

The Story Behind the Story
Francisco Jiménez

"The Circuit" is an autobiographical short story based on my experiences as a child growing up in a migrant family. "Roberto" is my older brother's real name; "Panchito" is my Spanish nickname.

The idea for the story goes back many years to the time when I was in Miss Bell's English class at Santa Maria High School. Miss Bell encouraged the class to write detailed narrative accounts of personal experiences. Even though I had difficulty expressing myself in English, I enjoyed the assignments, and with much effort I wrote about what I knew best. The remarks she made about what I wrote were so reassuring that long after I left her class I continued to reflect upon my life experiences and often thought of expressing them in writing. Whenever I could, I would jot down recollections on a piece of paper hoping to write about them in the future.

In 1972, I shared two autobiographical narrative accounts with Professor Andrés Iduarte, my mentor in graduate school. He liked them very much and urged me to publish my work.

Encouraged by his positive remarks, I decided to write a short story describing in detail the joys and disappointments I encountered as I grew up in a migrant setting. I chose to treat my experiences during the time I was in the sixth grade because that school year had a great influence on me, especially the relationship I had with Mr. Lema, the sixth-grade teacher.

Come along for a ride with . . .

The Sidewalk Racer
or
On the Skateboard

Lillian Morrison

Skimming
an asphalt sea
I swerve, I curve, I
sway; I speed to whirring
5   sound an inch above the
ground; I'm the sailor
and the sail, I'm the
driver and the wheel
I'm the one and only
10   single engine
human auto
mobile.

Chuck O'Rear

Reprinted by permission of Lothrop, Lee & Shepard Co. from *The Sidewalk Racer and Other Poems of Sports and Motion* by Lillian Morrison. Copyright © 1965, 1967, 1968, 1977 by Lillian Morrison.

Discussion

1. What images describe the setting and action?

2. (a) Read the poem aloud. Do you find that you speed up, slow down, or maintain a steady pace as you read? **(b)** What effect is created by the pace at which you read the poem?

3. (a) The speaker is like both "the sailor and the sail," both "the driver and the wheel." What feelings do these combined images suggest? **(b)** Is the sidewalk racer really "one and only"? Why do you suppose the speaker makes this claim in lines 9–12?

Lillian Morrison

Of *The Sidewalk Racer* Lillian Morrison says, "I love rhythms, the body movement implicit in poetry, explicit in sports. And there are emotions connected with sports, sometimes a kind of transcendence and beauty one wants to catch. One turns naturally to poetry to express these things."

Lillian Morrison has published two volumes of poetry and a very popular anthology of sports poems, *Sprints and Distances*. She is the Coordinator of Young Adult Services for the New York Public Library.

Long before the sun struck the face of Lookout Mountain, curls of smoke rose from the earth houses at its feet. Women hurried to the springs for water. Boys ran through the village. Dogs barked. The men brought out the weapons and gear of the hunt for admiration and repair. Today would begin the preparations for the ceremonial that would bring the buffalo from the land of the warm wind.

It was time. The long snows of winter had eaten deep into the caches of dried meat and corn and pumpkin rings. But soon there would be new meat for the pots and the drying racks, new robes and skins for sewing with the bone awls and needles of the women. And with these things would come great glory for the buffalo hunters.

Seeing this, young Birdman drew his robe around him and stalked out of the village, carrying neither bow nor arrow—only his flintheaded spear which everyone derided as much too heavy and much too strong for birds and rabbits.

Climbing the steep slope out of Reams Creek to the high plain spreading away southwestward, he circled back to where it broke in the high limestone-capped bluff called Lookout Mountain. There he squatted in his robe and scowled down upon the gray earth homes of his people, scattered in little groups far up and down the benches of the creek valley.

Below him the women moved about their labors. Several were working with bone diggers and willow baskets at the warming clay pits, for there was pottery to make, and the winter-bared patches of willow thatching on the house roofs must be covered before the late spring rains came. At the creek an old woman tied a long string of buffalo bladders to a stake to soak, complainingly, Birdman knew, and with no faith that there would

At first Birdman couldn't believe it. But even as he watched, it grew— the buffalo were coming straight toward him, heads down, running blindly, certain death to everything in their path.

The Birdman

Mari Sandoz

soon be fresh ones for the moulding of the pottery.

About the earth houses the men were preparing for the buffalo ceremonial and the coming of the herds from the south, the older with pipe and story and the sacred things for tomorrow's rites, the younger with mighty testing of bow and arrow and great plans for the surround. Others sharpened the knives and spears that might, with one blow under the shoulder, bring the buffalo to his knees.

But the testing of buffalo bows and the sharpening of spearheads was not for him on the top of Lookout Mountain. He was a birdman and sat long hours in the chill waters with an eye-holed pumpkin over his head. When the ducks came he moved slowly, very slowly, as though drifting in the evening winds, until he was among the gossiping birds. Then he pulled them under by the feet, each so swiftly that there was no time for outcry, their mates noticing only to watch this curious diving until Birdman had all his two hands could hold. And twice a year came the flying wedges of geese out of the evening horizon. Once he caught two white-throated geese at one time.

But Birdman was not so named for these things alone. Upon a far bluff was an old pit, and when the hunting eagle soared the sky like a flake of soot from burning cornstalks, the hunter threw the drifted sand from the pit with the shoulder blade of a buffalo and repaired the light covering of willows. When it was old to the eye he caught a young antelope or a rabbit, and with its side opened red, tied it firmly to a center pole. Then he waited in the pit and when the circling eagle dropped like a stone upon his prey, Birdman reached up from below and swiftly clutched the powerful legs. He must get them both, and in one hand, to leave the other free for

defense against the sharp tearing beak, the threshing wings.

In the first fierce rush of his anger, the eagle would beat down the light network of willow and strike again and again upon Birdman's unprotected head and shoulders, his sharp beak cutting and tearing the flesh, while the wings were as war clubs. But never once did the bird hunter release his hold and at last his thumb always closed on the sinewed, pulsing throat.

Sometimes it was hours before he could rise and bear his kill to the village, the wings spread longer than any man and the torn flesh of the hunter speaking of a battle that would bear recounting for many a moon.

He knew that it was no small thing to be called Birdman, but it was not enough. He would be a buffalo hunter also and as he looked down upon the earth houses of his people on the second bench above the river, Birdman was angry. Even now the house builders were perhaps seeking him to help place the center posts about the fire pit in a new house or to mould the clay about the firehole in the roof. Or perhaps his aunt wanted him to help plant the pumpkin in the

was as the ash fire in winter, soothing. Gradually he was drowsy too and slept for a long time.

He awoke to hunger and to a breathless stillness and a green-gray sky. Below him the women were flying to finish their work, to gather in the soaking bladders, the garments and the robes spread to air. Over them the clouds darkened and began to roll and tumble like the floodwaters of the creek rolled when they rose over the cornfields or perhaps even the lower houses, crumbling their earth shells.

Birdman watched the valley below darken into an unnatural opaqueness. The air sang with a high, thin sound that grew into a roar. A dust cloud swept out of the horizon toward Lookout Mountain. Then the wind struck, from every side at one time. The grass ran like milling buffalo. Trees leaned, turned half around, and went down like sticks.

Hard on the wind came sheets of rain and earth-shaking thunder. Birdman dropped over the limestone cap of the mountain, squeezed himself under an overhanging cliff, and pulled his robe about him. Let the storm howl like the wolves in midwinter, the

creek bends where the sod would yield to the shovel of bone from buffalo killed by those who were now sharpening their spears for the hunt.

As the sun climbed in the sky, a drowsiness settled over the gray earth houses above the tree-tufted creek. They were greening fast today, and on the horizon shimmered a pale heat dance. No wind stirred the spare sand grass upon the slope. Two grouse flew across the valley, cackling low, uneasily. Birdman marked their flight, but not as carefully as was his habit. The sun thunder fall like great boulders from high places!

A long time afterward the silence came back. Birdman stretched his cramped knees and looked out from his robe. Reams Creek was a swirling, gray river, scattering mud, branches, even whole trees over the lower cornfields. The new yellow clay was washed as paint over the ground. The trees tucked in the draws were broken; many that stood alone bared their uprooted feet to the air.

The creek lapped sullenly at the houses along the lower bench. The women ran for the higher ground with their bundles, shooing their children before them, while the men threw up earth embankments. Birdman saw that he must return to the village. As he wrapped his robe about him he heard a faint roar as of far but mighty thunder—a low, steady thunder that shook the earth. He looked around. Across the horizon lay a dark line. At first he could not believe it. But even as he watched, it grew—the buffalo were coming, stampeded by the storm.

One moment he hesitated before giving the customary signal. Then, without warning his village, he grasped his spear and clinging to his flying robe, he ran over the plain toward the herd, leaping gullies and washouts like an antelope. As the dark mass neared he saw that it was breaking. Little herds, unpressed from behind, were gradually swinging to the sides.

One of these dark fingers pointed along the breaks of Reams Creek. Birdman, recalling the many accounts of the great hunters of his people, thought swiftly. To the left was the broad plain down which the larger herd was sweeping. Coming straight toward him were about a hundred of the muddy animals, heads down, running blindly, certain death to everything in their path. For one instant he was only a birdman and,

wishing to rid himself of spear and robe, wanted to run as the antelope and the coyote ran, with no pretense of courage. But instead he threw himself into a washout to wait, the earth trembling under his body. Even now he wondered if he should not signal to the village for those who make the surrounds, those who do it well and bring meat to the drying racks. But already it was too late. Besides, his anger with himself stiffened his determination. As the dark herd was upon him he rose and with a loud cry he waved the dark robe before him.

For a second the leaders hesitated. Then the thrust of those behind drove them on. Birdman leaped sideways, flung his robe into the mud-caked faces, and with a mighty thrust buried his spear under the shoulder of the nearest. Inexpertly he overbalanced and went down but the herd, already swerved, swept past him toward the bluff. At the brink the leaders could not stop and those behind followed.

Birdman found himself unhurt. As he looked down upon the muddy, bleeding side of the dead buffalo, his spear deep, an exultation rose in him and he threw back his head and began to run. At the edge of the bluff overlooking Reams Creek he stopped and looked down. Below was a writhing mass of buffalo; some, less crippled, were dragging their heavy bodies onward.

And already up the benchland from the village came the first of the runners with their spears. Birdman stood straight and tall against the sky and signaled to his people. Here were robes enough to keep the women tanning for a long moon, fresh bladders about which to mould their pottery. Here was much meat for the pots and the drying racks and tongue and hump enough to feast all the people—to whom he would be Birdman no longer. □□

Discussion

1. (a) Where does this story take place? (b) What time of year is it? (c) What details can you find to indicate that this story might have taken place a long time ago?

2. (a) What kinds of preparations are the villagers engaged in? (b) What job does the Birdman perform in his community? (c) Is he happy in his work? Explain. (d) What mood is he in as the story opens? Why?

3. (a) What causes Birdman to try to kill a buffalo? (b) What conflicting emotions does he experience? (c) How much does the outcome depend on luck? on skill? (d) How might the villagers have reacted if he had been unsuccessful?

4. (a) What effect does the kill have on Birdman's self-image? (b) In what ways does he anticipate that his role in village life will change as a result of his action?

Vocabulary • Structure

Many difficult looking words are really familiar words with parts added to them. Recognizing the various parts in a word can often help you understand its meaning.

Words can be made up of three parts:

1. A root word such as *cook, bright, vigor, view,* or *move.* Root words are words to which parts can be added to form other words. The meaning of a root word gives you a clue to the meaning of the longer word formed from it.

2. Prefixes—word parts such as *in-, un-, re-,* and *pre-.* Prefixes are added to the beginning of a root word to change its meaning (*pre*cook, *re*move). A word may have more than one prefix, as in *unremoved* (*un* + *re* + moved).

3. Suffixes—word parts such as *-ous, -er, -ness, -ation,* and *-ly.* Suffixes are added to the end of a word (view*er*, vigor*ous*, bright*ly*) and usually determine whether a word is used as a noun, adjective, verb, or adverb. ("As the sun climbed in the sky, a *drowsiness* [noun] settled over the gray earth houses. . . . Gradually Birdman was *drowsy* [adjective] too and slept for a long time.") A word may have more than one suffix, as in *vigorously* (vigor + *ous* + *ly*).

The term *affix* is used to indicate both prefixes and suffixes. The word *reviewer* has two affixes, a prefix (*re-*) and a suffix (*-er*).

Analyze the italicized word in each sentence that follows, and then on your paper answer the questions.

1. Birdman thrust his spear *inexpertly* at the shoulder of the nearest buffalo.

a. What is the root word? What does it mean?

b. What is the prefix? What is the suffix? How do they change the meaning of the root word?

c. Did Birdman display great skill trying to kill the buffalo?

2. The men brought out the weapons of the hunt for *admiration* and repair.

a. What is the meaning of the root word? What part of speech is it?

b. What is the suffix?

c. What part of speech is the italicized word?

d. Were the men expecting to be praised or scolded when the weapons were examined?

3. Birdman awoke to hunger and a great *stillness* in the air.

a. What is the root word?

b. What part of speech is the italicized word?

c. What sounds did Birdman hear when he awoke?

4. Two grouse flew across the valley cackling *uneasily.*

a. What are the affixes in the italicized word?

b. Were the grouse behaving as if something were wrong? Which affix helped you decide?

A fortune—a regular fortune!
And she only had to wait ninety days.

I'll Give You Law

Molly Picon

When I read the newspaper, there is always a must section in it that I never pass by. This is the lost and found advertisements usually buried in the back pages. This is a habit I picked up from my grandmother. She always took a keen interest in who had lost what, and who was honestly reporting on items found. She could people a whole colony from just a couple of advertisements.

"Lost—one black puppy with a white patch around its eye. Answers to the name 'Spot.' Please call Beaver 6-5000. Reward."

From this my grandmother would draw for me a picture of a child sobbing itself to sleep at night, of parents out searching the streets anxiously, calling in hopeless voices, "Spot. Come on, Spot. Here, boy."

The picture was so real to both of us we used to sit there with tears in our eyes, willing Spot to answer, wanting the child to cry with joy and not in sorrow.

We thought about all the lost items with equal interest. We wondered about the found items as well, visualizing the happy claimants, and the honest finders handsomely rewarded. At such moments, God was in Heaven, and all was right with the world.

And then one day, we moved swiftly from the land of fantasy to a world of realities. My grandmother found something!

"What is it? What is it?" I asked, hopping with excitement.

"A lavaliere!"[1] My grandmother was absolutely overwhelmed. She had never found anything in her life, and now, here in her hand, was this magnificent lavaliere.

"It must be very expensive," I said, running my fingers over it.

"A fortune," my grandmother said positively. She held it up against her. "A regular fortune," she breathed.

"Are you going to keep it?" I asked.

She gave me a sharp look. If the thought entered her mind, she wasn't going to admit it to me.

"Am I going to keep it?" she asked. "Such a question." She threw her shawl over her head.

"Where are you going?" I asked. "Can I go, too?"

"I'm going to the police station. Let them worry about it. You can't come," she added firmly. "A police station is not respectable."

At the police station, the property clerk informed her politely that if the lavaliere was not claimed within ninety days, the police department would turn the jewelry over to her, and she would be its rightful and legal owner. He took her name and address and wrote it down. They would let her know, he said indifferently.

"Oh, I hope nobody claims it," I said fervently. "Oh, Grandma, I hope whoever lost it doesn't even know they lost it."

Such a dilemma for my grandmother. If ever she yearned for anything, it was for this lavaliere. On the other hand, her active imagination conjured up for her such tearful scenes that she couldn't wait for the loser to come and claim her property.

Meanwhile, my grandmother took to haunting the police station and the property clerk. "How are you," she would ask, "and how is the family?" In the beginning he would dismiss this with a curt "fine we haven't heard don't call on us we'll let you know" attitude. But my grandmother began to take a personal interest in the policemen at the precinct. She knew their names and the names of their wives and children. She knew how hard it was to make ends meet on a policeman's salary, what policeman was going to night school to study law and improve his station in life, what policeman was smarting at being passed over when promotions were handed out. Only the property clerk held out. When he would look up and see my grandmother, he would mutter and groan.

"Mrs. Ostrow," he would say, "don't you have anything to do at home?"

"Why don't I have something to do at home?" My grandmother would regard him scornfully. "You think I like to come here day after day?"

"So why do you come?" he would ask logically.

"To see what I have to see," she would tell him. And then she would demand to see the lavaliere with "my own eyes." And then she would subject him to a searching questioning. Who had come today, and what had they claimed, and wasn't it possible the lavaliere had belonged to one of the people who had come, and had he told anybody about it, and if he was keeping it such a big secret, how could anybody know he had it in the first place?

As hard as I prayed that no one would show up, he prayed that someone—anyone—would.

"Ninety days," he would cry, clutching his hair. "I'll never survive it."

I never knew that ninety days could last so long. But eventually the ninetieth day arrived, bringing with it much excitement. My grandmother and I dressed as though we were going to a party. She was going to allow me to go with her for the presentation. On the way we discussed her immense good fortune.

"When I die," she said to me, "I want you to have it."

"Please, Grandma," I said, uncomforta-

bly. It seemed like a grim note to inject in an otherwise cloudless day.

"No," she insisted seriously. "I want you to have it. It will be like a—what is the word I want, Molly?"

"An heirloom?"

"That's the word." She pounced on it with satisfaction. "And when you die, your children will have it."

In two sentences, my grandmother had disposed of us both.

At the police station, my grandmother was greeted with happy smiles, even from the property clerk. I should say, especially from the property clerk. It was the happiest day of his life.

When my grandmother finally held the lavaliere in her hand, her eyes misted over. She couldn't speak, but she nodded her head at the policemen.

"Don't be a stranger," they urged her. "Don't wait till you find something before you drop in."

"Such nice boys," my grandmother said, as we left the station. She touched her eyes with her handkerchief. "Such good boys, even him," she said, referring to the property clerk. "He had his eye on it, but out of respect, he didn't touch it." I believed my grandmother. I didn't see how that property clerk could have looked at that lavaliere for ninety days and so nobly fought off temptation.

When we got home, my grandmother promptly put the lavaliere on.

"I'll wear it night and day," she vowed. "I'll never take it off." For a week she was as good as her word.

Then one day there came a knock at the door, and tragedy swept in, escorted by an embarrassed property clerk from the police station.

"Where is it?" cried the woman he had

brought to the door. She looked at my grandmother. "My lavaliere she's wearing," she cried in horror, pointing to my grandmother.

My grandmother looked at both of them, shocked. Her hand went up automatically to clutch the lavaliere.

"It's mine," she said. "You told me, after ninety days . . ."

"That's right," the property clerk said promptly. "Legally it is yours. That's what I've been trying to tell this lady. She didn't claim it in ninety days, and the law says . . ."

"I'll give you law," the lady shouted vigorously, pounding him on the arm. "Does the law say after ninety days thieves and murderers can do whatever they want? Law! I'll give you law!"

"Please, lady," the property clerk pleaded. "Let's try to be calm."

"Calm!" she took up the cry. "I'll give you calm!"

My grandmother entered the fray briskly.

"So much commotion," she said. "You want the neighbors to think we're killing you on the doorstep. Come inside." She urged them in and closed the door. "So if you'll stop talking and tell me where you were," she said, guiding the distracted woman to a seat, "we'll listen and we'll be the same good friends."

"Where was I?" the woman said, shaking her head. "My daughter was having her baby, so she says to me, 'Ma,' she says, 'if you don't come, I won't have it, that's all.'

"So I had to go to Scranton yet. One month in advance, just in case. And then, with God's help, the baby comes. Now she's afraid to hold it, it might break. And she's afraid to wash it. It might come apart in the water. One month. Two months. Finally I say to her, 'Rebeccah,' I say, 'enough is enough already. Whatever you'll do, you'll do.' "

My grandmother was already making tea for everybody, bustling about the kitchen, putting crackers and jam on the table.

"The young people today," she commented.

"So when I come back, I first realized my lavaliere is gone. I'm not hung with jewelry, and between you and me and the lamppost," she added confidentially to my grandmother, "I need a lavaliere like I need a hole in the head. But when I need a little extra money in an emergency, that lavaliere saves my life."

"How does it save your life?" I asked.

"I bring it to the pawnshop and whatever few pennies he gives me . . ."

"The pawnshop!" I was indignant. "She doesn't even wear it, Grandma," I said passionately. "Don't give it back. You don't have to. The law says you don't have to."

"That's right," the property clerk said instantly. He was on his second cup of tea and using my grandmother's jam as if the jar had an endless bottom.

The woman opened her mouth to protest, but my grandmother stopped her by holding up her hand for silence.

"Molly," she said gently, "there is a law here, too." She laid her hand tenderly on my heart: "Look in your heart and tell me. Suppose it was your lavaliere. Suppose you lost it and somebody else found it. Ninety days, a thousand days . . . how would you feel?"

"I would want it back," I answered honestly.

She spread her hands out eloquently.

"So?" she asked me.

"That's not fair," I burst out.

"Fair? Who said anything about fair?" She reached up and took off the lavaliere. She fondled it for a moment, and then handed it over to the woman.

"Why should I complain?" she asked no one in particular and shrugged. "For three months I lived in a dream, and for five days I lived like a queen. Is that bad?" □□

Discussion

1. (a) What is Grandmother Ostrow's initial reaction to finding the lavaliere? (b) What does she do with it?

2. (a) How does Grandmother Ostrow's life change after she turns in the lavaliere? (b) What do you think her feelings are during the ninety-day waiting period? (c) What are the narrator's feelings?

3. (a) What does Grandmother Ostrow tell the narrator on the day they go to claim the lavaliere? (b) What does she do with the lavaliere when she finally gets it? (c) What does this reveal about her attitude toward the lavaliere?

4. (a) What does the real owner of the lavaliere mean when she cries, "I'll give you law"? (b) How does Grandmother Ostrow react to the woman's claim?

5. Contrast the two women's attitudes toward the piece of jewelry. Which woman is more interested in the lavaliere's monetary value? Why?

6. (a) What do you learn about the narrator and Grandmother Ostrow from what they say and do? (b) What do their feelings toward each other reveal? (c) What does the end of the story reveal about Grandmother Ostrow's sense of values?

Vocabulary
Pronunciation, Dictionary

When you can't determine the meaning or the correct pronunciation for a word from the context or structure, then you must use your dictionary. Look up the pronunciations and meanings of the italicized words in your Glossary and then on your paper answer the questions. Be sure you can spell all the italicized words.

1. Does the accented or stressed syllable in *claimant* rhyme with "day" or "farm"?

2. Does the accented syllable in *eloquent* rhyme with "bell" or "rock"? Is an *eloquent* person likely to be called on to give a talk?

3. Does the accented syllable in *commotion* rhyme with "some" or "toe"?

4. What is a rhyming word for *fray*? Which meaning of *fray* is intended in the sentence, "Everyone ran outside to see what the *fray* was about"?

Extension • Writing

These advertisements appeared in the lost-and-found section of a newspaper. Visualize a scene involving one of the people who wrote the ad. Write a paragraph describing how that person feels while waiting for the item to be returned or claimed.

Lost: Ring, plain silver, man's small size. Old, was my father's. Rwd. Janie. 243-9365.

Found: Squawky, small green parrot. On San Simeon Ave. Call 854-3232 immed.

Lost: Black leather attaché case, fitted with unbreakable lock. Large reward. No questions asked. Call 191-8080 or 923-8182 any time a.m. or p.m.

Discussion

1. (a) What, in general, are adults always saying to young people? (b) How do young people react to their elders' advice? (c) What, then, is the basic difference between the attitudes of youth and age?

2. (a) What is suggested by the lines

> youth goes
> right on
> gr
> owing old

(b) Is a change in outlook an unavoidable part of aging? Why or why not?

3. (a) What are some unusual features in the form of this poem? (b) What effect does the form have on you? (See the material on form in the biography of Cummings which follows.)

E. E. Cummings   1894 • 1962

A daring experimenter in both art and poetry, Cummings searched for new ways to convey sounds and movement in verse. He often ignored conventional spacing and punctuation. Sometimes he ran words together to suggest speed, or separated them, one to a line, for a slower pace. His poems are sprightly and forceful in their originality, not because they "look different," but because he succeeded in making the form of his poems fit the particular ideas and feelings he wished to express.

old age sticks

E. E. Cummings

old age sticks
up Keep
Off
signs)&

5 youth yanks them
down(old
age
cries No

Tres)&(pas)
10 youth laughs
(sing
old age

scolds Forbid
den Stop
15 Must
n't Don't

&)youth goes
right on
gr
20 owing old

Ron Benvenisti/MAGNUM PHOTOS

Veterans and novices alike had died on these icy slopes.
He was scared—and he knew it.

Mirror of Ice

GARY WRIGHT

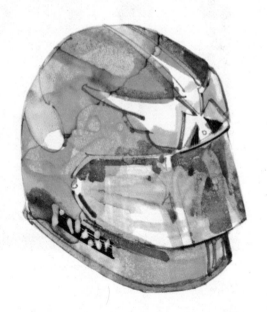

They called it the Stuka. It was a tortuous, twenty-kilometer path of bright ice, and in that distance—12.42 miles—it dropped 7,366 feet, carving a course down the alpine mountainside like the track of a great snake. It was thirty feet wide on the straights with corners curling as high as forty feet. It was made for sleds. . . .

He waited in the narrow cockpit and listened to the wind. It moaned along the frozen shoulder of the towering white peak and across the steep starting ramp, pushing along streamers of snow out against the hard blue sky, and he could hear it cry inside him with the same cold and lonely sound.

He was scared. And what was worse—he knew it.

Forward, under the sleek nose of his sled, the mountain fell away abruptly—straight down, it seemed—and the valley was far below. So very far.

. . . too far this time, buddyboy, too far forever . . .

The countdown light on the dash flickered a sudden blood red, then deliberately winked twice. At the same time two red rockets arced out over the valley and exploded into twin crimson fireballs.

Two minutes.

On both sides of the starting ramp, cantilevered gracefully from the mountainside, brightly bannered platforms were crowded with people. He glanced at the hundreds of blankly staring sunglasses, always the same, always turned to the ramp as if trying to see inside the helmets of these men, as if trying to pry into the reasons of their being there waiting to die. He looked back to the deep valley; today he wondered too.

. . . just one last time, wasn't that what

you told yourself? One last race and that's the end of it and good-by to the sleds! Wasn't that your personal promise?

Then what are you doing here? That "last race" was last month's race. Why are you in this one?

No answer.

All he could find inside were cold questions and a hollow echo of the wind. He gripped the steering wheel, hard, until cramps began in his hands; he would think about his sled. . . .

It was his eleventh sled, and like the others it was a brilliant red, not red for its particular flash, but because of a possible crash far from the course in deep snow. He wanted to be found and found fast. Some of the Kin had never been found in time.

. . . they didn't find Bob Lander until that summer—

He forced himself back.

Empty, the sled weighed 185 pounds and looked very much like the body-shell of a particularly sleek racer but with a full bubble canopy and with runners instead of wheels. It was a mean-looking missile, low and lean, hardly wider than his shoulders, clearing the ice by barely two inches. He sat nearly reclining, the half wheel in his lap, feet braced on the two edging pedals—and this was the feature that made these sleds the awesome things they were. They could tilt their runners—four hollowground, chrome-steel "skis"—edging them against the ice like wide skate blades. This was what had changed bobsledding into . . . *this:* this special thing with its special brotherhood, this clan apart, this peculiar breed of men set aside for the wonder of other men. The Kin, they called themselves.

. . . someone once, laughing, had said, "Without peer, we are the world's fastest suicides."

He snapped himself back again and checked his brakes.

By pulling back on the wheel, two electrically operated flaps—actually halves of the sled's tail section—swung out on either side. Silly to see, perhaps. But quite effective when this twelve and a half square feet hit the airstream at eighty mph. A button under his right thumb operated another braking system: with each push it fired forward a solid rocket charge in the nose of the sled. There were seven charges, quite often not enough. But when everything failed, including the man, there was the lever by his left hip. The Final Folly, it was called; a firm pull and, depending on a hundred unknown "if's" and "maybe's," he might be lucky enough to find himself hanging from a parachute some 300 feet up. Or it might be the last voluntary act of his life.

He had used it twice. Once streaking into the tall wall of the Wingover, he had lost a runner . . . and was almost fired into the opposite grandstand, missing the top tier of seats by less than four feet. Another time six sleds suddenly tangled directly in front of him, and he had blasted himself through the over-hanging limbs of a large fir tree.

But others had not been so lucky.

Hans Kroger: they finally dug his body out of eighteen feet of snow; he'd gone all the way to the dirt. His sled had been airborne when he blew—and upside-down!

Jarl Yorgensen: his sled tumbling and he ejected directly under the following sleds. No one was certain that all of him was ever found!

Max Conrad: a perfect blowout! At least 350 feet up and slightly downhill . . . His chute never opened.

Wayne Barley:—

He jarred himself hard in the cockpit and

felt the sudden seizure of his G-suit.[1] He wanted to hit something. But he could feel the watching eyes and the TV cameras, and there wasn't room in the cockpit to get a decent swing anyway.

His countdown light flickered for attention and blinked once, and a single red rocket flashed into the sky.

One minute—had time stopped?

But that was part of it all: the waiting, the awful waiting, staring down at the valley over a mile below. And how many men had irrevocably slammed back their canopy in this lifetime of two minutes and stayed behind? A few, yes. And he could too. Simply open his canopy, that was the signal, and when the start came the other sleds would dive down and away and he would be sitting here alone. But so alone! And he would be alone for the rest of his life. He might see some of the Kin again, sometime, somewhere. But they would not see him. It was a kind of death to stay behind.

. . . and a real death to go. Death, the silent rider with every man in every race . . .

He frowned at the other sleds, sixteen in staggered rows of eight. Sixteen bright and beautiful, trim fast projectiles hanging from their starting clamps. He knew them, every one; they were his brothers. They were the Kin—but not here. Not now.

Years ago when he was a novice he had asked old Franz Cashner, "Did you see the way I took Basher Bend right beside you?"

And Franz told him, "Up there I see nobody! Only sleds! Down here you are you, up there you are nothing but another sled. That's all! And don't forget that! That's all! And don't forget that!"

. . . and it had to be that way . . . On the course sleds crashed and were no more. . . . Only later, in the valley, were there men missing.

Of these sixteen, chances were that nine would finish. With luck, maybe ten. And chances also said that only fourteen of these men would be alive tonight. Those were the odds, as hard and cold as the ice, the fascinating frosting for this sport. Violent death! Assured, spectacular, magnetic death in a sport such as the world had never known. Incredible men with incredible skills doing an incredible thing.

Back in the Sixties they claimed an empty sled with its steering locked would make a course all by itself. An empty sled here would not last two corners. The Stuka was a cold killer, not a thrill ride. And it was not particular. It killed veterans and novices alike. But there was $20,000 for the man who got to the end of it first, and a whole month before he had to do it again. Money and fame and all the girls in the world. Everything and anything for the men who rode the Stuka.

Was that why they did it?

. . . yes, always that question: "Why do you do it?" And before he had died on the Plummet, Sir Robert Brooke had told them, "Well, why not?"

And it was an answer as good as any.

But was it good enough this time?

No answer.

He only knew there was but one way off this mountain for him now and that was straight ahead, and for the first time since his novice runs, his legs were trembling. Twelve and a half miles, call it, and the record was 9 minutes, 1.14 seconds! An average speed of 82.67 mph, and that was *his* record. They would at least remember him by that!

His countdown light flashed, a green

---

1. *G-suit,* garment worn by pilots and astronauts to counteract the effects of increased gravitational forces and to prevent blackout.

rocket rose and burst, and there was a frozen moment . . . the quiet click of the release hook, the lazy, slow-motion start, the sleds sliding forward in formation over the edge . . . then he was looking once again into the terrible top of the Stuka—that 45-degree, quarter-mile straight drop. In six seconds he was doing over 60 mph, and the mouth of the first corner was reaching up.

. . . Carl's Corner, for Carl Rasch, who went over the top of it nine years ago; and they found him a half-mile down the glacier . . . what was left of him . . .

He glanced to his right. It was clear. He eased his flap brakes, dropped back slightly and pulled right. The leading sleds were jockeying in front now, lining for this long left. Brakes flapped like quick wings, and they started around, sleds riding up the vertical ice wall and holding there, ice chips spraying back like contrails from those on the lower part of the wall as they edged their runners against the turn. He came in far right and fast, riding high on the wall and diving off with good acceleration.

The ice was a brilliant blur underneath now, and he could feel the trembling rumble of his sled. They rattled into the Chute, a steep traverse, still gaining speed, still bunched and jostling for position. He was in the rear but this was good; he didn't like this early crowding for the corners.

The sheer wall of Basher Bend loomed, a 120-degree right that dropped hard coming out. He was following close in the slipstream of the sled in front of him, overtaking because of the lessened wind resistance. The corner came, and they were on the wall again. With his slightly greater speed he was able to go higher on the wall, nearly to the top and above the other sled. His G-suit tightened. They swarmed out of the corner

and into the Strafing Run, a long, steep dive with a hard pull-out.

A roar rose from the mountain now as the sleds reached speed, a dull rumble like that of avalanche . . . and that is actually what they were now—an avalanche of sleds, and just as deadly.

He pulled ahead of the other sled in the dive and hit the savage pull-out right on the tail of another, and the next turn curved up before them: Hell's Left, a double corner, an abrupt left falling into a short straight with another sharp left at the bottom. He was still overtaking, and they went up the wall side by side, he on the inside, under the other. He eased his left pedal, using edges for the first time, holding himself away from the other by a safe six inches. The course dropped away, straight down the mountain to the second half of the corner, and he felt the sickening sudden smoothness of leaving the ice—he had tried it too fast, and the course was falling away under him. . . .

. . . old Rolf De Kepler, "The Flying Dutchman," laughing over his beer and saying, "Always I am spending more time off the ice than on, hah? So this is more easy to my stomach. Already I have four G-suits to give up on me."

. . . and he had made his last flight three years ago off the top at the bottom of Hell's Left . . . 400 yards, they claimed.

He held firm and straight on the wheel and pulled carefully, barely opening his brakes. The sled touched at a slight angle, lurched, but he caught it by edging quickly. The other sled had pulled ahead. He tucked in behind it. The second left was rushing up at them, narrow and filled with sleds. They dove into it less than a foot apart. Ice chips streamed back from edging runners, rattling against his sled like a storm of bullets. There was an abrupt lurching, the quick left-right slam of air turbulence. A sled was braking hard somewhere ahead. Perhaps two or three. Where? He couldn't see. He reacted automatically . . . full air brakes, hard onto his left edges and steer for the inside; the safest area if a wreck was trying to happen. His sled shivered with the strain of coming off the wall, holding against the force of the corner now only with the knifelike edges of its runners. But the force was too great. He began to skid, edges chattering. He eased them off a little, letting the sled drift slightly sideways. Two others had sliced down to the inside too, edges spraying ice. For a moment he was blinded again, but the corner twisted out flat, and he was through and still on the course, and he knew he was too tight, too hard with his control; he was fighting his sled instead of working with it. . . .

. . . a tourist once asked Erik Sigismund how he controlled his sled, and he answered, "Barely." And even that had failed when he flipped it a year ago and four others ran over him.

An old, lurking thought pounced into him again . . . he couldn't stop this sled now if he wanted to. There was no such thing as stopping, outside of a crash. He had to ride until it ended, and he was suddenly certain that was not going to be at the bottom. Not this time. He had crashed before, too many times, but he had never had this feeling of fear before. Not *this* fear. It was different, and he couldn't say why, and he was letting it affect him. And that was the greatest wrong.

They were thundering into the Jackhammer now, 300 yards of violent dips. Every sled had its brakes out, and there were fast flashes as some fired braking rockets. But where the walls of the course sloped upward the ice was comparatively smooth. He eased left, to the uphill side, and leaned on his left

pedal, holding the sled on the slope with its edges. Then he folded his air brakes and started gaining again. It was necessary; one did not hold back from fear. If that was one's style of life, he would never be a sledder in the first place.

Suddenly from the middle of the leading blurs a sled became airborne from the crest of one of the bumps. It hit once and twisted into the air like something alive. Sleds behind it fired rockets and tried to edge away. One skidded broadside, then rolled. A shattered body panel spun away; the two sleds were demolishing themselves. Someone blew-out, streaking into the sky, canopy sparkling high in the sun—and that meant another sled out of control. He pulled full air brakes and fired a rocket, the force slamming him hard against his chest straps. His left arm was ready to fire the charge under the seat. But if he waited too long. . . .

. . . Kurt Schnabel was proud to be the only man who had never ejected . . . but the one time he had tried he had waited the barest fraction of a moment too long, and his chute came down with his shattered corpse.

The three wild sleds whirled away, spinning out of sight over the low retaining walls. He folded his brakes. There was a trembling in his arms and legs like the slight but solid shuddering of a flywheel out of balance, involuntary and with a threat of getting worse. He cursed himself. He could have blown-out too. No one would have blamed him with that tangle developing in front. But he hadn't . . . and it was too late now.

. . . only one man had ever blown-out without an apparent reason and gotten away with it: Shorty Case in his first race. And when he was asked about it afterwards, asked in that over casual, quiet tone, he had answered, "You bet I blew! 'Cause if I hadn't, man . . ."

But he didn't blow-out that day on the Fallaways, the day his sled somersaulted and sowed its wreckage down the course for a half mile . . . and him too . . .

No, there were no quitters here; only the doers or the dead. And which was he going to be tonight?

. . . drive, don't think . . .

The Jackhammer smoothed out and plunged downward, and they were hurtling now into the Wingover at over 90 mph. Here were the second biggest grandstands on the course, the second greatest concentration of cameras.

Here two ambulance helicopters stood by, and a priest too. The Wingover. . . .

Imagine an airplane peeling off into a dive . . . imagine a sled doing the same on a towering wall of ice, a wall rising like a great, breaking wave, frozen at the moment of its overhanging curl. . . . The Wingover was a monstrous, curving scoop to the right, nearly fifty feet high, rolling the sleds up, over, and hurling them down into a 65-degree pitch when twisted into a 6-G pull-out[2] to the left.

. . . "Impossible!" When Wilfrid von Gerlach laid out the Stuka that is what they told him about the Wingover. "It cannot be done!"

But von Gerlach had been a Grand Prix[3] racer and a stunt pilot, and when the Stuka was finished he took the first sled through. At the finish he sat quietly for a moment, staring back at the mountain. "At the Wingover I was how fast?" he asked thoughtfully. They replied that he'd been radared there at 110 mph. He nodded, then made the state-

---

2. hurling . . . 6-G pull-out. The sleds pull out of the curve at a steep, downhill angle (65 degrees from the horizontal), and they are going so fast that the pressure on them is equal to six times the force of gravity.

3. Grand Prix (grän prē), an annual international series of long-distance automobile races.

*ment the sledders had carried with them ever
since.*

"It's possible."

He watched the leading sleds line up for
that shining sheer curve and felt the fear
freeze through him again. A man was little
more than a captive in his sled here. If he
was on the right line going in, then it was
beautiful; if not, well. . . .

*. . . the brotherly beers and the late
talk . . .*

*"Remember when Otto Domagk left Crip-
ple's Corner in that snow storm?"*

*"Ya, und ven him vas digged out—Vas?
Two hours?—he vas so sleeping."*

"And not a mark on him, remember?"

. . . Remember, remember . . .

He followed in line barely four feet from
the sled in front of him and felt the savage,
sickening blow as the wall raised and rolled
him. A flicker of shadow, a glimpse of the
valley nearly upsidedown, then the fall and
the increasing shriek of wind and runners,
and he was pointing perfectly into the pull-
out, still lined exactly with the sled ahead—
but there was one sled badly out of line . . .

*And someone pulled their air brakes full
open.*

Sleds began weaving in the violent turbulence of those brakes. Rockets flashed. A
sled went sideways, rolling lazily above the
others, and exploded against the wall of the
pull-out. He pulled the ejection lever . . .
nothing happened!

He was dead, he knew that. He saw two
sleds tumbling into the sky, another shattered to pieces and sliding along the course.
All that was necessary was to hit one of
those pieces . . . but the corner was suddenly gone behind. The course unwound into a
long left traverse. He remembered to
breathe. There were tooth chips in his mouth

and the taste of blood. He swerved past a
piece of wreckage, then another . . .

*. . . how many were dead now? Himself
and how many others? But it wasn't fear of
death—what was it? What was it that he'd
walled off inside—that something secret always skirted as carefully as a ship veers from a
hidden reef, knowing it is there—what? And
now the wall was down, and he was
facing. . . .*

His sled shuddered. He was driving badly, too harsh with his edge control. He
narrowly made it through the Boot and
Cripple's Corner, spraying ice behind him,
but it was not the sled that was out of
control. It was him. And he was diving now
straight for the gates of hell at over 110 mph.

It was called the Plummet. It began with
an innocent, wide left, steeply banked, then
the world fell away. It dove over a half mile
headlong down a 50-degree slope straight
into a ravine and up the other side, then into
a full 180-degree uphill hairpin to the right, a
steep straight to the bottom of the ravine
again, and finally into a sharp left and a long,
rolling straight. It had killed more men than
any other part of the course.

Here were the biggest grandstands and
the most hungry eyes of the cameras. Here
there were three clergy, and emergency operating rooms. Here . . .

*. . . here he would complete the formality
of dying.*

He came into the left too low, too fast for
the edges to hold. The sled skidded. He
reacted automatically, holding slight left
edges and steering into the skid. The sled
drifted up the wall, arcing toward the top
where nothing showed but the cold blue of
the sky. He waited, a part of him almost
calm now, waiting to see if the corner would
straighten before he went over the top. It
did, but he was still skidding, close to the

retaining wall, plunging into the half-mile drop nearly sideways. He increased his edges. The tail of the sled brushed the wall and it was suddenly swinging the opposite way. He reversed his wheel and edges, anticipating another skid, but he was not quick enough. The sled bucked, careening up on its left runners. It grazed the wall again, completely out of control now—but he kept trying . . .

. . . now that was it; you kept trying. Over and over. No matter how many times you faced yourself it had to be done again. And again. The Self was never satisfied with single victories—you had to keep trying . . .

And he was empty no more.

The hospital. How many times had he awakened here? And it was always wonderfully the same: gentle warmth and his body finally relaxed and he would test it piece by piece to see what was bent and broken this time; and always the newsmen and the writers and the other assorted ghouls, and always the question and answer period. Punchlining, they called it. . . .

"How did it happen?"

"I dozed off."

"Why didn't you eject?"

"Parachuting is dangerous."

"When did you realize you were out of control?"

"At the starting line."

"What will you do now?"

"Heal."

"Will you race again?"

. . . "It's possible."

Outside, the wind was blowing. ☐☐

Discussion

1. What events in the story made you feel the greatest tension?

2. (a) Where do the events in this story take place? (b) Describe the race course. Which aspects make it a particularly dangerous course?

3. (a) Describe the racing sled. (b) What special features distinguish this sled from an ordinary bobsled?

4. The main character in this story is engaged in several struggles. (a) In what way is he struggling against the other racers? against the race course? (b) In what way is he engaged in a struggle within himself? (c) Which of these struggles do you think is the most important?

5. (a) What specific information about the main character is given in the story? (b) What type of person do you think the racer represents?

6. On page 36 the racer asks himself, "How many were dead now? Himself and how many others?" How do you interpret this remark in view of the fact that the racer is not actually dead?

7. Reread page 37a, 1, in which the racer explains why he keeps trying to race the Stuka. (a) What are some benefits that can result from continually testing oneself in difficult or hazardous situations? (b) When might it be unwise to keep trying to do something "over and over . . . again and again"?

8. This story was written as science fiction. (a) Cite elements that make it seem believable. (b) Which details and events seem unbelievable?

9. Some science-fiction authors use their stories to make a comment on the wisdom or foolishness of human behavior. What point, if any, do you think this author is trying to make?

Extension • Writing

Write a newspaper advertisement or a television commercial to publicize the Stuka. What features would you emphasize? At whom would you direct the commerical?

See **PLOT** Handbook of Literary Terms

"Leave him alone," the hired hand said angrily. "It's his pony." Indeed, could anyone in his family be expected to feel about the pony the way Jody did?

The Gift John Steinbeck

At daybreak Billy Buck emerged from the bunkhouse and stood for a moment on the porch looking up at the sky. He was a broad, bandy-legged little man with a walrus mustache, with square hands, puffed and muscled on the palms. His eyes were a contemplative, watery gray and the hair which protruded from under his Stetson hat was spiky and weathered. Billy was still stuffing his shirt into his blue jeans as he stood on the porch. He unbuckled his belt and tightened it again. The belt showed, by the worn shiny places opposite each hole, the gradual increase of Billy's middle over a period of years. When he had seen to the weather, Billy cleared each nostril by holding its mate closed with his forefinger and blowing fiercely. Then he walked down to the barn, rubbing his hands together. He curried and brushed two saddle horses in the stalls, talking quietly to them all the time; and he had hardly finished when the iron triangle started ringing at the ranch house. Billy stuck the brush and currycomb together and laid them on the rail, and went up to breakfast. His action had been so deliberate and yet so wasteless of time that he came to the house while Mrs. Tiflin was still ringing the triangle. She nodded her gray head to him and withdrew into the kitchen. Billy Buck sat down on the steps, because he was a cow hand, and it wouldn't be fitting that he should go first into the dining room. He heard Mr. Tiflin in the house, stamping his feet into his boots.

The high jangling note of the triangle put the boy Jody in motion. He was only a little boy, ten years old, with hair like dusty yellow grass, and with shy polite gray eyes, and with a mouth that worked when he thought. The triangle picked him up out of sleep. It didn't occur to him to disobey the harsh note. He never had: no one he knew ever had. He brushed the tangled hair out of his eyes and skinned his nightgown off. In a moment he was dressed—blue chambray shirt and overalls. It was late in the summer, so of course there were no shoes to bother with. In the kitchen he waited until his mother got from in front of the sink and went back to the stove. Then he washed himself and brushed back his wet hair with his fingers. His mother turned sharply on him as he left the sink. Jody looked shyly away.

"I've got to cut your hair before long," his mother said. "Breakfast's on the table. Go on in, so Billy can come."

Jody sat at the long table which was covered with white oilcloth washed through to the fabric in some places. The fried eggs lay in rows on their platter. Jody took three eggs on his plate and followed with three thick slices of crisp bacon. He carefully scraped a spot of blood from one of the egg yolks.

Billy Buck clumped in. "That won't hurt you," Billy explained. "That's only a sign the rooster leaves."

Jody's tall stern father came in then and Jody knew from the noise on the floor that he was wearing boots, but he looked under the table anyway, to make sure. His father turned off the oil lamp over the table, for plenty of morning light now came through the windows.

Jody did not ask where his father and Billy Buck were riding that day, but he wished he might go along. His father was a disciplinarian. Jody obeyed him in everything without questions of any kind. Now, Carl Tiflin sat down and reached for the egg platter.

From *The Red Pony* by John Steinbeck. Copyright © 1933, 1961 by John Steinbeck. Reprinted by permission of The Viking Press and McIntosh and Otis, Inc.

"Got the cows ready to go, Billy?" he asked.

"In the lower corral," Billy said. "I could just as well take them in alone."

"Sure you could. But a man needs company. Besides your throat gets pretty dry." Carl Tiflin was jovial this morning.

Jody's mother put her head in the door. "What time do you think to be back, Carl?"

"I can't tell. I've got to see some men in Salinas.[1] Might be gone till dark."

The eggs and coffee and big biscuits disappeared rapidly. Jody followed the two men out of the house. He watched them mount their horses and drive six old milk cows out of the corral and start over the hill toward Salinas. They were going to sell the old cows to the butcher.

When they had disappeared over the crown of the ridge Jody walked up the hill in back of the house. The dogs trotted around the house corner hunching their shoulders and grinning horribly with pleasure. Jody patted their heads—Doubletree Mutt with the big thick tail and yellow eyes, and Smasher, the shepherd, who had killed a coyote and lost an ear in doing it. Smasher's one good ear stood up higher than a collie's ear should. Billy Buck said that always happened. After the frenzied greeting the dogs lowered their noses to the ground in a businesslike way and went ahead, looking back now and then to make sure that the boy was coming. They walked up through the chicken yard and saw the quail eating with the chickens. Smasher chased the chickens a little to keep in practice in case there should ever be sheep to herd. Jody continued on through the large vegetable patch where the green corn was higher than his head. The cow pumpkins were green and small yet. He went on to the sagebrush line where the cold spring ran out of its pipe and fell into a round wooden tub. He leaned over and drank close to the green mossy wood where the water tasted best. Then he turned and looked back on the ranch, on the low, whitewashed house girded with red geraniums, and on the long bunkhouse by the cypress tree where Billy Buck lived alone. Jody could see the great black kettle under the cypress tree. That was where the pigs were scalded. The sun was coming over the ridge now, glaring on the whitewash of the houses and barns, making the wet grass blaze softly. Behind him, in the tall sagebrush, the birds were scampering on the ground, making a great noise among the dry leaves; the squirrels piped shrilly on the side hills. Jody looked along at the far buildings. He felt an uncertainty in the air, a feeling of change and of loss and of the gain of new and unfamiliar things. Over the hillside two big black buzzards sailed low to the ground and their shadows slipped smoothly and quickly ahead of them. Some animal had died in the vicinity. Jody knew it. It might be a cow or it might be the remains of a rabbit. The buzzards overlooked nothing. Jody hated them as all decent things hate them, but they could not be hurt because they made away with carrion.

After a while the boy sauntered down hill again. The dogs had long ago given him up and gone into the brush to do things in their own way. Back through the vegetable garden he went, and he paused for a moment to smash a green muskmelon with his heel, but he was not happy about it. It was a bad thing to do, he knew perfectly well. He kicked dirt over the ruined melon to conceal it.

Back at the house his mother bent over his rough hands, inspecting his fingers and nails. It did little good to start him clean to school, for too many things could happen on the way. She sighed over the black cracks on

1. **Salinas** (sə lē′nəs), city in west central California.

his fingers, and then gave him his books and his lunch and started him on the mile walk to school. She noticed that his mouth was working a good deal this morning.

Jody started his journey. He filled his pockets with little pieces of white quartz that lay in the road, and every so often he took a shot at a bird or at some rabbit that had stayed sunning itself in the road too long. At the crossroads over the bridge he met two friends and the three of them walked to school together, making ridiculous strides and being rather silly. School had just opened two weeks before. There was still a spirit of revolt among the pupils.

It was four o'clock in the afternoon when Jody topped the hill and looked down on the ranch again. He looked for the saddle horses, but the corral was empty. His father was not back yet. He went slowly, then, toward the afternoon chores. At the ranch house, he found his mother sitting on the porch, mending socks.

"There's two doughnuts in the kitchen for you," she said. Jody slid to the kitchen, and returned with half of one of the doughnuts already eaten and his mouth full. His mother asked him what he had learned in school that day, but she didn't listen to his doughnut-muffled answer. She interrupted, "Jody, tonight see you fill the woodbox clear full. Last night you crossed the sticks and it wasn't only about half full. Lay the sticks flat tonight. And Jody, some of the hens are hiding eggs, or else the dogs are eating them. Look about in the grass and see if you can find any nests."

Jody, still eating, went out and did his chores. He saw the quail come down to eat with the chickens when he threw out the grain. For some reason his father was proud to have them come. He never allowed any shooting near the house for fear the quail might go away.

When the woodbox was full, Jody took his twenty-two rifle up to the cold spring at the brush line. He drank again and then aimed the gun at all manner of things, at rocks, at birds on the wing, at the big black pig kettle under the cypress tree, but he didn't shoot, for he had no cartridges and wouldn't have until he was twelve. If his father had seen him aim the rifle in the direction of the house he would have put the cartridges off another year. Jody remembered this and did not point the rifle down the hill again. Two years was enough to wait for cartridges. Nearly all of his father's presents were given with reservations which hampered their value somewhat. It was good discipline.

The supper waited until dark for his father to return. When at last he came in with Billy Buck, Jody could smell the delicious brandy on their breaths. Inwardly he rejoiced, for his father sometimes talked to him when he smelled of brandy, sometimes even told things he had done in the wild days when he was a boy.

After supper, Jody sat by the fireplace and his shy polite eyes sought the room corners, and he waited for his father to tell what it was he contained, for Jody knew he had news of some sort. But he was disappointed. His father pointed a stern finger at him.

"You'd better go to bed, Jody. I'm going to need you in the morning."

That wasn't so bad. Jody liked to do things he had to do as long as they weren't routine things. He looked at the floor and his mouth worked out a question before he spoke it. "What are we going to do in the morning, kill a pig?" he asked softly.

"Never you mind. You better get to bed."

When the door was closed behind him, Jody heard his father and Billy Buck chuckling and he knew it was a joke of some kind. And later, when he lay in bed, trying to make words out of the murmurs in the other room, he heard his father protest, "But, Ruth, I didn't give much for him."

Jody heard the hoot owls hunting mice down by the barn, and he heard a fruit tree limb tap-tapping against the house. A cow was lowing when he went to sleep.

When the triangle sounded in the morning, Jody dressed more quickly even than usual. In the kitchen, while he washed his face and combed back his hair, his mother addressed him irritably. "Don't you go out until you get a good breakfast in you."

He went into the dining room and sat at the long white table. He took a steaming hot cake from the platter, arranged two fried eggs on it, covered them with another hot cake and squashed the whole thing with his fork.

His father and Billy Buck came in. Jody knew from the sound on the floor that both of them were wearing flat-heeled shoes, but he peered under the table to make sure. His father turned off the oil lamp, for the day had arrived, and he looked stern and disciplinary, but Billy Buck didn't look at Jody at all. He avoided the shy questioning eyes of the boy and soaked a whole piece of toast in his coffee.

Carl Tiflin said crossly, "You come with us after breakfast!"

Jody had trouble with his food then, for he felt a kind of doom in the air. After Billy had tilted his saucer and drained the coffee which had slopped into it, and had wiped his hands on his jeans, the two men stood up from the table and went out into the morning light together, and Jody respectfully followed a little behind them. He tried to keep his mind from running ahead, tried to keep it absolutely motionless.

His mother called, "Carl! Don't you let it keep him from school."

They marched past the cypress, where a single-tree hung from a limb to butcher the pigs on, and past the black iron kettle, so it was not a pig killing. The sun shone over the hill and threw long, dark shadows of the trees and buildings. They crossed a stubble field to short-cut to the barn. Jody's father unhooked the door and they went in. They had been walking toward the sun on the way down. The barn was black as night in contrast and warm from the hay and from the beasts. Jody's father moved over toward the one box stall. "Come here!" he ordered. Jody could begin to see things now. He looked into the box stall and then stepped back quickly.

A red pony colt was looking at him out of the stall. Its tense ears were forward and a light of disobedience was in its eyes. Its coat was rough and thick as an airdale's fur and its mane was long and tangled. Jody's throat collapsed in on itself and cut his breath short.

"He needs a good currying," his father said, "and if I ever hear of you not feeding him or leaving his stall dirty, I'll sell him off in a minute."

Jody couldn't bear to look at the pony's eyes any more. He gazed down at his hands for a moment, and he asked very shyly, "Mine?" No one answered him. He put his hand out toward the pony. Its gray nose came close, sniffing loudly, and then the lips drew back and the strong teeth closed on Jody's fingers. The pony shook its head up and down and seemed to laugh with amusement. Jody regarded his bruised fingers. "Well," he said with pride—"Well, I guess he can bite all right." The two men laughed, somewhat in relief. Carl Tiflin went out of the barn and walked up a side hill to be by himself, for he was embarrassed, but Billy Buck stayed. It was easier to talk to Billy Buck. Jody asked again—"Mine?"

Billy became professional in tone. "Sure! That is, if you look out for him and break him right. I'll show you how. He's just a colt. You can't ride him for some time."

Jody put out his bruised hand again, and this time the red pony let his nose be rubbed. "I ought to have a carrot," Jody said. "Where'd we get him, Billy?"

"Bought him at a sheriff's auction," Billy explained. "A show went broke in Salinas and had debts. The sheriff was selling off their stuff."

The pony stretched out his nose and shook the forelock from his wild eyes. Jody stroked the nose a little. He said softly, "There isn't a—saddle?"

Billy Buck laughed. "I'd forgot. Come along."

In the harness room he lifted down a little saddle of red morocco leather. "It's just a show saddle," Billy Buck said disparagingly. "It isn't practical for the brush, but it was cheap at the sale."

Jody couldn't trust himself to look at the saddle either, and he couldn't speak at all. He brushed the shining red leather with his finger tips, and after a long time he said, "It'll look pretty on him though." He thought of the grandest and prettiest things he knew. "If he hasn't a name already, I think I'll call him Gabilan Mountains," he said.

Billy Buck knew how he felt. "It's a pretty long name. Why don't you just call him Gabilan? That means hawk. That would be a fine name for him." Billy felt glad. "If you will collect tail hair, I might be able to make a hair rope for you sometime. You could use it for a hackamore."

Jody wanted to go back to the box stall. "Could I lead him to school, do you think—to show the kids?"

But Billy shook his head. "He's not even halter-broke yet. We had a time getting him here. Had to almost drag him. You better be starting for school though."

"I'll bring the kids to see him here this afternoon," Jody said.

Six boys came over the hill half an hour early that afternoon, running hard, their

heads down, their forearms working, their breath whistling. They swept by the house and cut across the stubble field to the barn. And then they stood self-consciously before the pony, and then they looked at Jody with eyes in which there was a new admiration and a new respect. Before today Jody had been a boy, dressed in overalls and a blue shirt—quieter than most, even suspected of being a little cowardly. And now he was different. Out of a thousand centuries they drew the ancient admiration of the footman for the horseman. They knew instinctively that a man on a horse is spiritually as well as physically bigger than a man on foot. They knew that Jody had been miraculously lifted out of equality with them, and had been placed over them. Gabilan put his head out of the stall and sniffed them.

"Why'n't you ride him?" the boys cried. "Why'n't you braid his tail with ribbons like in the fair?" "When you going to ride him?"

Jody's courage was up. He too felt the superiority of the horseman. "He's not old enough. Nobody can ride him for a long time. I'm going to train him on the long halter. Billy Buck is going to show me how."

"Well, can't we even lead him around a little?"

"He isn't even halter-broke," Jody said. He wanted to be completely alone when he took the pony out the first time. "Come and see the saddle."

They were speechless at the red morocco saddle, completely shocked out of comment. "It isn't much use in the brush," Jody explained. "It'll look pretty on him though. Maybe I'll ride bareback when I go into the brush."

"How you going to rope a cow without a saddle horn?"

"Maybe I'll get another saddle for every day. My father might want me to help him with the stock." He let them feel the red saddle, and showed them the brass chain throatlatch on the bridle and the big brass buttons at each temple where the headstall and brow band crossed. The whole thing was too wonderful. They had to go away after a little while, and each boy, in his mind, searched among his possessions for a bribe worthy of offering in return for a ride on the red pony when the time should come.

Jody was glad when they had gone. He took brush and currycomb from the wall, took down the barrier of the box stall and stepped cautiously in. The pony's eyes glittered, and he edged around into kicking position. But Jody touched him on the shoulder and rubbed his high arched neck as he had always seen Billy Buck do, and he crooned, "So-o-o boy," in a deep voice. The pony gradually relaxed his tenseness. Jody curried and brushed until a pile of dead hair lay in the stall and until the pony's coat had taken on a deep red shine. Each time he finished he thought it might have been done better. He braided the mane into a dozen little pigtails, and he braided the forelock, and then he undid them and brushed the hair out straight again.

Jody did not hear his mother enter the barn. She was angry when she came, but when she looked in at the pony and at Jody working over him, she felt a curious pride rise up in her. "Have you forgot the woodbox?" she asked gently. "It's not far off from dark and there's not a stick of wood in the house, and the chickens aren't fed."

Jody quickly put up his tools. "I forgot, ma'am."

"Well, after this do your chores first. Then you won't forget. I expect you'll forget lots of things now if I don't keep an eye on you."

"Can I have carrots from the garden for him, ma'am?"

She had to think about that. "Oh—I guess so, if you only take the big tough ones."

"Carrots keep the coat good," he said, and again she felt the curious rush of pride.

Jody never waited for the triangle to get him out of bed after the coming of the pony. It became his habit to creep out of bed even before his mother was awake, to slip into his clothes and to go quietly down to the barn to see Gabilan. In the gray quiet mornings when the land and the brush and the houses and the trees were silver-gray and black like a photograph negative, he stole toward the barn, past the sleeping stones and the sleeping cypress tree. The turkeys, roosting in the tree out of coyotes' reach, clicked drowsily. The fields glowed with a gray frostlike light and in the dew the tracks of rabbits and of field mice stood out sharply. The good dogs came stiffly out of their little houses, hackles up and deep growls in their throats. Then they caught Jody's scent, and their stiff tails rose up and waved a greeting—Doubletree Mutt with the big thick tail, and Smasher, the incipient shepherd—then went lazily back to their warm beds.

It was a strange time and a mysterious journey to Jody—an extension of a dream. When he first had the pony he liked to torture himself during the trip by thinking Gabilan would not be in his stall, and worse, would never have been there. And he had other delicious little self-induced pains. He thought how the rats had gnawed ragged holes in the red saddle, and how the mice had nibbled Gabilan's tail until it was stringy and thin. He usually ran the last little way to the barn. He unlatched the rusty hasp of the barn door and stepped in, and no matter how quietly he opened the door, Gabilan was always looking at him over the barrier of the box stall and Gabilan whinnied softly and stamped his front foot, and his eyes had big sparks of red fire in them like oakwood embers.

Sometimes, if the work horses were to be used that day, Jody found Billy Buck in the barn harnessing and currying. Billy stood with him and looked long at Gabilan and he told Jody a great many things about horses. He explained that they were terribly afraid for their feet, so that one must make a practice of lifting the legs and patting the hoofs and ankles to remove their terror. He told Jody how horses love conversation. He must talk to the pony all the time, and tell him the reasons for everything. Billy wasn't sure a horse could understand everything that was said to him, but it was impossible to say how much was understood. A horse never kicked up a fuss if someone he liked explained things to him. Billy could give examples, too. He had known, for instance, a horse nearly dead-beat with fatigue to perk up when told it was only a little farther to his destination. And he had known a horse paralyzed with fright to come out of it when his rider told him what it was that was frightening him. While he talked in the mornings, Billy Buck cut twenty or thirty straws into neat three-inch lengths and stuck them into his hatband. Then during the whole day, if he wanted to pick his teeth or merely to chew on something, he had only to reach up for one of them.

Jody listened carefully, for he knew and the whole country knew that Billy Buck was a fine hand with horses. Billy's own horse was a stringy cayuse with a hammerhead,[2] but he nearly always won the first prizes at the stock trials. Billy could rope a steer, take a double half-hitch about the horn with his riata, and dismount, and his horse would play the steer as an angler plays a fish, keeping a tight rope until the steer was down or beaten.

Every morning, after Jody had curried and brushed the pony, he let down the barrier of the stall, and Gabilan thrust past him and raced down the barn and into the

---

2. *cayuse* (kī ūs′) *with a hammerhead,* an Indian pony with a head shaped like a double-headed hammer.

corral. Around and around he galloped, and sometimes he jumped forward and landed on stiff legs. He stood quivering, stiff ears forward, eyes rolling so that the whites showed, pretending to be frightened. At last he walked snorting to the water trough and buried his nose in the water up to the nostrils. Jody was proud then, for he knew that was the way to judge a horse. Poor horses only touched their lips to the water, but a fine spirited beast put his whole nose and mouth under, and only left room to breathe.

Then Jody stood and watched the pony, and he saw things he had never noticed about any other horse, the sleek, sliding flank muscles and the cords of the buttocks, which flexed like a closing fist, and the shine the sun put on the red coat. Having seen horses all his life, Jody had never looked at them very closely before. But now he noticed the moving ears which gave expression and even inflection of expression to the face. The pony talked with his ears. You could tell exactly how he felt about everything by the way his ears pointed. Sometimes they were

stiff and upright and sometimes lax and sagging. They went back when he was angry or fearful, and forward when he was anxious and curious and pleased; and their exact position indicated which emotion he had.

Billy Buck kept his word. In the early fall the training began. First there was the halter-breaking, and that was the hardest because it was the first thing. Jody held a carrot and coaxed and promised and pulled on the rope. The pony set his feet like a burro when he felt the strain. But before long he learned. Jody walked all over the ranch leading him. Gradually he took to dropping the rope until the pony followed him unled wherever he went.

And then came the training on the long halter. That was slower work. Jody stood in the middle of a circle, holding the long halter. He clucked with his tongue and the pony started to walk in a big circle, held in by the long rope. He clucked again to make the pony trot, and again to make him gallop. Around and around Gabilan went thundering and enjoying it immensely. Then he called,

"Whoa," and the pony stopped. It was not long until Gabilan was perfect at it. But in many ways he was a bad pony. He bit Jody in the pants and stomped on Jody's feet. Now and then his ears went back and he aimed a tremendous kick at the boy. Every time he did one of these bad things, Gabilan settled back and seemed to laugh to himself.

Billy Buck worked at the hair rope in the evenings before the fireplace. Jody collected tail hair in a bag, and he sat and watched Billy slowly constructing the rope, twisting a few hairs to make a string and rolling two strings together for a cord, and then braiding a number of cords to make the rope. Billy rolled the finished rope on the floor under his foot to make it round and hard.

The long halter work rapidly approached perfection. Jody's father, watching the pony stop and start and trot and gallop, was a little bothered by it.

"He's getting to be almost a trick pony," he complained. "I don't like trick horses. It takes all the—dignity out of a horse to make him do tricks. Why, a trick horse is kind of like an actor—no dignity, no character of his own." And his father said, "I guess you better be getting him used to the saddle pretty soon."

Jody rushed for the harness room. For some time he had been riding the saddle on a sawhorse. He changed the stirrup length over and over, and could never get it just right. Sometimes, mounted on the sawhorse in the harness room, with collars and hames and tugs hung all about him, Jody rode out beyond the room. He carried his rifle across the pommel. He saw fields go flying by; and he heard the beat of the galloping hoofs.

It was a ticklish job, saddling the pony the first time. Gabilan hunched and reared and threw the saddle off before the cinch could be tightened. It had to be replaced again and again until at last the pony let it stay. And the cinching was difficult, too. Day by day Jody tightened the girth a little more until at last the pony didn't mind the saddle at all.

Then there was the bridle. Billy explained how to use a stick of licorice for a bit until Gabilan was used to having something in his mouth. Billy explained, "Of course we

could force-break him to everything, but he wouldn't be as good a horse if we did. He'd always be a little bit afraid, and he wouldn't mind because he wanted to."

The first time the pony wore the bridle he whipped his head about and worked his tongue against the bit until the blood oozed from the corners of his mouth. He tried to rub the headstall off on the manger. His ears pivoted about and his eyes turned red with fear and with general rambunctiousness. Jody rejoiced, for he knew that only a mean-souled horse does not resent training.

And Jody trembled when he thought of the time when he would first sit in the saddle. The pony would probably throw him off. There was no disgrace in that. The disgrace would come if he did not get right up and mount again. Sometimes he dreamed that he lay in the dirt and cried and couldn't make himself mount again. The shame of the dream lasted until the middle of the day.

Gabilan was growing fast. Already he had lost the long-leggedness of the colt; his mane was getting longer and blacker. Under the constant currying and brushing his coat lay as smooth and gleaming as orange-red lacquer. Jody oiled the hoofs and kept them carefully trimmed so they would not crack.

The hair rope was nearly finished. Jody's father gave him an old pair of spurs and bent in the side bars and cut down the strap and took up the chainlets until they fitted. And then one day Carl Tiflin said:

"The pony's growing faster than I thought. I guess you can ride him by Thanksgiving. Think you can stick on?"

"I don't know," Jody said shyly. Thanksgiving was only three weeks off. He hoped it wouldn't rain, for rain would spot the red saddle.

Gabilan knew and liked Jody by now. He nickered when Jody came across the stubble field, and in the pasture he came running when his master whistled for him. There was always a carrot for him every time.

Billy Buck gave him riding instructions over and over. "Now when you get up there, just grab tight with your knees and keep your hands away from the saddle, and if you get throwed, don't let that stop you. No matter how good a man is, there's always some horse can pitch him. You just climb up again before he gets to feeling smart about it. Pretty soon, he won't throw you no more, and pretty soon he *can't* throw you no more. That's the way to do it."

"I hope it don't rain before," Jody said.

"Why not? Don't want to get throwed in the mud?"

That was partly it, and also he was afraid that in the flurry of bucking Gabilan might slip and fall on him and break his leg or his hip. He had seen that happen to men before, had seen how they writhed on the ground like squashed bugs, and he was afraid of it.

He practiced on the sawhorse how he would hold the reins in his left hand and a hat in his right hand. If he kept his hands thus busy, he couldn't grab the horn if he felt himself going off. He didn't like to think of what would happen if he did grab the horn. Perhaps his father and Billy Buck would never speak to him again, they would be so ashamed. The news would get about and his mother would be ashamed too. And in the school yard—it was too awful to contemplate.

He began putting his weight in a stirrup when Gabilan was saddled, but he didn't throw his leg over the pony's back. That was forbidden until Thanksgiving.

Every afternoon he put the red saddle on the pony and cinched it tight. The pony was learning already to fill his stomach out unnaturally large while the cinching was going on, and then to let it down when the straps were fixed. Sometimes Jody led him up to the brush line and let him drink from the round green tub, and sometimes he led him up through the stubble field to the hilltop from which it was possible to see the white town of Salinas and the geometric fields of the great valley, and the oak trees clipped by the sheep. Now and then they broke through the brush and came to little cleared circles so hedged in that the world was gone and only the sky and the circle of brush were left from the old life. Gabilan liked these trips and showed it by keeping his head very high and by quivering his nostrils with interest. When the two came back from an expedition they smelled of the sweet sage they had forced through.

Time dragged on toward Thanksgiving, but winter came fast. The clouds swept down and hung all day over the land and brushed the hilltops, and the winds blew shrilly at night. All day the dry oak leaves drifted down from the trees until they covered the ground, and yet the trees were unchanged.

Jody had wished it might not rain before Thanksgiving, but it did. The brown earth turned dark and the trees glistened. The cut ends of the stubble turned black with mildew; the haystacks grayed from exposure to the damp, and on the roofs the moss, which had been all summer as gray as lizards, turned a brilliant yellow-green. During the week of rain, Jody kept the pony in the box stall out of the dampness, except for a little time after school when he took him out for exercise and to drink at the water trough in the upper corral. Not once did Gabilan get wet.

The wet weather continued until little new grass appeared. Jody walked to school dressed in a slicker and short rubber boots.

At length one morning the sun came out brightly. Jody, at his work in the box stall, said to Billy Buck, "Maybe I'll leave Gabilan in the corral when I go to school today."

"Be good for him to be out in the sun," Billy assured him. "No animal likes to be cooped up too long. Your father and me are going back on the hill to clean the leaves out of the spring." Billy nodded and picked his teeth with one of his little straws.

"If the rain comes, though—" Jody suggested.

"Not likely to rain today. She's rained herself out." Billy pulled up his sleeves and snapped his arm bands. "If it comes on to rain—why a little rain don't hurt a horse."

"Well, if it does come on to rain, you put him in, will you, Billy? I'm scared he might get cold so I couldn't ride him when the time comes."

"Oh sure! I'll watch out for him if we get back in time. But it won't rain today."

And so Jody, when he went to school, left Gabilan standing out in the corral.

Billy Buck wasn't wrong about many things. He couldn't be. But he was wrong about the weather that day, for a little after noon the clouds pushed over the hills and the rain began to pour down. Jody heard it start on the schoolhouse roof. He considered holding up one finger for permission to go to the outhouse and, once outside, running for home to put the pony in. Punishment would be prompt both at school and at home. He gave it up and took ease from Billy's assurance that rain couldn't hurt a horse. When school was finally out, he hurried home through the dark rain. The banks at the sides of the road spouted little jets of muddy water. The rain slanted and swirled under a cold and gusty wind. Jody dog-trotted home, slopping through the gravelly mud of the road.

From the top of the ridge he could see Gabilan standing miserably in the corral. The red coat was almost black, and streaked with water. He stood head down with his rump to the rain and wind. Jody arrived running and threw open the barn door and led the wet pony in by his forelock. Then he found a gunny sack and rubbed the soaked hair and rubbed the legs and ankles. Gabilan stood patiently, but he trembled in gusts like the wind.

When he had dried the pony as well as he could, Jody went up to the house and brought hot water down to the barn and soaked the grain in it. Gabilan was not very hungry. He nibbled at the hot mash, but he was not very much interested in it, and he still shivered now and then. A little steam rose from his damp back.

It was almost dark when Billy Buck and Carl Tiflin came home. "When the rain started we put up at Ben Herche's place, and the rain never let up all afternoon," Carl Tiflin explained. Jody looked reproachfully at Billy Buck and Billy felt guilty.

"You said it wouldn't rain," Jody accused him.

Billy looked away. "It's hard to tell, this time of year," he said, but his excuse was lame. He had no right to be fallible, and he knew it.

"The pony got wet, got soaked through."

"Did you dry him off?"

"I rubbed him with a sack and I gave him hot grain."

Billy nodded in agreement.

"Do you think he'll take cold, Billy?"

"A little rain never hurt anything," Billy assured him.

Jody's father joined the conversation then and lectured the boy a little. "A horse," he said, "isn't any lap-dog kind of thing." Carl Tiflin hated weakness and sickness, and he held a violent contempt for helplessness.

Jody's mother put a platter of steaks on the table and boiled potatoes and boiled squash, which clouded the room with their steam. They sat down to eat. Carl Tiflin still grumbled about weakness put into animals and men by too much coddling.

Billy Buck felt bad about his mistake. "Did you blanket him?" he asked.

"No. I couldn't find any blanket. I laid some sacks over his back."

"We'll go down and cover him up after we eat, then." Billy felt better about it then. When Jody's father had gone in to the fire and his mother was washing dishes, Billy found and lighted a lantern. He and Jody walked through the mud to the barn. The barn was dark and warm and sweet. The horses still munched their evening hay. "You hold the lantern!" Billy ordered. And he felt the pony's legs and tested the heat of the flanks. He put his cheek against the pony's gray muzzle and then he rolled up the eyelids to look at the eyeballs and he lifted the lips to see the gums, and he put his fingers inside the ears. "He don't seem so chipper," Billy said. "I'll give him a rubdown."

Then Billy found a sack and rubbed the pony's legs violently and he rubbed the chest and the withers. Gabilan was strangely spiritless. He submitted patiently to the rubbing. At last Billy brought an old cotton comforter from the saddle room, and threw it over the pony's back and tied it at neck and chest with string.

"Now he'll be all right in the morning," Billy said.

Jody's mother looked up when he got back to the house. "You're late up from bed," she said. She held his chin in her hand and brushed the tangled hair out of his eyes

and she said, "Don't worry about the pony. He'll be all right. Billy's as good as any horse doctor in the country."

Jody hadn't known she could see his worry. He pulled gently away from her and knelt down in front of the fireplace until it burned his stomach. He scorched himself through and then went in to bed, but it was a hard thing to go to sleep. He awakened after what seemed a long time. The room was dark but there was a grayness in the window like that which precedes the dawn. He got up and found his overalls and searched for the legs, and then the clock in the other room struck two. He laid his clothes down and got back into bed. It was broad daylight when he awakened again. For the first time he had slept through the ringing of the triangle. He leaped up, flung on his clothes and went out of the door still buttoning his shirt. His mother looked after him for a moment and then went quietly back to her work. Her eyes were brooding and kind. Now and then her mouth smiled a little but without changing her eyes at all.

Jody ran on toward the barn. Halfway there he heard the sound he dreaded, the hollow rasping cough of a horse. He broke into a sprint then. In the barn he found Billy Buck with the pony. Billy was rubbing its legs with his strong thick hands. He looked up and smiled gaily. "He just took a little cold," Billy said. "We'll have him out of it in a couple of days."

Jody looked at the pony's face. The eyes were half closed and the lids thick and dry. In the eye corners a crust of hard mucus stuck. Gabilan's ears hung loosely sideways and his head was low. Jody put out his hand, but the pony did not move close to it. He coughed again and his whole body constricted with the effort. A little stream of fluid ran from his nostrils.

Jody looked back at Billy Buck. "He's awful sick, Billy."

"Just a little cold, like I said," Billy insisted. "You go get some breakfast and then go back to school. I'll take care of him."

"But you might have to do something else. You might leave him."

"No, I won't. I won't leave him at all. Tomorrow's Saturday. Then you can stay with him all day." Billy had failed again, and he felt bad about it. He had to cure the pony now.

Jody walked up to the house and took his place listlessly at the table. The eggs and bacon were cold and greasy, but he didn't notice it. He ate his usual amount. He didn't even ask to stay home from school. His mother pushed his hair back when she took his plate. "Billy'll take care of the pony," she assured him.

He moped through the whole day at school. He couldn't answer any questions nor read any words. He couldn't even tell anyone the pony was sick, for that might make him sicker. And when school was finally out he started home in dread. He walked slowly and let the other boys leave him. He wished he might continue walking and never arrive at the ranch.

Billy was in the barn, as he had promised, and the pony was worse. His eyes were almost closed now, and his breath whistled shrilly past an obstruction in his nose. A film covered that part of the eyes that was visible at all. It was doubtful whether the pony could see any more. Now and then he snorted, to clear his nose, and by the action seemed to plug it tighter. Jody looked dispiritedly at the pony's coat. The hair lay rough and unkempt and seemed to have lost all of its old luster. Billy stood quietly beside the stall. Jody hated to ask, but he had to know.

"Billy, is he—is he going to get well?"

Billy put his fingers between the bars under the pony's jaw and felt about. "Feel here," he said and he guided Jody's fingers to a large lump under the jaw. "When that gets bigger, I'll open it up and then he'll get better."

Jody looked quickly away, for he had heard about that lump. "What is the matter with him?"

Billy didn't want to answer, but he had to. He couldn't be wrong three times. "Strangles," he said shortly, "but don't you worry about that. I'll pull him out of it. I've seen them get well when they were worse than Gabilan is. I'm going to steam him now. You can help."

"Yes," Jody said miserably. He followed Billy into the grain room and watched him make the steaming bag ready. It was a long canvas nose bag with straps to go over a horse's ears. Billy filled it one-third full of bran and then he added a couple of handfuls of dried hops. On top of the dry substance he poured a little carbolic acid and a little turpentine.

"I'll be mixing it all up while you run to the house for a kettle of boiling water," Billy said.

When Jody came back with the steaming kettle, Billy buckled the straps over Gabilan's head and fitted the bag tightly around his nose. Then through a little hole in the side of the bag he poured the boiling water on the mixture. The pony started away as a cloud of strong steam rose up, but then the soothing fumes crept through his nose and into his lungs, and the sharp steam began to clear out the nasal passages. He breathed loudly. His legs trembled in an ague, and his eyes closed against the biting cloud. Billy poured in more water and kept the steam rising for fifteen minutes. At last he set down the kettle and took the bag from Gabilan's nose. The pony looked better. He breathed freely, and his eyes were open wider than they had been.

"See how good it makes him feel," Billy said. "Now we'll wrap him up in the blanket again. Maybe he'll be nearly well by morning."

"I'll stay with him tonight," Jody suggested.

"No. Don't you do it. I'll bring my blankets down here and put them in the hay. You can stay tomorrow and steam him if he needs it."

The evening was falling when they went to the house for their supper. Jody didn't even realize that someone else had fed the chickens and filled the woodbox. He walked up past the house to the dark brush line and took a drink of water from the tub. The spring water was so cold that it stung his mouth and drove a shiver through him. The sky above the hills was still light. He saw a hawk flying so high that it caught the sun on its breast and shone like a spark. Two blackbirds were driving him down the sky, glittering as they attacked their enemy. In the west, the clouds were moving in to rain again.

Jody's father didn't speak at all while the family ate supper, but after Billy Buck had taken his blankets and gone to sleep in the barn, Carl Tiflin built a high fire in the fireplace and told stories. He told about the wild man who ran naked through the country and had a tail and ears like a horse, and he told about the rabbit-cats of Moro Cojo that hopped into the trees for birds. He revived the famous Maxwell brothers who found a vein of gold and hid the traces of it so carefully that they could never find it again.

Jody sat with his chin in his hands; his mouth worked nervously and his father gradually became aware that he wasn't listening very carefully. "Isn't that funny?" he asked.

Jody laughed politely and said, "Yes, sir." His father was angry and hurt, then. He didn't tell any more stories. After a while, Jody took a lantern and went down to the barn. Billy Buck was asleep in the hay, and, except that his breath rasped a little in his lungs, the pony seemed to be much better. Jody stayed a little while, running his fingers over the red rough coat, and then he took up the lantern and went back to the house. When he was in bed, his mother came into the room.

"Have you enough covers on? It's getting winter."

"Yes, ma'am."

"Well, get some rest tonight." She hesitated to go out, stood uncertainly. "The pony will be all right," she said.

Jody was tired. He went to sleep quickly and didn't awaken until dawn. The triangle sounded, and Billy Buck came up from the barn before Jody could get out of the house.

"How is he?" Jody demanded.

Billy always wolfed his breakfast. "Pretty good. I'm going to open that lump this morning. Then he'll be better maybe."

After breakfast, Billy got out his best knife, one with a needle point. He whetted the shining blade a long time on a little carborundum stone. He tried the point and the blade again and again on his calloused thumb ball, and at last he tried it on his upper lip.

On the way to the barn, Jody noticed how the young grass was up and how the stubble was melting day by day into the new green crop of volunteer. It was a cold sunny morning.

As soon as he saw the pony, Jody knew he was worse. His eyes were closed and sealed shut with dried mucus. His head hung so low that his nose almost touched the straw of his bed. There was a little groan in each breath, a deep-seated, patient groan.

Billy lifted the weak head and made a quick slash with the knife. Jody saw the yellow pus run out. He held up the head while Billy swabbed out the wound with weak carbolic acid salve.

"Now he'll feel better," Billy assured him. "That yellow poison is what makes him sick."

Jody looked unbelieving at Billy Buck. "He's awful sick."

Billy thought a long time what to say. He nearly tossed off a careless assurance, but he saved himself in time. "Yes, he's pretty sick," he said at last. "I've seen worse ones get well. If he doesn't get pneumonia, we'll pull him through. You stay with him. If he gets worse, you can come and get me."

For a long time after Billy went away, Jody stood beside the pony, stroking him behind the ears. The pony didn't flip his head the way he had done when he was well. The groaning in his breathing was becoming more hollow.

Doubletree Mutt looked into the barn, his big tail waving provocatively, and Jody was so incensed at his health that he found a hard black clod on the floor and deliberately threw it. Doubletree Mutt went yelping away to nurse a bruised paw.

In the middle of the morning, Billy Buck came back and made another steam bag. Jody watched to see whether the pony improved this time as he had before. His breathing eased a little, but he did not raise his head.

The Saturday dragged on. Late in the afternoon Jody went to the house and brought his bedding down and made up a place to sleep in the hay. He didn't ask permission. He knew from the way his mother looked at him that she would let him do almost anything. That night he left a lantern burning on a wire over the box stall. Billy had told him to rub the pony's legs every little while.

At nine o'clock the wind sprang up and howled around the barn. And in spite of his worry, Jody grew sleepy. He got into his blankets and went to sleep, but the breathy groans of the pony sounded in his dreams. And in his sleep he heard a crashing noise which went on and on until it awakened him. The wind was rushing through the barn. He sprang up and looked down the lane of stalls. The barn door had blown open, and the pony was gone.

He caught the lantern and ran outside into the gale, and he saw Gabilan weakly shambling away into the darkness, head down, legs working slowly and mechanically. When Jody ran up and caught him by the forelock, he allowed himself to be led back and put into his stall. His groans were louder, and a fierce whistling came from his nose. Jody didn't sleep any more then. The hissing of the pony's breath grew louder and sharper.

He was glad when Billy Buck came in at dawn. Billy looked for a time at the pony as though he had never seen him before. He felt the ears and flanks. "Jody," he said, "I've got to do something you won't want to see. You run up to the house for a while."

Jody grabbed him fiercely by the forearm. "You're not going to shoot him?"

Billy patted his hand. "No. I'm going to open a little hole in his windpipe so he can breathe. His nose is filled up. When he gets well, we'll put a brass button in the hole for him to breathe through."

Jody couldn't have gone away if he had wanted to. It was awful to see the red hide cut, but infinitely more terrible to know it was being cut and not to see it. "I'll stay right here," he said bitterly. "You sure you got to?"

"Yes. I'm sure. If you stay, you can hold his head. If it doesn't make you sick, that is."

The fine knife came out again and was whetted again just as carefully as it had been the first time. Jody held the pony's head up and the throat taut, while Billy felt up and down for the right place. Jody sobbed once as the bright knife point disappeared into the throat. The pony plunged weakly away and then stood still, trembling violently. The blood ran thickly out and up the knife and across Billy's hand and into his shirt sleeve. The sure square hand sawed out a round hole in the flesh, and the breath came bursting out of the hole, throwing a fine spray of blood. With the rush of oxygen, the pony took a sudden strength. He lashed out with his hind feet and tried to rear, but Jody held his head down while Billy mopped the new wound with carbolic salve. It was a good job. The blood stopped flowing and the air puffed out the hole and sucked it in regularly with a little bubbling noise.

The rain brought in by the night wind began to fall on the barn roof. Then the triangle rang for breakfast. "You go up and eat while I wait," Billy said. "We've got to keep this hole from plugging up."

Jody walked slowly out of the barn. He was too dispirited to tell Billy how the barn door had blown open and let the pony out. He emerged into the wet gray morning and sloshed up to the house, taking a perverse pleasure in splashing through all the puddles. His mother fed him and put dry clothes on. She didn't question him. She seemed to know he couldn't answer questions. But when he was ready to go back to the barn she brought him a pan of steaming meal. "Give him this," she said.

But Jody did not take the pan. He said, "He won't eat anything," and ran out of the house. At the barn, Billy showed him how to fix a ball of cotton on a stick, with which to swab out the breathing hole when it became clogged with mucus.

Jody's father walked into the barn and stood with them in front of the stall. At length he turned to the boy. "Hadn't you better come with me? I'm going to drive over the hill." Jody shook his head. "You better come on, out of this," his father insisted.

Billy turned on him angrily. "Let him alone. It's his pony, isn't it?"

Carl Tiflin walked away without saying another word. His feelings were badly hurt.

All morning Jody kept the wound open and the air passing in and out freely. At noon the pony lay wearily down on his side and stretched his nose out.

Billy came back. "If you're going to stay with him tonight, you better take a little nap," he said. Jody went absently out of the barn. The sky had cleared to a hard thin blue. Everywhere the birds were busy with worms that had come to the damp surface of the ground.

Jody walked to the brush line and sat on the edge of the mossy tub. He looked down at the house and at the old bunkhouse and at the dark cypress tree. The place was familiar, but curiously changed. It wasn't itself any more, but a frame for things that were happening. A cold wind blew out of the east now, signifying that the rain was over for a little while. At his feet Jody could see the little arms of new weeds spreading out over the ground. In the mud about the spring were thousands of quail tracks.

Doubletree Mutt came sideways and embarrassed up through the vegetable patch, and Jody, remembering how he had thrown the clod, put his arm about the dog's neck and kissed him on his wide black nose. Doubletree Mutt sat still, as though he knew some solemn thing was happening. His big tail slapped the ground gravely. Jody pulled a swollen tick out of Mutt's neck and popped it dead between his thumbnails. It was a nasty thing. He washed his hands in the cold spring water.

Except for the steady swish of the wind, the farm was very quiet. Jody knew his mother wouldn't mind if he didn't go in to eat his lunch. After a little while he went slowly back to the barn. Mutt crept into his own little house and whined softly to himself for a long time.

Billy Buck stood up from the box and surrendered the cotton swab. The pony still lay on his side and the wound in his throat bellowsed in and out. When Jody saw how dry and dead the hair looked, he knew at last that there was no hope for the pony. He had seen the dead hair before on dogs and cows, and it was a sure sign. He sat heavily on the box and let down the barrier of the box stall. For a long time he kept his eyes on the moving wound, and at last he dozed, and the afternoon passed quickly. Just before dark his mother brought a deep dish of stew and left it for him and went away. Jody ate a little of it, and, when it was dark, he set the lantern on the floor by the pony's head so he could watch the wound and keep it open. And he dozed again until the night chill awakened him. The wind was blowing fiercely, bringing the north cold with it. Jody brought a blanket from his bed in the hay and wrapped himself in it. Gabilan's breathing was quiet at last; the hole in his throat moved gently. The owls flew through the hayloft, shrieking and looking for mice. Jody put his hands down on his head and slept. In his sleep he was aware that the wind had increased. He heard it slamming about the barn.

It was daylight when he awakened. The barn door had swung open. The pony was gone. He sprang up and ran out into the morning light.

The pony's tracks were plain enough, dragging through the frost-like dew on the young grass, tired tracks with little lines between them where the hoofs had dragged. They headed for the brush line halfway up the ridge. Jody broke into a run and followed them. The sun shone on the sharp white quartz that stuck through the ground here and there. As he followed the plain trail, a shadow cut across in front of him. He looked up and saw a high circle of black buzzards, and the slowly revolving circle dropped lower and lower. The solemn birds soon disappeared over the ridge. Jody ran faster then, forced on by panic and rage. The trail entered the brush at last and followed a winding route among the tall sage bushes.

At the top of the ridge Jody was winded. He paused, puffing noisily. The blood pounded in his ears. Then he saw what he was looking for. Below, in one of the little clearings in the brush, lay the red pony. In the distance, Jody could see the legs moving slowly and convulsively. And in a circle around him stood the buzzards, waiting for the moment of death they know so well.

Jody leaped forward and plunged down the hill. The wet ground muffled his steps and the brush hid him. When he arrived, it was all over. The first buzzard sat on the pony's head and its beak had just risen dripping with dark eye fluid. Jody plunged into the circle like a cat. The black brother-

hood arose in a cloud, but the big one on the pony's head was too late. As it hopped along to take off, Jody caught its wing tip and pulled it down. It was nearly as big as he was. The free wing crashed into his face with the force of a club, but he hung on. The claws fastened on his leg and the wing elbows battered his head on either side. Jody groped blindly with his free hand. His fingers found the neck of the struggling bird. The red eyes looked into his face, calm and fearless and fierce; the naked head turned from side to side. Then the beak opened and vomited a stream of putrefied fluid. Jody brought up his knee and fell on the great bird. He held the neck to the ground with one hand while his other found a piece of sharp white quartz. The first blow broke the beak sideways and black blood spurted from the twisted, leathery mouth corners. He struck again and missed. The red fearless eyes still looked at him, impersonal and unafraid and detached. He struck again and again, until the buzzard lay dead, until its head was a red pulp. He was still beating the dead bird when Billy Buck pulled him off and held him tightly to calm his shaking.

Carl Tiflin wiped the blood from the boy's face with a red bandana. Jody was limp and quiet now. His father moved the buzzard with his toe. "Jody," he explained, "the buzzard didn't kill the pony. Don't you know that?"

"I know it," Jody said wearily.

It was Billy Buck who was angry. He had lifted Jody in his arms, and had turned to carry him home. But he turned back on Carl Tiflin. "'Course he knows it," Billy said furiously, "Man, can't you see how he'd feel about it?" □□

Discussion

1. (a) Describe Jody's physical appearance. (b) Which of his mannerisms reveals most about him? (c) Which of the following character traits does Jody possess: *obedience; belligerence; forcefulness; patience; shyness; responsibility?* Find evidence in the story to support your answers.

2. What does Jody reveal about his feelings for the red pony when he names it Gabilan Mountains?

3. (a) What ideas about discipline does Carl Tiflin have? (b) How does he demonstrate his ideas in giving Jody the twenty-two? (c) What restrictions does he put upon Jody's use of the pony? (d) Describe the relationship between Jody and his father.

4. (a) What bond exists between Jody and Billy Buck? (b) Why is there no such bond between Jody and his father?

5. (a) What in Jody's nature prevents him from leaving school when it starts to rain? (b) How much blame for the pony's death does Billy Buck take upon himself? (c) Is Jody in part responsible for Gabilan's death? Explain.

6. (a) How does Jody's mother express her sympathy during the pony's illness? (b) How does Carl Tiflin show his sympathy? (c) How do you think Steinbeck wants you to feel toward Carl Tiflin? Cite evidence to support your answer.

7. (a) Find the first mention of buzzards in the story. (b) At this point, what attitude does Jody display toward the birds? (c) If Gabilan hadn't died, would Jody ever have attacked a buzzard? How do you know?

(d) What motivates him to do so? (e) Why is he able to kill a bird almost as large as he is?

8. (a) As the story ends, why is Billy Buck so angry at Carl Tiflin? (b) What is the meaning of Billy's final exclamation?

9. (a) Identify the various conflicts—both external and internal—that are present in "The Gift." (b) Which one, do you think, is the main conflict?

10. (a) What in your opinion is the climax or turning point of the story? (b) List the events that lead up to the climax. (c) How is the main conflict resolved?

11. Characters in good fiction are often described as being "alive." (a) What does this statement mean? (b) Which character in "The Gift" seemed particularly lifelike to you? (c) Find details in the story which make that character seem real.

Vocabulary
Context, Structure, Pronunciation, Dictionary

In the preceding vocabulary exercises, you learned the three aids a good reader uses to determine the meanings and pronunciations of unfamiliar words. Review these aids (page 9). Then read each sentence below and answer the questions that follow by using context clues, structure clues, or the Glossary.

1. She had never been a *contemplative* person, but had always acted without much thought.

a. What does *contemplative* mean? What context clues helped you determine its meaning?
b. How is it pronounced? (Say it to yourself.)

2. Because he had no particular place to go and was in no hurry, he *sauntered* down the walk.

a. How was he walking?
b. What is a synonym for *saunter?*

3. The child gave us a *reproachful* look, as if to say, "You didn't bring me a present."

a. What part of speech is *reproachful?*
b. Write a sentence containing another reproachful remark.

4. He looked *dispiritedly* at the pony's tangled and matted coat.

a. What is the root word in *dispiritedly?* What does the root mean here?
b. The prefix is *di-*. What do you think this prefix might mean?
c. When saying the word, which syllable should you accent?

John Steinbeck 1902 • 1968

Ranch hands, fruit pickers, grocers, or simple drifters were the kinds of people about whom John Steinbeck most often wrote. In his early career he was at one time or another a ranch hand, fruit picker, and bricklayer, but his determination to write eventually earned him the Nobel Prize in Literature, the highest honor an author can receive. The Swedish Academy which gave him the prize in 1962 explained that in Steinbeck ". . . we find the American temperament . . . expressed in his great feeling for nature, for the tilled soil, the wasteland, the mountains, and the ocean coasts. . . ."

California's Salinas valley, where he was born and where he spent much of his life, is the setting of many of his works, including *The Red Pony*, from which "The Gift" is taken.

1: Encounters

CONTENT REVIEW

1. In the stories in Unit 1 all the main characters face a problem. **(a)** Whose problem seems the most difficult to you? Why do you think so? **(b)** Which person faces the predicament with the most intense feelings? **(c)** Which characters show the most patience and self-control?

2. What characteristics do Teruo in "Say It with Flowers" and the Birdman have in common?

3. Compare the feelings expressed by the speaker in "The Sidewalk Racer" with those expressed by the bobsled racer in "Mirror of Ice."

4. (a) In what ways are the family relationships in "The Circuit" similar to the family relationships in "I'll Give You Law"? **(b)** In what ways are these relationships different from those in "The Gift"?

5. Identify the *main conflict* in each of the following selections and indicate whether the conflict is an *external* one or an *internal* one:

  (a) "Say It with Flowers."

  (b) "The Birdman."

  (c) "I'll Give You Law."

6. In which selections in the unit does *setting* play an important part besides serving as background for the action? Why?

Unit 1, Test I
INTERPRETATION: NEW MATERIAL

Read the short story below. Then complete the sentences that follow by writing the letter identifying the correct completion. You may refer to the selection when necessary.

Stolen Day
Sherwood Anderson

    It must be that all children are actors. The whole thing started with a boy on our street named Walter, who had inflammatory rheumatism.[1] That's what they called it. He didn't have to go to school.

    Still he could walk about. He could go fishing in the creek or the waterworks pond. There was a place up at the pond where in the spring the water came tumbling over the dam and formed a deep pool. It was a good place. Sometimes you could get some big ones there.

Reprinted by permission of Harold Ober Associates Incorporated. Copyright © 1941 by United Newspapers Magazine Corporation. Renewed 1968 by Eleanor Copenhaver Anderson.

1. *inflammatory rheumatism,* a disease of the joints, usually marked by heat, redness, swelling, and pain.

I went down that way on my way to school one spring morning. It was out of my way but I wanted to see if Walter was there.

He was, inflammatory rheumatism and all. There he was, sitting with a fish pole in his hand. He had been able to walk down there all right.

It was then that my own legs began to hurt. My back too. I went on to school but, at the recess time, I began to cry. I did it when the teacher, Sarah Suggett, had come out into the schoolhouse yard.

She came right over to me.

"I ache all over," I said. I did, too.

I kept on crying and it worked all right.

"You'd better go on home," she said.

So I went. I limped painfully away. I kept on limping until I got out of the schoolhouse street.

Then I felt better. I still had inflammatory rheumatism pretty bad but I could get along better.

I must have done some thinking on the way home.

"I'd better not say I have inflammatory rheumatism," I decided. "Maybe if you've got that you swell up."

I thought I'd better go around to where Walter was and ask him about that, so I did—but he wasn't there.

"They must not be biting today," I thought.

I had a feeling that, if I said I had inflammatory rheumatism, Mother or my brothers and my sister Stella might laugh. They did laugh at me pretty often and I didn't like it at all.

"Just the same," I said to myself, "I have got it." I began to hurt and ache again.

I went home and sat on the front steps of our house. I sat there a long time. There wasn't anyone at home but Mother and the two little ones. Ray would have been four or five then and Earl might have been three.

It was Earl who saw me there. I had got tired sitting and was lying on the porch. Earl was always a quiet, solemn little fellow.

He must have said something to Mother for presently she came.

"What's the matter with you? Why aren't you in school?" she asked.

I came pretty near telling her right out that I had inflammatory rheumatism but I thought I'd better not. Mother and Father had been speaking of Walter's case at the table just the day before. "It affects the heart," Father had said. That frightened me when I thought of it. "I might die," I thought. "I might just suddenly die right here; my heart might stop beating."

On the day before I had been running a race with my brother

Irve. We were up at the fairgrounds after school and there was a half-mile track.

"I'll bet you can't run a half mile," he said. "I bet you I could beat you running clear around the track."

And so we did it and I beat him, but afterward my heart did seem to beat pretty hard. I remembered that lying there on the porch. "It's a wonder, with my inflammatory rheumatism and all, I didn't just drop down dead," I thought. The thought frightened me a lot. I ached worse than ever.

"I ache, Ma," I said. "I just ache."

She made me go in the house and upstairs and get into bed.

It wasn't so good. It was spring. I was up there for perhaps an hour, maybe two, and then I felt better.

I got up and went downstairs. "I feel better, Ma," I said.

Mother said she was glad. She was pretty busy that day and hadn't paid much attention to me. She had made me get into bed upstairs and then hadn't even come up to see how I was.

I didn't think much of that when I was up there but when I got downstairs where she was, and when, after I had said I felt better and she only said she was glad and went right on with her work, I began to ache again.

I thought, "I'll bet I die of it. I bet I do."

I went out to the front porch and sat down. I was pretty sore at Mother.

"If she really knew the truth, that I have inflammatory rheumatism and I may just drop down dead any time, I'll bet she wouldn't care about that either," I thought.

I was getting more and more angry the more thinking I did.

"I know what I'm going to do," I thought; "I'm going to go fishing."

I thought that, feeling the way I did, I might be sitting on the high bank just above the deep pool where the water went over the dam, and suddenly my heart would stop beating.

And then, of course, I'd pitch forward, over the bank into the pool and, if I wasn't dead when I hit the water, I'd drown sure.

They would all come home to supper and they'd miss me.

"But where is he?"

Then Mother would remember that I'd come home from school aching.

She'd go upstairs and I wouldn't be there. One day during the year before, there was a child got drowned in a spring. It was one of the Wyatt children.

Right down at the end of the street there was a spring under a birch tree and there had been a barrel sunk in the ground.

Everyone had always been saying the spring ought to be kept covered, but it wasn't.

So the Wyatt child went down there, played around alone, and fell in and got drowned.

Mother was the one who had found the drowned child. She had gone to get a pail of water and there the child was, drowned and dead.

This had been in the evening when we were all at home, and Mother had come running up the street with the dead, dripping child in her arms. She was making for the Wyatt house as hard as she could run, and she was pale.

She had a terrible look on her face, I remembered then.

"So," I thought, "they'll miss me and there'll be a search made. Very likely there'll be someone who has seen me sitting by the pond fishing, and there'll be a big alarm and all the town will turn out and they'll drag the pond."

I was having a grand time, having died. Maybe, after they found me and had got me out of the deep pool, Mother would grab me up in her arms and run home with me as she had run with the Wyatt child.

I got up from the porch and went around the house. I got my fishing pole and lit out for the pool below the dam. Mother was busy—she always was—and didn't see me go. When I got there I thought I'd better not sit too near the edge of the high bank.

By this time I didn't ache hardly at all, but I thought:

"With inflammatory rheumatism you can't tell," I thought.

"It probably comes and goes," I thought.

"Walter has it and he goes fishing," I thought.

I had got my line into the pool and suddenly I got a bite. It was a regular whopper. I knew that. I'd never had a bite like that.

I knew what it was. It was one of Mr. Fenn's big carp.

Mr. Fenn was a man who had a big pond of his own. He sold ice in the summer and the pond was to make the ice. He had bought some big carp and put them into his pond and then, earlier in the spring when there was a freshet, his dam had gone out.

So the carp had got into our creek and one or two big ones had been caught—but none of them by a boy like me.

The carp was pulling and I was pulling and I was afraid he'd break my line, so I just tumbled down the high bank, holding onto the line and got right into the pool. We had it out, there in the pool. We struggled. We wrestled. Then I got a hand under his gills and got him out.

He was a big one all right. He was nearly half as big as I was myself. I had him on the bank and I kept one hand under his gills and I ran.

I never ran so hard in my life. He was slippery, and now and then he wriggled out of my arms; once I stumbled and fell on him, but I got him home.

So there it was. I was a big hero that day. Mother got a washtub and filled it with water. She put the fish in it and all the neighbors came to look. I got into dry clothes and went down to supper—and then I made a break that spoiled my day.

There we were, all of us, at the table, and suddenly Father asked what had been the matter with me at school. He had met the teacher, Sarah Suggett, on the street and she had told him how I had become ill.

"What was the matter with you?" Father asked, and before I thought what I was saying I let it out.

"I had the inflammatory rheumatism," I said—and a shout went up. It made me sick to hear them, the way they all laughed.

It brought back all the aching again, and like a fool I began to cry.

"Well, I *have* got it—I *have*, I *have*," I cried, and I got up from the table and ran upstairs.

I stayed there until Mother came up. I knew it would be a long time before I heard the last of the inflammatory rheumatism. I was sick all right, but the aching I now had wasn't in my legs or in my back. □□

1. Walter's rheumatism makes a deep impression on the narrator because, as a result of the illness, Walter (a) is not able to walk well; (b) does not have to go to school; (c) has been forbidden to go to the pool; (d) seems to be in great pain.

2. This story is told from the viewpoint of (a) Walter; (b) the mother; (c) someone outside the story; (d) the person who experiences the events.

3. At home the narrator *first* calls attention to his condition by (a) crying; (b) going immediately to bed; (c) complaining to his brother Earl; (d) lying on the front porch.

4. The cause of his temporary recovery is (a) his two hours' bed rest; (b) his mother's frantic worry; (c) boredom and the fact that it is spring; (d) his mother's wish to call the doctor.

5. Imagining his death gives him pleasure because it would be a good way to get even with (a) his mother for always being too busy; (b) the town for not having boarded up the well; (c) Walter for being able to fish on a school day; (d) his family for laughing at him.

6. The greatest joy he experiences from catching the huge fish is (a) the struggle to land the fish; (b) the fact that catching the fish makes him a hero; (c) the fact that he can provide the evening meal; (d) that he is the only one ever to have caught a fish there before.

7. The day is spoiled when the narrator (a) reveals why he wasn't in school; (b) is sent to

bed by his father; **(c)** is scolded by his mother; **(d)** meets Miss Suggett on the street.

8. The boy's new aches are caused by his **(a)** rheumatism; **(b)** humiliation and embarrassment; **(c)** being spanked by his father; **(d)** failure to finish his supper.

9. The most important conflict in the story is **(a)** between the boy and Walter; **(b)** between the boy and his mother; **(c)** within the boy; **(d)** between the boy and the fish.

10. The chief method the author uses to tell us about the main character involves **(a)** revealing the boy's inner thoughts and feelings; **(b)** including dialogue between the main characters; **(c)** describing the boy's effect on other characters; **(d)** describing physical characteristics and setting in detail.

COMPOSITION

Choose any *one* of the following assignments to write about.

1. Describe an older person you know well. Be as specific as possible and include, if you can, an incident involving that person that reveals his or her personality or character.

2. In "Old Age Sticks," "The Gift," and "Stolen Day," each writer expresses opinions about the relationships between adults and young people. These opinions are summarized below. Choose one opinion. Then write a letter to the author telling him why you agree or disagree with him.

a. The conflict between adults and young people is a kind of war that adults always win because young people grow up to accept adult viewpoints.

("Old Age Sticks")

b. It is difficult for parents to be both good friends with their children and strict with their children.

("The Gift")

c. Adults often make fun of a child's opinions or statements because they forget what it is like to be a child.

("Stolen Day")

3. Assume that you are an editorial writer for a newspaper of the future. A law has been proposed to ban events such as the race on the Stuka in "Mirror of Ice." Write an editorial telling why you do or do not agree with the proposed law.

Some understandings come in time to be acted upon;

some do not.

Some understandings bring comfort;

some bring more problems.

Some understandings provide new ways of

looking at things, acting, dealing with people.

In one way or another, our lives change

whenever we experience **INSIGHTS**

See **IRONY** Handbook of Literary Terms

"But I'm blind!" the beggar screamed, "and you've been standing here laughing at me...."

A Man Who Had No Eyes

MacKinlay Kantor

A beggar was coming down the avenue just as Mr. Parsons emerged from his hotel.

He was a blind beggar, carrying the traditional battered cane, and thumping his way before him with the cautious, half-furtive effort of the sightless. He was a shaggy, thicknecked fellow; his coat was greasy about the lapels and pockets, and his hand splayed over the cane's crook with a futile sort of clinging. He wore a black pouch slung over his shoulder. Apparently he had something to sell.

The air was rich with spring; sun was warm and yellowed on the asphalt. Mr. Parsons, standing there in front of his hotel and noting the *clack-clack* approach of the sightless man, felt a sudden and foolish sort of pity for all blind creatures.

And, thought Mr. Parsons, he was very glad to be alive. A few years ago he had been little more than a skilled laborer; now he was successful, respected, admired. . . . Insurance. . . . And he had done it alone, unaided, struggling beneath handicaps. . . . And he was still young. The blue air of spring, fresh from its memories of windy pools and lush shrubbery, could thrill him with eagerness.

He took a step forward just as the tap-tapping blind man passed him by. Quickly the shabby fellow turned.

"Listen, guv'nor. Just a minute of your time."

Mr. Parsons said, "It's late. I have an appointment. Do you want me to give you something?"

"I ain't no beggar, guv'nor. You bet I ain't. I got a handy little article here"—he fumbled until he could press a small object into Mr. Parsons' hand—"that I sell. One buck. Best cigarette lighter made."

Mr. Parsons stood there, somewhat annoyed and embarrassed. He was a handsome figure with his immaculate gray suit and gray hat and malacca stick. Of course the man with the cigarette lighters could not see him. . . . "But I don't smoke," he said.

"Listen. I bet you know plenty people who smoke. Nice little present," wheedled the man. "And, mister, you wouldn't mind helping a poor guy out?" He clung to Mr. Parsons' sleeve.

Mr. Parsons sighed and felt in his vest pocket. He brought out two half dollars and pressed them into the man's hand. "Certainly. I'll help you out. As you say, I can give it to someone. Maybe the elevator boy would—" He hesitated, not wishing to be boorish and inquisitive, even with a blind peddler. "Have you lost your sight entirely?"

The shabby man pocketed the two half dollars. "Fourteen years, guv'nor." Then he added with an insane sort of pride: "Westbury, sir. I was one of 'em."

"Westbury," repeated Mr. Parsons. "Ah, yes. The chemical explosion. . . . The papers haven't mentioned it for years. But at the time it was supposed to be one of the greatest disasters in—"

"They've all forgot about it." The fellow shifted his feet wearily. "I tell you, guv'nor, a man who was in it don't forget about it. Last thing I ever saw was C shop going up in one grand smudge, and gas pouring in all the busted windows."

Mr. Parsons coughed. But the blind peddler was caught up with the train of his one dramatic reminiscence. And, also, he was thinking that there might be more half dollars in Mr. Parsons' pocket.

"Just think about it, guv'nor. There was a hundred and eight people killed, about two

---

"A Man Who Had No Eyes" by MacKinlay Kantor. Copyright ©
1931 by *Liberty Magazine*. Reprinted by permission of Paul R.
Reynolds, Inc., 599 Fifth Avenue, New York, New York 10017.

hundred injured, and over fifty of them lost their eyes. Blind as bats—" He groped forward until his dirty hand rested against Mr. Parsons' coat. "I tell you, sir, there wasn't nothing worse than that in the war. If I had lost my eyes in the war, okay. I would have been well took care of. But I was just a workman, working for what was in it. And I got it. You're darn right I got it, while the capitalists were making their dough! They was insured, don't worry about that. They—"

"Insured," repeated his listener. "Yes. That's what I sell—"

"You want to know how I lost my eyes?" cried the man. "Well, here it is!" His words fell with the bitter and studied drama of a story often told, and told for money. "I was there in C shop, last of all the folks rushing out. Out in the air there was a chance, even with buildings exploding right and left. A lot of guys made it safe out the door and got away. And just when I was about there, crawling along between those big vats, a guy behind me grabs my leg. He says, 'Let me past, you—!' Maybe he was nuts. I dunno. I try to forgive him in my heart, guv'nor. But he was bigger than me. He hauls me back and climbs right over me! Tramples me into the dirt. And he gets out, and I lie there with all that poison gas pouring down on all sides of me, and flame and stuff. . . . " He swal-

lowed—a studied sob—and stood dumbly expectant. He could imagine the next words: *Tough luck, my man. Now, I want to—*

"That's the story, guv'nor."

The spring wind shrilled past them, damp and quivering.

"Not quite," said Mr. Parsons.

The blind peddler shivered crazily. "Not quite? What do you mean, you—?"

"The story is true," Mr. Parsons said, "except that it was the other way around."

"Other way around?" He croaked unamiably. "Say, guv'nor—"

"I was in C shop," said Mr. Parsons. "It was the other way around. You were the fellow who hauled back on me and climbed over me. You were bigger than I was, Markwardt."

The blind man stood for a long time, swallowing hoarsely. He gulped: "Parsons. I thought you—" And then he screamed fiendishly: "Yes. Maybe so. Maybe so. But I'm blind! I'm blind, and you've been standing here letting me spout to you, and laughing at me every minute! I'm blind."

People in the street turned to stare at him.

"You got away, but I'm blind! Do you hear? I'm—"

"Well," said Mr. Parsons, "don't make such a row about it, Markwardt. . . . So am I." □□

Discussion

1. Did you expect the story to end the way it did? Why or why not?

2. (a) Why do you think the beggar lies about what happened during the fire? (b) Where in the story do you learn that the beggar apparently has told this lie often? (c) What reason is implied for his having done so?

3. Several key words and phrases are used to describe the physical appearance and the character of the beggar. Identify the words and phrases and explain what they imply about him.

4. Describe the physical appearance and the character of Mr. Parsons. Find words and phrases in the story to support your description.

5. What hints can you find early in the story to suggest that Mr. Parsons is also blind?

6. (a) Which one of the three types of irony discussed in the Handbook of Literary Terms occurs at the end of this story? (b) What is ironic about the ending?

Extension • Speaking

Pretend that you are Mr. Parsons and that you are applying for a job. You are confronting the personnel director who has just mentioned that your visual disability makes you unfit to work. What would you say to the personnel director? How would you prove you were fit? For what jobs? (Address your remarks to your classmates.)

Or, you may use the same situation, pretending that you are the beggar.

MacKinlay Kantor
1904 • 1977

Newspaper reporter, columnist, free-lance writer, and author of 43 books, MacKinlay Kantor once offered the harsh opinion that although many of his stories had appeared in an incredible number of magazines, they had little value except as entertaining reading. He added, however, that the discipline involved in producing such a volume of writing helped him to refine his craft—particularly his command of plot and construction. The highly compressed plot of "A Man Who Had No Eyes" provides an early example of the success he achieved through such discipline.

Born in Webster City, Iowa, MacKinlay Kantor lived for a while in Chicago and New York City before settling for most of his adult life in Sarasota, Florida. During World War II he lived in Britain, serving as a war correspondent for *The Saturday Evening Post* and *Esquire*.

Glory for Me, his critically unsuccessful novel, was adapted into the award-winning movie "The Best Years of Our Lives." *Andersonville,* a novel of life in a Confederate prisoner-of-war camp during the Civil War, won Kantor the Pulitzer Prize for fiction in 1956.

See **FLASHBACK** Handbook of Literary Terms

The hunt for Bandit produced the biggest turnout the hills had known, and all time-honored rules of the fox chase were broken to bring the wily fox down.

Last Cover

Paul Annixter

I'm not sure I can tell you what you want to know about my brother; but everything about the pet fox is important, so I'll tell all that from the beginning.

It goes back to a winter afternoon after I'd hunted the woods all day for a sign of our lost pet. I remember the way my mother looked up as I came into the kitchen. Without my speaking, she knew what had happened. For six hours I had walked, reading signs, looking for a delicate print in the damp soil or even a hair that might have told of a red fox passing that way—but I had found nothing.

"Did you go up in the foothills?" Mom asked.

I nodded. My face was stiff from held-back tears. My brother, Colin, who was going on twelve, got it all from one look at me and went into a heartbroken, almost silent, crying.

Three weeks before, Bandit, the pet fox Colin and I had raised from a tiny kit, had disappeared, and not even a rumor had been heard of him since.

"He'd have had to go off soon anyway," Mom comforted. "A big, lolloping fellow like him, he's got to live his life same as us. But he may come back. That fox set a lot of store by you boys in spite of his wild ways."

"He set a lot of store by our food, anyway," Father said. He sat in a chair by the kitchen window mending a piece of harness. "We'll be seeing a lot more of that fellow, never fear. That fox learned to pine for table scraps and young chickens. He was getting to be an egg thief, too, and he's not likely to forget that."

"That was only pranking when he was little," Colin said desperately.

From the first, the tame fox had made tension in the family. It was Father who said we'd better name him Bandit, after he'd made away with his first young chicken.

"Maybe you know," Father said shortly. "But when an animal turns to egg sucking he's usually incurable. He'd better not come pranking around my chicken run again."

It was late February, and I remember the bleak, dead cold that had set in, cold that was a rare thing for our Carolina hills. Flocks of sparrows and snowbirds had appeared to peck hungrily at all that the pigs and chickens didn't eat.

"This one's a killer," Father would say of a morning, looking out at the whitened barn roof. "This one will make the shoats squeal."

A fire snapped all day in our cookstove and another in the stone fireplace in the living room, but still the farmhouse was never warm. The leafless woods were bleak and empty, and I spoke of that to Father when I came back from my search.

"It's always a sad time in the woods when the seven sleepers are under cover," he said.

"What sleepers are they?" I asked. Father was full of woods lore.

"Why, all the animals that have got sense enough to hole up and stay hid in weather like this. Let's see, how was it the old rhyme named them?

Surly bear and sooty bat,
Brown chuck and masked coon,
Chippy-munk and sly skunk,
And all the mouses
'Cept in men's houses.

"And man would have joined them and made it eight, Granther Yeary always said, if he'd had a little more sense."

"I was wondering if the red fox mightn't make it eight," Mom said.

Father shook his head. "Late winter's a high time for foxes. Time when they're out deviling, not sleeping."

My chest felt hollow. I wanted to cry like Colin over our lost fox, but at fourteen a boy doesn't cry. Colin had squatted down on the floor and got out his small hammer and nails to start another new frame for a new picture. Maybe then he'd make a drawing for the frame and be able to forget his misery. It had been that way with him since he was five.

I thought of the new dress Mom had brought home a few days before in a heavy cardboard box. That box cover would be fine for Colin to draw on. I spoke of it, and Mom's glance thanked me as she went to get it. She and I worried a lot about Colin. He was small for his age, delicate and blond, his hair much lighter and softer than mine, his eyes deep and wide and blue. He was often sick, and I knew the fear mom had that he might be predestined. I'm just ordinary, like Father. I'm the sort of stuff that can take it—tough and strong—but Colin was always sort of special.

Mom lighted the lamp. Colin began cutting his white cardboard carefully, fitting it into his frame. Father's sharp glance turned on him now and again.

"There goes the boy making another frame before there's a picture for it," he said. "It's too much like cutting out a man's suit for a fellow that's say, twelve years old. Who knows whether he'll grow into it?"

Mom was into him then, quick. "Not a single frame of Colin's has ever gone to waste. The boy has real talent, Sumter, and it's time you realized it."

"Of course he has," Father said. "All kids have 'em. But they get over 'em."

"It isn't the pox we're talking of," Mom sniffed.

"In a way it is. Ever since you started talking up Colin's art, I've had an invalid for help around the place."

Father wasn't as hard as he made out, I knew, but he had to hold a balance against all Mom's frothing. For him the thing was the land and all that pertained to it. I was following in Father's footsteps, true to form, but Colin threatened to break the family tradition with his leaning toward art, with Mom "aiding and abetting him," as Father liked to put it. For the past two years she had had dreams of my brother becoming a real artist and going away to the city to study.

It wasn't that Father had no understanding of such things. I could remember, through the years, Colin lying on his stomach in the front room making pencil sketches, and how a good drawing would catch Father's eye halfway across the room, and how he would sometimes gather up two or three of them to study, frowning and muttering, one hand in his beard, while a great pride rose in Colin, and in me too. Most of Colin's drawings were of the woods and wild things, and there Father was a master critic. He made out to scorn what seemed to him a passive "white-livered" interpretation of nature through brush and pencil instead of rod and rifle.

At supper that night Colin could scarcely eat. Ever since he'd been able to walk, my brother had had a growing love of wild things, but Bandit had been like his very own, a gift of the woods. One afternoon a year and a half before, Father and Laban Small had been running a vixen through the hills with their dogs. With the last of her strength the she-fox had made for her den, not far from our house. The dogs had overtaken her and killed her just before she reached it. When Father and Laban came up, they'd found Colin crouched nearby holding her cub in his arms.

Father had been for killing the cub, which was still too young to shift for itself, but Colin's grief had brought Mom into it. We'd taken the young fox into the kitchen, all of us, except Father, gone a bit silly over the little thing. Colin had held it in his arms and fed it warm milk from a spoon.

"Watch out with all your soft ways," Father had warned, standing in the doorway. "You'll make too much of him. Remember, you can't make a dog out of a fox. Half of that little critter has to love, but the other half is a wild hunter. You boys will mean a whole lot to him while he's kit, but there'll come a day when you won't mean a thing to him and he'll leave you shorn."

For two weeks after that Colin had nursed the cub, weaning it from milk to bits of meat. For a year they were always together. The cub grew fast. It was soon following Colin and me about the barnyard. It turned out to be a patch fox, with a saddle of darker fur across its shoulders.

I haven't the words to tell you what the fox meant to us. It was far more wonderful owning him than owning any dog. There was something rare and secret like the spirit of the woods about him, and back of his calm, straw-gold eyes was the sense of a brain the equal of a man's. The fox became Colin's whole life.

Each day, going and coming from school, Colin and I took long side trips through the woods, looking for Bandit. Wild things' memories were short, we knew; we'd have to find him soon or the old bond would be broken.

Ever since I was ten I'd been allowed to hunt with Father, so I was good at reading signs. But, in a way, Colin knew more about the woods and wild things than Father or me. What came to me from long observation, Colin seemed to know by instinct.

It was Colin who felt out, like an Indian, the stretch of woods where Bandit had his den, who found the first slim, small fox-print in the damp earth. And then, on an afternoon in March, we saw him. I remember the day well, the racing clouds, the wind rattling the tops of the pine trees and swaying the Spanish moss. Bandit had just come out of a clump of laurel; in the maze of leaves behind him we caught a glimpse of a slim red vixen, so we knew he had found a mate. She melted from sight like a shadow, but Bandit turned to watch us, his mouth open, his tongue lolling as he smiled his old foxy smile. On his thin chops, I saw a telltale chicken feather.

Colin moved silently forward, his movements so quiet and casual he seemed to be standing still. He called Bandit's name, and the fox held his ground, drawn to us with all his senses. For a few moments he let Colin actually put an arm about him. It was then I knew that he loved us still, for all of Father's warnings. He really loved us back, with a fierce, secret love no tame thing ever gave. But the urge of his life just then was toward his new mate. Suddenly, he whirled about and disappeared in the laurels.

Colin looked at me with glowing eyes. "We haven't really lost him, Stan. When he gets through with his spring sparking he may come back. But we've got to show ourselves to him a lot, so he won't forget."

"It's a go," I said.

"Promise not to say a word to Father," Colin said, and I agreed. For I knew by the chicken feather that Bandit had been up to no good.

A week later the woods were budding and the thickets were rustling with all manner of wild things scurrying on the love scent. Colin managed to get a glimpse of Bandit every few days. He couldn't get close though, for the spring running was a lot more important to a fox than any human beings were.

Every now and then Colin got out his framed box cover and looked at it, but he never drew anything on it; he never even picked up his pencil. I remember wondering if what Father had said about framing a picture before you had one had spoiled something for him.

I was helping Father with the planting now, but Colin managed to be in the woods every day. By degrees he learned Bandit's range, where he drank and rested and where he was likely to be according to the time of day. One day he told me how he had petted Bandit again, and how they had walked together a long way in the woods. All this time we had kept his secret from Father.

As summer came on, Bandit began to live up to the prediction Father had made. Accustomed to human beings he moved without fear about the scattered farms of the region, raiding barns and hen runs that other foxes wouldn't have dared go near. And he taught his wild mate to do the same. Almost every night they got into some poultry house, and by late June Bandit was not only killing chickens and ducks but feeding on eggs and young chicks whenever he got the chance.

Stories of his doings came to us from many sources, for he was still easily recognized by the dark patch on his shoulders. Many a farmer took a shot at him as he fled and some of them set out on his trail with dogs, but they always returned home without even sighting him. Bandit was familiar with all the dogs in the region, and he knew a hundred tricks to confound them. He got a reputation that year beyond that of any fox our hills had known. His confidence grew, and he gave up wild hunting altogether and lived entirely off the poultry farmers. By September the hill farmers banded together to hunt him down.

It was Father who brought home that news one night. All time-honored rules of the fox chase were to be broken in this hunt; if the dogs couldn't bring Bandit down, he was to be shot on sight. I was stricken and furious. I remember the misery of Colin's face in the lamplight. Father, who took pride in all the ritual of the hunt, had refused to be a party to such an affair, though in justice he could do nothing but sanction any sort of hunt, for Bandit, as old Sam Wetherwax put it, had been "purely getting in the Lord's hair."

The hunt began next morning, and it was the biggest turnout our hills had known. There were at least twenty mounted men in the party and as many dogs. Father and I were working in the lower field as they passed along the river road. Most of the hunters carried rifles, and they looked ugly.

Twice during the morning I went up to the house to find Colin, but he was nowhere around. As we worked, Father and I could follow the progress of the hunt by the distant hound music on the breeze. We could tell just where the hunters first caught sight of the fox and where Bandit was leading the dogs during the first hour. We knew as well as if we'd seen it how Bandit roused another fox along Turkey Branch and forced it to run for him, and how the dogs swept after it for twenty minutes before they sensed their mistake.

Noon came, and Colin had not come in to eat. After dinner Father didn't go back to the field. He moped about, listening to the hound talk. He didn't like what was on any more

than I did, and now and again I caught his smile of satisfaction when we heard the broken, angry notes of the hunting horn, telling that the dogs had lost the trail or had run another fox.

I was restless, and I went up into the hills in midafternoon. I ranged the woods for miles, thinking all the time of Colin. Time lost all meaning for me, and the short day was nearing an end, when I heard the horn talking again, telling that the fox had put over another trick. All day he had deviled the dogs and mocked the hunters. This new trick and the coming night would work to save him. I was wildly glad, as I moved down toward Turkey Branch and stood listening for a time by the deep, shaded pool where for years we boys had gone swimming, sailed boats, and dreamed summer dreams.

Suddenly, out of the corner of my eye, I saw the sharp ears and thin, pointed mask of a fox—in the water almost beneath me. It was Bandit, craftily submerged there, all but his head, resting in the cool water of the pool and the shadow of the two big beeches that spread above it. He must have run forty miles or more since morning. And he must have hidden in this place before. His knowing, crafty mask blended perfectly with the shadows and a mass of drift and branches that had collected by the bank of the pool. He was so still that a pair of thrushes flew up from the spot as I came up, not knowing he was there.

Bandit's bright, harried eyes were looking right at me. But I did not look at him direct. Some woods instinct, swifter than thought, kept me from it. So he and I met as in another world, indirectly, with feeling but without sign or greeting.

Suddenly I saw that Colin was standing

almost beside me. Silently as a water snake, he had come out of the bushes and stood there. Our eyes met, and a quick and secret smile passed between us. It was a rare moment in which I really "met" my brother, when something of his essence flowed into me and I knew all of him. I've never lost it since.

My eyes still turned from the fox, my heart pounding. I moved quietly away, and Colin moved with me. We whistled softly as we went, pretending to busy ourselves along the bank of the stream. There was magic in it, as if by will we wove a web of protection about the fox, a ring-pass-not that none might penetrate. It was so, too, we felt, in the brain of Bandit, and that doubled the charm. To us he was still our little pet that we had carried about in our arms on countless summer afternoons.

Two hundred yards upstream, we stopped beside slim, fresh tracks in the mud where Bandit had entered the branch. The tracks angled upstream. But in the water the wily creature had turned down.

We climbed the far bank to wait, and Colin told me how Bandit's secret had been his secret ever since an afternoon three months before, when he'd watched the fox swim downstream to hide in the deep pool. Today he'd waited on the bank, feeling that Bandit, hard pressed by the dogs, might again seek the pool for sanctuary.

We looked back once as we turned homeward. He still had not moved. We didn't know until later that he was killed that same night by a chance hunter, as he crept out from his hiding place.

That evening Colin worked a long time on his framed box cover that had lain about the house untouched all summer. He kept at it all the next day too. I had never seen him work so hard. I seemed to sense in the air the feeling he was putting into it, how he was *believing* his picture into being. It was evening before he finished it. Without a word he handed it to Father. Mom and I went and looked over his shoulder.

It was a delicate and intricate pencil drawing of the deep branch pool, and there was Bandit's head and watching, fear-filled eyes hiding there amid the leaves and shadows, woven craftily into the maze of twigs and branches, as if by nature's art itself. Hardly a fox there at all, but the place where he was—or should have been. I recognized it instantly, but Mom gave a sort of incredulous sniff.

"I'll declare," she said, "it's mazy as a puzzle. It just looks like a lot of sticks and leaves to me."

Long minutes of study passed before Father's eye picked out the picture's secret, as few men's could have done. I laid that to Father's being a born hunter. That was a picture that might have been done especially for him. In fact, I guess it was.

Finally he turned to Colin with his deep, slow smile. "So that's how Bandit fooled them all," he said. He sat holding the picture with a sort of tenderness for a long time, while we glowed in the warmth of the shared secret. That was Colin's moment. Colin's art stopped being a pox to Father right there. And later, when the time came for Colin to go to art school, it was Father who was his solid backer. □□

Discussion

1. Explain what the narrator means when he describes himself as being "just ordinary" but says that Colin "was always sort of special."

2. How does each member of the family react to Colin's special qualities?

3. The events below are listed in the order in which they are presented in the story. Rearrange the list so that the events are in the order in which they actually happened.

a. The narrator spends a winter afternoon hunting in the woods for Bandit.

b. Bandit runs away.

c. Colin's father suggests that the family name the fox Bandit.

d. Colin finds a fox cub and brings it home.

e. The farmers organize a hunt to catch Bandit.

f. The narrator discovers Bandit's hiding place.

g. Bandit is killed.

4. (a) At what point does the author interrupt the story to tell you about something that occurred before the story began? **(b)** What technique does he use to do this?

5. (a) Describe the circumstances under which Bandit became a member of the family. **(b)** Why was Colin's father opposed to the family's plan to keep Bandit as a pet? **(c)** Give evidence from the story to show that Colin's father had sympathetic feelings for Bandit.

6. In what ways is the narrator's relationship to Colin similar to Colin's relationship to Bandit?

7. What finally changed the father's mind about Colin's art? Why do you think he changed his mind?

Vocabulary • Dictionary

Being familiar with the *etymology* (et′ ə mol′ ə jē), or origin of a word, can often help you remember the meaning of that word. Most dictionaries give the etymology of a word at the end of its definition, in a form like this:

invalid . . . [< French *invalide* < Latin *invalidus* < *in-* not + *validus* strong]

The bracketed information tells you that (1) *invalid* was derived from the French word *invalide* (the symbol < means "taken or derived from"); (2) *invalide* came from the Latin word *invalidus;* and (3) *invalidus* was formed from the prefix *in-*, meaning "not," plus *validus,* meaning "strong."

Use the etymologies in your Glossary to answer the following questions. Be sure you know the meaning of the italicized word in each question.

1. Did the word *harry* come into English from French, Old English, or Latin?

2. What is the meaning of the Middle English word that *wily* is derived from?

3. Did *confound* come into English from Latin or Old French?

4. What did *pertain* mean in its Latin form *pertinere?*

5. What is the original word that *sanction* is derived from? What is the meaning of the original word?

Paul Annixter 1894 •

This short story is one of about five hundred that Howard Allison Sturtzel has published under the pseudonym Paul Annixter. Regarding the rural fox hunt, he says, "The most important rule and the one I referred to in the story is that only the dogs may do the killing. The fox hunters carry no weapons. The shooting of a fox is a grave misdemeanor in any fox-hunting territory. Having the fox killed at all is regrettable to most hunt clubs. The same fox is run time after time, season after season, and it is the chase, not the kill, that is important."

The Fox and the Grapes

Marianne Moore

A fox of Gascon, though some say of Norman descent,[1]
When starved till faint gazed up at a trellis to which grapes were tied—
    Matured till they glowed with a purplish tint
    As though there were gems inside.
5 Now grapes were what our adventurer on strained haunches chanced to crave,
    But because he could not reach the vine
He said, "These grapes are sour; I'll leave them for some knave."
Better, I think, than an embittered whine.

"The Fox and the Grapes" translated by Marianne Moore. From *The Marianne Moore Reader* (British title: *Complete Poems of Marianne Moore).* Copyright 1954 by Marianne Moore. Reprinted by permission of The Viking Press and Faber and Faber Limited.

1. **Gascon . . . Norman descent.** The speaker is unsure of what part of France the fox comes from. Gascony and Normandy are names of provinces in southwestern and northern France, respectively.

Discussion

1. (a) Summarize the incident described in the poem. (b) What doubt does the speaker express in the first line? (c) Does this doubt give the incident an air of reality or unreality? Explain.

2. (a) What description does the speaker give you of the grapes? (b) In what way does the description help you understand the fox's predicament?

3. The speaker does not merely report the facts but comments on them as well. (a) What attitude does the speaker adopt as commentator? (b) Find words and phrases that indicate this attitude.

4. The fable on which this poem is based usually ends with a line such as, "It is easy to despise what you cannot have." Does the last line of the poem suggest the same meaning? Explain.

Marianne Moore
1887 • 1972

The language of poetry, said Marianne Moore, substitutes "compactness for confusion." Miss Moore, who once told *The New Yorker,* "I don't call myself a poet. . . . I'm just like anybody else," was fascinated by everything that happened around her. She revealed in her writing keen insights into humankind and nature. In her own words, she "watched life with affection." Her poems, she once said, presented "imaginary gardens with real toads in them."

See **CHARACTERIZATION** Handbook of Literary Terms

Cal Crawford had lived with Indians and fought against them.
He had sat in council with chiefs, had taken scalps and
never lost his own. But in that last summer of his life,
he was only a blind old man, looked after by his Indian daughter.
Why, then, was young Buck so terrified of him?

A Time of Greatness

Dorothy Johnson

I was ten years old the summer I worked for old Cal Crawford. For years afterward I remembered it as a time of terror. I was grown up before I understood it had been a time of greatness, too.

Cal Crawford did not hire me and probably did not know I was working for him. He never remembered my name—he called me "Boy" when he noticed me at all—and at the end, he got the idea that through some misfortune he had to look after me, instead of the other way around.

But I was hired to look after him, because he was blind and very old. If my father hadn't needed the money desperately, he would not have let me go to the Crawford place. Old Cal's daughter, who hired me, was half-Indian. White people didn't work for Indians. It was unthinkable.

She looked immensely old, older than Cal Crawford himself, for he was tall and straight, while she was short and stooped. I never knew her name but got around it by calling her "Missus." What most people called her was "Monkeyface."

She wore her purple silk dress the day she came to our place. My sister Geraldine saw her through the window and said, "The old squaw's coming this way. Aren't we being honored, though! And all dressed up in silk. *I* haven't got a silk dress."

Geraldine snickered at the sight. She had little enough to make her laugh those days. Her young man had gone West without her, because she had to stay home and look after Pa. She didn't think she would ever see her man again.

I laughed, too, at the old Indian woman, and was sorry later. If I hadn't laughed at Monkeyface, then maybe I wouldn't have had to go away with her that day. Maybe it was a punishment. But she did look ridiculous in the purple silk dress, astride an old white horse and slumped like a sack of meal. Her gray hair hung in frowzy braids from under a red kerchief. When she got close enough, you saw the dress was grease-spotted and dull with dirt.

Monkeyface had little English, but she kept saying, "Mistah? Mistah?" and making the Indian sign for "man."

"She wants to see Pa," I explained to Geraldine. I answered the old woman with the sign for "sick," and added, "He's got a broken leg."

She still wanted to see him, so Geraldine took her into the bedroom. Any visitor broke the monotony.

Pa and Monkeyface had quite a talk, in her mangled English and sign language, and I shivered because she kept motioning toward me.

A boy of ten does not expect his own father will give him away, but that was how it looked. And dreadful things not expected had happened lately in our cabin, like the way my sister cried at night because she had to stay home instead of go West with her man. It wasn't Pa that made her stay, though. It was her conscience.

"You want a summer job, Buck?" my father asked.

I took heart. "Sure." Herding cows, maybe. I wasn't big enough for much else.

"She wants you to look after her father," Pa explained. "Cal Crawford, the old mountain man."

"Look after him how?" I demanded, getting suspicious. I had few skills and little ability, nothing to be proud of. If I had been big enough to amount to anything, I could have been taking care of Pa so Geraldine wouldn't have had to stay home. She sometimes told me so.

"Just see he don't stray off," Pa explained. "He's blind, and he wanders. She don't want him to get hurt or lost." He added, "They'll give you your keep and a dollar a month wages."

I had no choice, really. It was a big thing to relieve the folks of feeding me, and a bigger one to earn that much money.

So I went to Cal Crawford's place, twenty miles away, on a pinto pony, trailing behind Cal's half-Indian daughter. I was scared all the way, and all summer.

That was before he became a legend, and after he had stopped being one, you might say. He was like a deposed god. He had gloried and drunk deep with his peers, had dared much and suffered much, had gained and lost. But all his peers were dead. Conestoga wagons had swayed westward along trails he had unwittingly helped mark, and as the frontier crept forward, settlements nestled where his campfires had starred the vast and silent night.

After he had gone, historians resurrected the legends and found most of them were true. He had trapped beaver and traded furs with the Indians, had lived with Indians and fought against them. He had traveled the wild Missouri and the Roche Jaune, or Yellowstone, had seen a mountain of black glass and the place where hell broke through the earth's surface to spout boiling water toward the sky. He had sat in council with chiefs, had taken scalps and never lost his own. But when I worked for him, nobody was left who had known him when he was young and strong and in his glory.

In that last summer of his life, he was only a blind old man, looked after by his Indian daughter.

She never gave me any orders. She showed me a pallet on the floor by his bunk and signed, "You sleep there." The cabin had two rooms. She slept in the other one, the kitchen.

Cal Crawford rode into the yard on a tired old white horse, herded by a tired old black dog. Monkeyface made a gesture toward him as if to say, This is what you are here for, to help the horse and the dog keep him from getting lost.

So I went outside and stood around while he dismounted. I cleared my throat and asked, "Want me to take the saddle off, Mr. Crawford?"

He looked over my head with his blazing blue blind eyes, scowling, his defiant chin held high, and said, "No!" He didn't want me there, and if I had to be there, he didn't care to be reminded.

There was no conversation at supper. Monkeyface had changed from her silk dress to a faded gray one, such as any farm woman might wear. She cut up his meat and murmured to him, but he didn't answer.

He would not stay in the house or near it, and rain didn't matter, except that he would turn his face up to catch it. And sometimes he would get off his horse and kneel down in a field, reaching with his hands to see how high the grain had grown.

Uncounted miles of tipped mountains and rolling prairie had passed beneath his moccasin-clad feet when he was young and had his sight. He had been at home in tepees and brush shelters, and fifteen years had passed in one stretch without his ever setting foot in a house. When he was old, he did not like houses but wandered on horseback, with the old dog to herd him home.

When he was not riding, he walked around the yard, prodding ahead with a long stick. I kept quiet and out of his way, and when he saddled his old horse, I scrambled bareback onto the pinto.

Cal knew I was there, but he acted as if I had never been born. Once or twice he asked irritably, "Boy, you there?" but most of the time he preferred to forget me.

Once, when he was walking to the house, he prodded me with his pole by accident—I hadn't jumped fast enough when he turned around—but he wasn't sorry. He challenged, "Well?" while I rubbed my shin.

I said apologetically, "Sorry I got in the way, Mr. Crawford," and was mad at myself for being such a ninny.

Then came the morning when he whistled as usual for the dog but the dog did not come stiffly out of the shed. He whistled again, scowling, and seemed lost in his darkness. For the first time, I was sorry enough for him to forget being scared.

"I'll get him," I offered.

The dog was too tired to get up. I went out of the shed and reported, "Dog's sick, Mr. Crawford."

The old man prodded in with his stick and was not grateful when I touched his arm and said, "He's to your right."

He hunkered down and the dog inched himself over and put his head on the old man's groping hand, wagging his tail feebly. After a while, Cal Crawford stopped petting him and grumbled, "Well, he's dead."

When Monkeyface found out, she handed me a shovel and I dug a grave for the dog. Cal didn't pay any attention except that he was impatient because his daughter wouldn't let him ride anywhere while I was busy.

When the dog was gone, I felt more useful, but I never bossed old Cal. I followed him and warned when he came to a fence or a creek.

I was desperately lonesome and homesick, with nobody to tell about it. The Indian woman never talked to me, and the tall, stiff-jointed mountain man usually would not admit I was there. I suppose each of them was lonely, too. The old man looked blindly through me or over my head, and Monkeyface sometimes glanced at me with no expression—wondering, I think now, whether this boy who was her last hope would stay while she needed him.

Back home, my sister would be crying for her lost love or shouting angrily at my father, and he would be helpless and melancholy, as dependent as Cal Crawford but lacking his defense of arrogance. Nevertheless, it was home, and I wanted to be there.

Homesickness was bad enough, but something worse happened. One day, old Cal began to talk to people I could not see. We were riding along beside a grove. I was watching so as to warn him when he came to a creek with a steep bank. Suddenly he chuckled.

He pointed ahead and said, "Good beaver there last year. Plenty Blackfeet, too. Waugh!"

"Did you want to go back now, Mr. Crawford?" I asked.

He swung around, scowling, and said something in a language that was not English. Then he ignored the interruption and went on talking loudly in some tongue unknown to me, gesturing, telling a story. Along with the spoken language he used the sign talk of the prairie tribes, but more gracefully, more swiftly, than I had ever seen it. I got a few of the signs—men riding,

an evil person, somebody dead. To the rider on his left he spoke, and to the rider on his right. I was on his right, but it was not to me he told his story. It was to someone I could not see, someone who wasn't there.

And the comrades of long ago must have answered, because once in a while he laughed. He pointed off toward the place where prairie met sky, and kicked his horse into a faster walk.

I was afraid to warn him of the creek. He sat easy in his battered saddle as his horse slid down the bank, waded across, and lunged up the other side. I kept behind him, shivering.

Long afterward, when historians revived the legend of Cal Crawford, I knew in what company I had ridden that day. The ghosts were bearded trappers in fringed buckskin, long-haired men with shapeless headgear of fur, moccasined men who rode like wary kings, who had forgotten fear but not caution. And Indians, too, rode with us, half-naked, curious, cruel, with paint stripes on their dark faces and hair in long black locks like snakes.

It was I who was invisible. Cal Crawford was young again in a time long years before I was born.

I did not guide him home that day. His horse turned and headed back to the cabin with him. But I did not desert him. I rode with him all the way, and did not know when we lost those other riders only he could see and hear.

I was going to tell his daughter at first, but what was the use? There comes a time when you have to look out for yourself, and I figured it had come. I decided to leave that night, sneak out of the cabin and walk the twenty miles back home.

But he slept poorly. He mumbled and

tossed, and when he groaned, how could I leave?

He cried out, "Arrowhead under my shoulder, boy. Dig it out! Dig it out!"

With some hazy conviction that it would be cowardly for me to leave him wounded, I went over to him and said firmly, "It's all right, Mr. Crawford. Everything's all right."

He turned toward me and threw out his hand, groping, and I took hold of it.

"Don't leave me, boy," he whispered. He was not speaking to those lost, unseen comrades. I was the one he called "Boy."

"I won't leave you," I promised.

The next morning he pretended as usual that I wasn't there. He may not have remembered my promise, but I did. It worried me. How could I stay there, being scared all the time? Well, I hadn't said I would never leave him. Any day I was free to go, I thought. That was how I endured staying, just one day at a time, always knowing I could go.

One day he told me a story—or maybe he told it to someone else, but I could hear it, and he talked in English.

"My little girl," he said, chuckling. "Right smart young one, she is. I got her at a mission school, where they can bring her up right. Wouldn't have been there if I hadn't went to a lot of trouble. Her mother died, you know."

I made a sound indicating I was listening.

"Shoshone woman, her mother was. Died when we was camped on Little Muddy. If I'd knowed how sick she was, I'd have gotten her back to her people some way, but we was all alone. And the baby only three months old.

"Well, now, how was I going to feed the baby? No other woman around to give her to. Had to get out to someplace there'd be milk. But we was five hundred miles from a settlement. So I rode for buffalo country.

"I fed the young one on juice from chewed-up meat, but she cried all the time, getting weaker so she sounded like a sick kitten. First buffalo I seen was a dry cow, didn't do me no good. Then I come on a little herd of 'em, and there was milk to be had."

He laughed, remembering.

"You can't make no buffalo cow stand still to be milked. I had to shoot 'em. A dead cow you can get milk from. I fixed up a buckskin sack to nurse her with, and you should have seen her light into that milk! Every time she yelled for dinner and the sack was dry, I'd kill another buffalo cow.

"And did I ride! The last two days she got awful hungry, because the closer I came to the settlement, the scarcer the buffaloes was. But we made it through. I saved her. The Sisters at the mission took her.

"That girl baby was more darned trouble! I got me boys, too—Cheyenne, Sioux, Crow, Nez Percé—lots of boys, but darned if I know what become of 'em. They wasn't no trouble to me, and I wasn't no trouble to them. It's that little girl that was all the trouble."

He went back into silence, and after a while he talked to someone not present.

Seldom did anyone come to the Crawford place. A distant neighbor sometimes, looking for strayed stock, would ride in and stare with curiosity, nodding a brief greeting at Monkeyface and perhaps shouting, "Hello there, Cal, how are you?"

The old man might answer angrily, "Think I'm deaf as well as blind?" or he might stare with those blazing blue eyes and not answer at all.

The few visitors were curious about me, but beyond asking whether I was any relation, they seldom bothered to speak. A lordly boy of fifteen or so did condescend to conversation. He asked, grinning, "The old man been fighting any Injuns lately?"

Cal's wandering mind was known to him, apparently, but a burst of loyalty prevented me from admitting anything.

I said stiffly, "You crazy? No Injun fighting around here."

"The old squaw's man been around this summer?" he asked. "Long-hair Injun, comes to see her once in a long while."

"Nobody's been here. I don't know who you mean."

"He's her man. Wants her to go back to the tribe, but she stays with her pa," the boy explained. "She's waiting to inherit all his property. She don't want to live with the savages anyhow, not when she can have everything good like white folks, silk dress and all."

"She's got it good here, all right," I agreed, jumping to the conclusion that anything white was bound to be better than anything Indian.

He rode on after a while. He was the only boy I saw all that summer, and I used to wish he would come again.

The tax collector came one day when Cal and I had just got back from riding and the old man was lying on his bunk, tired out. I was in the yard, throwing chips at the chickens, when a rig turned in from the road. I went to tell Monkeyface, and she seemed disturbed. She woke up her father, and he was angry.

He shouted at her and groped out with his long stick to face the enemy. Monkeyface scowled at me and ordered, "You stay!"—the only time she ever gave me a direct order. This was private business, humiliating, not for me to know.

But even in the house I could hear the conversation, because the tax collector was one of the people who took it for granted that Cal Crawford, being blind, must be deaf as well.

"This ain't no place for you, Cal," he pleaded. "Come winter, what you going to do? We got a county farm. You'd be well took care of there, wouldn't have to worry about nothing."

"I got nothing to worry about now," Cal roared.

"But this place is going to be sold for taxes, I tell you. You could keep it, did you have the tax money."

Monkeyface snatched the purple silk dress from its nail by the door and put it on over her other dress and walked out to stand by her father, glaring at the visitor.

I saw a thing then that struck me with pity, young as I was and lacking in understanding. Cal put out his hand and touched the silk of the dress and took new strength from it. He expected it to be there, and it was.

"I look after my own," he boasted. "Bought my daughter a nice white-woman dress. You think I ain't got money? I can pay them taxes any time I please to!"

"Then pay me now, Cal, and save trouble," the tax collector pleaded. "It's not that anybody wants to put you off. But you don't need this place. You'd be better took care of on the county farm."

"Hundred and sixty acres," muttered Cal Crawford. "And he says I don't need all that." He stared blindly at the man in the rig and said with pride, "Young feller, once I owned half the continent. Me and a few others, we shared it and all that was in it. I ain't got much room to spread out in any more, but what I got, I need. And I'm going to keep it till I go under."

The man in the rig looked as if he might cry. "It's only what I'm supposed to do," he defended.

Cal lifted his stick in a vast, threatening gesture. "I'm going to keep what I got as long as I need it," he said, spacing the words. "I'll kill the man that tries to put me off."

The tax collector swatted his team with the whip and drove out fast.

At that moment, I loved old Cal. For the ring of truth was in his voice. *I'll kill him, that's what I'll do.* When other men said that, the threat was a crutch for weakness. But old Cal had killed, he could kill. If necessary, he would.

He turned toward the house, probing out ahead with his stick. Walking behind him, I straightened my shoulders. I was still afraid of him, but I was not lonely any more.

Cal lay down in his bunk again, one arm across his eyes. I hunkered on the floor, willing to wait as long as need be. Where was he then? In that Kansas cabin, maybe, thinking about the tax collector. Or maybe he was behind the log walls of a trading post far to the westward, planning defense against painted savages.

Wherever he was, he knew I was there, too. Because after a while he said, "Bring my gun."

I was honored to be so commanded, but I didn't know which gun he wanted. He had four, hanging on the wall of the kitchen. I had not touched them but had admired them from a distance. I was ignorant, but how could I confess it? Guns belonged to men, so a man naturally knew all about guns. But only one of Cal's looked like the rifle we had at home.

Cal Crawford's life had spanned two great developments in firearms. Flintlocks had been his weapons in his younger days. As civilization crept westward, he had used percussion arms. Before his sight went dim, metal cartridges and breech-loading rifles were available. So he had three kinds on the

wall. One of them was a flintlock with the stock scarred and set with brass-headed tacks.

I climbed on a chair and reached for the flintlock because it was the strongest. Monkeyface objected, "Uh! Uh!" and I told her, "He wants his gun."

She did not try again to stop me. I carried the strange, long old rifle carefully to the other room and put it in Cal's hands.

He knew it by touch and smiled. "Not that one, boy." He fondled it. "I took that off Bull Back in forty-three, lost it twice, and got it again. See this here, boy?" He fingered a bit of long black hair on a scrap of leather, attached to the trigger guard. "That there is Bull Back's scalp lock."

Shrinking, I touched it and thought, Now I have touched an Indian scalp, and I know the man who took it.

"Bring me the rest, boy. And the ammunition."

I carried the guns in one at a time, with more journeys for the dirty beaded and quill-worked bags for lead balls and percussion caps, two powder horns so thin you could see light through them, a couple of metal powder containers, and a box of cartridges.

"Lay 'em down here," Cal Crawford ordered. "And git out."

When I came back, half an hour later, I was disappointed. The old man was sleeping, and Monkeyface had put the weapons back where they belonged.

After that day, Cal never went riding any more. He stayed to defend the last vestige of his empire, the little hundred and sixty acres. And for the first time, he fretted. A couple of times he whistled for the dog, and I was afraid to remind him the dog couldn't answer his signal any more. He stayed in the cabin for hours at a time, going over the logs with his hands, measuring the windows, getting his bearings.

His Indian daughter fretted, too, but silently. Sometimes she stood looking to the west, always looking west, as if waiting for somebody. Cal Crawford was waiting, too, but not for the same person.

But someone came for me before anyone came for either of them. A man from town, on his way out to our home place with a wagon load of lumber, drove in to say, "Your pa said I might's well pick you up and carry you home, Buck, seeing's I'm going right by there."

He got down from the wagon and walked around, loosening up his muscles, looking things over. Monkeyface came out, but she didn't say anything. She only looked at me.

"This here's a friend of Pa's," I explained. "Pa says I'm to come home now."

She didn't answer. She turned to the house to get the pay I had coming, the three silver dollars.

"I'll get my stuff," I told the driver. "Be with you in a minute."

Getting my possessions didn't take long. But my extra shirt was in the room where Cal lay on his bunk, and it was only decent to tell him I was going.

"G'by, Mr. Crawford," I said politely. "A man's come for me, going to give me a lift home."

He was silent for a while, with one arm over his eyes. Then he said bitterly, "All right. You don't need to stay. I'll stand 'em off."

So something was going to happen, and if I went home then, I might never get the straight of it. That wasn't the important thing, though. What mattered was that I mattered to Cal Crawford.

"Shucks, I needn't go yet," I told him.

"There's no hurry. I'll tell him I'm going to stay around a while more."

"Whatever you want to do," Cal Crawford answered. He would not beg. He gave me pride I had never had before. I could afford to stay.

When I explained to the driver, he thought I was crazy and said so.

Neither Cal nor Monkeyface said anything about how I was a good boy and thank you. They just went on waiting.

One morning before dawn, the way Cal was fighting for breath woke me out of a sound sleep, or maybe it was his daughter's presence that woke me. She held an oil lamp high and was looking at Cal, speaking to him in her own language. She put a gnarled brown hand on his forehead and he shook it off angrily.

She looked at me with pleading. When she went outside, I saw in the dim light that she had a rope to catch up a horse with, so I guessed she was going for a doctor. I was more afraid than ever before in my life. I guessed what was coming for Cal Crawford.

He had faced it often before, stared it down, fought it off, conquered it, got away. Now he was going to fight it again, or maybe he thought it was some other enemy.

"Get my gun, boy," he gasped. "Help me sit up."

The breech-loading cartridge rifle was the one he had preferred before, so I brought that, but he disdained it.

"What's this thing?" he demanded. "Give me one a man can shoot with! And see the flint's sharp and the powder's dry."

So I got the old long flintlock with the bit of Bull Back's scalp dangling from the trigger guard. His hands claimed and caressed it.

"'Tain't Old Fury," he muttered, "but it'll do. Look around the rocks, boy, and tell me what you see. Keep your head down."

My voice wasn't above a whisper. "Nothing coming yet, Mr. Crawford."

"Stay clear and give me room, that's all I ask," he said. His breathing was full and fast by then. "And listen, boy, if I go under, you run and hide. Don't worry none. If they take you, likely they'll raise you like one of their own." He managed a grating chuckle. "There's worse ways to live than like an Injun."

I wanted to run, not from the Indians but from Cal Crawford and the enemy. I had not reckoned on staying alone with him while Monkeyface rode for a doctor. I still wonder why she did it. Probably because she was proud he maintained her in the style of a white woman and she wanted to go on to the end doing, for his sake, what a white woman would try to do.

Cal loaded the battered old flintlock. He didn't need to see. He put the lead ball in his cupped hand and spilled powder so the ball was almost covered. Getting the right amount of powder into the pan was harder, and he spilled some.

When he had the charge rammed home, he was tired out. He lay back, commanding, "Watch for 'em, boy, and let me know when they come up over the hill."

I never saw them come, and he never spoke again.

It was near noon when Monkeyface came with the doctor. I was crouching in a corner with my face turned away from the bunk. But I had not retreated.

Maybe it was not an enemy who came for Cal Crawford. Maybe it was the mountain men, riding in to guide him on a journey through a country of wonders even he had never glimpsed.

His daughter let me go home that day on the pinto pony.

It was good to be home, better than if I

had gone scared and retreating. I went as one who had earned the right because the job was finished and the duty done. I didn't tell them much, only that the old man was dead.

Pa was better, he could walk with a cane. Geraldine went around with a look on her face as if she had seen angels. She had a letter from her man, the first one since he went West without her. She wouldn't let us read it. But she hummed at her work and her steps were light.

About a week after I went home, Geraldine said, "Some old Injun is riding in with a squaw following. Now, what would they want?"

The Indian man stayed mounted, but when the squaw got down, I saw it was Cal's daughter. She was not wearing the purple silk dress. She had a striped shawl over an old cotton dress, and a kerchief on her head, squaw-fashion.

"It's Monkeyface," I said. "And that must be her husband, come to take her back to the tribe."

"She waited long enough," Geraldine said, "to get what old Cal left her. She earned it."

I suddenly understood something. "That wasn't why she stayed with him. She ain't got much of a pack on that horse. He didn't have anything to leave. She was just looking after her old pa because he needed her."

"Faithful," Geraldine whispered softly. "Faithful. That's what John says I am. He said it in the letter." She began to cry in a happy, sparkling way, and ran out to make a fuss over Monkeyface.

They had come for the pinto, so I went out and roped it. And Monkeyface gave me something for a remembrance of her pa.

Then they rode on, the man ahead and Cal Crawford's daughter following, leading the pinto, going home, wherever that was. Somewhere west, in the direction she used to look.

"There *is* faith and trust," my sister said softly. "She knew her man would wait till she could leave her pa. I wonder what she did with her purple dress."

We heard later. She left it hanging on a nail in the cabin. She left almost everything there. She had no use for anything white women treasured.

I don't know what happened to Cal Crawford's things, except that his daughter brought me the flintlock rifle he had held when he made his last stand. ☐☐

Discussion

1. In the first paragraph Buck says, "For years afterward I remembered it as a time of terror. I was grown up before I understood it had been a time of greatness, too." (a) For whom was it "a time of terror"? (b) For whom was it "a time of greatness"?

2. Buck says that he went to work for Cal "before he became a legend, and after he had stopped being one." What does Buck mean by this statement?

3. Which of the following might explain why Cal lives in the past? Be sure you can defend your answers with evidence that is either stated or suggested in the story. (a) He is lonely and longs for the company of men like himself. (b) He is afraid to admit he is old and defeated. (c) He fears death, and living in the past helps him to dismiss thoughts of it from his mind. (d) He is rebelling against civilization. (e) He finds the past more glorious than the present.

4. (a) What inner conflict does Buck undergo throughout most of his stay at the Crawford place? (b) At what point does he definitely settle this conflict? (c) What does he

mean when he says Cal "gave me pride I never had before. I could afford to stay"?

5. (a) What effect does the tax collector's visit have on Cal? **(b)** While talking to the collector, Cal touches his daughter's dress. What strength does he find in this action? **(c)** What does the collector represent to Cal? **(d)** Why does Cal's encounter with the collector cause Buck to love the old man?

6. What was Cal fighting during his last stand?

7. (a) While at the Crawfords', how does Buck feel about Monkeyface? **(b)** What does he finally come to realize about her? **(c)** Why does Monkeyface bring Buck her father's flintlock rifle?

8. In the biography below, Dorothy Johnson is quoted as saying, "I don't care to write about people I don't admire for at least one quality. I admire the people in this story because of their loyalty to one another." If you admired the characters in the story, what qualities in each did you admire most?

9. In her detailed portrait of Cal Crawford, Dorothy Johnson has created an especially vivid character. **(a)** What do you learn about Cal from the author's physical description of him? **(b)** How do Cal's words and actions increase your understanding of his character? **(c)** What more do you learn about Cal from Buck's observation of him? **(d)** Which of the above techniques of character-

ization revealed Cal most vividly for you?

Vocabulary • Dictionary

Use your Glossary to answer the questions following each of these sentences.

1. Rainy weather makes me feel *melancholy.*

a. Is the *ch* in *melancholy* pronounced like the *ch* in *charm* or like the *ch* in *character?*
b. Write one synonym for *melancholy.*
c. What are the meanings of the two Greek words from which *melancholy* comes?

2. The speaker's *arrogance* angered everyone.

a. What does *arrogance* mean?
b. Write the adjective form of *arrogance.*
c. What language did these two words come from?

3. Be *wary* of riding your bike after dark.

a. Is *wary* closer in meaning to *war* or to *beware?*
b. What two Old English words contributed two meanings for *ware* to modern English?

4. A crumbled stone temple was the only *vestige* of the lost city.

a. What meaning of *vestige* is intended in this sentence?
b. How is the meaning of the

Latin word from which *vestige* is derived related to the current meaning of *vestige?*

5. Where did you *resurrect* that old cabinet?

a. From what English word is *resurrect* derived?
b. What is the meaning of *resurrect* in sentence 5?

Dorothy Johnson 1905 •

Of "A Time of Greatness" Dorothy Johnson says, "Some of the details are true. I was tremendously moved by one small statement in a biography of the famous mountain man Jim Bridger: when he was old and blind, he used to kneel down and feel how tall the grain was growing. My stories always grow from an emotion. In this case it was deep pity.

"Jim Bridger, whose nickname was Old Gabe even when he was young, became Cal Crawford. Jim Bridger did have a half-Indian daughter, whose life he saved with buffalo milk.

"I don't care to write about people I can't admire for at least one quality. I admire the people in this story because of their loyalty to one another. Such loyalty often results in sacrifice."

An honorary member of the Blackfeet tribe, Miss Johnson has spent most of her life in Montana. A number of her western stories—including "The Man Who Shot Liberty Valance"—have been made into movies.

Venturing out into the great sea,
the Eskimo sings songs of joy.

Two Songs

Uvavnuk

I

The great sea
Has sent me adrift.
It moves me
As the weed in a great river.
5 Earth and the great weather
Move me,
Have carried me away
And move my inward parts with joy.

II

And I think over again
My small adventures
When with a shore wind I drifted out
In my kayak
5 And thought I was in danger.
My fears,
Those small ones
That I thought so big
For all vital things
10 I had to get and to reach.

And yet, there is only
One great thing,
The only thing:
To live and to see in huts and on journeys
15 The great day that dawns,
And the light that fills the world.

From ANERCA by Edmund Carpenter published by J. M. Dent &
Sons (Canada) Limited. © Edmund Carpenter, 1959.

Discussion

1. (a) In the first song does the speaker feel large or small in relation to the sea, the earth, and the weather? **(b)** Do you think the speaker is disturbed by this relationship?

2. What emotions does the speaker reveal in the first stanza of the second song?

3. What is the "one great thing" that the speaker talks about in the second stanza?

4. What main idea is expressed in both poems? (See biography below for related information.)

Uvavnuk

In Eskimo, the word "to make poetry" is the same as the word "to breathe." The songs and recitations of the Eskimo are especially rich in the observation of nature for nature's sake.

The two songs printed here are healing songs attributed to the poet-muse Uvavnuk. The first song has an interesting history. Among the arctic Eskimo, Uvavnuk was believed to possess magical powers. According to one account, Uvavnuk was struck unconscious one day while seeking a vision for her people. When she recovered, she sang this healing song.

Healing songs such as these are intended to instill feelings of joy and to help avoid dwelling too long on sorrows. In the cold, bleak environment of the arctic, such songs are an important and welcome part of the Eskimo's daily life.

See **THEME** Handbook of Literary Terms

The plans for killing the dolphin had already been made.
What could Helen possibly do to save him?

Let Me Hear
You Whisper

Paul Zindel

CHARACTERS

HELEN, a little old cleaning lady who lives alone in a one-room apartment and spends most of her spare time feeding stray cats and dogs. She has just been hired to scrub floors in a laboratory that performs rather strange experiments with dolphins.

MISS MORAY, a briskly efficient custodial supervisor who has to break Helen in to her new duties at the laboratory. She has a face that is so uptight she looks like she either throws stones at pigeons or teaches Latin.

DR. CROCUS, the dedicated man of science who devises and presides over the weird experiments.

MR. FRIDGE, assistant to Dr. Crocus. He is so loyal and uncreative that if Dr. Crocus told him to stick his head in the mouth of a shark, he'd do it.

DAN, a talky janitor, also under Miss Moray's control, who at every chance ducks out of the Manhattan laboratory for a beer at the corner bar.

A DOLPHIN, the subject of an experiment being performed by Dr. Crocus.

SETTING: *The action takes place in the hallway, laboratory and specimen room of a biology experimentation association located in Manhattan near the Hudson River.*

TIME: *The action begins with the night shift on a Monday and ends the following Friday.*

ACT I

SCENE I

(DR. CROCUS *and* MR. FRIDGE *are leaving the laboratory where they have completed their latest experimental tinkering with a dolphin, and they head down a corridor to the elevator. The elevator door opens and* MISS MORAY *emerges with* HELEN.)

MISS MORAY. Dr. Crocus. Mr. Fridge. I'm so glad we've run into you. I want you to meet Helen.

HELEN. Hello.

(DR. CROCUS *and* MR. FRIDGE *nod and get on elevator.*)

MISS MORAY. Helen is the newest member of our Custodial Engineering Team.

(MISS MORAY *and* HELEN *start down the hall.*)

MISS MORAY. Dr. Crocus is the guiding heart here at the American Biological Association Development for the Advancement of Brain Analysis. For short, we call it "Abadaba."

HELEN. I guess you have to.

(*They stop at a metal locker at the end of the hall.*)

MISS MORAY. This will be your locker and your key. Your equipment is in this closet.

HELEN. I have to bring in my own hangers, I suppose.

MISS MORAY. Didn't you find Personnel pleasant?

HELEN. They asked a lot of crazy questions.

MISS MORAY. Oh, I'm sorry. (*pause*) For instance.

HELEN. They wanted to know what went on in my head when I'm watching television in my living room and the audience laughs. They asked if I ever thought the audience was laughing at *me*.

MISS MORAY (*laughing*). My, oh, my! (*pause*) What did you tell them?

HELEN. I don't have a TV.

MISS MORAY. I'm sorry.

HELEN. I'm not.

MISS MORAY. Yes. Now, it's really quite simple. That's our special soap solution. One tablespoon to a gallon of hot water, if I may suggest.

(HELEN *is busy running water into a pail which fits into a metal stand on wheels.*)

MISS MORAY. I'll start you in the laboratory. We like it done first. The specimen room next, and finally the hallway. By that time we'll be well toward morning, and if there are a few minutes left, you can polish the brass strip. (*She points to brass strip which runs around the corridor, halfway between ceiling and floor.*) Ready? Fine.

(*They start down the hall,* MISS MORAY *thumbing through papers on a clipboard.*)

MISS MORAY. You were with one concern for fourteen years, weren't you? Fourteen years with the Metal Climax Building.

That's next to the Radio City Music Hall,[1] isn't it, dear?

HELEN. Uh-huh.

MISS MORAY. They sent a marvelous letter of recommendation. My! Fourteen years on the seventeenth floor. You must be very proud. Why did you leave?

HELEN. They put in a rug.

(MISS MORAY *leads* HELEN *into the laboratory, where* DAN *is picking up.*)

MISS MORAY. Dan, Helen will be taking Marguerita's place. Dan is the night porter for the fifth through ninth floors.

DAN. Hiya!

HELEN. Hello. *(She looks around.)*

MISS MORAY. There's a crock on nine you missed, and the technicians on that floor have complained about the odor.

(HELEN *notices what appears to be a large tank of water with a curtain concealing its contents.*)

HELEN. What's that?

MISS MORAY. What? Oh, that's a dolphin, dear. But don't worry about anything except the floor. Dr. Crocus prefers us not to touch either the equipment or the animals.

HELEN. Do you keep him cramped up in that all the time?

MISS MORAY. We have a natatorium for it to exercise in, at Dr. Crocus's discretion.

HELEN. He really looks cramped.

(MISS MORAY *closes a curtain which hides the tank.*)

MISS MORAY. Well, you must be anxious to begin. I'll make myself available at the reception desk in the hall for a few nights in case any questions arise. Coffee break at two and six A.M. Lunch at four A.M. All clear?

HELEN. I don't need a coffee break.

MISS MORAY. Helen, we all need Perk-You-Ups. All of us.

HELEN. I don't want one.

MISS MORAY. They're compulsory. *(pause)* Oh, Helen, I know you're going to fit right in with our little family. You're such a *nice* person. *(She exits.)*

(HELEN *immediately gets to work, moving her equipment into place and getting down on her hands and knees to scrub the floor.* DAN *exits.* HELEN *gets in a few more rubs, glances at the silhouette of the dolphin's tank behind the curtain, and then continues. After a pause, a record begins to play.*)

RECORD. "Let me call you sweetheart,
　　　　 I'm in love with you.
　　　　 Let me hear you whisper
　　　　 That you love me, too."

(HELEN'S *curiosity makes her open the curtain and look at the dolphin. He looks right back at her. She returns to her work, singing* "Let Me Call You Sweetheart" *to herself, missing a word here and there; but her eyes return to the dolphin. She becomes uncomfortable under his stare and tries to ease her discomfort by playing peek-a-boo with him. There is no response and she resumes scrubbing and humming. The dolphin then lets out a bubble or two and moves in the tank to bring his blowhole to the surface.*)

DOLPHIN. Youuuuuuuuuuuu.

(HELEN *hears the sound, assumes she is mistaken, and goes on with her work.*)

DOLPHIN. Youuuuuuuuuuuu.

(HELEN *has heard the sound more clearly this time. She is puzzled, contemplates a moment, and then decides to get up off the floor. She closes the curtain on the dolphin's tank and leaves the laboratory. She walks the length of the hall to* MISS MORAY, *who is sitting at a reception desk near the elevator.*)

MISS MORAY. What is it, Helen?

---

1. *Radio City Music Hall,* movie theater in New York City, famous for lavish stage shows.

HELEN. The fish is making some kinda funny noise.

MISS MORAY. Mammal, Helen. It's a mammal.

HELEN. The mammal's making some kinda funny noise.

MISS MORAY. Mammals are supposed to make funny noises.

HELEN. Yes, Miss Moray.

(HELEN *goes back to the lab. She continues scrubbing.*)

DOLPHIN. Youuuuuuuuuuu.

(*She apprehensively approaches the curtain and opens it. Just then* DAN *barges in. He goes to get his reaching pole, and* HELEN *hurriedly returns to scrubbing the floor.*)

DAN. Bulb out on seven.

HELEN. What do they have that thing for?

DAN. What thing?

HELEN. That.

DAN. Yeah, he's something, ain't he? *(pause)* They're tryin' to get it to talk.

HELEN. Talk?

DAN. Uh-huh, but he don't say nothing. They had one last year that used to laugh. It'd go "heh heh heh heh heh heh heh." Then they got another one that used to say, "Yeah, it's four o'clock." Everybody took pictures of that one. All the magazines and newspapers.

HELEN. It just kept saying "Yeah, it's four o'clock"?

DAN. Until it died of pneumonia. They talk outta their blowholes, when they can talk, that is. Did you see the blowhole?

HELEN. No.

DAN. Come on and take a look.

HELEN. I don't want to look at any blowhole.

DAN. Miss Moray's at the desk. She won't see anything.

(HELEN *and* DAN *go to the tank. Their backs are to the lab door and they don't see* MISS MORAY *open the door and watch them.*)

DAN. This one don't say anything at all. They been playing that record every seven minutes for months, and it can't even learn a single word. Don't even say "Polly want a cracker."

MISS MORAY. Helen?

(HELEN *and* DAN *turn around.*)

MISS MORAY. Helen, would you mind stepping outside a moment?

HELEN. Yes, Miss Moray.

DAN. I was just showing her something.

MISS MORAY. Hadn't we better get on with our duties?

DAN. All right, Miss Moray.

(MISS MORAY *guides* HELEN *out into the hall, and puts her arm around her as though taking her into her confidence.*)

MISS MORAY. Helen, I called you out here because . . . well, frankly, I need your help.

HELEN. He was just showing me . . .

MISS MORAY. Dan is an idle-chatter breeder. How many times we've told him, "Dan, this is a scientific atmosphere you're employed in and we would appreciate a minimum of subjective communication." So—if you can help, Helen—and I'm sure you can, enormously—we'd be so grateful.

HELEN. Yes, Miss Moray.

(MISS MORAY *leads* HELEN *back to the lab.*)

MISS MORAY. Now, we'll just move directly into the specimen room. The working conditions will be ideal for you in here.

(HELEN *looks ready to gag as she looks around the specimen room. It is packed with specimen jars of all sizes. Various animals and parts of animals are visible in their formaldehyde baths.[2]*)

---

2. **formaldehyde** (fôr mal′də hīd) **baths,** solutions containing the colorless, toxic gas formaldehyde, used as a preservative.

MISS MORAY. Now, you will be responsible not only for the floor area but the jars as well. A feather duster—here—is marvelous.

(MISS MORAY *smiles and exits. The sound of music and voice from beyond the walls floats over.*)

RECORD. "Let me call you sweetheart . . ."

(HELEN *gasps as her eyes fall upon one particular jar in which is floating a preserved human brain. The lights go down, ending Act I, Scene 1.*)

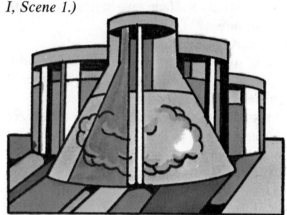

SCENE 2

(*It is the next evening.* HELEN *pushes her equipment into the lab. She opens the curtain so she can watch the dolphin as she works. She and the dolphin stare at each other.*)

HELEN. Youuuuuuuuuuu. (*She pauses, watches for a response.*) Youuuuuuuuuuuu. (*Still no response. She turns her attention to her scrubbing for a moment.*) Polly want a cracker? Polly want a cracker? (*She wrings out a rag and resumes work.*) Yeah, it's four o'clock. Yeah, it's four o'clock. Polly want a cracker at four o'clock?

(*She laughs at her own joke, then goes to the dolphin's tank and notices how sad he looks. She reaches her hand in and just touches the*

top of his head. He squirms and likes it.)

HELEN. Heh heh heh heh heh heh heh heh heh.

(MISS MORAY *gets off the elevator and hears the peculiar sounds coming from the laboratory. She puts her ear against the door.*)

HELEN. Heh heh heh heh heh . . .

MISS MORAY (*entering*). Look how nicely the floor's coming along! You must have a special rinsing technique.

HELEN. Just a little vinegar in the rinse water.

MISS MORAY. You brought the vinegar yourself. Just so the floors . . . they are sparkling, Helen. Sparkling! (*She pauses—looks at the dolphin, then at* HELEN.) It's marvelous, Helen, how well you've adjusted.

HELEN. Thank you, Miss Moray.

MISS MORAY. Helen, the animals here are used for experimentation, and. . . . Well, take Marguerita. She had fallen in love with the mice. All three hundred of them. She seemed shocked when she found out Dr. Crocus was . . . using . . . them at the rate of twenty or so a day in connection with electrode implanting.[3] She noticed them missing after a while and when I told her they'd been decapitated, she seemed terribly upset.

HELEN. What do they want with the fish—mammal?

MISS MORAY. Well, dolphins may have an intelligence equal to our own. And if we can teach them our language—or learn theirs—we'll be able to communicate.

HELEN. I can't understand you.

MISS MORAY (*louder*). Communicate! Wouldn't it be wonderful?

HELEN. Oh, yeah. . . . They chopped the

---

3. electrode implanting, the insertion into the mice's heads of devices to measure the electrical activity of their brains.

heads off three hundred mice? That's horrible.

MISS MORAY. You're so sensitive, Helen. Every laboratory in the country is doing this type of work. It's quite accepted.

HELEN. Every laboratory cutting off mouse heads!

MISS MORAY. Virtually . . . .

HELEN. How many laboratories are there?

MISS MORAY. I don't know. I suppose at least five thousand.

HELEN. Five thousand times three hundred . . . that's a lot of mouse heads. Can't you just have one lab chop off a couple and then spread the word?

MISS MORAY. Now, Helen—this is exactly what I mean. You will do best not to become fond of the subject animals. When you're here a little longer you'll learn . . . well . . . there are some things you just have to accept on faith.

(MISS MORAY *exits, leaving the lab door open for* HELEN *to move her equipment out.*)

DOLPHIN. Whisper. . . . (HELEN *pauses a moment.*) Whisper to me. (*She exits as the lights go down, ending the scene.*)

SCENE 3

(*It is the next evening.* HELEN *goes from her locker to the laboratory.*)

DOLPHIN. Hear . . . .

HELEN. What?

DOLPHIN. Hear me . . . .

(DAN *barges in with his hamper, almost frightening* HELEN *to death. He goes to dolphin's tank.*)

DAN. Hiya, fella! How are ya? That reminds me. Gotta get some formaldehyde jars set up by Friday. If you want anything just whistle.

(*He exits.* HELEN *goes to the tank and reaches her hand out to pet the dolphin.*)

HELEN. Hear. (*pause*) Hear.

DOLPHIN. Hear.

HELEN. Hear me.

DOLPHIN. Hear me.

HELEN. That's a good boy.

DOLPHIN. Hear me . . . .

HELEN. Oh, what a pretty fellow. Such a pretty fellow.

(MISS MORAY *enters.*)

MISS MORAY. What are you doing, Helen?

HELEN. I . . . uh . . . .

MISS MORAY. Never mind. Go on with your work.

(MISS MORAY *surveys everything, then sits on a stool.* DAN *rushes in with large jars on a wheeled table.*)

DAN. Scuse me, but I figure I'll get the formaldehyde set up tonight.

MISS MORAY. Very good, Dan.

HELEN (*noticing the dolphin is stirring*). What's the formaldehyde for?

MISS MORAY. The experiment series on . . . the dolphin will . . . terminate on Friday. That's why it has concerned me that you've apparently grown . . . fond . . . of the mammal.

HELEN. They're gonna kill it?

DAN. Gonna sharpen the handsaws now. Won't have any trouble getting through the skull on this one, no, sir. (*He exits.*)

HELEN. What for? Because it didn't say anything? Is that what they're killing it for?

MISS MORAY. Helen, no matter how lovely our intentions, no matter how lonely we are and how much we want people or animals . . . to like us . . . we have no right to endanger the genius about us. Now, we've spoken about this before.

(HELEN *is dumbfounded as* MISS MORAY *exits.* HELEN *gathers her equipment and* looks at the dolphin, which is staring desperately at her.)

DOLPHIN. Help. *(pause)* Please help me.

(HELEN *is so moved by the cries of the dolphin she looks ready to burst into tears as the lights go down, ending Act I.)*

ACT II

(The hall. It is the night that the dolphin is to be dissected. Elevator doors open and HELEN *gets off, nods, and starts down the hall.* MISS MORAY *comes to* HELEN *at closet.)*

MISS MORAY. I hope you're well this evening.

HELEN. When they gonna kill it?

MISS MORAY. Don't say kill, Helen. You make it sound like murder. Besides, you won't have to go into the laboratory at all this evening.

HELEN. How do they kill it?

MISS MORAY. Nicotine mustard,[4] Helen. It's very humane. They inject it.

HELEN. Maybe he's a mute.

MISS MORAY. Do you have all your paraphernalia?

HELEN. Some human beings are mute, you know. Just because they can't talk we don't kill them.

MISS MORAY. It looks like you're ready to open a new box of steel wool.

HELEN. Maybe he can type with his nose. Did they try that?

MISS MORAY. Now, now, Helen—

HELEN. Miss Moray, I don't mind doing the lab.

MISS MORAY. Absolutely not! I'm placing it off limits for your own good. You're too emotionally involved.

HELEN. I can do the lab, honest. I'm not emotionally involved.

MISS MORAY *(motioning her to the speci-*

men-room door). Trust me, Helen. Trust me.

HELEN *(reluctantly disappearing through the door).* Yes, Miss Moray.

(MISS MORAY *stations herself at the desk near the elevator and begins reading her charts.* HELEN *slips out of the specimen room and into the laboratory without being seen. The lights in the lab are out and moonlight from the window casts eerie shadows.)*

DOLPHIN. Help.

(HELEN *opens the curtain. The dolphin and she look at each other.)*

DOLPHIN. Help me.

HELEN. You don't need me. Just say something to them. Anything. They just need to hear you say something. . . . You want me to tell 'em? I'll tell them. I'll just say I heard you say "Help." *(pauses, then speaks with feigned cheerfulness)* I'll go tell them.

DOLPHIN. Noooooooooooooooo.

(HELEN *stops. Moves back toward tank.)*

HELEN. They're gonna kill you!

DOLPHIN. Plaaaaan.

HELEN. What?

DOLPHIN. Plaaaaaaaan.

HELEN. Plan? What plan?

(DAN *charges through the door and snaps on the light.)*

DAN. Uh-oh. Miss Moray said she don't want you in here.

(HELEN *goes to* DR. CROCUS's *desk and begins to look at various books on it.)*

HELEN. Do you know anything about a plan?

DAN. She's gonna be mad. What plan?

HELEN. Something to do with . . . . *(She indicates the dolphin.)*

DAN. Hiya, fella!

HELEN. About the dolphin . . . .

---

4. **Nicotine** (nik′ə tēn′) **mustard,** a colorless poison derived from tobacco.

DAN. They got an experiment book they write in.

HELEN. Where?

DAN. I don't know.

HELEN. Find it and bring it to me in the animals' morgue. Please.

DAN. I'll try. I'll try, but I got other things to do, you know.

(HELEN *slips out the door and makes it safely back into the specimen room.* DAN *rummages through the desk and finally finds the folder. He is able to sneak into the specimen room.*)

DAN. Here.

(HELEN *grabs the folder and starts going through it.* DAN *turns and is about to go back out into the hall when he sees that* MISS MORAY *has stopped reading.* HELEN *skims through more of the folder. It is a bulky affair. She stops at a page discussing uses of dolphins.* MISS MORAY *gets up from the desk and heads for the specimen-room door.*)

DAN. She's coming.

HELEN. Maybe you'd better hide. Get behind the table. Here, take the book.

(DAN *ducks down behind one of the specimen tables, and* HELEN *starts scrubbing away.* MISS MORAY *opens the door.*)

MISS MORAY. Perk-You-Up time, Helen. Tell Dan, please. He's in the laboratory.

(HELEN *moves to the lab door, opens it, and calls into the empty room.*)

HELEN. Perk-You-Up time.

MISS MORAY. Tell him we have ladyfingers.

HELEN. We have ladyfingers.

MISS MORAY. Such a strange thing to call a confectionery, isn't it? It's almost macabre.

HELEN. Miss Moray . . . .

MISS MORAY. Yes, Helen?

HELEN. I was wondering why they wanna talk with . . . .

MISS MORAY. Now now now!

HELEN. I mean, supposing dolphins *did* talk?

MISS MORAY. Well, like fishing, Helen. If we could communicate with dolphins, they might be willing to herd fish for us. The fishing industry would be revolutionized.

HELEN. Is that all?

MISS MORAY. All? Heavens, no. They'd be a blessing to the human race. A blessing. They would be worshipped in oceanography. Checking the Gulf Stream . . . taking water temperatures, depth, salinity readings.[5] To say nothing of the contributions they could make in marine biology, navigation, linguistics![6] Oh, Helen, it gives me the chills.

HELEN. It'd be good if they talked?

MISS MORAY. God's own blessing.

(DAN *opens the lab doors and yells over* HELEN'S *head to* MISS MORAY.*)

DAN. I got everything except the head vise. They can't saw through the skull bone without the head vise.

MISS MORAY. Did you look on five? They had it there last week for . . . what they did to the St. Bernard.

(*From the laboratory, music drifts out. They try to talk over it.*)

DAN. I looked on five.

MISS MORAY. You come with me. It must have been staring you in the face.

(DAN *and* MISS MORAY *get on the elevator.*)

MISS MORAY. We'll be right back, Helen.

(*The doors close and* HELEN *hurries into the laboratory. She stops just inside the door, and it is obvious that she is angry.*)

---

5. *Gulf Stream . . . salinity readings.* The Gulf Stream is a warm ocean current flowing north along the east coast of the U.S. Salinity readings are measurements of salt content of the ocean.

6. *marine biology, navigation, linguistics* (ling gwis′tiks). Marine biology is the scientific study of plant and animal life of the sea. Navigation is the science of finding a ship's or plane's position and course. Linguistics is the science of language.

DOLPHIN. Booooooooook.

HELEN. I looked at your book. I looked at your book all right!

DOLPHIN. Booooooooook.

HELEN. And you want to know what I think? I don't think much of you, that's what I think.

DOLPHIN. Booooooooook.

HELEN. Oh, shut up. Book book book book book. I'm not interested. You eat yourself silly—but to get a little fish for hungry humans is just too much for you. Well. I'm going to tell 'em you can talk.

(The dolphin moves in the tank, lets out a few warning bubbles.)

HELEN. You don't like that, eh? Well, I don't like lazy selfish people, mammals or animals.

(The dolphin looks increasingly desperate and begins to make loud blatt and beep sounds. He struggles in the tank.)

HELEN. Cut it out—you're getting water all over the floor.

DOLPHIN. Booooooooook!

(HELEN looks at the folder on the desk. She picks it up, opens it, closes it, and sets it down again.)

HELEN. I guess you don't like us. I guess you'd die rather than help us . . . .

DOLPHIN. Hate.

HELEN. I guess you do hate us . . . .

(She returns to the folder.)

HELEN *(reading).* Military implications . . . war . . . plant mines in enemy waters . . . deliver atomic warheads . . . war . . . nuclear torpedoes . . . attach bombs to submarines . . . terrorize enemy waters . . . war. . . . They're already thinking about ways to use you for war. Is that why you can't talk to them? *(pause)* What did you talk to me for? *(pause)* You won't talk to them, but you . . . you talk to me because . . . you want something . . .

there's something . . . I can do?

DOLPHIN. Hamm . . . .

HELEN. What?

DOLPHIN. Hamm . . . .

HELEN. Ham? I thought you ate fish.

DOLPHIN *(moving with annoyance).* Ham . . . purrrr.

HELEN. Ham . . . purrrr? I don't know what you're talking about.

DOLPHIN *(even more annoyed).* Ham . . . purrr.

HELEN. Ham . . . purrrr. What's a purrrr?

(Confused and scared, she returns to scrubbing the hall floor just as the doors of the elevator open, revealing MISS MORAY, DAN, *and* MR. FRIDGE. DAN *pushes a dissection table loaded with shiny instruments toward the lab.)*

MISS MORAY. Is the good doctor in yet?

MR. FRIDGE. He's getting the nicotine mustard on nine. I'll see if he needs assistance.

MISS MORAY. I'll come with you. You'd better leave now, Helen. It's time. *(She smiles and the elevator doors close.)*

DAN *(pushing the dissection table through the lab doors).* I never left a dirty head vise. She's trying to say I left it like that.

HELEN. Would you listen a minute? Ham . . . purrrr. Do you know what a ham . . . purrrr is?

DAN. The only hamper I ever heard of is out in the hall.

(HELEN darts to the door, opens it, and sees the hamper at the end of the hall.)

HELEN. The hamper!

DAN. Kazinski left the high-altitude chamber[7] dirty once, and I got blamed for that, too. *(He exits.)*

HELEN *(rushing to the dolphin).* You want me to do something with the hamper.

---

7. **high-altitude chamber,** a closed container in which air pressure can be varied.

What? To get it? To put . . . you want me to put you in it? But what'll I do with you? Where can I take you?

DOLPHIN. Sea . . . .

HELEN. See? See what?

DOLPHIN. Sea . . . .

HELEN. I don't know what you're talking about. They'll be back in a minute. I don't know what to do!

DOLPHIN. Sea . . . sea . . . .

HELEN. See? . . . The sea! That's what you're talking about! The river . . . to the sea!

(She darts into the hall and heads for the hamper. Quickly she pushes it into the lab,

and just as she gets through the doors unseen, MISS MORAY *gets off the elevator.)*

MISS MORAY. Helen?

(She starts down the hall. Enters the lab. The curtain is closed in front of the tank.)

MISS MORAY. Helen? Are you here? Helen?

(She sees nothing and is about to leave when she hears a movement behind the curtain. She looks down and sees HELEN'*s shoes.* MISS MORAY *moves to the curtain and pulls it open. There is* HELEN *with her arms around the front part of the dolphin, lifting it a good part of the way out of the water.)*

MISS MORAY. Helen, what do you think

you're hugging?

(HELEN *drops the dolphin back into the tank.*)

MR. FRIDGE *(entering).* Is anything wrong, Miss Moray?

MISS MORAY. No . . . nothing wrong. Nothing at all. Just a little spilled water.

(HELEN *and* MISS MORAY *grab sponges from the lab sink and begin to wipe up the water around the tank.* DR. CROCUS *enters and begins to fill a hypodermic syringe while* MR. FRIDGE *expertly gets all equipment into place.* DAN *enters.*)

MR. FRIDGE. Would you like to get an encephalogram[8] during the death process, Dr. Crocus?

DR. CROCUS. Why not?

(MR. FRIDGE *begins to implant electrodes in the dolphin's head. The dolphin commences making high-pitched distress signals.*)

MISS MORAY. Come, Helen. I'll see you to the elevator.

(MISS MORAY *leads her out to the hall.* HELEN *gets on her coat and kerchief.*)

MISS MORAY. Frankly, Helen, I'm deeply disappointed. I'd hoped that by being lenient with you—and heaven knows I have been—you'd develop a heightened loyalty to our team.

HELEN *(bursting into tears and going to the elevator).* Leave me alone.

MISS MORAY *(softening as she catches up to her).* You really are a nice person, Helen. A very nice person. But to be simple and nice in a world where great minds are giant-stepping the micro- and macrocosms,[9] well—one would expect you'd have the humility to yield in unquestioning awe. I truly am very fond of you, Helen, but you're fired. Call Personnel after nine A.M.

(As MISS MORAY *disappears into the laboratory, the record starts to play.*)

RECORD. "Let me call you sweetheart,
   I'm in love with you.
   Let me hear you whisper. . . ."

(*The record is roughly interrupted. Instead of getting on the elevator,* HELEN *whirls around and barges into the lab.*)

HELEN. Who do you think you are? *(pause)* Who do you think you *are? (pause)* I think you're a pack of killers, that's what I think.

MISS MORAY. Doctor. I assure you this is the first psychotic outbreak she's made. She did the entire brass strip . . . .

HELEN. I'm very tired of being a nice person, Miss Moray. I'm going to report you to the ASPCA,[10] or somebody, because . . . I've decided I don't like you cutting the heads off mice and sawing through skulls of St. Bernards . . . and if being a nice person is just not saying anything and letting you pack of butchers run around doing whatever you want, then I don't want to be nice anymore. *(pause)* You gotta be very stupid people to need an animal to talk before you know just from looking at it that it's saying something . . . that it knows what pain feels like. I'd like to see you all with a few electrodes in your heads. Being nice isn't any good. *(looking at dolphin)* They just kill you off if you do that. And that's being a coward. You gotta talk back. You gotta speak up against what's wrong and bad, or you can't ever stop it. At least you've gotta try. *(She bursts into tears.)*

MISS MORAY. Nothing like this has ever happened with a member of the Custodial Engineering . . . . Helen, dear . . . .

---

8. *encephalogram* (en sef/ə lə gram/), a chart measuring the electrical activity of the brain.
9. *great minds . . . macrocosms.* Scientists are making great advances in understanding our world as well as the universe beyond.
10. *ASPCA,* American Society for Prevention of Cruelty to Animals.

HELEN. Get your hands off me. *(yelling at the dolphin)* You're a coward, that's what you are. I'm going.

DOLPHIN. Loooooooooveeeeeeeee.

(Everyone turns to stare at the dolphin.)

DOLPHIN. Love.

DR. CROCUS. Get the recorder going.

(HELEN pats the dolphin, exits. The laboratory becomes a bustle of activity.)

DOLPHIN. Love . . . .

DR. CROCUS. Is the tape going?

MR. FRIDGE. Yes, Doctor.

DOLPHIN. Love . . . .

DR. CROCUS. I think that woman's got something to do with this. Get her back in here.

MISS MORAY. Oh, I fired her. She was hugging the mammal . . . and . . . .

DOLPHIN. Love . . . .

DR. CROCUS. Just get her. *(to MR. FRIDGE)* You're sure the machine's recording?

MISS MORAY. Doctor, I'm afraid you don't understand. That woman was hugging the mammal . . . .

DR. CROCUS. Try to get another word out of it. One more word . . . .

MISS MORAY. The last thing in the world I want is for our problem in Custodial Engineering to . . . .

DR. CROCUS *(furious)*. Will you shut up

and get that washwoman back in here?

MISS MORAY. Immediately, Doctor.

(She hurries out of the lab. HELEN *is at the end of the hall waiting for the elevator.)*

MISS MORAY. Helen? Oh, Helen? Don't you want to hear what the dolphin has to say? He's so cute! Dr. Crocus thinks that his talking might have something to do with you. Wouldn't that be exciting? *(pause)* Please, Helen. The doctor . . . .

HELEN. Don't talk to me, do you mind?

MISS MORAY. It was only in the heat of argument that I . . . of course, you won't be discharged. All right? Please, Helen, you'll embarrass me . . . .

(The elevator doors open and HELEN *gets on to face* MISS MORAY. *She looks at her a moment and then lifts her hand to press the button for the ground floor.)*

MISS MORAY. Don't you dare . . . Helen, the team needs you, don't you see? You've done so well—the brass strip, the floors. The floors have never looked so good. Ever. Helen, please. What will I do if you leave?

HELEN. Why don't you get a rug?

(HELEN helps slam the elevator doors in MISS MORAY'S *face as the lights go down, ending the play.)* □□

Discussion

1. (a) What do you learn about Helen from her conversations with Miss Moray? (b) What do you learn about Miss Moray?

2. (a) What is Helen's reaction to learning that the dolphin is going to be killed? (b) What advice does she give the dolphin? (c) Why does she get angry at the dolphin? (d) What changes her attitude toward the dolphin's reluctance to speak?

3. (a) What does the dolphin want Helen to do? (b) What prevents Helen from helping him?

4. (a) After being fired for her actions, what does Helen say to the scientists before she leaves? (b) What does she say to the dolphin? (c) Do you agree with Helen's accusations? Why or why not?

5. (a) What do you think is the significance of the dolphin's response to Helen? (b) What

results from his having spoken? (c) What do you think will happen to the dolphin?

6. (a) Find examples of humor in the play. (b) Do you think the humor is intended for its own sake only, or does it serve another purpose as well? Explain your answer.

7. Read the four statements below and choose the one that comes the closest in your opinion to expressing the theme of the play. Explain your choice. (a) Dolphins are not capable of learning how to perform military functions. (b) Sentiment has no place in scientific research. (c) People sometimes find that they have to take a stand against something that they think is wrong, even if that something is done in the name of science. (d) If you become too involved in your work, you run the risk of getting into trouble.

Vocabulary • Context

Use the context clues in the sentences below to figure out the meaning of the italicized words. Then write the letter of the correct meaning on your paper.

1. So that his parents would not know he was listening to their conversation, Jim *feigned* sleep. (a) wanted; (b) tried; (c) pretended; (d) expected.

2. The audience watched *apprehensively* as the tight-rope walker struggled to regain his balance on the high wire. (a) fearfully; (b) wisely; (c) happily; (d) angrily.

3. Attendance at the next club meeting will be *compulsory;* any member not present will be fined one dollar. (a) enjoyable; (b) required; (c) costly; (d) relaxed.

4. The protesters demanded better living conditions and more *humane* treatment for the prisoners. (a) merciful; (b) enthusiastic; (c) disciplined; (d) possessive.

5. Herb was careful to make no direct statements, but by *implication* he cast doubt on Jack's honesty. (a) accusation; (b) whispering; (c) indirect suggestion; (d) lying.

6. Five minutes after the show had ended, the auditorium was *virtually* empty; only a handful of students remained. (a) completely; (b) unnecessarily; (c) for no reason; (d) for all practical purposes.

7. Elena didn't swear us to secrecy about the plan, but she did say to use *discretion* in discussing it with other people. (a) simple language; (b) charts and diagrams; (c) careful judgment; (d) compassion.

Extension • Writing

Scientists are confronted every day by issues similar to ones that are raised in *Let Me Hear You Whisper.* Pretend that you are a scientist in the following situation:

You are conducting laboratory tests on monkeys to determine if a certain new drug is successful in treating heart disease. Many of the monkeys have suffered serious side effects from the drug. Some have died. A representative of the ASPCA sends you a letter protesting your inhumane treatment of the monkeys. Write a reply explaining why you think it is important and necessary to continue the tests on the monkeys.

If you prefer, pretend that you are the representative of the ASPCA. Compose a letter to the scientist explaining why you are opposed to conducting tests on the monkeys.

If Dolphins Could Talk, What Would They Say?

Let Me Hear You Whisper is not completely fantasy. Recently two young lab assistants were arrested for "liberating" two dolphins from the Hawaii Institute of Marine Biology in Honolulu. They released the animals because, they claimed, "man has no right to capture or hold in captivity intelligent feeling beings." The two dolphins were last seen far from shore, heading out into the open sea.

For thousands of years we have known that of all the creatures that live in the sea, the air-breathing mammals called *cetaceans*—whales, porpoises, and dolphins—are the most unusual. Sailors have always considered the appearance of dolphins and porpoises a sign of good luck, and dolphins in particular seem to take special pleasure in leaping and frolicking around ships at sea. Eyewitnesses tell of drowning men saved by dolphins.

Dolphins are among the gentlest creatures on earth, and probably are among the most intelligent. Although some dolphins can stun, even kill, large sharks with a single blow, not one report has ever been received of a dolphin intentionally harming a person. On the contrary, dolphins are curious, playful, often friendly. But when they draw near a ship it is *they* who are in danger of being maimed, taken captive, or killed.

Our treatment of dolphins seems especially cruel when one considers their behavior toward their own kind. They often mate for life, and they nurture and protect their young in openly affectionate ways. They cooperate in groups or families: often an individual will make dramatic sacrifices to help the larger group. They protect their sick and their old, sometimes helping weakened dolphins to the surface to breathe. Isolated from their fellows in captivity, they live far shorter lives and often die from refusing to eat. The most astonishing fact about dolphins, and the one we still know least about, is their remarkable intelligence. Recent experiments with dolphins prove that they communicate with each other using a "language" of what sounds (to humans) like squeals, grunts, and clicks. But some researchers think the dolphins' underwater communication system may be ten times more complex than human speech. Other experiments have shown that dolphins can learn to "talk" to people using symbols or voice commands. Most intriguing are reports that dolphins seem to be *interested* in communicating with people.

Dolphin intelligence may in fact be superior to human intelligence in certain ways. In the areas of the brain that govern memory, imagination, creative and social behavior, most dolphins have three to four times more brain mass than humans. What does this mean? Is it possible that dolphins, and their larger cousins the porpoises and whales, may yet prove to be better thinkers, poets, philosophers, even engineers—if they survive?

Lately, many people have become concerned about the fate of all cetaceans. The blue whale, once the largest mammal on earth, has recently been hunted to extinction. At least four other types of whale are close to being wiped out. Dolphins, too, are often victims. They are caught and drowned in the huge nets of tuna boats; they are hunted and killed for food in some areas of the world; they are captured and kept in tanks for scientific experiments or trained to entertain people at aquariums. They are also slowly being poisoned by the world-wide pollution of the seas.

If dolphins are indeed trying to communicate with us, we should have little trouble inferring what a part of their message might be.

A Haircut

I.S. Nakata

John Von Dorn

People have trouble deciding what I am. Indians mistake me for one of their own; in Chinatown they give me a menu written in Chinese; and once even a Japanese kid asked me if I was Korean. My ancestors are full-blooded Japanese, but I have had to get used to people thinking I'm something else.

Like that time I went to the barber college on North Clark Street for my cut-rate haircut. It's a place where student-barbers get on-the-job training, and that's where I met this guy. He was last in line, and he kept staring at me as I walked in. I just stared back.

Finally he smiled and said with a southern drawl straight out of Alabama, "Say, you're Indian, aren't you?"

I looked into the long mirror on the opposite wall. "No," I told the guy, "I'm not an Indian."

"Not an Indian?" Alabama said. "I would have sworn you were."

"I'm not."

Alabama shook his head and said, "You can't fool me. I've been all over the country. Seen all kinds of Indians. Cherokees in the Carolinas and Georgia and Alabama. Navajos in Arizona and New Mexico. Winnebagos in Wisconsin, and even some Shastas once in the mountains of California. I know you're some kind of Indian."

I shook my head, crossed my arms in front of my chest, and took a deep breath. "No."

"Cherokee?"

"No, not Cherokee."

"Not Sioux, are you?"

"Never been in North or South Dakota," I said.

"Winnebago?"

I didn't answer. I knew a lot about the

I. S. Nakata. "A Haircut" from *The Husk* (March 1966), Vol. XLV, No. 3.

Winnebagos. After World War II at an army post just outside Paris, I had met a Winnebago Indian from Black River Falls, Wisconsin. Jameson, I think his name was. A medic. And in the week or so that we were at the army post we spent a lot of time talking and eating. Every night we would go and buy a couple of long loaves of bread fresh from the baker's oven, and we would eat and talk for hours. He made me promise to visit him in Wisconsin when I got back to the States.

"That's God's country—where the Winnebagos live," I told Alabama. "Plenty of hunting and fishing, especially for muskellunge."

"Muskellunge, huh?" Alabama said. He looked impressed.

"Yeah, muskellunge. Most people call them muskies. Good eating, too. Salted, fried, or broiled in the ashes of hickory wood."

"Wish you was there, huh, Chief?"

"Yeah, nice place," I said.

"So you're a Winnebago?" he said with a happy nod.

"I never said that. I am not a Winnebago." I turned away.

"Now, now, Chief. Don't get mad," Alabama said. "I'm your friend. Yes, sir, I'm truly your friend. I've worked with Indians and helped lots of them working for Standard Oil. The reason I thought you were Winnebago is because you know so much about them."

"I don't know so much."

"You do. You sure do, Chief." He looked slyly around and then lowered his voice. "You running away from there, Chief? Maybe from the police?"

"I AM NOT RUNNING AWAY FROM THE POLICE," I told him.

"OK, Chief," he said quickly. "I didn't mean no harm."

For a long time Alabama didn't say anything. Some of the guys ahead of us moved up in line and we moved along, too. Soon Alabama had a choice of sitting or standing. He sat down on the bench and slid over to make room for me. Then he began again.

"So you're not a Winnebago, huh?"

I didn't answer him.

"Crow?"

"No, I am not a Crow," I said very sharply, although I had nothing against that tribe.

He rubbed his chin with his left hand and thought hard. "Arapaho?"

I shook my head.

"Navajo, then?"

I smiled. The Navajos were a tribe that I'd be proud to be part of. Great weavers, great in handicrafts, and among the best when it came to farming. I'd once gone to an art school in Kansas City with Custer Begay—a Navajo and a fine artist. I started thinking about Custer and his beautiful drawings of Indians on horseback. Then I remembered some of the great times we'd had and I began to laugh.

Alabama slapped his knee and said, "You're a Navajo! From Arizona."

This guy would not give up!

"Well," I said with a sigh, "I *was* once on a reservation in Arizona."

I really had been, too. I'd been sent to Arizona to live in a relocation camp for Japanese-Americans during World War II,[1] before I volunteered for the army.

Alabama's eyes lit up. "I knew it! You couldn't fool me. What reservation was it, Chief?"

"Poston, Arizona," I said, remembering the wartime internment camp. "On the Colorado River."

"I mean," Alabama moaned, "what tribe was it?"

"Nipponese.[2] We were scattered a bit until Uncle Sam gathered us up and put us all together again."

Alabama nodded a couple of times. "Well, I sure do think that was the best thing to do, having the government look after you all. Nipponese, eh? That must be a very small tribe. Never heard of it, Chief."

I had enjoyed my joke. Alabama wanted me to be something else, but I wasn't going to be anyone else but myself.

"A Nipponese is a Japanese. I am Japanese." I spoke slowly, feeling a little self-conscious as I wondered how I am supposed to say I am what I am.

Alabama rubbed his chin and looked puzzled. "Jap, eh? Wouldn't think it to look at you. You could pass for Indian any day."

"Japanese," I said.

"Sure, sure, Jap-a-nees. Japanese. But you were born in the USA, weren't you? You can't talk American like that without your being born here."

"I was born in Hawaii."

"Well, you're American like the rest of us, then. A man should be proud of what he is. Aren't you?"

Did I sense a threatening tone in his voice?

"I am pleased that I am who I am, Alabama," I told him. "It's good to be alive."

"Sure is, all right," he said. "But you're wrong about me. I don't come from Alabama."

"No?"

"No!" He stood up because it was finally

---

1. *relocation camp . . . World War II.* After Japanese planes attacked Pearl Harbor on December 7, 1941, the United States government forcibly evacuated from their homes all persons of Japanese ancestry on the West Coast. The government relocated these people in inland detention camps. At the time, the government defended its action as being in the best interests of national security.
2. *Nipponese* (nip′ə nēz′).

his turn to get a haircut. "I'm from Georgia," he said in a loud voice, "and proud of it."

"Sorry I made the mistake," I told him.

Then I shrugged. For the life of me I couldn't see what difference it made if he came from Georgia or Alabama. ☐☐

Discussion

1. (a) With what groups has the narrator been mistakenly identified? (b) What is the narrator's ancestry?

2. What does "Alabama" imply about the way he views Indians when he says, "You can't fool me. I've . . . seen all kinds of Indians. . . . I know you're some kind of Indian"?

3. Why do you think "Alabama" continues to insist that the narrator is an Indian, even after the narrator has denied it firmly three times?

4. (a) At what points in the conversation does the narrator seem irritated? (b) Why, in your opinion, didn't the narrator reveal his true identity to "Alabama" right away?

5. Explain the joke that the narrator plays on "Alabama."

6. What does the narrator reveal about himself when he admits that he doesn't see what difference it makes if "Alabama" came from Georgia or Alabama?

7. Explain the irony in the last sentence of the story.

Extension · Reading

If you want to learn more about the Japanese-American experience, the following books provide a good introduction:

Toshio Mori's *Yokohama, California* is a collection of short stories dealing with the everyday lives of first- and second-generation immigrants in and around Mori's boyhood home of San Leandro, California.

Farewell to Manzanar, by Jeanne Wakatsuki Houston and James D. Houston, is the true story of Jeanne Wakatsuki and her family, who were forced to live in a relocation camp during World War II.

If some aspect of the Japanese-American experience interests you in particular, pursue the subject further. Do research on the subject in your library and report what you learn to the rest of the class.

It was the most important race of his life, the one that it meant most to win. Why, then, did Graham decide to lose it?

Win or Lose

Brian Glanville

In Leipzig.[1] A very hot day, one of those days that burn the strength out of you as you run. Sieloff, the big German, in front of me, because I'd let him go in front of me. And knowing that if I wanted to catch him, I could still catch him, but if I left it any longer, even two seconds, then I couldn't. The most important race I'd ever run in my life, the one that it meant most to win; and the one it would mean most to lose. Because I could win it or lose it. It was up to me. That was what I thought, as the crowd started shouting him on. All those thousands of East Germans. It's not up to him; it's up to me. I could win it, or I could lose it.

I think the first time Dad took me out running I must have been about three. Running round a track, that is. The other, just running in the room or running round the garden, that began earlier, when I was two. Of course I can't remember it, but he's told me about it often enough, how he'd give me a candy if I could get right round the dining room in less than a minute. Two candies for under half-a-minute. "You should have seen yourself!" he says. "Especially if it was chocolate. You'd do anything for chocolate."

And of course, it's all in the books, the notebooks he's kept on me from the beginning, the great pile of them that he's got in his study. Records of everything, right back to the first day, even of how many times I ran round the garden and how long it took me. Incredible, really. Then, later on, my height; every month, we had that. My

From *Boys' Life*, April 1971. Reprinted by permission of the author and *Boys' Life*, published by the Boy Scouts of America.

1. *Leipzig*, city in the southern half of East Germany.

weight; every week. My pulse rate, when we started interval training—that was when I was 12. And later still, when we'd been out to the Sports Institute at Düsseldorf,[2] and he'd got taken with this German coach's theories, Emmerich, then there was a record of my heartbeats too.

The thing about Dad was, he was a runner himself in his time, but never as good as he'd wanted to be. He's told me about it so often, I know it almost by heart, now. "The thing is, Graham, I had ability, but I didn't have opportunity. You have ability, *and* you have opportunity, because I've seen to it that you *do* have opportunity. I always swore to myself, long before I met your mother, long before I got married, if ever I have a son, he's not going to be frustrated the way I was." And then I'd get all the old stuff about what a great runner he was as a boy, how he ran a mile in 4:45 when he was 16, which wasn't bad going in those days, and then how the war came along and put an end to everything. He was called up almost straightaway and put into the Royal Engineers.[3]

"But it wasn't just the war," he'd say. "People like me, Graham, they never had a chance. I left school at 14 to be apprenticed, and after that it was work, work, work. I trained when I could. I'd go slogging round the streets before I'd had my breakfast, or else as soon as I got home; didn't matter how tired I was. I remember how people used to turn and laugh at me, running past them.

"Britain wasn't sports-minded then, Graham. At the Berlin Olympics,[4] this country was a laughingstock. I remember every morning I looked at the times recorded by our athletes in the middle-distance races, and they were shameful times, son, most of them, times I knew I could have beaten with ease, if only I had had the chance to train—

the way the Germans and the Finns and the Americans had. Paavo Nurmi; that was the runner I admired more than any other. The Flying Finn. This little man; there was nothing of him. But year after year he came in ahead of the world.

"Paavo Nurmi; and in England, Sidney Wooderson."

In fact he had pictures of both of them up, Nurmi in the dining room, Wooderson in his study. Wooderson had been a miler, a tiny little skinny fellow, you'd have thought he'd be pushed to run across the road, but he'd won the European Championship in 1946, or whenever it was. Anyway, before I was born.

"Sheer willpower," Dad used to say. "That man prevailed on sheer guts and determination. Now you, Graham, you have no excuse for failure, son. You are physically exceptional, and between us, we're going to see you have the right mental attitude, as well."

Dad was very hot on mental attitudes. And diet. And sleep. In fact, on practically everything that had to do with running, even in the most indirect way, even when it came to what I read, what films he thought I ought to see. As for television, he wouldn't have one in the house. Well, not for years, anyway. His idea was it was a distraction; instead of going out to train, you sat at home goggling at the box and filling up your mind with rubbish.

What changed him was when they started showing athletics on the box. First of all, he hired one. Just for the weekend, he said when he got it, just to watch the European Games, from Bucharest.[5] And then, just for

2. *Düsseldorf,* city on the Rhine River in West Germany.
3. *Royal Engineers,* the corps of engineers of the British Army.
4. *Berlin Olympics,* Olympic Games held in Berlin, Germany, in 1936.
5. *Bucharest,* capital city of Rumania.

the week. And after that, well, just for the month. He said, "After all, we've paid for a month," and so it stayed.

I was talking about that first time, though, that first time Dad took me out running at the track, over at Parliament Hill Fields, which was about the nearest, then, to where we were living. That I *do* remember, or rather, I remember things about it. Number one, I remember it being cold, I remember I was shivering; I didn't want to take my warm-up suit off, this little one he'd had specially made for me, but the old man insisted. I can imagine what he must have said, more or less, because I've had the same kind of thing dozens of times, over the years. "Look, son, look, Graham, let's do the thing properly, or let's not do it at all." So I took the warm-up suit off and I froze and I ran crying all the time and when we got home I was still shaking, and Mum gave him the devil for making me do it.

Mum. It wasn't very often she got like that. Less and less over the years, in fact. Mostly Dad got his own way. She's small, always very quiet, she gives in too much. He's tall and thin, white hair and glasses. They married very young, started poor, then gradually got richer and richer till now, well, he's rich, Dad, that's the only word for it, and as for me, I'm the only child, born pretty late.

And I never went to school. It's hard to believe, isn't it? To be dead accurate, I did go just for a couple of years or so. I suppose it must have been during the time Dad was still wondering had I got it or hadn't I? Then when he'd decided that I had, it was out of school and private tutors, and if you think that was a pretty lonely kind of life, you're right. I hardly knew any other kids, really; the only time I'd meet them was when I was running against them.

I had quite a few different tutors. First it was women, later on it was men. The old man had it all worked out. He said, "This won't only benefit your running; in this way you'll get a better education, Graham. You'll learn more from them than you ever would at school."

Some I learned from and some I didn't. A lot of it may have been me. Whatever the old man said, he knew and I knew what the real point of it all was, it was to give me more time for running, and knowing it came first, what incentive was there to work hard at things like Math and Latin? History I quite enjoyed, particularly the way one strange bloke taught it to me, though he only stayed a couple of months.

His name was Buglass, and he was the first chap I ever met who actually made fun of running, which I'm sure was what made the old man get rid of him as quickly as he did. There were times when I'd egg him on, if Dad happened to be in the room, just because I liked hearing the two of them going at it. It was easy for Dad to make fun of Buglass, who looked as if he'd never done a day's exercise.

Buglass would say, "A sound mind in a healthy body, that was the Roman ideal, my dear Graham. You've achieved half of it, at the expense of the other. You have a superbly healthy body, and no mind at all."

"What about the Greeks?" Dad asked him. "Who invented the Olympic Games, then?"

Buglass said, "I have personally always regarded the Olympic Games as a most unfortunate aberration on the part of the Greeks. Of course I admire them. The Greeks were the exponents of the Golden Mean.[6] They engaged in sport purely to

---

6. *Golden Mean,* safe, sensible way of doing things; the avoidance of extremes.

exercise their bodies. It was only in their period of decadence that they stooped to producing specialized athletes, like circus animals."

You should have seen the old man's face, then. Puce. "How can you achieve anything without specialization?" he said. If there was one thing he believed in, it was that.

"On the contrary," Buglass told him, "you achieve nothing through specialization except the specialty."

When I was 16, I took half-a-dozen of the O-level exams that you have to pass if you want to go on studying to try for a university. I passed in History, Geography, and English, and I failed the rest. Quite honestly, it didn't worry either of us, either the old man or me. I think our main reaction, his and mine, was that we were glad to get it out of the way. Now we could just concentrate on training.

That winter, we all three of us went out to Santa Barbara, to California, which was great, the sunshine and the beaches, instead of all the London cold and rain, even if the old man wouldn't let me swim much; he said it was bad for the running muscles. I trained with the Santa Barbara Striders, Dad had arranged that through his contacts. They had a very good coach there called Joe Watson who taught me a lot, he worked on my starts and my stride and my arm action. At that time, I was still doing the 100 yards, gradually moving up to competitive 220s, but Joe convinced me I'd never have the basic speed for the hundred. He said, "Shoot for the 220 the next couple of years, then when you're a little stronger, I reckon you'll be running the quarter."

Dad was always trying out different coaches. I suppose at the bottom of it was that he wanted to be my only coach, himself, just as he always was till I was about 14. But

then I think he realized that he couldn't do it all alone; he needed professional coaches for me. At the same time, he couldn't reconcile himself to this, so what would happen, time and time again, was that he'd pick on a coach he'd think was fabulous, maybe in the States, maybe in England, maybe in Germany or Scandinavia, take me to this fellow, then, after a time, fall out with him.

As I grew up, Dad's attitude towards me changed quite a lot, I suppose. When I was just a kid, it was, "Do this, do that," but I shot up very quickly and got big, all the more so with the weight training that I hated when he first made me do it, so it got to be more, "Please, Graham," or, "I want you to do it for *me,* Graham." He was very fond of saying, when there were people there, "We're pals, we two, aren't we, Graham?"

In a way this made it harder for me, knowing he was expecting so much, not wanting to let him down. Every time I ran a race, I was running for the both of us, and the more I won, the more difficult it got, because people knew about me, they were keener to beat me; and because of all the publicity, too.

It started from the summer I turned 16 and set a new junior record for the hundred. I was running for the Ajax Club, then. I think if Dad had had his way I wouldn't have run for any club, but since I didn't go to school and couldn't compete in school championships, there was nothing else for it. With the clubs, it was more or less the same as with the coaches; I've never stayed with one for long, because Dad finished up quarreling with the officials—who, I must say, it's very easy to quarrel with. They wanted their way, he wanted his.

So after Ajax it was East London, and after that, Nemean. It got to the point where other athletes would say, "Well, how long will you be staying with us, then?" They were never very friendly to me, other athletes, and I suppose this was another thing that started me resenting Dad. They seemed to have the idea that I'd been spoon-fed. Dad would say, "They're jealous of you, son, that's all," and I suppose they were.

If *I'd* known that while I'd been slogging through school, somebody else had gone all over the world just to run and train, I'd probably have felt the same. All this stuff in the papers about "Britain's Test-Tube Runner," and "British Whiz Kid" didn't help much, either. But there was more to it, as well.

Dad's point was that this was simply something that had to be faced. He said, "Dilettantism, that's always been the curse of British sport, son. I fought against it while I was a runner, but it beat me. I'll fight against it now, and between us, we'll win."

We usually won—or rather, I usually won. It's hard to get out of the habit of saying "we," I'm so used to hearing Dad. First it was the Southern Junior, then the National Junior, then, when I was 17—last year, that was—the Nationals, the AAA's, all in the 220 yards. I remember afterwards all the newspapermen clustering round, it was at the White City; there's a little sort of bend there in the railings where runners come and talk to the press, I was terrified, to tell the truth, but Dad called me over there, and, as usual, he did all the talking.

"After this," he said, "Graham is turning to the 440. Our aim is the 400 meters in next year's European Games, isn't it, Graham?" All I could do was nod. As far as I was concerned, I was going to try the 440, I was going to run both distances for a time, then make up my mind which suited me best.

Dad told them, "Graham has the basic strength for the 440. He has speed and strength; the two great requisites. We have three years until the next Olympics, then he'll be 20, and I think he'll be capable of standing up to anybody in the world."

One of them asked him, "Don't you think he'll be a little young, Mr. Rogerson?"

"No," said Dad. "Don't forget Graham has been in training virtually since the age of three."

They made great play of that, I can tell you. It made me feel like a freak. Dad told me, "I did that for one reason, Graham, to set you a standard. It's often a wonderful idea to have a goal, even if in the end you don't achieve it. The mere fact you know it's there means that you're striving toward it."

By this time, I was right in the middle of the whole athletics thing, where people didn't get at me for being single-minded, because everybody else was too. Some of them were so fanatical, I even thought at times perhaps I wasn't taking it seriously enough.

And now I know you're waiting for me to come to the race and tell you why I did what I did; which I shall. But everything I've said so far was necessary; it was all part of it. You can't understand what I did without knowing what had gone before.

It was in Leipzig, of course: the finals of the European 400 meters. I hated everything about that city, except for the stadium, which was a nice one, out among the trees, full of wooden benches. I hated the atmosphere, I hated the grayness of everything. I hated the loudspeakers in the streets that suddenly began spouting at you, even if you couldn't understand a word of it, and when they took us round their Sports Institute that they were so proud of, I didn't even like *that.* I'd seen things like it before, of course, but here, going round it, I suddenly remembered what my tutor, Buglass, had said that time. These athletes, they were what he said: circus animals. They did their tricks and you threw them a bun or a peanut.

The old man was with me, too, raving about everything. "Look at it, Graham. No wonder they produce so many champions. I've done this for you, but I've done it with my own money."

I think it must have been then that the idea came to me: I was going to lose. Yes, lose. You find that hard to believe, don't you? After all the preparation, all the victories. Lose—because if I lost, it would let me off the hook. If I lost, it would free me from *him*, I could make up my own mind and maybe I'd decide to go on running, maybe I wouldn't; at least I'd have done something for myself. Because if this was the big one to win, then it had to be the big one to lose. And in this place that I hated: this Leipzig.

Then, when the moment came, I couldn't lose. As you know, I won, but what you don't know is how near I came to throwing it away; deliberately. I cruised through the heats, I coasted through the semifinals, and when it came to the final, I was running so well I knew there were only two of them who could live with me—Davidescu of Rumania, who got away quicker than me, and the East German, Sieloff, who had a better finish.

I admit I had a plan, and it was a strange plan. I was going to get off to a flying start, stay with Davidescu, lose him on the first bend, go into the straight neck and neck with Sieloff, pull ahead of him to show I could beat him if I wanted—even if I only showed myself—then let him go, and finish maybe third, even fourth.

Which was exactly how it went; until that last bit.

I stayed with Davidescu, just as I planned I would. I left him behind in the back straight, I was way out in front, and then I could hear Sieloff coming, on the outside. I held him all the way to the bend, then he caught me as we came into the home straight; then I clenched my teeth and gave it everything and got ahead of him again.

We were about 90 yards out when I eased up and let him pass me, but the moment he did, the moment I saw him ahead, something happened, like a reflex action: *snap!* I couldn't let him get away with it, it was just bred into me, all the years of slogging my guts out, and I went after him again, even though what it meant was winning it twice. At 50 yards I was still a yard behind him. My chest felt as if it was bursting, my legs were turning to paper. Then I was right on his heels, then swerving round him, then level; then I was slinging myself at the tape, going through it, falling, knowing I'd won.

Afterwards I went on down into the interview room. It was packed with people. Dad was there; I couldn't look at him. So pleased. Beaming all over his face. One of the British reporters called out, "What next, Graham?" and I said, "Nothing's next, I've retired."

You could have heard a pin drop; or rather, you could once the Germans had explained to one another, once everyone had grasped it. This reporter asked, "Do you mean it, Graham? Are you serious?"

From the corner of my eye I could see Dad's face; the most astonished look I think I've ever come across. "Yes," I said, "I've never been more serious." Then I got up and walked out. I still didn't look at Dad. All I could think of was the talk we were going to have, hours and hours, like two records playing in turn. "I don't understand, Graham," he'd say. "I just don't understand you."

Outside in the sunshine, I suddenly realized something. I was happy. I was really happy. I could start running for myself, now. □□

Discussion

1. (a) What impression does Graham give of his father? of his mother? (b) What kind of person do you think Graham is, on the basis of what he says and does? Give examples.

2. (a) What does Buglass have to say about athletes? (b) What indication is there that Buglass might be prejudiced? (c) What kind of impression do Buglass's words make on Graham's father? (d) At what point is Graham reminded of Buglass's words? Do they influence him? In what ways?

3. Would you call Graham's decision at the end of the story courageous or selfish? Explain.

4. (a) What changes in attitude toward his father does Graham experience as he grows up? (b) Does his father's attitude toward him change also? How? (c) Is there any possibility that the father will ever be able to understand Graham's decision to retire from competitive running? (d) Do you think Graham might ever return to competitive running?

Brian Glanville 1931 •

"Win or Lose," with its emphasis on the human situation, is typical of all of Brian Glanville's sports writing. One of the busiest and most prolific journalists in England, Glanville currently is a sports columnist for London's *Sunday Times*. "My column," he says, "is for people who don't want to read about sport just as sport, but want to read about people and human experience."

Unit Review Tests 2: Insights

CONTENT REVIEW

1. Each selection in this unit features a main character who either uses insight in dealing with a situation or gains insight from having dealt with a situation. Explain how each character listed below fits one or the other category:

(a) Markwardt in "A Man Who Had No Eyes."

(b) The father in "Last Cover."

(c) The fox in "The Fox and the Grapes."

(d) Buck in "A Time of Greatness."

(e) Helen in "Let Me Hear You Whisper."

(f) Graham in "Win or Lose."

2. Choose one of the characters below and describe him or her in detail:

Colin in "Last Cover."

Helen in "Let Me Hear You Whisper."

Alabama in "A Haircut."

Graham in "Win or Lose."

(a) What physical description of the character does the author provide? **(b)** What do you learn about the character from his or her own words and actions? **(c)** What do you learn from other characters? **(d)** Which of these sources reveals the most about the character?

3. (a) Besides "Last Cover," what other selection in Unit 3 contains a *flashback?* **(b)** What information is given in that flashback? **(c)** What reason might the author have had for using a flashback to help tell the story?

4. (a) Explain the difference between the subject of a selection and the *theme* of a selection. **(b)** What is the subject of "A Man Who Had No Eyes"? of "The Fox and the Grapes"? of "Win or Lose"? **(c)** What, in your opinion, is the theme of each of these selections?

Unit 2, Test I
INTERPRETATION: NEW MATERIAL

Read the following story, then on your paper write the answers to the questions. You may refer to the story when necessary.

The Conjurer's Revenge
Stephen Leacock

"Now, ladies and gentlemen," said the conjurer, "having shown you that the cloth is absolutely empty, I will proceed to take from it a bowl of goldfish. Presto!"

All around the hall people were saying, "Oh, how wonderful! How does he do it?"

But the Quick Man on the front seat said in a big whisper to

"The Conjurer's Revenge" from *Literary Lapses* by Stephen Leacock. Reprinted by permission of the U.S. publisher, Dodd, Mead & Company; the Canadian publisher, McClelland and Stewart Limited, Toronto; and the British publisher, The Bodley Head.

the people near him, "He—had—it—up—his—sleeve."

Then the people nodded brightly at the Quick Man and said, "Oh, of course"; and everybody whispered round the hall, "He—had—it—up—his—sleeve."

"My next trick," said the conjurer, "is the famous Hindostanee rings. You will notice that the rings are apparently separate; at a blow they all join (clang, clang, clang)—Presto!"

There was a general buzz of stupefaction till the Quick Man was heard to whisper, "He—must—have—had—another—lot—up—his—sleeve."

Again everybody nodded and whispered, "The—rings—were—up—his—sleeve."

The brow of the conjurer was clouded with a gathering frown.

"I will now," he continued, "show you a most amusing trick by which I am enabled to take any number of eggs from a hat. Will some gentleman kindly lend me his hat? Ah, thank you—Presto!"

He extracted seventeen eggs, and for thirty-five seconds the audience began to think that he was wonderful. Then the Quick Man whispered along the front bench, "He—has—a—hen—up—his—sleeve," and all the people whispered it on. "He—has—a—lot—of—hens—up—his—sleeve."

The egg trick was ruined.

It went on like that all through. It transpired from the whispers of the Quick Man that the conjurer must have concealed up his sleeve, in addition to the rings, hens, and fish, several packs of cards, a loaf of bread, a doll's cradle, a live guinea-pig, a fifty-cent piece, and a rocking-chair.

The reputation of the conjurer was rapidly sinking below zero. At the close of the evening he rallied for a final effort.

"Ladies and gentlemen," he said, "I will present to you, in conclusion, the famous Japanese trick recently invented by the natives of Tipperary. Will you, sir," he continued, turning toward the Quick Man, "will you kindly hand me your gold watch?"

It was passed to him.

"Have I your permission to put it into this mortar and pound it to pieces?" he asked savagely.

The Quick Man nodded and smiled.

The conjurer threw the watch into the mortar and grasped a sledge hammer from the table. There was a sound of violent smashing. "He's—slipped—it—up—his—sleeve," whispered the Quick Man.

"Now, sir," continued the conjurer, "will you allow me to take your handkerchief and punch holes in it? Thank you. You see, ladies and gentlemen, there is no deception, the holes are visible to the eye."

The face of the Quick Man beamed. This time the real mystery of the thing fascinated him.

"And now, sir, will you kindly pass me your silk hat and allow me to dance on it? Thank you."

The conjurer made a few rapid passes with his feet and exhibited the hat crushed beyond recognition.

"And will you now, sir, take off your celluloid collar and permit me to burn it in the candle? Thank you, sir. And will you allow me to smash your spectacles for you with my hammer? Thank you."

By this time the features of the Quick Man were assuming a puzzled expression. "This thing beats me," he whispered, "I don't see through it a bit."

There was a great hush upon the audience. Then the conjurer drew himself up to his full height and, with a withering look at the Quick Man, he concluded:

"Ladies and gentlemen, you will observe that I have, with this gentleman's permission, broken his watch, burnt his collar, smashed his spectacles, and danced on his hat. If he will give me the further permission to paint green stripes on his overcoat, or to tie his suspenders in a knot, I shall be delighted to entertain you. If not, the performance is at an end."

And amid a glorious burst of music from the orchestra the curtain fell, and the audience dispersed, convinced that there are some tricks, at any rate, that are not done up the conjurer's sleeve. ☐☐

1. "The Conjurer's Revenge" is told by (a) the conjurer; (b) the Quick Man; (c) a woman in the audience; (d) a narrator from outside the story.

2. The story takes place (a) at an outdoor booth at a county fair; (b) at a large party; (c) in a hall; (d) in a park.

3. What is another word for conjurer?

4. Calling the Quick Man "quick" is probably meant to show that the man (a) thinks himself to be very clever; (b) is in a hurry to leave; (c) is impatient with the audience; (d) understands all the tricks immediately.

5. The term below that best describes the Quick Man is (a) mind reader; (b) conjurer; (c) intellectual; (d) heckler.

6. The audience reacts to the Quick Man by (a) telling him he's very clever; (b) asking him to speak up so they can hear him better; (c) believing everything he says; (d) telling him he's very rude.

7. List at least two items mentioned in the story that would be unlikely to be pulled out of the conjurer's sleeve.

8. What is the Quick Man's reaction when the conjurer smashes his watch? (a) He is puzzled because he can't figure out the trick. **(b)** He thinks the conjurer has actually slipped the watch up his sleeve. **(c)** He begins to be impressed with the conjurer. **(d)** He begins to get annoyed.

9. It can be inferred from the "great hush upon the audience" (page 124) that **(a)** the audience is beginning to understand what the conjurer is really doing; **(b)** the audience doesn't understand the trick; **(c)** the audience is silent because the Quick Man has stopped talking; **(d)** the audience is getting bored and sleepy.

10. The irony in what happens to the Quick Man is that **(a)** he finally makes the conjurer angry; **(b)** he has his clothes destroyed by the conjurer; **(c)** although he thinks he understands all the conjurer's tricks, he doesn't catch on to the one played on him; **(d)** although he has explained all the conjurer's tricks to the audience, the audience turns on him at the end.

11. The main conflict in the story is between **(a)** the Quick Man and the audience; **(b)** the conjurer and the Quick Man; **(c)** the conjurer and the rest of the audience; **(d)** the conjurer and his unsuccessful tricks.

12. The saying below that best sums up the meaning of this story is **(a)** All the world's a stage; **(b)** He who laughs last laughs best; **(c)** What a tangled web we weave when first we practice to deceive; **(d)** You can fool some of the people all of the time.

Unit 2, Test II
COMPOSITION

Choose any *one* of the following assignments to write about.

1. Mr. Parsons in "A Man Who Had No Eyes" is a good example of a person who has refused to allow a physical handicap to interfere with his life. Write a composition about someone you know who has overcome a physical handicap in a similar way. Describe the person's handicap, and explain the specific ways you think he or she has overcome it.

2. Assume that you are Uvavnuk, author of "Two Songs." You are making a tour of the United States, and every evening you write in a journal an account of that day's events and your reaction to them. Write two journal entries, one for the day you visited Abadaba (the biology laboratory in "Let Me Hear You Whisper") and another for the time you spent with the family in "Last Cover."

Before writing, you should decide whether you (as Uvavnuk) visited the places during or after the events described in the play and short story.

3. The narrator in "A Time of Greatness" is not pleased when he first learns that he is to take care of old Cal Crawford. By the end of the story, however, he has learned to respect both Cal and his daughter. Write a composition for your classmates explaining at least three specific incidents that cause the narrator to change his mind about the Crawford family.

Sometimes who you are doesn't seem to matter as much

as what you are or where you are:

>you may be a stranger in a new town;

>you may look or speak differently

>from those around you;

>you may simply have your own ways of feeling

>and looking at things.

Each of us at some time in our lives has probably been

in the position of **THE OUTSIDER**

See **SYMBOL** Handbook of Literary Terms

The shopowner's knowing look
had dismissed her as a person
of no importance at all;
but Sister Opal determined
she was going to do something about it.

The Baroque Marble

E. A. Proulx

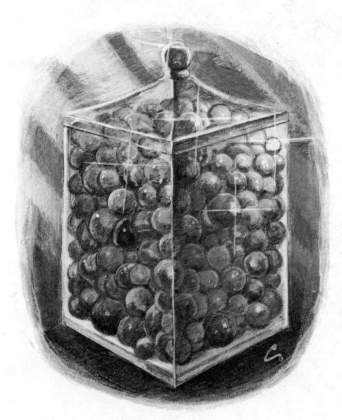

Late autumn rain again. Sister Opal woke up in a Polaroid yellow light with her head hanging off the bed all sideways. Down in the street children's voices slid under the window muffled and changed by the damp morning. Sister Opal thought the children sounded as if they were speaking Russian or Basque[1]—some queer, garbled language. She pretended she was in another country where she didn't know a word of the language and where she would have to make signs to get breakfast in a few minutes when she went downstairs. False panic began to rise in her, then subsided. From her position of suspension over the edge of the bed, the furniture looked darker, and the unfamiliar angle gave it a sinister look. The bureau loomed, a skyscraper in dull, dark varnish. Perhaps there were tiny people and offices inside. The chair arms seemed to have clenched hands at their ends, like brown old men sitting anxiously in the doctor's office waiting to hear the bad news.

Sister Opal twisted her head around toward the yellow window. On the sill was a square glass jar of marbles, reddish brown, yellow and white glassies and a very large blue one. Most of them were mob marbles, as much alike as the faces of the crowd to a dictator on his balcony. Off to one side of the jar there was a white marble, deformed and not a true round—a lopsided freak of a marble—her favorite one. When this marble sat alone on the splendor of Sister Opal's blue velvet best dress, it took on a silver, translucent glow. In the jar, it was dirty-

1. **Basque,** language of a people who live in and around the Pyrenees, a mountain range of northern Spain and southern France.

white, opaque and with more space around it than the other marbles, as if they avoided getting too close to it.

The jar of marbles was a kind of wealth. It was the most Sister Opal owned. Eight hundred and forty-three marbles. She took a miser's satisfaction in pouring them out onto the bed, watching them roll into the valleys, gathering up their heavy, glassy weight, cold but soon warming in her hand. Each marble was individually beautiful. A kind of classic Greek perfection shone in their roundness. Under Sister Opal's father's magnifying glass the perfect marbles disclosed blemishes, pits and scratches. Sister Opal liked them unmagnified; in their smallness she found their greatest value.

She touched the shade and it leaped up, startled, to the top of the wooden roller where it chattered a few seconds in fright, and then clung, tightly wound. Her warm breath made a milky fog on the window glass and her warm finger wrote, "All the sailors have died of scurvy, yours truly, Opal Foote."

Downstairs, Sister Opal's family sat at the table. Dark and sullen, they crunched toast, stabbed at their eggs and made whirlpools in their coffee with spoons. Except for Sister Opal, it was a bad-tempered family in the mornings and the only conversations were mumbles to each other to pass the sugar or salt. By noontime the family would be chatty and warm, and by suppertime everyone was in high spirits. Sister Opal's four brothers (except for Roy, who worked on the night shift at GE) were very jovial at suppertime when Sister Opal was weary. This morning Sister Opal's father asked about homework. Sister Opal thought of homework as yellow leaves dropping softly down, like the yellow blank pages she had dropped into the wastepaper basket last night. Guilty, Sister Opal went outside with jammy toast, hearing something from her father about being home right after school to make up Roy's dinner pail and to start supper because Mama had to work late. Sister Opal sang a private song as she walked along the wet sidewalk hopping the shallow puddles which were out to ruin her good shoes.

Sailors died of scurvy, oh,
They threw them in the sea.
Pack Roy's dinner pail tonight
With a thermos bottle of tea.

The rain outside had transmuted to yellow light and threatened afternoon lightning. Somewhere Sister Opal had read that yellow was the favorite color of insane people. The woman down the street had had a nervous breakdown last summer only a week after her husband had painted their house yellow. Across the street some white boys from Sister Opal's class at school were walking in the same direction. They pushed and shoved each other. One of them yelled, "Hey, turkey!" at Sister Opal. Sister Opal laughed because their faces looked yellow. Immediately they became hostile, thinking she was laughing at their existence, their being. Sister Opal's dignity did not allow her to hear their jeers.

At three-thirty Sister Opal was not on her way back home to pack up Roy's dinner pail. Instead, she was walking thoughtfully down Essex Street, peering into all the windows of the silver and antique shops. Art class that afternoon had completely enthralled Sister Opal. Mrs. Grigson had shown a film about ordinary people who started art collections with inexpensive things that became rare and valuable as time went by. Sister Opal envisioned herself someday in her own apartment with rare items of art in glass cases and white walls hung with glowing works of great artists which she, Sister Opal, had picked up years before for just a song. Even though she had only a few dollars in her savings account (a birthday present from her grandmother), and little hope of getting more, she was looking for something really good and fine on Essex Street. The film had indicated that all the people who built up enviable art collections had started off with the things they really liked. This was Sister Opal's primary mission: to find something she really liked. Then she would face the money problem. She had quite forgotten about Roy's empty dinner pail, the cold stove, and Mama working late.

As she splashed through the puddles of Essex Street, she dismissed old silver, all lumpy with twisted roses and crests, and dark with tarnish. She rejected the idea of collecting glass—too space-consuming and bothersome. She didn't really like sculpture, and she didn't know where she could buy real paintings or prints. The rain began again and Sister Opal's shoes were sodden and squishy. Past shops with small, dirty windows she went, discarding ceramics, carved wooden figures, vases, chandeliers, toy soldiers, andirons, dog-grates, lacquerware and crystal.

Then, in the window of R. Sonnier's, she saw *it*. On a piece of blue velvet, quite like Sister Opal's best dress, there lay a large, glowing, misshapen marble. Sister Opal drew in her breath and exhaled slowly. This was it. She would collect marbles, rare ones from China, ancient ones from Peru, Roman marbles, marbles Genghis Khan[2] had played with, marbles from Napoleon's[3] cabinets, from Istanbul and Alexandria, marbles of solid gold, of azure, of lapis lazuli, of wood and stone and jewel. And she would begin

with the marble in this very window! In she marched, a thin black girl with wet shoes, whose older brother was going to go supperless on the night shift.

The shop inside was crowded with objects stacked on shelves, in corners or looming down from the ceiling, crumpled, dusty dark things. A fat, middle-aged white man was reading a book in a leather chair behind the counter. He looked up when the door opened and then back to his book. Sister Opal did not waste time looking around the shop. She marched briskly up to R. Sonnier, or as briskly as one can march with wet shoes.

"Excuse me, how much is that marble in the window, and do you have any other kinds?"

"*What* marble in the window? I haven't got any marble that I know of in there. This is an antique shop, not a toy store." Sister Opal went to the curtain that hung behind the window to give a background for the objects displayed and pulled it aside.

"There," she said simply, pointing to the fat, lucent sphere.

"Young lady," said R. Sonnier, highly amused, "that is *not* a marble. That is a baroque pearl, an antique baroque pearl, and even though I am letting it go at an unbelievably low price, I doubt you could afford it." He looked her up and down, seeing the wet shoes, the cotton dress in late October, the brown skin and thinness that was Sister Opal. "It is for sale for four hundred and fifty dollars. A bargain for those who can afford such things. Marbles I believe you'll find at Woolworth's."

Sister Opal felt a horrible combination of

---

2. **Genghis Khan,** early 13th century Mongol leader who conquered much of Asia.

3. **Napoleon's,** Napoleon Bonaparte, French Emperor who in the early 19th century conquered a large part of Europe.

shame, embarrassment, anger, pride and sadness rise in her. She carried as a memory for the rest of her life R. Sonnier's knowing look that dismissed her as a person of no importance at all. Sister Opal, in a burst of pride and fantasy, said in a haughty voice, "*I prefer to think of baroque pearls as marbles. And I would definitely like that marble. Please save it for me because it might be quite a while before I can pick it up. My name is Opal Foote.*"

R. Sonnier digested this information and repeated, "Then you want me to save this baroque pearl for you? You intend to buy it?"

"Yes," said Sister Opal. "Opal Foote is the name." She gave him her address and then left with her shoes squelching softly. She was committed to the baroque marble which R. Sonnier was saving for her. Suddenly she remembered Roy's dinner pail and the gloomy apartment without one picture or really nice thing in it. There were only the family photographs kept in an old candy box and a plastic vase filled with plastic flowers. She ran home hoping that Roy hadn't left for work yet.

At the table that night Sister Opal's father looked on her with disfavor. His cheerful supper face was cloudy, and Sister Opal knew the storm would break before she poured out his coffee. Roy had had to go to work without any dinner, supper had been late and Opal had broken three eggs by slamming the old refrigerator door so hard that the eggs had shot out of their aluminum nest and run all over everything inside. Sister Opal's father finished the last bit of mashed potato on his plate and leaned back, glaring at Sister Opal.

"Well, girl, how come you didn't get home to fix your brother's dinner pail or start the supper? Everybody in this family's got to do his part. Now I'm waiting to hear."

There was no escape. Sister Opal took a deep breath and began telling about the art class and Essex Street and the baroque pearl in R. Sonnier's shop. Her father's face was first incredulous, then angry, then sad. He said nothing for a long time. Opal sat miserably waiting for the lecture. Her brother Andrew got up and poured the coffee and patted Opal's shoulder as he passed behind her chair. Her father began to speak, slowly at first.

"Well, Sister, I think for a family in the kind of situation we got, where we all work to keep some kind of decency in our lives, and where we are trying to work toward an education for all you kids, an education of *some* kind, that any ideas about collecting art are just plain *crazy.* We are poor people and it's no use you pretending otherwise. Maybe someday your children, or more likely, grandchildren can collect art, but right now, girl, we can't gather enough money together to collect milk bottles! Wait!" (Sister Opal had uttered a furious "But!")

"Now just wait! I don't want to crush you down like a pancake. I *know* how you felt when that antique man looked you up and down and made his remarks. Every person in this family knows how you felt. And I understand how you answered him back pridefully about how you'd *get* that pearl or marble or whatever it is. But now, Opal, you got to swallow your pride and forget that marble, or else you got to do something about it. You got any ideas? Because I personally do not."

"I am old enough and able enough to get a job after school in the evenings and earn enough money to *buy* that baroque pearl myself, and I am going to do it!" Opal spoke slowly.

Her father looked at Opal, sadder than ever, and said, "If you are old enough to get a job, Sister Opal, you are old enough to save that job money for college or for helping this big family to get along. How would it be if I decided to save the money I make at Quadrant for buying myself a Picasso[4] or something? Or suppose Roy decided not to kick in money for groceries and things but to buy himself a—a—harpsichord[5] or a statue?" The idea of big, quiet Roy, clumsy and inarticulate, buying himself a harpsichord or a statue sent half the table snorting with laughter. "Besides," continued her father, "who's going to pack up Roy's dinner pail and start the supper while you are at some job?"

Sister Opal's brother Andrew stood up. "I am sick and tired of hearing about Roy's dinner pail. I expect the sun isn't going to

---

4. Picasso, work by Pablo Picasso (1881–1973), important Spanish painter and sculptor.
5. harpsichord, musical instrument much like a piano except that the strings are plucked instead of hammered, causing a more delicate and tinkling sound.

come up and set anymore—no, it's going to be Roy's dinner pail! I say that if Sister Opal sees more in life than groceries and trying to get along, she should at least have the chance to try. I can get home a little earlier and start supper myself, and Roy can pack up his *own* dinner pail. You've told us yourself, Papa, that if a person wants something bad enough, and works hard enough *for* it, he'll get it. I'm willing to see Opal get that baroque pearl. I wouldn't mind seeing a few nice things around here myself."

The great argument broke out and raged around the supper table and took on fresh vigor when Sister Opal's mother came in, tired and with a sharp edge to her tongue. The final resolution, near midnight, was that if Sister Opal got a job, she could save half the money for the baroque pearl and half for college. Sister Opal felt triumphant and like a real art collector.

It took her three days to find a job. She was to work at Edsall's drugstore after school until ten-thirty from Monday to Friday and all day Saturday. She dipped out ice cream, made sodas and cherry Cokes, mixed Alka-Seltzer for gray-faced men, sold cigars and newspapers, squeezed her homework in between customers and wiped off the sticky counter with a yellow sponge (Mr. Edsall had bought five hundred yellow sponges at a bargain sale the year before and Sister Opal got to despise those yellow sponges). She made change for people to use in the phone booth, she cleaned out the Pyrex coffeepots and made fresh coffee a thousand times a day, sold cough drops and throat lozenges all through the winter and dispensed little plastic hats to ladies when the spring rains came. She got home at eleven o'clock each night with aching legs and red eyes, and Sunday mornings she slept late, catching up. In little ways, her mother showed an extra tenderness for her only daughter's great desire for a beautiful object. Her father surprised Sister Opal by Scotch-taping a reproduction of a Picasso painting over the kitchen calendar. He had cut *The Three Musicians* out of an old magazine. When Roy said, "What's that!?" Sister Opal's father remarked loftily, "I always did like Picasso."

"Yeah," said Andrew to Roy, "at least he doesn't go in for harpsichords and statues." This joke about harpsichords and statues was one that Roy had never quite fathomed, and he eventually grew so confused on the matter that he was convinced that he really did take an extraordinary interest in keyboard music and sculpture. It was even suspected by the family that on his night off he had once gone, not to a night baseball game, but to a concert.

Sister Opal's weeks turned into months, and the long drugstore nights dragged through winter into spring. She had two bank accounts, one for college money and one for the baroque pearl. In March on a

Friday night, she had four hundred dollars in the school account, and four hundred fifty in the pearl account. It was enough. She got permission from Mr. Edsall to take the next day off to go to R. Sonnier's to buy the pearl.

Early in the morning Sister Opal woke to pale yellow spring sun. She leaped up with her heart beating hard and dressed the part of a baroque pearl buyer. Something special was needed. Her blue velvet best dress had been outgrown and remade during the winter into a blue velvet best skirt. She put it on and borrowed her mother's white silk blouse. She shined her shoes until the cracks didn't show and rushed downstairs to breakfast. Everybody knew she was going to buy the pearl that day but nobody said anything. The whole family was shy and quiet with anticipation. Andrew sat breathing quietly on his coffee.

At nine o'clock Sister Opal was walking along Essex Street. She went past the dusty windows displaying lumpy silverware, ceramic mugs with gold decorations, wooden candelabra from Spain, and then she came to R. Sonnier's shop. In his window there was a display of silver and gold watches and clocks under glass bells. Sister Opal smiled, thinking of the baroque pearl hidden secretly in a box, waiting for Sister Opal all those long months. She went inside. R. Sonnier sat in his chair behind the counter, reading a book. Nothing had changed. Stuff was still stacked to the ceiling, stuff still hung down to the floor. R. Sonnier looked up. His eyes were flat, incurious.

"Can I help you?"

"It's me, Mr. Sonnier. Opal Foote. I've come to get my baroque marble that you've been saving for me."

"What marble? I don't have any marbles."

Patiently Sister Opal explained about the

baroque pearl she had asked him to save for her last fall, and then she expectantly waited for the shock of recognition, the rummaging in a desk drawer and the uncovering of the baroque pearl. She hadn't even yet seen it up close or held it. R. Sonnier looked annoyed.

"Listen, young lady, I had a baroque pearl last fall, and I sold it to a very nice lady who comes in here often to buy things. I never save anything except for my good customers. This lady paid me by check right away. I don't run any lay-away plan here, and that baroque pearl was priced at almost five hundred dollars."

"You sold it? But it was supposed to be *mine!* I worked after school all fall and winter long, and I earned the money for it!" Sister Opal pulled out her wad of money. R. Sonnier looked astounded.

"Little lady, how was I to know you were serious? We get people in here every day saying they like something and they'll be back the next day or next week. They never show up, never! So when somebody comes in and says I'll take that ring or that vase, here, here's the money, why I *sell* it to them. I'd go out of business if I believed everything people tell me. But since you've worked all that time, maybe you'd like to see some nice earrings I've got, jade and . . ."

"No. I was starting a famous marble collection. I don't want anything else." Sister Opal tucked her worthless money away in her old purse and went out with her back straight and stiff.

She walked around downtown all day long, looking into bookstores, department stores, stationery shops, jewelry stores, boutiques, but nothing seemed attractive to her. She thought it was strange that all the times she hadn't had any money hundreds and hundreds of things in the store windows had looked so great and she had really

wanted them. Now that she had a lot of money nothing interested her. She stared at the most exotic clothes without even a twinge of desire. Her beautiful baroque pearl belonged to somebody else; she didn't want any other thing. She put off going home as long as possible, but when the lights began to come on she knew it was time to go back.

The family was at supper. Every head turned to Sister Opal as she came in and slumped into her chair.

"Well!" boomed Roy, who didn't work Saturday nights. "Let's see that solid gold marble you got!" Sister Opal's mother, who saw something was wrong, said, "Well, what's the trouble, Sister? Was the store closed?" Sister Opal, who had not cried, or even felt much of anything except emptiness and loss, burst into a howl she didn't even know was inside her.

"He sold it to somebody else a long time ago-o-oo-o!" Between sobs, hiccups and tears dripping into her plate, Sister Opal told the family about R. Sonnier and how he had sold the pearl. Andrew was indignant and declared that if he was ever in the market for a baroque pearl, he would rather die in the gutter than buy it from R. Sonnier. But Sister Opal's father said judiciously, "Well, Sister, he didn't do it out of spite and meanness. He was just being businesslike. If you were a store man and somebody breezed in and said, 'Here, you hold on to that stuffed elephant for me, I'll be back someday and pay for it,' and a week later somebody else came in and said, 'Here, here's a thousand dollars for that stuffed elephant,' you *know* you are going to sell that elephant right there and then. Sister Opal, you should have checked back with that R. Sonnier every week or so, so that he'd know you were really serious about

buying it. I know you're disappointed. I'm disappointed myself. I was looking forward to seeing that baroque pearl and knowing somebody in our family owned it." This brought a fresh howl from Sister Opal which her father silenced by continuing.

"As I see it, Sister, you can either curl up and die because you didn't get your fancy marble, or you can hurry up and quit crying and think about the future. Probably you should take that pearl money and put it with the college money so that you can study up on baroque pearls when you get to college. So you got to adopt a long range plan now and think about education and a career . . ."

Sister Opal heard her father talking on in a kindly way about his favorite subject, education and getting knowledge and getting ahead and having a career. She knew that most of what he was saying was sensible, but she had heard it all so many times she didn't want to hear it again. Her father didn't *know* how it felt to be a girl and to want a beautiful thing very badly. Sister Opal excused herself from the table and went up to her room. She flung herself on the bed sideways and dangled her head off the edge, looking at the pale rectangle of the window. The marble jar was dark in the twilight and it glittered along one side from the reflected light of the street lamp. Sister Opal reached out for the marble jar, tipped the contents onto the bed with a rich, sensuous, rolling sound. Her thin hand slid through the marble pile in the darkening room until she touched the familiar lopsided marble. Warming it in the hollow of her hand, she could just make out its ephemeral glow, its waxy luster against the darkness of her hand and the darkness of the oncoming night. She rolled it slightly in her palm and said softly to the warmed, heavy marble, "Oh, what a beautiful baroque pearl." ☐☐

Discussion

1. (a) What do you learn of Sister Opal's character from her thoughts and actions at the beginning of the story?
(b) What makes her first decide to buy the baroque pearl? **(c)** In what way does R. Sonnier's treatment of her influence Sister Opal's actions?

2. (a) What does the baroque pearl symbolize to Sister Opal? **(b)** What does it represent to her family? **(c)** In what ways does Sister Opal's decision to buy the pearl change her life and the lives of those in her family?

3. (a) What kind of man is R. Sonnier? In your response take into account both his attitude and Sister Opal's attitude toward the baroque pearl.
(b) In your opinion, is Sonnier's treatment of Sister Opal acceptable or unacceptable? **(c)** Do you agree with Sister Opal's father's explanation of why Sonnier sold the pearl to someone else? Why or why not?

4. (a) Why is Sister Opal unable to spend her $450 for something else? **(b)** Does she learn anything from losing the pearl? If so, what?

5. (a) Does Sister Opal seem changed at the end of the story? Explain your answer.
(b) What reasons can you give for her actions in the last paragraph of the story?

6. In your own interpretation of the story, does the baroque pearl symbolize anything additional, or different from what it means to Sister Opal and her family? Explain.

7. One reader of this story said, "Sister Opal is lucky to have a nearly perfect family who support and try to understand her; next to this her loss of the pearl is secondary." Do you agree or disagree with this interpretation? Why?

Extension • Speaking

Sister Opal learned in art class about collections started with inexpensive things that became rare and valuable as time went by. Successful collectors seem to have started off with the things they really liked; in Sister Opal's case, those things were marbles.

Speak to your class about what you collect or would enjoy collecting. Your choice of topic should be something you really like. (You may pretend here that money, travel, etc., present no problem. But keep in mind that today, when comic books and old glass bottles are considered collectors' items, your collectable need not be expensive and may be very common indeed.)

You should include some information about your item, perhaps how you first became acquainted with it. Your presentation will be more interesting if you can relate a personal experience you have had. Is the item symbolic to you? In what way?

Plan carefully what you're going to say; your talk should run no longer than five minutes. Then share with the class your hopes and ideas for being a collector.

E. A. Proulx

"Yes, I know what it feels like to be an outsider. It's terribly hard." So speaks a character in another of E. A. Proulx's short stories. Proulx (whose real name is Ann Lang) lives in the small town of St. Albans, Vermont, away from the busy pace and pressures of the kind of large city in which "The Baroque Marble" is set. Yet in her writing she uses as settings small towns and cities, past, present, and even the future, for she has written some science fiction, as well. Many of her stories have been published in the magazine *Seventeen*.

How important is it to be important?

I'm Nobody

Emily Dickinson

I'm nobody! Who are you?
Are you nobody, too?
Then there's a pair of us—don't tell!
They'd banish us, you know.

5 How dreary to be somebody!
How public, like a frog
To tell your name the livelong day
To an admiring bog.

Poems of Emily Dickinson, Second Series, edited by T. W. Higginson and Mabel Loomis Todd. (Boston: Roberts Brothers), 1891.

Scott, Foresman and Company Staff

1. (a) Whom does the speaker mean by "they" in line 4? **(b)** How are "they" likely to react to this pair of nobodies? Why? **(c)** Why might a person who chooses to be a nobody be regarded as an outsider?

2. (a) How does the speaker feel about being important?

(b) Explain the comparison the speaker makes in the second stanza.

3. (a) What comment on human nature is made in this poem? **(b)** Do you agree or disagree with the speaker's view? Why?

notes and comments

Too "Modern" for Her Time

Emily Dickinson and her poetry never fully belonged to their own time. She was an individualist who never conformed to "what was expected," and her poetry reflected her individuality.

Dickinson was born in 1830, and she lived all her life in Amherst, Massachusetts. In her youth, she was a lively and fun-loving girl. But the society she grew up in was very strict, with precise ideas about manners and beliefs "proper" for young women.

Dickinson wrote her poems secretly on scraps of paper— used envelopes, backs of reci-pes. Some poems she copied into little booklets; the rest she tied up with thread and stuffed in drawers. There are hints in her letters that she recognized the quality and possible impor-tance of her work; yet—like the speaker in "I'm Nobody" —she maintained that she had no wish for recognition in her own time.

The first of her poems to ap-pear in print was published without her permission, and the publisher had changed the poem without her consent. Dickinson was greatly dis-turbed. From that point on she insisted that her poems not be published rather than be tam-pered with. Only seven of her 1,775 poems were published during her lifetime. After her death in 1886, relatives gath-ered her manuscripts for publi-cation.

Today more than ever, Dick-inson's poetry seems to be widely read and greatly appre-ciated. Her popularity further increased when actress Julie Harris toured the country in a one-woman show based on Dickinson's life and works. Harris won Broadway's Tony award for her characterization of Emily Dickinson, *The Belle of Amherst.*

*Fiona Farmer discovers a world
she never knew existed—
and is given a new name, besides.*

Nancy

Elizabeth Enright

Fiona Farmer was seven years old. Her mother was forty-six, her father was fifty-five, her nurse was sixty-one, and her grandmother and grandfather with whom they were all spending the summer had reached such altitudes of age that no one remembered what they were. From these great heights Fiona was loved and directed.

She wore her hair as her mother had worn it in 1914, braided tight and tied back in pretzel loops with big stiff ribbons. In winter she was the only girl at school to wear a flannel petticoat and underwear with sleeves. Her mother read her all the books she had loved in her childhood: *Rebecca of Sunnybrook Farm,* and *The Five Little Peppers,* and *Under the Lilacs.* Her grandmother read her the books *she* had loved as a child: Macé's *Fairy Tales,* and Grimm's *Fairy Tales,* and *The Princess and Curdie.* On this mixed diet of decorum and brutality Fiona was rapidly turning into a "quaint little creature." She was a pensive child with large attentive eyes and rather elderly manners; all her play was quiet, accompanied at times by nothing noisier than a low continuous murmuring, so it was strange that the ranks of dolls on her nursery shelves were scalped, and eyeless, like the victims of a Sioux massacre.

"What on earth does she do to them?" her mother said to Nana, the nurse. "Why, when I was little my dollies were really like babies to me. I took such *care* of them, I *loved* them so. . . ."

"I honestly don't know, Mrs. Farmer," Nana said. "She'll be as quiet as a mouse in here for hours at a time, and then I'll come in and find all this—this destruction! It seems so unlike her!"

Fiona's grandmother reproached her quietly. "How would you like it if your dear mother pulled all your hair out of your head and broke your arms and legs? Your dolls are your little responsibilities, your *children* in a way. . . . "

Her admonishments though frequent were always mild. When Fiona scratched her head, or picked her nose, she would say: "That's not very pretty, dear, is it? We don't do those things, do we?" . . . She was a lofty, dignified, conventional lady, and she smelled like an old dictionary among whose pages many flowers have been dried and pressed. She taught Fiona how to make a sachet and a pomander ball and play parcheesi.

Fiona liked her grandfather the best. He was a man of wonderful patience and politeness, deaf as a post. Every morning she followed him out to the vegetable garden where, in his old loose button-down-the-front sweater and his white canvas golf hat that sagged in a ruffle around his head, he worked along the rows of beets and cabbages with his hoe and rake. Fiona followed at his heels, speaking ceaselessly; it did not matter to her that he never heard a word she said, she told him everything. Now and then he would stop, resting on his hoe handle, and look down at her appreciatively. "Well," he would say. "You're a pleasant little companion, aren't you?" Then he would reach out his old parched hand (he was so old that he never sweated any more) and give her a brittle tap or two on the shoulder or head, and he and Fiona would smile at each other out of a mutual feeling of benevolence.

Sooner or later, though, Nana's voice would begin to caw: "Fee-ona! Fee-ona!" and she would have to go back to the house to pick up her toys or change her dress or eat a meal, or some other dull thing.

Her grandparents' house was big and cool inside. All the rooms were full of greenish light reflected from the maple trees outdoors; the floors were dark and gleaming, the carpets had been taken up for the summer and the furniture had linen dresses on. There was no dust anywhere, not even in the corners of the empty fireplaces, for Cora and Mary, the maids who had been there for thirty years, spent their lives seeing that there was not.

Cora had arthritis, and on Sundays when Fiona had noon dinner with the whole family she marveled at the extreme slowness with which the maid moved about the table, like a running-down toy. Her face looked very still and concentrated then, relaxing only when she served Fiona, whispering: "Eat it all up now, dear, every bit, so I can tell Mary."

Oh food! People were always speaking of food to Fiona; the Sunday dinners were a trial to toil through. "Eat it all up, dear," and "Clean your plate" were phrases that were ugly in her ears.

After Sunday dinner everyone went to sleep for a while and the house droned with different pitches of snoring. Wearing nothing but a pink wrapper Fiona would lie on the big white bed while Nana sat in an armchair by the window rattling the Sunday paper. Out of doors the cicadas sounded hot as drills; the lazy air coming in the window brought a smell of grass, and Fiona wished that Nana would fall asleep so that she could get up and find something to play with, but Nana would not fall asleep.

But once she did.

Once on Sunday after the usual slow massive dinner, as Fiona lay in the extremity of boredom counting mosquito bites and listening to herself yawn, she heard another sound; a new one that might promise much. Quietly she raised herself to her elbows, hardly daring to believe, and saw that the impossible had happened at last. Nana lay in the armchair, abandoned, with her head thrown back and her hair coming down and her mouth wide open like that of a fish; a faint guttural sound came out of it each time she breathed.

A great light seemed to flood the room, and a voice from on high addressed Fiona: "Get up and dress, but do not put on your shoes. Carry them in your hand till you get outside, and close the front door quietly behind you."

Fiona got up at once, dressed with the silence and speed of light, and departed. The upstairs hall hummed and trumpeted with the noises of sleeping; no one heard her running down the stairs.

Out of doors it was bright and hot; she sat on the front step and put on her sandals with her heart galloping in her chest. Though old, the members of her family were tall, their legs were long as ladders, and if they came after her they would surely catch her. Leaving the sandal straps unbuckled, Fiona ran out of the gate and down the street, terrified and exhilarated. She ran till she was giddy and breathless, but when at last she stopped and looked behind her the street on which she found herself was still and empty; steeped in Sunday.

She walked for a long time. Her heart stopped racing and her breathing became comfortable again. Her fear, too, gave way to pleasure and pride. It was a beautiful afternoon. The street was very high with elms. The light that came through their roof of leaves was green and trembling like light through water. Fiona became a little crab crawling among the roots of seaweed. The parked cars were fishes which would eat her

up, danger was everywhere. . . . She walked sideways, made claws out of her thumbs, hid behind trees, and felt that her eyes grew out on stems. But not for long. Suddenly, as sometimes happened, the fancy collapsed, betrayed her completely. There was no danger; the cars were cars only. Nothing was any better than real; in the end somebody would catch her and take her home or she would return of her own accord, driven by hunger or conscience, and everything would be as it had always been.

The houses sat back from their green laps of lawn, silent and substantial, regarding her like people wearing glasses. There was a smell of privet and hot asphalt in the still air; a boring smell. . . . Intolerable boredom amounting to anguish drove Fiona to turn abruptly and kick the iron palings of a fence that she was passing; a kick that hurt right through her shoe.

The big street came to an end finally at a small Civil War monument and branched out beyond it in three roads. She chose the right-hand one because there was a dog asleep on the sidewalk there, but when she got to him she saw the flies strolling up and down his face and he looked up at her balefully with a low ripple of sound in his throat and she hurried on.

This street had few trees; it was broader, and the houses, while farther apart, were shabbier. The afternoon sun was in her eyes, drawing her along the gilded road. The wind had sprung up, too, warm and lively, blowing from the west.

On the outskirts of the town she came upon her destination, though at first she did not realize it. For some time the wind had been bringing her great blasts of radio music; and she saw now that these had their source in a gray frame house that fairly trembled with melody. Though not small, this was the seediest of all the houses. It stood in the middle of a yard as full of tall grass as a field. There were paths through the field and bald patches where people had stamped and trampled, and many souvenirs abandoned and half grown over: a rusted little wagon with no wheels, somebody's shoe, an old tire . . .

The house had a queer shape, fancy, but with everything coming off or breaking. Some of the shutters hung by one hinge only; the cupola on top was crooked and so was the porch from which half the palings were gone. The fence, too, had lost many of its pickets and stood propped against the tangle like a large comb with teeth missing; but it had kept its gate and hanging onto this and swinging slowly back and forth were three little girls. Fiona walked more slowly.

One of the girls had a bandanna tied tightly around her head but the other two regarded her from under untrimmed dusty bangs, like animals peering out from under ferns. The gate gave a long snarl of sound as they pushed it forward. "Where are you going?" said the tallest one.

Fiona could not be sure of the tone of this question: was it a friendly or a hostile challenge? She moved still more slowly touching each picket with her forefinger.

"No place," she said guardedly.

"What's your name?" demanded the girl with the bandanna. She smelled of kerosene.

"Fiona Farmer," said Fiona.

"That's a funny name. My name's Darlene, and hers is Pearl, and *hers* is Merle. Nancy is a nice name."

Fiona saw that all of them were wearing red nail polish and asked a question of her own.

"Are you all three sisters?"

"Yes, and there's more of us. *Them,*"

said Pearl, the tallest girl, jerking her head. "In the swing."

Beyond the house Fiona now saw for the first time an old double-rocker swing full of boys.

"There's Norman and Stanley and Earl," Darlene said. "And in the house we got a baby sister named Marilyn, and down to the picture theater we got a big sister named Deanna. Come on in."

"Will they let me swing in the swing?" said Fiona.

"Sure they will. *What* did you say your name was?"

"Fiona," she admitted. "Fiona Farmer."

"Gee," said Pearl.

"We'll call her Nancy," said Darlene, who, though younger, seemed to be a leader in her way. "Come on, Nancy, you wanna swing on the gate? Get off, Merle."

Merle got off obediently, sucking her thumb.

"I would like to swing in the *swing,*" Fiona said.

She came into the yard gazing up at the tipsy cupola. "Can you get up there into that kind of little tower?"

"Sure," said Darlene. "Come on up and we'll show you."

Fiona followed them through the interesting grass in which she now saw a broken doll, somebody's garter, somebody's hat, and many weathered corncobs and beer cans.

On the porch which swayed when they walked on it there were a tough-looking baby buggy, two sleds, a bent tricycle, a lot of chairs and boxes and bushel baskets and peck baskets and a baby pen and a wagon wheel and some kindling wood. The screen door was full of holes and instead of a doorknob there was a wooden thread spool to turn.

The noise of music was stunning as they went indoors; it kept the Mason jars[1] ringing on the shelves. They walked right into it, into the thrilling heart of noise which was the kitchen, where a woman was sitting nursing a baby and shouting random conversation at an old, old woman with a beak nose.

The music ceased with a flourish and the radio announcer's tremendous tones replaced it, but this did not stop the shouted discourse of the woman with the baby. As the girls crossed the kitchen she turned for a moment to look at them, saw Fiona and said, "Who's she?"

"She's Nancy," called Darlene, against the radio.

"Who?"

"Nancy! She dropped in."

"That's Mom," Pearl said.

Fiona went over to the lady to shake her hand. She made her usual curtsy and said, "How do you do?"

Mom's hand felt limp and rather damp and startled. She was a big woman with a wide face and tired blue eyes.

"The old one's Gramma," Darlene said, so Fiona curtsied to the old lady too, and shook her hand which felt like a few twigs in a glove.

"And that's my father," Darlene added, a few seconds later when they had gone up the loud bare stairs to the next floor; Fiona peeked in the doorway of the dim strong-smelling room but all she saw of *him* was the soles of his socks and she heard him snoring.

"Just like at home," she said. "Sunday afternoon they all sleep."

"Heck, he sleeps all *day* on Sundays," Darlene said, and Fiona felt a little humiliated for her own father.

"This is Gramma's room" Pearl threw open the door. "She likes flowers."

The room was a jungle steeped in musky twilight. A vine of some kind had crawled all over the window and parts of the wall, and on the sill, the sash, the floor below, were pots and jars and coffee tins in which stout lusty plants were growing and flowering.

"How does she open the window at night?" Fiona wondered.

"*She* don't open no windows day or night," Darlene said. "Heck, she's *old,* she's gotta stay *warm.*"

They went up another flight of stairs, narrow steep ones, crowded with magazines and articles of clothing and decayed toys. "Up here's where we sleep," Darlene said. "Us girls, all of us except Marilyn. Pearl and me and Merle sleep in the big bed and Deanna she sleeps in the cot. This is the attic like."

The big bed was made of iron with the post knobs missing. It dipped in the middle like a hammock and there, Fiona knew, the little girls would lie at night, dumped together in a tangle, quarreling or giggling in whispers.

"Look at all the comic books!" she cried, and indeed they lay everywhere in tattered profusion, a drift of stained, disordered leaves.

"We got about a hundred or a thousand of 'em, I guess," Pearl said. "You want some?"

"Could I really, Pearl? Could you spare them?"

"*Atom Annie's* a good one," Pearl said. "We got a lot about her, and here's one called *Hellray* that's real good, real scarey. Take these."

Fiona looked at them longingly.

"I don't know if my mother—she doesn't

---

1. *Mason jars,* jars used for canning fruits and vegetables. Mason is a brand name.

like for me to have comics."

"Heck, why not?"

"Well, maybe this time she won't mind," Fiona said, taking the books, determined that everything would be all right for once. "Thank you very, very much, Darlene and Pearl."

"Here's the stairs to the lookout," Darlene said. "Get out of the way, Merle, you wait till last."

They climbed the ladder steps in the middle of the room. Pearl pushed open the trap door and one by one they ascended into the tiny chamber.

It was a tipped little cubicle like a ship's cabin in stiff weather, and stiflingly hot. It seemed remote, high, cozy, and its four soiled windows showed four different views of the town faded and reduced as pictures in an old book. Flies buzzed and butted at the hot glass. Fiona felt disappointed when she saw the steeple of the church that stood across the street from her grandfather's house. She had not thought it was so near.

"Jump!" cried Darlene. They all began to jump, and the cupola jarred and trembled under the pounding.

"Won't it break?" cried Fiona, pounding with the rest. "Won't it fall off?"

"Naw, it won't break," Darlene called back. "It never did yet."

"But it might some day, though," shouted Pearl encouragingly.

It was fun to jump riotously and yell, as the tiny tower rocked and resounded.

There was an interruption from below.

"Get out of there!" bawled Mom up the stairs. "How many times I told you kids to stay down out of there! You want to get your backs broke? You want to get killed? You scram down!"

"Get out of the way, Merle, let Nancy go first," Pearl said.

Mom stood at the foot of the steps wearing the baby around her neck. Anxiety had made her furious. "That place ain't safe, you know that!" she cried. "How many times have I told you?" She gave Pearl a slap on the cheek and would have given one to Darlene, too, if Darlene had not bent her neck adroitly.

"You let me catch you up there one more time and I'll get your father to lick you good!"

"Aw, climb a tree," said Darlene.

Fiona was aghast. What would happen now?

But nothing happened. Merle still quietly sucked her thumb, Darlene and Pearl seemed cool and jaunty, and as they descended through the house Mom's anger dried up like dew.

"You kids want a snack?" she said. "You didn't eat since breakfast."

"Can Nancy stay?"

"Why sure, I guess. Why not?"

"Oh, thank you very, very much. . . ."

The kitchen, like the rest of the house, had a rich bold musty smell. It smelled of constant usage and memories of usage. It was crowded and crusted with objects: pots, pans, kettles, boxes, jars, cans, buckets, dippers. There were two alarm clocks, one lying on its side, and each asserting a different hour, and four big Coca-Cola calendars on the wall, none for the current year. The radio was still thundering music, and close beside it warming herself at the noise sat Gramma, dark as a crow, chewing and chewing on her empty gums.

The stove was named Ebony Gem, and behind it in a cardboard box there was something alive; something moved. . . .

"It's kittens," said Merle, removing her thumb from her mouth and speaking for the first time. "Our cat had kittens."

"Oh, let me see!" Fiona knelt by the box. There inside it lay a bland and happy group: mother cat with her yellow eyes half closed and her paws splayed out in pleasure; kittens lined up all along her, sucking.

Merle put out her little forefinger with its chipped red nail polish, stroking first one infant, then the next. "The black one's name is Blackie and the white one's name is Whitey and we call *this* one Butch because he's so . . ."

"My father usually drowns them, all but one," Darlene interrupted. She bent her kerchiefed head close to Fiona's, so that there was a blinding smell of kerosene. "Tomorrow probably," she whispered. "We don't tell Merle, it makes her feel so bad." Then she raised her voice. "She knows it's going to happen but she don't know when, huh, Merle?"

"You could take one, Nancy," Merle said, still gazing at the kittens. "You could keep it and be good to it."

"Do you mean honestly and truly?"

Fiona's joy was suffocating.

"Any one? Any one at all?"

"Except Butch," Darlene said. "We're going to keep him to help with the rats."

"Could I have Blackie? Really for keeps?"

Merle plucked the dark little thing from the mother as if she were plucking off a burr and gave it to Fiona.

"I can feel its little tiny heart," Fiona said. "I'll give it milk all the time and brush its fur and it can sleep in the doll cradle. Oh look at its ears, oh Merle, oh thank you!"

Shamed by gratitude Merle put her thumb back in her mouth and looked away.

"You kids get out from under my feet," Mom said. "Sit up to the table now, it's all ready. Come on Mama, come on *boys!*" She opened the screen door and put her head

out, shouting so hard that great cords stood out on her neck.

They sat around the big table with its oilcloth cover, everything in easy reach: cereal in paper boxes, sugar, catsup. . . . They had cornflakes and milk, Swiss cheese sandwiches with catsup, cream soda in bottles, and little cakes out of a box with pink and green beads on them. Fiona ate everything.

"Nancy eats good, don't she, Mom?" Darlene said.

"I never had catsup before," said Fiona. "My, it certainly is delicious, isn't it?"

The table was a family battlefield. Fiona had never seen anything like it in her life. Stanley and Norman threw pieces of sandwich at each other, Earl took one of Merle's cakes and Merle cried and Mom slapped Earl; Darlene stole big swigs from Pearl's soda bottle, was loudly accused and loudly defended herself.

"You kids shut up," Mom said, eating over Marilyn's head and giving her occasional bits of cake dipped in tea. Gramma was the only quiet one; she sat bent over, all wrapped and absorbed in her old age, gazing into her cup as she drank from it with a long purring sound. Blackie was quiet, too, asleep in Fiona's lap. She kept one hand on his little velvet back. Mom pointed at Fiona with her spoon. "Looks like Margaret O'Brien[2] used to, don't she? The ribbons and all."

"Margaret who?" said Fiona.

"O'Brien, you know, the kid in the movies," Darlene said.

"Oh, I never go to movies," said Fiona. "I'm not allowed."

"Not allowed!" cried Darlene incredulously. "Heck, we go all the time, don't we, Mom? Even Deanna goes. We could take Nancy with us sometimes, couldn't we, Mom?"

"Maybe, if her folks say yes."

"Oh if I went with you it would be all right, I'm sure," cried Fiona joyously. Drunk with noise, strange flavors, gifts, and new friendship, she really believed this.

Afterward, still with catsup on their upper lips, they went outdoors to play hide-and-seek.

"You be her partner, Stanley," ordered Darlene, who was "it." "You kind of look after her, she don't know our places to hide."

Then she hid her eyes with her arm, cast herself against a tree like a girl in grief, and began to count out loud.

"The cellar," hissed Stanley, grabbing Fiona's hand. He was a big eight-year-old boy, and still clutching the kitten Fiona ran with him willingly, hesitating only for a second at sight of the dark abyss. On the steps were many cans and beer crates, but Stanley led her safely down among these and into the black deep tunnel beyond. Fiona could feel that there were solid things all around them; probably more boxes, more beer crates, but she could see nothing. Stanley's hand was warm and firm, it just fitted hers, and she liked having him lead her.

"We can stop now," he said, "but keep quiet."

Darlene could still be heard, faintly. Her counting voice sounded deserted and defiant: "Ninety-five, ninety-six, ninety-seven" . . . The blackness throbbed and shimmered and the air had a dense aged smell.

"Coming, ready or not!" called the faraway defiant voice.

"We're safe here anyways," Stanley said. "She won't come down here, she's scared to." He laughed silently and gave Fiona's hand a squeeze. "There's rats down

2. **Margaret O'Brien,** a child movie star, popular in the late 1940's and early 1950's.

here."

"Oh no, oh no! Oh, Stanley, let's go up again," cried Fiona, tears of panic in her voice.

But Stanley held onto her hand. "You going to be a sissy too?" he demanded. "We got the *cat,* ain't we?"

Fiona strained the tiny kitten to her chest. Her heart was banging terribly and she wanted to cry but she would not. All around the rats were closing in, large as dogs and smiling strangely; smiling like people. She almost sobbed when Stanley said, "Now we can go, hurry up, and keep still!"

They were the first ones back.

For a long time they played and Stanley always was her partner. He knew the best places to hide: up in the boughs of a pear tree, under the porch steps, in the fearful little dark privy with its different-sized "family accommodations," and flat on their stomachs under the folded-back cellar door. Darlene was "it" till she caught Merle and Merle was "it" for hours. Fiona got spider webs in her mouth and gnats up her nose, tore her dress, scraped her knee, lost one hair ribbon, and gave the other to Merle, who had admired it.

When they were through with hide-and-seek they all got into the rocker swing and played gangsters. The swing leapt to and fro, to and fro, screaming wildly at the joints; surely it would break, and soon! That was the thrilling thing about this place: so many features of it—the tower, the swing, the porch—trembled at the edge of ruin, hung by a thread above the fatal plunge. Earl and Stanley and Norman leaned over the back of one of the seats firing at the enemy. "Step on it, you guys," yelled Stanley, "they got a gat!"

"They got a rod!" yelled Norman. "They got a lotta rods!"

"What's a rod?" cried Fiona. "What's a gat?"

"Guns he means," Darlene told her. "Rods and gats is guns."

"Shoot 'em, Stanley," yelled Fiona. "With your gat, shoot the eyes out of 'em!"

Clutching the clawing kitten to her collarbone, her hair in her open mouth, she bawled encouragement to them. The swing accelerated ever more wildly: soon it would take off entirely, depart from its hinges, fly through the air, burn a hole through the sky! . . .

"Fee-ona Farmer!"

The cry was loud enough to be heard above all sounds of war and wind and radio music.

Beside the swing stood Nana, so tall, so highly charged with hurry and emotion, that the children stopped their play at once.

"Who's she?" Stanley asked.

"She's my nurse," Fiona murmured.

"Your nurse! What's the matter, are you sick?"

"No . . . she just—takes care of me."

"Takes *care* of you!"

"You get out of that swing and come this in-stant!"

Having struck the bottom of disgrace, Fiona stepped down and slowly went to Nana. From the swing the others watched as still as children posing for a photograph.

"Put down that cat and come at once."

"Oh no!" Fiona said. "It's mine, they gave it to me."

"Put. Down. That. Cat."

Darlene came to stand beside Fiona. "But we did give it to her, we want for her to have it."

Nana struck the kitten from Fiona's arms. "You will not take that creature home! It's filthy, it has fleas!"

"Oh my kitty!" shrieked Fiona, diving

after Blackie, but Nana caught her wrist.

"You come!"

Fiona pulled, struggled, cast a glare of anguish at all the rapt photograph-faces in the swing.

"You should be punished. You should be whipped. Whipped!" Nana whistled the cruel words; Nana, who was never cruel! Her fingers on Fiona's wrist were hard.

"Let me say good-by to them, Nana, let me say good-by to their *mother!* You said I should *always* say good-by to the mother!"

"Not this time, this time it doesn't matter," Nana said. "You're going straight home and into the tub. Heaven knows what you will have caught!" Upon Fiona's friends she turned a single brilliant glance like one cold flash from a lighthouse.

There was nothing to commend Fiona's departure; dragged by the hand, whimpering, she looked back at her friends in desperation. "Oh, Darlene!"

But it was easy to see that Darlene had detached herself. "Good-by, Nancy," she said, not without a certain pride. She did not smile or say anything else, but her attitude showed Fiona and Nana that she had no need for either of them, could not be hurt by them, and would not think of them again. As they went out the gate she turned her back and skipped away, and Fiona heard the rocker swing resume its screaming tempo.

Halfway home Nana's recriminations began to modify, gradually becoming reproaches: "How could you have, Fiona, run away like that, why it's only by the grace of God I ever found you at all! And all the time I was half sick with worry I never said a word to your father and mother! I didn't want *them* to worry!"

Somewhere deep inside her Fiona understood exactly why Nana had said nothing to her parents, but she just kept on saying: "I want my kitty, I want my kitty."

Finally Nana said: "If you're a good girl maybe we'll get you another kitten."

"I don't want another, I want that one."

"Oh for pity's sakes, it had fleas, or worse. Anything belonging to the Fadgins would be bound to have—"

"Do *you* know them?"

"I know *about* them, everybody does. They're the dirtiest, the shiftlessest, the most down-at-the-heel tribe in this whole town!"

"They are not, they're nice, I love them!"

Nana relented a little. "Maybe it's hard not to be shiftless when you're that poor."

"*They* aren't poor. You should see all the things they've got! More than Grandmother's got in her whole house!"

"All right now, dearie, all right. We'll forget about it, shall we? It will be our secret and we'll never tell anyone because we don't want them to worry, do we? But you must promise me never, never to do such a thing again, hear?"

"I want my kitty," droned Fiona.

Her grandparents' house smelled cool and sweetish. There was a bowl of white and pink stock on the hall table and her grandmother's green linen parasol leaned in a corner among the pearly company of her grandfather's canes.

In the shaded living room Fiona saw her mother knitting and her grandmother at the piano playing the same kind of music she always played, with the loose rings clicking on her fingers.

"Is that my baby?" called her mother— but Nana answered hastily, "I'm getting her right into her bath, Mrs. Farmer. She's simply fil-thy."

Upstairs Nana went in to run the water in the tub. Fiona kicked off one sandal, then the other. A terrible pain took hold of her; it began in her mind and spread down to her stomach. She had never been homesick before and did not know what ailed her: she knew only that she wanted to sleep at night in a big twanging bed full of children and to eat meals at a crowded table where people threw bread at each other and drank pop. She wanted Stanley's hand to guide her and Darlene's voice to teach her and Blackie's purr to throb against her chest. . . .

Beyond the window she saw her grandfather's wilted golf hat bobbing among the cornstalks and escaped again, running on bare feet down the back stairs and out of doors across the billowing lawn which seemed to be colliding with the trees and sky and shadows, all flooded and dazzled with tears. Blindly she flung open the garden gate and pushed her way through the green-paper corn forest to her grandfather who dropped his hoe and held out his arms when he saw her face.

"Come here now," he said in his gentle deaf voice. "Well, well, this won't do, no it won't, not at all. Come sit here with Grandpa, sit here in the arbor. Did you hurt yourself?"

He led her to the seat under the green grape trellis where he sometimes rested from the hot sun. He put his arm around her shoulders, offering himself as a support for grief, and Fiona howled against his waistcoat till the wet tweed chapped her cheek and there was not a tear left in her. He did not interrupt or ask questions but kept patting her shoulder in a sort of sympathetic accompaniment to her sobs, which he could not hear but which he felt. What's the cause of it all, he wondered. A broken toy? A scolding? Children's tragedies, he thought, children's little tragedies: there are bigger ones in store for you, Fiona, a world of them. The thought did not move him deeply; everyone must suffer, but for an instant he was not sorry to be old.

Fiona leaned against him and after a while between the hiccups left from sobbing she could hear the ancient heart inside his chest tick-tocking steadily, as tranquil and unhurried as he was himself. All the wild performance of her sorrow had not quickened its tempo by a single beat, and this for some reason was a comfort.

The sound of her grandmother's music, sugary and elegant, came sparkling from the house, and upstairs in the bedroom or the hall Nana began to call. "Fee-ona?" she cried. "Oh, Fee-*ona?*"

There was a hint of panic in her voice, now, but no response came from under the green trellis: Fiona's grandfather could not hear the calling, and Fiona, for the time being, did not choose to answer. □□

Discussion

1. (a) List details from the story that indicate it does not take place today. (b) Could this story take place today? Explain your answer.

2. (a) Before Fiona meets the Fadgins, what kind of life does she lead? (b) Who is her one friend? (c) Why does she enjoy his company so much?

3. (a) How is the Fadgin home different from the Farmer home? (b) In what ways are the families different? (c) How do the attitudes of the adults toward the children differ in the two homes?

4. Compare Fiona's reactions to each of the following things at the Fadgins' with her reactions to similar things at home: (a) the comic books; (b) the kitten; (c) the meal; (d) the attitudes of the children toward the adults.

5. (a) What is Fiona's reaction to going home with Nana? (b) How does Darlene react to Fiona's leaving? (c) Why do you suppose Darlene behaves in this way?

6. (a) What is the terrible pain Fiona experiences while waiting for her bath? (b) Why could she not have felt this way before? (c) Why isn't her grandfather more concerned about the cause of her tears?

7. (a) Why do you suppose Fiona is so impressed with the Fadgins that she tells her nurse, "I love them"? (b) Why doesn't Fiona object to being called Nancy during the time she is at the Fadgins'? (c) Do you feel "Nancy" is an appropriate name for this story? Why or why not?

Vocabulary • Structure

You have already learned that many seemingly unfamiliar words are simple words with affixes added to them. The longer words may look difficult because a number of affixes can be confusing.

When you recognize one or more suffixes in a word, you can sometimes spot those same suffixes in another word, and so find its root more easily. For example, knowing that *joyously = joy + ous + ly,* you should have little trouble with *riotously.*

It is important to keep in mind that spelling changes may occur when suffixes are added. Some of the most common changes are dropping final *e,* as in *desperat(e) + ion;* changing final *y* to *i,* as in *accompan(y)i + ment;* doubling of final consonant, as in *wrap(p) + er.*

Copy the following words on your paper. After each, write the root word. If there is a spelling change, indicate it in parentheses. Notice that your analysis of structure does help you understand the meanings of some of these words.

1. departure
2. massive
3. ceaselessly
4. boredom
5. extremity
6. appreciative
7. defiant
8. musky
9. brutality
10. stiflingly

Elizabeth Enright 1909 • 1968

Because Elizabeth Enright's father was a cartoonist and her mother an artist, it seemed natural that she should be interested in art. After studying at the School of Applied Art in Paris, Enright began illustrating children's books. Only after she'd done the art work for several books written by other people did she attempt to write one of her own. Her first book, *Kintu,* which she wrote and illustrated, was honored for its literary content as well as its art work. Her second, *Thimble Summer,* won the Newbery Medal.

In this true account, Richard Wright tells
of the night his mother taught him to stand up and fight for himself.

Hunger

Richard Wright

Hunger stole upon me so slowly that at first I was not aware of what hunger really meant. Hunger had always been more or less at my elbow when I played, but now I began to wake up at night to find hunger standing at my bedside, staring at me gauntly. The hunger I had known before this had been no grim, hostile stranger; it had been a normal hunger that had made me beg constantly for bread, and when I ate a crust or two I was satisfied. But this new hunger baffled me, scared me, made me angry and insistent. Whenever I begged for food now my mother would pour me a cup of tea which would still the clamor in my stomach for a moment or two; but a little later I would feel hunger nudging my ribs, twisting my empty guts until they ached. I would grow dizzy and my vision would dim. I became less active in my play, and for the first time in my life I had to pause and think of what was happening to me.

"Mama, I'm hungry," I complained one afternoon.

"Jump up and catch a kungry," she said, trying to make me laugh and forget.

"What's a *kungry?*"

"It's what little boys eat when they get hungry," she said.

"What does it taste like?"

"I don't know."

"Then why do you tell me to catch one?"

"Because you said that you were hungry," she said, smiling.

I sensed that she was teasing me and it made me angry.

"But I'm hungry. I want to eat."

"You'll have to wait."

"But I want to eat now."

"But there's nothing to eat," she told me.

"Why?"

"Just because there's none," she explained.

"But I want to eat," I said, beginning to cry.

"You'll just have to wait," she said again.

"But why?"

"For God to send some food."

"When is He going to send it?"

"I don't know."

"But I'm hungry!"

She was ironing and she paused and looked at me with tears in her eyes.

"Where's your father?" she asked me.

I stared in bewilderment. Yes, it was true that my father had not come home to sleep for many days now and I could make as much noise as I wanted. Though I had not known why he was absent, I had been glad that he was not there to shout his restrictions at me. But it had never occurred to me that his absence would mean that there would be no food.

"I don't know," I said.

"Who brings food into the house?" my mother asked me.

"Papa," I said. "He always brought food."

"Well, your father isn't here now," she said.

"Where is he?"

"I don't know," she said.

"But I'm hungry," I whimpered, stomping my feet.

"You'll have to wait until I get a job and buy food," she said.

As the days slid past the image of my father became associated with my pangs of hunger, and whenever I felt hunger I thought of him with a deep biological bitterness.

My mother finally went to work as a cook and left me and my brother alone in the flat each day with a loaf of bread and a pot of tea. When she returned at evening she would be tired and dispirited and would cry a lot. Sometimes, when she was in despair, she would call us to her and talk to us for hours, telling us that we now had no father, that our lives would be different from those of other children, that we must learn as soon as possible to take care of ourselves, to dress ourselves, to prepare our own food; that we must take upon ourselves the responsibility of the flat while she worked. Half frightened, we would promise solemnly. We did not understand what had happened between our father and our mother and the most that

these long talks did to us was to make us feel a vague dread. Whenever we asked why father had left, she would tell us that we were too young to know.

One evening my mother told me that thereafter I would have to do the shopping for food. She took me to the corner store to show me the way. I was proud; I felt like a grownup. The next afternoon I looped the basket over my arm and went down the pavement toward the store. When I reached the corner, a gang of boys grabbed me, knocked me down, snatched the basket, took the money, and sent me running home in panic. That evening I told my mother what had happened, but she made no comment; she sat down at once, wrote another note, gave me more money, and sent me out to the grocery again. I crept down the steps and saw the same gang of boys playing down the street. I ran back into the house.

"What's the matter?" my mother asked.

"It's those same boys," I said. "They'll beat me."

"You've got to get over that," she said. "Now, go on."

"I'm scared," I said.

"Go on and don't pay any attention to them," she said.

I went out of the door and walked briskly down the sidewalk, praying that the gang would not molest me. But when I came abreast of them someone shouted, "There he is!"

They came toward me and I broke into a wild run toward home. They overtook me and flung me to the pavement. I yelled, pleaded, kicked, but they wrenched the money out of my hand. They yanked me to my feet, gave me a few slaps, and sent me home sobbing. My mother met me at the door.

"They b-beat m-me," I gasped. "They t-t-took the m-money."

I started up the steps, seeking the shelter of the house.

"Don't you come in here," my mother warned me.

I froze in my tracks and stared at her.

"But they're coming after me," I said.

"You just stay right where you are," she said in a deadly tone. "I'm going to teach you this night to stand up and fight for yourself."

She went into the house and I waited, terrified, wondering what she was about. Presently she returned with more money and another note; she also had a long heavy stick.

"Take this money, this note, and this stick," she said. "Go to the store and buy those groceries. If those boys bother you, then fight."

I was baffled. My mother was telling me to fight, a thing that she had never done before.

"But I'm scared," I said.

"Don't you come into this house until you've gotten those groceries," she said.

"They'll beat me; they'll beat me," I said.

"Then stay in the streets; don't come back here!"

I ran up the steps and tried to force my way past her into the house. A stinging slap came on my jaw. I stood on the sidewalk, crying.

"Please, let me wait until tomorrow," I begged.

"No," she said. "Go now! If you come back into this house without those groceries, I'll whip you!"

She slammed the door and I heard the key turn in the lock. I shook with fright. I was alone upon the dark, hostile streets and gangs were after me. I had the choice of being beaten at home or away from home. I clutched the stick, crying, trying to reason. If I were beaten at home, there was absolutely nothing that I could do about it; but if I were beaten in the streets, I had a chance to fight and defend myself. I walked slowly down the sidewalk, coming closer to the gang of boys, holding the stick tightly. I was so full of fear that I could scarcely breathe. I was almost upon them now.

"There he is again!" the cry went up.

They surrounded me quickly and began to grab for my hand.

"I'll kill you!" I threatened.

They closed in. In blind fear I let the

stick fly, feeling it crack against a boy's skull. I swung again, lamming another skull, then another. Realizing that they would retaliate if I let up for but a second, I fought to lay them low, to knock them cold, to kill them so that they could not strike back at me. I flayed with tears in my eyes, teeth clenched, stark fear making me throw every ounce of my strength behind each blow. I hit again and again, dropping the money and the grocery list. The boys scattered, yelling, nursing their heads, staring at me in utter disbelief. They had never seen such frenzy. I stood panting, egging them on, taunting them to come on and fight. When they refused, I ran after them and they tore out for their homes, screaming. The parents of the boys rushed into the streets and threatened me, and for the first time in my life I shouted at grownups, telling them that I would give them the same if they bothered me. I finally found my grocery list and the money and went to the store. On my way back I kept my stick poised for instant use, but there was not a single boy in sight. That night I won the right to the streets of Memphis. □□

Discussion

1. (a) In the first paragraph, to what does Wright compare his hunger? (b) What words and phrases make that hunger seem real?

2. (a) What impression do you get of Richard Wright's mother? (b) What does she do to provide a home for her two sons after their father has left? (c) How does she try to make them feel better about their living conditions?

3. (a) What were her motives for sending young Richard out on the street with a stick? (b) How did she teach him to be courageous? (c) What do you think of her methods?

4. (a) Find passages which give clues to Wright's youth and to his innocence in this selection. (b) Has he changed by the end of the selection? In what way(s)?

Richard Wright 1908 • 1960

To Richard Wright, childhood meant hunger and unhappiness and endless moving. When Wright was five, his father deserted the family, and for the next five years Mrs. Wright tried desperately to keep her two sons with her. But the only work she could get was as a domestic, and domestics worked for starvation wages. For a time she had to put her sons in an orphan asylum; when they refused to stay there, she borrowed from relatives to feed and shelter them. Finally, Mrs. Wright, who had been ill for years, became completely paralyzed, and the two boys became wholly dependent on their relatives.

But Richard Wright was rude and hard to manage. He could not get along with the aunts and uncles and cousins who wanted to make him over into a "good" boy. So, unlike his brother who lived with one family, Richard was shuffled from relative to relative, from town to town.

At fifteen Wright discovered the joys of reading, and he realized he wanted to be a writer. He wrote short stories which he showed to no one for fear of being ridiculed. He worked at whatever jobs were available until he had enough money to move to Chicago. It was there that he published his first book and wrote his most important works, including *Black Boy,* an autobiographical account of his childhood and young manhood from which "Hunger" was taken. He eventually moved with his family to Paris, where he continued to write until his death. Today, Wright is remembered for the realism and sensitivity of all his works.

See **TONE** Handbook of Literary Terms

*Who would be such Bad Sports as to swindle trusting relatives,
destroy an innocent leader's reputation, terrorize sweet little fellow campers
—and even counterfeit a yellow-billed cuckoo?*

A Loud Sneer for Our Feathered Friends

Ruth McKenney

From childhood, my sister and I have had a well-grounded dislike for our friends the birds. We came to hate them when she was ten and I was eleven. We had been exiled by what we considered an unfeeling family to one of those loathsome girls' camps where Indian lore is rife and the management puts up neatly lettered signs reminding the clients to be Good Sports. From the moment Eileen and I arrived at dismal old Camp Hi-Wah, we were Bad Sports, and we liked it.

We refused to get out of bed when the bugle blew in the morning, we fought against scrubbing our teeth in public to music, we sneered when the flag was ceremoniously lowered at sunset, we avoided doing a good deed a day, we complained loudly about the food, which was terrible, and we bought some chalk once and wrote all over the Recreation Cabin, "We hate Camp Hi-Wah." It made a wonderful scandal, although unfortunately we were immediately accused of the crime. All the other little campers *loved* dear old Camp Hi-Wah, which shows you what kind of people they were.

The first two weeks Eileen and I were at Camp Hi-Wah, we sat in our cabin grinding our teeth at our counselor and writing letters to distant relatives. These letters were, if I say so myself, real masterpieces of double dealing and heartless chicanery. In our childish and, we hoped, appealing scrawl, we explained to Great-Aunt Mary Farrel and Second Cousin Joe Murphy that we were having such fun at dear Camp Hi-Wah making Indian pocketbooks.

"We would simply L-O-V-E to make you a pocketbook, dear Aunt Mary," we wrote, "only the leather costs $1 for a small pocketbook or $1.67 for a large size pocketbook, which is much nicer because you can carry more things in it, and the rawhide you sew it up with, just exactly the way the Indians did, costs 40 cents more. We burn pictures on the leather but that doesn't cost anything. If we O-N-L-Y had $1 or $1.67 and 40 cents for the rawhide, we could make you the S-W-E-L-L-E-S-T pocketbook."

As soon as we had enough orders for Indian pocketbooks with pictures burnt on them, we planned to abscond with the funds sent by our trusting relatives and run away to New York City, where, as we used to explain dramatically to our cabin-mates, we intended to live a life of sin. After a few days, our exciting plans for our immediate future were bruited all over the camp, and admirers came from as far away as Cabin Minnehaha, which was way down at the end of Hiawatha Alley, just to hear us tell about New York and sin.

Fame had its price, however. One of the sweet little girls who lived in our cabin turned out to be such a Good Citizen ("Camp Hi-Wah Girls Learn to Be Good Citizens") that she told our dreadful secret to our counselor. Our mail was impounded for weeks, and worst of all, we actually had to make several Indian pocketbooks with pictures burnt on them. My pictures were all supposed to be snakes, although they were pretty blurred. Eileen specialized in what she believed to be the likeness of a were-

wolf, but Cousin Joe, who had generously ordered three pocketbooks, wrote a nice letter thanking Eileen for his pretty pocketbooks with the pretty pictures of Abraham Lincoln on them. We were terribly disgusted by the whole thing.

It was in this mood that we turned to birds. The handicraft hour at Camp Hi-Wah, heralded by the ten-thirty A.M. bugle, competed for popularity with the bird walks at the same hour. You could, as Eileen had already somewhat precociously learned how to say, name your own poison. After three weeks of burning pictures on leather, we were ready for anything, even our feathered friends.

So one hot morning in July, the two McKenney sisters, big and bad and fierce for their age, answered the bird-walk bugle call, leaving the Indian-pocketbook teacher to mourn her two most backward pupils. We were dressed, somewhat reluctantly, to be sure, in the required heavy stockings for poison ivy and brambles, and carried, each of us, in our dirty hands a copy of a guide to bird lore called *Bird Life for Children.*

Bird Life for Children was a volume that all the Good Citizens in Camp Hi-Wah pretended to find engrossing. Eileen and I thought it was stupefyingly dull. Our favorite literary character at the time was Dumas' Marguerite de Valois,[1] who took her decapitated lover's head home in a big handkerchief for old times' sake. Eileen, in those days, was always going to name her first girl child Marguerite de Valois.

Bird Life for Children was full of horrid pictures in full color of robins and pigeons

---

1. ***Dumas' Marguerite de Valois.*** Alexander Dumas, a French writer, wrote *Marguerite de Valois* in 1845. The real Marguerite de Valois was the wife of Henry IV, a sixteenth-century French king. However, she did not really perform the acts Dumas attributed to her in his book.

and redbirds. Under each picture was a loathsomely whimsical paragraph describing how the bird in question spent his spare time, what he ate, and why children should love him. Eileen and I hated the book so, we were quite prepared to despise birds when we started off that morning on our first bird walk, but we had no idea of what we were going to suffer, that whole awful summer, because of our feathered friends. In the first place, since we had started off making leather pocketbooks, we were three weeks behind the rest of the Hi-Wah bird-lovers. They had been tramping through blackberry bushes for days and days and had already got the hang of the more ordinary bird life around camp, whereas the only bird I could identify at the time was the vulture. Cousin Joe took me to a zoo once, and there was a fine vulture there, a big, fat one. They fed him six live rats every day in lieu of human flesh. I kept a sharp eye out for a vulture all summer, but one never turned up at Camp Hi-Wah. Nothing interesting ever happened around that place.

On that first bird walk, Eileen and I trotted anxiously along behind the little band of serious-minded bird-lovers, trying desperately to see, or at least hear, even one bird, even one robin. But alas, while other bird-walkers saw, or pretended to see—for Eileen and I never believed them for a moment—all kinds of hummingbirds and hawks and owls and whatnot, we never saw or heard a single, solitary feathered friend, not one.

By the time we staggered into camp for lunch, with stubbed toes, scratched faces, and tangled hair, Eileen and I were soured for life on birds. Our bird logs, which we carried strapped to our belts along with the *Guide,* were still chaste and bare, while all the other little bird-lovers had fulsome entries, such as "Saw and heard redbird at 10:37 A.M. Molting."

Still, for the next three days we stayed honest and suffered. For three terrible mornings we endured being dolts among bird-walkers, the laughingstock of Camp Hi-Wah. After six incredibly tiresome hours, our bird logs were still blank. Then we cracked under the strain. The fourth morning we got up feeling grim but determined. We sharpened our pencils before we started off on the now-familiar trail through the second-growth forest.

When we got well into the woods and Mary Mahoney, the premier bird-walker of Camp Hi-Wah, had already spotted and logged her first redbird of the morning, Eileen suddenly stopped dead in her tracks. "Hark!" she cried. She had read that somewhere in a book. "Quiet!" I echoed instantly.

The bird-walkers drew to a halt respectfully and stood in silence. They stood and stood. It was not good form even to whisper while fellow bird-walkers were logging a victim, but after quite a long time the Leader, whose feet were flat and often hurt her, whispered impatiently, "Haven't you got him logged yet?"

"You drove him away," Eileen replied sternly. "It was a yellow-billed cuckoo."

"A yellow-billed cuckoo?" cried the Leader incredulously.

"Well," Eileen said modestly, "at least *I* think it was." Then, with many a pretty hesitation and thoughtful pause, she recited the leading features of the yellow-billed cuckoo, as recorded in *Bird Life for Children.*

The Leader was terribly impressed. Later on that morning I logged a kingfisher, a red-headed woodpecker, and a yellow-bellied sapsucker, which was all I could remember at the moment. Each time, I kept the bird-walkers standing around for an interminable period, gaping into blank space and listening desperately to the rustle of the wind in the trees and the creak of their shoes as they went from one foot to another.

In a few days Eileen and I were the apple of our Leader's eye, the modest heroes of the Camp Hi-Wah bird walks. Naturally, there were base children around camp, former leading bird-walkers, who spread foul rumors up and down Hiawatha Alley that Eileen and I were frauds. We soon stopped this ugly talk, however. Eileen was the pitcher, and a very good one, too, of the Red Bird ball team and I was the first base. When Elouise Pritchard, the worst gossip in Cabin Sitting Bull, came up to bat, she got a pitched ball right in the stomach. Of course it was only a soft ball, but Eileen could throw it pretty hard. To vary this routine, I tagged Mary Mahoney, former head bird-walker, out at first base, and Mary had a bruise on her thigh for weeks. The rumors stopped abruptly.

We had begun to get pretty bored with logging rare birds when the game took on a new angle. Mary Mahoney and several other bird-walkers began to see the same birds we did on our morning jaunts into the forest. This made us pretty mad, but there wasn't much we could do about it. Next, Mary Mahoney began to see birds we weren't logging. The third week after we joined the Camp Hi-Wah Bird Study Circle, everybody except the poor, dumb Leader and a few backward but honest bird-lovers was logging the rarest birds seen around Camp Hi-Wah in twenty years. Bird walks developed into a race to see who could shout "Hark!" first and keep the rest of the little party in fidgety silence for the next five minutes.

The poor bird-walk Leader was in agony. Her reputation as a bird-lover was in shreds. Her talented pupils were seeing rare birds right and left, while the best she could log for herself would be a few crummy old redbirds and a robin or so. At last our Leader's morale collapsed. It was the day when nearly everybody in the study circle swore that she saw and heard a bona-fide nightingale.

"Where?" cried our Leader desperately, after the fourth nightingale had been triumphantly logged in the short space of five minutes. Heartless fingers pointed to a vague bush. The Leader strained her honest eyes. No notion of our duplicity crossed her innocent, unworldly mind.

"I can't see any nightingale," our Leader cried, and burst into tears. Then, full of shame, she sped back to camp, leaving the Camp Hi-Wah bird-lovers to their nightingales and guilty thoughts.

Eileen and I ate a hearty lunch that noon

because we thought we would need it. Then we strolled down Hiawatha Alley and hunted up Mary Mahoney.

"We will put the Iron Cross on you if you tell," Eileen started off, as soon as we found Mary.

"What's the Iron Cross?" Mary squeaked, startled out of her usual haughty poise.

"Never mind," I growled. "You'll find out if you tell."

We walked past Cabin Sitting Bull, past the flagpole, into the tall grass beyond the ball field.

"She'll tell," Eileen said finally.

"What'll we do?" I replied mournfully. "They'll try us at campfire tonight."

They did, too. It was terrible. We denied everything, but the Head of Camp, a mean old lady who wore middy blouses and pleated serge bloomers, sentenced us to no desserts and eight-o'clock bedtime for two weeks. We thought over what to do to Mary Mahoney for four whole days. Nothing seemed sufficiently frightful, but in the end we put the wart curse on her. The wart curse was simple but horrible. We dropped around to Cabin Sitting Bull one evening and in the presence of Mary and her allies we drew ourselves up to our full height and said solemnly in unison, "We put the wart curse on you, Mary Mahoney." Then we stalked away.

We didn't believe for a moment in the wart curse, but we hoped Mary would. At first she was openly contemptuous, but to our delight, on the fourth evening she developed a horrible sty on her eye. We told everybody a sty was a kind of a wart and that we had Mary in our power. The next day Mary broke down and came around to our cabin and apologized in choked accents. She gave Eileen her best hair ribbon and me a little barrel that had a picture of Niagara Falls inside it, if you looked hard enough. We were satisfied. □□

Discussion

1. **(a)** Describe how Ruth and Eileen behave during their stay in camp. **(b)** How do they justify their behavior?

2. **(a)** How do the sisters plan to escape from Camp Hi-Wah? **(b)** What happens to spoil their scheme?

3. **(a)** Why do the sisters finally turn to bird-watching? **(b)** Explain their attitude toward bird-watching as they begin to do it. **(c)** What happens to turn them into "the modest heroes of the Camp Hi-Wah bird walks"? **(d)** What results from their apparent success as bird-watchers?

4. What one victory do the sisters actually achieve during their stay at camp?

5. **(a)** What do you suppose Camp Hi-Wah thought of the McKenney girls? **(b)** How do Ruth and Eileen think of themselves? **(c)** Do you see them in the same way as they see themselves? **(d)** What overall impression does Ruth McKenney give you of Camp Hi-Wah?

6. **(a)** What is the tone of this selection? **(b)** What elements in the selection are clues to this tone?

Vocabulary
Context, Structure,
Pronunciation, Dictionary

Using context, structure, or the Glossary, determine the meaning and pronunciation of each italicized word. Then on your paper, write "true" or "false" in answer to the statements which follow.

1. After Ann and Janie left the party, theories were *rife* on where they had gone.

a. The vowel sound in *rife* is the same as the vowel sound in the word *stiff*.

b. Ann and Janie's leaving caused talk among the guests.

2. Old Mr. Quince's *chicanery* caused his family much grief.

a. *Chicanery* is accented on the first syllable.

b. Mr. Quince's family grieved because of his serious illness.

3. Molly may at times hurt people's feelings with her honesty, but she could never be accused of *duplicity*.

a. Molly is dishonest.

b. The accented syllable in *duplicity* rhymes with *miss*.

4. With a *contemptuous* look at the porter, Arianna picked up her luggage and walked through the doors.

a. Something the porter did pleased Arianna very much.

b. *Contemptuous* has three syllables.

5. After what seemed to her an *interminable* wait, Clara saw Tom hurrying down the stairs.

a. Clara felt that Tom kept her waiting too long.

b. The prefix in *interminable* is *inter-*.

Extension • Writing

In the story, Ruth and Eileen think of themselves as big and bad and fierce, but through her use of tone, author Ruth McKenney makes us see these characters as innocent and basically good girls, who are the more amusing for trying so hard to be Bad Sports.

How would the story be different if Ruth and Eileen were just like "all the other little campers" who *"loved* dear old Camp Hi-Wah"?

Pretend you are one of the other campers at Camp Hi-Wah. Write a letter home to your parents describing one incident from the story. Be sure to use a tone different from the overall tone of the selection.

Ruth McKenney

Ruth McKenney claims that it took her twenty years to learn how to spell the name of her home town—Mishawaka, Indiana. Growing up in Cleveland, Ohio, she and her sister Eileen must have been at least a little like the characters in this story, for they were once barred from Sunday school there. McKenney began her career in literature as a printer (she considers herself a pretty good one). Later, she moved on to become a feature writer for a New York newspaper; still later, she started writing books.

*Indescribably terrible things can happen
when you refuse to take the garbage out!*

Sarah Cynthia Sylvia Stout
Would Not Take the Garbage Out

Shel Silverstein

Sarah Cynthia Sylvia Stout
Would not take the garbage out!
She'd scour the pots and scrape the pans,
Candy the yams and spice the hams,
5 And though her daddy would scream and shout,
She simply would not take the garbage out.
And so it piled up to the ceilings:
Coffee grounds, potato peelings,
Brown bananas, rotten peas,
10 Chunks of sour cottage cheese.
It filled the can, it covered the floor,
It cracked the window and blocked the door
With bacon rinds and chicken bones,
Drippy ends of ice cream cones,
15 Prune pits, peach pits, orange peel,
Gloppy glumps of cold oatmeal,
Pizza crusts and withered greens,
Soggy beans and tangerines,
Crusts of black burned buttered toast,
20 Gristly bits of beefy roasts . . .
The garbage rolled on down the hall,
It raised the roof, it broke the wall . . .
Greasy napkins, cookie crumbs,
Globs of gooey bubble gum,
25 Cellophane from green baloney,
Rubbery blubbery macaroni,
Peanut butter, caked and dry,
Curdled milk and crusts of pie,
Moldy melons, dried-up mustard,
30 Eggshells mixed with lemon custard,

Cold french fries and rancid meat,
Yellow lumps of Cream of Wheat.
At last the garbage reached so high
That finally it touched the sky.
35 And all the neighbors moved away,
And none of her friends would come to play.
And finally Sarah Cynthia Stout said,
"OK, I'll take the garbage out!"
But then, of course, it was too late . . .
40 The garbage reached across the state,
From New York to the Golden Gate.
And there, in the garbage she did hate,
Poor Sarah met an awful fate,
That I cannot right now relate
45 Because the hour is much too late.
But children, remember Sarah Stout
And always take the garbage out!

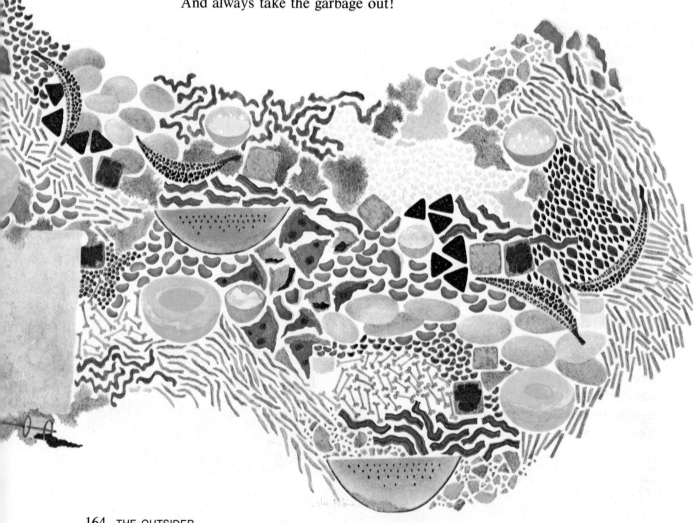

Discussion

1. Do you find this poem funny? Why or why not?

2. **(a)** Cite examples of exaggeration in the poem. **(b)** What effect is created by the exaggeration?

3. **(a)** "Potato peelings" and "brown bananas" are examples of combinations of words having the same initial sound. List as many as you can of two- and three-word combinations that begin with the same sound. **(b)** In your opinion do these combinations add to or subtract from the humorous effect?

4. **(a)** Words like "rotten," "sour," and "drippy" are used in the poem to describe food. List as many as you can of words like these. **(b)** What feeling do they arouse in you? **(c)** Choose a few of these words from your list and explain how they are especially appropriate to the foods they describe.

5. **(a)** Years ago stories written for children frequently showed "bad" or "naughty" boys and girls coming to horrible ends. Such stories always had a *moral,* or lesson, to teach young readers how they should or should not behave. Find such a moral in "Sarah

Cynthia. . . ." **(b)** Is the moral meant to be taken seriously in this poem, or not? Why do you think so?

6. **(a)** Why do you suppose the speaker does not tell what "awful fate" Sarah met, before giving the moral at the end? **(b)** In your opinion is the poem more or less effective because Sarah's fate is not told?

Extension • Writing

"Poor Sarah met an awful fate,
That I cannot right now
        relate. . . ."

What happened to Sarah? The speaker does not tell, but instead forces each reader to use his or her imagination to fill in the "awful" details. Use your imagination now to tell what did happen.

Take the first line above, "Poor Sarah met an awful fate," as your first line, and proceed from there. Poor Sarah does not have to die, of course; you may be able to think of several other "awful" possibilities. Write in paragraph form, using appropriate and effective descriptive words. Or, you may wish to write in poetic form. In that case, you can use the rest of the poem as a model, or you can follow your own form.

Try to relate Sarah's fate in terms "awful" enough to convince your readers to "always take the garbage out."

Shel Silverstein

Shel Silverstein keeps in touch with the contemporary scene. His songs—for which he writes both words and music—have made a hit with country/western and pop singers and their vast audiences. Before turning to writing songs and poetry, he was already widely known as a cartoonist, then as a writer and illustrator of children's books.

Silverstein travels a great deal all over the world, but when he is not wandering he lives on a houseboat off Sausalito, California, where he keeps a piano, a guitar, a saxophone, a trombone, and a camera. He is experimenting with all these things—"just to see if I can come up with anything"—and is planning to write a couple of plays, as well. He feels he is free to go wherever he pleases, do whatever he wants. "I believe everyone should live like that," he has said. "Don't be dependent on anyone else—man, woman, child or dog. I want to go everywhere, look at and listen to everything. You can go crazy with some of the wonderful stuff there is in life."

Moving Camp Too Far

Nila Northsun

i can't speak of
many moons
moving camp on travois
i can't tell of
5   the last great battle
counting coup or
taking scalps
i don't know what it
was to hunt buffalo
10 or do the ghost dance
but

i can see an eagle
almost extinct
on slurpee plastic cups
15 i can travel to pow wows
in campers & winnebagos
i can eat buffalo meat
at the tourist burger stand
i can dance to indian music
20 rock-n-roll hey-a-hey-o
i can
& unfortunately
i do.

J. R. Holland/STOCK, BOSTON

1. (a) What things does the speaker mention that she cannot do? **(b)** Why do you suppose she cannot do these things?

2. (a) What things does the speaker mention that she can do? **(b)** What is the difference between these things and the things she cannot do?

3. (a) What is the speaker's attitude toward the things she can—and does—do? **(b)** Why do you think she feels this way? **(c)** How does the title of the poem relate both to things the speaker does and to her attitude toward them?

Nila Northsun

Nila Northsun has published poetry in *Vagabond, Wormwood,* and *Pembroke* magazines, and is co-editor of the poetry magazine *Scree,* in Missoula, Montana. She is a member of the Shoshoni and Chippewa tribes.

notes and comments

Between Two Cultures

How to be an Indian in the twentieth century? How to be modern without destroying what is left of the Indian way of life? Over 800,000 native Americans today experience the problems of living between two cultures.

One way for Indians to identify with their heritage is to live on a reservation. There are more than 300 reservations in the U.S., ranging from one acre to the size of West Virginia. But life can be difficult on a reservation. Water supplies may be scarce, electricity and plumbing nonexistent. Unemployment rates are often very high. School facilities are sometimes inadequate. Or, students may attend boarding schools far from their homes.

Many reservations have organized their own schools and community centers—even their own small industries. Tourism has for years been a source of income, and some reservations are now building and staffing their own vacation resorts.

In the city, native Americans work at all kinds of jobs and live in all kinds of homes, maintaining their ancestral identity by attending annual tribal festivals or pow-wows.

Some have not fared so well in the city where they must pay rent—perhaps for the first time in their lives—wear different clothes, mingle with strangers, and handle a new vocabulary. Indian centers try to help ease this "culture shock."

Generally, Indian young people want what others want: a chance to work at a decent job, to raise a family, to live where they please, to pursue their own pleasures and ambitions. Those who find themselves growing away from the old culture still would not care to lose it completely. They know that if they reject their Indian heritage, they lose more than they gain. They realize that they are part of the American experience that started centuries before Columbus. Many simply want to get a good education, then go back to the reservation to work and live with their people.

There is certainly a resurgence of Indian pride in their ancestry and in their various tribal cultures. Native Americans today produce an astonishing variety of art, music, and crafts that are new and contemporary, yet rooted in native traditions. The tension between cultures has provided many Indians with new strength, new determination, and new directions.

Miss Lowy could get stirred up over beauty and truth and skylarks.
"Me," thought Jeanie, "I'd be glad to see some sky. . . ."

Beauty Is Truth

Anna Guest

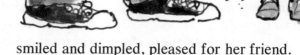

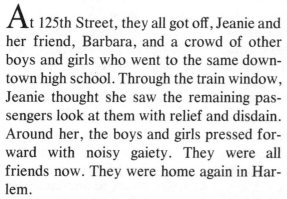

At 125th Street, they all got off, Jeanie and her friend, Barbara, and a crowd of other boys and girls who went to the same downtown high school. Through the train window, Jeanie thought she saw the remaining passengers look at them with relief and disdain. Around her, the boys and girls pressed forward with noisy gaiety. They were all friends now. They were home again in Harlem.

A tall boy detached himself from a group, bowed low and swept his cap before him in a courtly salute.

"Greetings, Lady Jeanie. Greetings, Barbara."

Jeanie bit her lip. Frowning, she pulled her coat closer and shrugged. Barbara smiled and dimpled, pleased for her friend.

"I told you he likes you," she whispered. "Look, he's waiting. Want me to go on ahead?"

Jeanie really was wasting an opportunity. Norman was keen. She saw Jeanie's head, slightly bowed and thrust forward. It was no use. She was an odd girl, but Barbara liked her anyway. The boy swung gracefully back to his group.

"Coming to the show tonight?" Barbara asked.

"No, I can't. I'm so far behind in my homework, I'd better try to do some before

"Beauty Is Truth" by Anna Guest from *Stories from Seventeen*.

they decide to throw me out." Jeanie still frowned.

"Want a Coke or something?" asked Barbara as they passed the big ice-cream parlor window, cluttered with candy boxes and ornate with curly lettering. They could see the juke box near the door and some boys and girls sitting down at a table. It looked warm and friendly.

Jeanie shook her head, one brief shake.

"I think I'll stop in. I'm awful thirsty," said Barbara.

Jeanie shrugged.

"So long then."

"So long."

She walked along the busy street, aimlessly looking in the store windows, turned the corner, and walked the few blocks to her house. Though it was chilly, each brownstone or gray stoop had its cluster of people clinging to the iron railings. Some children on skates played a desperate game of hockey with sticks that were not hockey sticks.

When a car approached, they did not interrupt their game until it was almost too late. Amid shouts from the driver and wild jeers from the children, the car passed, and the game was resumed in all its concentrated intensity.

Her little brother Billy was playing in front of the stoop with three or four other kids. They were bending over something on the sidewalk, in a closed circle. Pitching pennies again, she thought with repugnance.

She was going to pass them, and started up the three stone steps to the doorway. A window on the ground floor opened, and Fat Mary leaned out, dressed only in a slip and a worn, brown sweater.

"Now you're going to catch it, Billy Boy. Your sister's going to tell your mama you been pitching pennies again."

Jeanie did not pause.

Billy sprang up, "Hi, Jeanie. Jeanie, gimmie a nickel. I need a nickel. A nickel, a nickel. I gotta have a nickel."

The other little boys took up the chant. "A nickel, a nickel. Billy needs a nickel."

She threw them a furious glance and went in. Two little girls sat on the second landing, playing house. They had a set of toy dishes spread out on the top stair, and held dolls in their laps. She stepped over them, careful not to disturb their arrangements.

The kitchen smelled dank and unused, and the opening of the door dislodged a flake of green-painted plaster. It fell into the sink, with a dry powdering. A black dress someone had given her mother lay over the chair before the sewing machine. It reminded her that her sleeve had torn half out, dressing after gym. She really should sew it, but the sight of the black dress waiting to be made over made her dislike the thought of sewing. She would just have to wear her coat in school tomorrow. Lots of kids did.

She hung her coat on a hook in the room she shared with her mother, and stood irresolute. Her mother would be coming in soon, and would expect to find the potatoes peeled and the table laid. She caught sight of a comic book and, unwillingly attracted by the garish colors, read one side. "Ah!" she thought in disgust. "Billy!" She thought of her homework. She was so far behind in social studies that she could probably never make it up. It was hardly worth trying.

Mercantilism. The rise of the merchant class. She would probably fail. And gym, all those cuts in gym. Miss Fisher, her grade adviser, had called her down yesterday and warned her. "Ah!" she said again. Miss Fisher was all right. She had even been encouraging. "I know you can do it," she had said.

She sat down on the bed and opened her looseleaf notebook at random. A page fell out. She was about to jam it back in, when the freshly inked writing caught her eye. Today's English. Some poem about a vase, and youths and maidens. Miss Lowy had brought in some pictures of vases with people on them, dressed in togas or whatever they were, spinning and reading from scrolls. Why did everybody get so excited about the Greeks? It was so long ago. "Wonderful! Wonderful!" Miss Lowy had exclaimed. How could anybody get so stirred up over a poem? She meant it too. You could tell from her expression.

"Listen, boys and girls. Listen." A lifted arm enjoined them.

Beauty is truth, truth beauty,—
that is all
Ye know on earth, and all ye need
to know.[1]

There it was, copied into her notebook. Caught by something in the lines, she tried to find the poem in her tattered anthology, not bothering about the index, but riffling the pages to and fro. John Keats, at last—"On First Looking into Chapman's Homer." More Greeks. Here it was—"Ode on a Grecian Urn." The poem, all squeezed together in

---

1. *Beauty . . . know,* the concluding lines of "Ode on a Grecian Urn," by the English poet John Keats (1795–1821). The poem explores ideas inspired by pictures of men and women which decorate an ancient vase.

the middle of the page, looked dry and dusty, withered and far away, at the bottom of a dry well. She saw, not so much words, as an uninteresting, meandering pattern. The big THOU at the opening repelled her. She turned the page to find that the poem went on. Recognizing the last lines, she heard them again, falling so roundly, so perfectly, from the lips of Miss Lowy. She turned back to the beginning. Why "Grecian," why not "Greek"? With an effort, she began to dig the poem out of its constricted print.

Thou foster child of silence and slow time," its soft susurrus carried her on. She read the poem through to the end, trying to remember her teacher's cadences.

"Write about beauty and truth. Write about life," Miss Lowy had said.

She tore a page out of her notebook and opened her pen. Pulling over a chair, she rested her book on the sooty window sill. She stared out at the dusk falling sadly, sadly, thickening into darkness over the coal yards.

A crash of the kitchen door caused a reverberation in the window sill. The notebook slipped out of her hands.

"Where'd you get that bottle of pop?" she heard her mother's voice, hard and sounding more Southern than usual.

A high-pitched, wordless sniveling came in reply. "I asked you. Where'd you get that pop? You better tell me."

"A lady gave me a nickel. A lady came down the street and ask me—"

"You lying. I know where you got that money. Gambling, that's what you was doing."

"I was only pitching pennies, Ma. It's only a game, Ma."

"Gambling and stealing and associating with bad friends. I told you to stay away from them boys. Didn't I? Didn't I?" Her mother's voice rose. "I'm going to give you a beating you ain't going to forget."

Billy wailed on a long descending note.

Jeanie could hear each impact of the strap and her mother's heavy breathing.

"I want you to grow up good, not lying and gambling and stealing," her mother gasped, "and I'm going to make you good. You ain't never going to forget this." When it had been going on forever, it stopped. A final slap of the strap. "And you ain't going to get any supper either. You can go now. You can go to bed and reflect on what I told you."

He stumbled past her, whimpering, fists grinding into eyes, and into the dark little alcove which was his room. Jeanie heard the groan of the bed as he threw himself on it. She felt a pain in her fingers and saw them still pressed tightly around the pen.

Her mother appeared in the doorway. She wore her hat and coat.

"Come help me get supper, Jeanie. You should have got things started." Her voice was tired and tremulous, and held no reproach.

"I don't want any supper, Ma."

Her mother came in and sat down heavily on the bed, taking off her hat, and letting her coat fall open.

"I had a hard day. I worked hard every minute," she said. "I brought you something extra nice for dessert. I stood in line to get some of them tarts from Sutter's."

Jeanie rose and silently put her mother's hat on the shelf. She held out her hand for her mother's coat, and hung it up.

Together they opened the paper bags on the kitchen table. She set the water to boil.

As they ate in silence, the three tarts shone like subtle jewels on a plate, at one end of the chipped porcelain table. Her mother looked tired and stern.

"You better fix your brother up a plate," she said, still stern. "Put it on a tray. Here, take this." And she put on the tray the most luscious, the most perfect of the tarts. "Wait." She went heavily over to her swollen black handbag, took out a small clasp purse, opened it, and carefully, seriously, deliberately, picked out a coin, rejected it, and took out another. "Give him this." It was a quarter.

After the dishes were washed, Jeanie brought her books into the kitchen and spread them out under the glaring overhead light. Billy had been asleep, huddled in his clothes. Tears had left dusty streaks on his face.

Her mother sat in the armchair, ripping out the sides of the black dress. Her spectacles made her look strange.

"Beauty is truth," Jeanie read in her notebook. Hastily, carelessly, defiantly disregarding margins and doubtful spellings, letting her pen dig into the paper, she began to write: "Last night my brother Billy got a terrible beating. . . ."

Scramble to borrow the social studies homework from a girl in her homeroom, say hello to Barbara, undress for gym, dress again, the torn sleeve, bookkeeping—a blot, get another piece of ledger paper. "This is the third I've given you. You might say thank you." Get to English early. Slip her composition in under the others, sit in the last seat. Don't bother me. I am in a bad mood. Rows and rows of seats. Rows and rows of windows opposite. She could even read the writing on some of the blackboards, but who cared? A boy leaned far out of the window before closing it. Other heads turning. Would he fall? No, he was safe. Heads turned back. A poem about a skylark. From where she sat, she could see about a square foot of sky, drained of all color by the looming school walls. Miss Lowy read clearly, standing all alone at the front of the room in her clean white blouse and with her smooth blonde hair.

Miss Lowy, maybe you see skylarks. Me, I'd be glad to see some sky, she thought and nearly uttered it. Around her, students were writing in their notebooks. Miss Lowy was about to speak to her. Better start writing something. Sullen, Mr. MacIver had called her last week. She felt about for her notebook and pen. It had been a mistake to write as she had done about her brother's beating. They would laugh if they knew. Shirley, who was the class secretary, and Saul, with the prominent forehead. No, he would not laugh. He was always writing about space ships and the end of the world. No danger, though, that her story would be read. Only the best manuscripts were read. She remembered keenly the blotched appearance of the paper, the lines crossed out, and the words whose spelling she could never be sure of. Oh, well, she didn't care. Only one more period and then the weekend. "Lady Jeanie's too proud to come to our party. Jeanie, what are you waiting for? Jeanie's waiting for a Prince Charming with a red Cadillac to come and take her away." If Barbara asked her again, she would go with her, maybe. There was going to be a party at Norma's Saturday night, with Cokes and sandwiches and records and dancing, everybody chipping in. "Jeanie, I need a nickel. Mama, I need a dollar. I need, I need."

The bell rang, and the pens dropped, the books were closed with a clatter. She slipped out ahead of the pushing, jostling boys and girls.

Monday, Miss Lowy had on still another perfect white blouse. She stood facing the class, holding a sheaf of papers in her hand. Most of the students looked at her expectantly. Marion, who nearly always got ninety, whispered to her neighbor. Michael, who had but recently come from Greece—ah, but that was a different Greece—grumbled and shifted in his seat. He would have to do his composition over. He always did.

"I spent a very enjoyable time this weekend, reading your work," said Miss Lowy, waiting for the class to smile.

"Seriously, though, many of your pieces were most interesting, even though they were a trifle unconventional about spelling and punctuation." A smile was obviously indicated here too, and the class obeyed. She paused. "Sometimes, however, a piece of writing is so honest and human, that you have to forgive the technical weaknesses. Not that they aren't important," she said hastily, "but what the writer has to say is more significant."

The three best students in the class looked confused. It was their pride not to have technical errors.

"When you hear this," Miss Lowy continued, "I think you'll agree with me. I know it brought tears to my eyes." The class looked incredulous.

"It's called 'Evening Comes to 128th Street.' " Her face took on that rapt look.

Jeanie's heart beat painfully. She picked up a pencil, but dropped it, so unsteady were her fingers. Even the back of Shirley's head was listening. Even the classes in the other wing of the building, across the courtyard, seemed fixed, row on row, in an attitude of listening. Miss Lowy read on. It was all there, the coal yards and Fat Mary, the stoop and the tarts from Sutter's, Billy asleep with tears dried on his face, the clasp purse and the quarter.

"The funny part of it was, when I woke him, Billy wasn't mad. He was glad about the quarter, and ate his supper, dessert and all, but Mama never did eat her tart, so I put it away."

A poignancy of remembrance swept over Jeanie, then shame and regret. It was no business of theirs, these strange white people.

No one spoke. The silence was unbearable. Finally Marion, the incomparable Marion, raised her hand.

"It was so real," she said, "you felt you were right there in that kitchen."

"You didn't know who to feel sorry for," said another student. "You wanted to cry with the mother and you wanted to cry with Billy."

"With the girl too," said another.

Several heads nodded.

"You see," said Miss Lowy. "It's literature. It's life. It's pain and truth and beauty."

Jeanie's heart beat so, it made a mist come before her eyes. Through the blur she heard Miss Lowy say it was good enough to be sent in to *Scholastic*.[2] It showed talent, it showed promise. She heard her name called and shrank from the eyes turned upon her.

After school, she hurried out and caught the first train that you could catch only if you left immediately and did not stroll or stop the least little bit to talk to someone. She did not want to meet anyone, not even Barbara.

Was that Billy among the kids on the stoop?

"Billy," she called, "Billy."

What would she say to him? Beauty is truth, truth beauty?

"Billy," she called again urgently.

Billy lifted his head, and seeing who it was, tore himself reluctantly away from his friends, and took a step toward her. □□

---

2. **Scholastic,** literary magazine for high schools which periodically publishes student compositions.

Discussion

1. (a) What do you learn of Jeanie's personality from the story? (b) How is Jeanie different from her friends? (c) What causes this difference?

2. Find at least three details that create strong sense impressions of each of the following: (a) Miss Lowy's classroom; (b) 128th Street; (c) Jeanie's home.

3. (a) What kind of home life does Jeanie have? (b) Compare Jeanie's home life with the sort of things she is learning at school. (c) To what degree do her school studies apply to her home life, as far as Jeanie is concerned? (d) How does her home life affect her feelings toward school and the work she does?

4. (a) What is Jeanie's attitude or state of mind as she starts writing the essay? (b) What does she write about?

5. (a) What are Jeanie's feelings while Miss Lowy reads her essay aloud? (b) How do Miss Lowy and the students react to Jeanie's essay? (c) What causes them to react in this way?

6. The Keats poem that Miss Lowy reads—and the title of the story—states that beauty is truth, but it also states that truth is beauty. How is the idea that truth is beauty given meaning in this story?

7. (a) Why doesn't Jeanie want to meet anyone after school following the reading of her composition? (b) Has Jeanie learned anything from her experience that will influence her life? Explain your answer.

Vocabulary • Pronunciation

A. "Beauty Is Truth" contains a number of words with meanings you were probably able to get from context but with pronunciations that you may have had difficulty figuring out. Look up the words below in the Glossary and study their pronunciations in parentheses. Say each word softly to yourself several times.

> cadence
> irresolute
> meandering
> poignancy
> repugnance
> susurrus

B. Read the following sentences aloud in preparation for reading them to the class.

1. During the parade, the regular cadence of the drum helped the cadets to stay in formation.

2. He had sworn to stick to his diet, but, seeing the taco stand on one side of the street and the ice-cream parlor on the other, Charlie became irresolute.

3. While the rest of the group painstakingly searched the ground for arrowheads, Elsie and Victor went meandering off to pick wildflowers.

4. The poignancy of the scene between Anna and her son left Kelly in tears.

5. With a feeling of repugnance, Nate picked the snail from his arm and placed the little creature on a nearby rock.

6. The susurrus ended abruptly when the President appeared on the platform.

Extension • Writing

Choose a room in your own home to describe in terms that will give your reader strong sensory impressions of the place. First, list as many details as you can think of to appeal to sight, hearing, taste, smell, and touch.

Write a brief description of your room. You will have to choose details carefully from your lists in order to get the most effect, but you should include at least one detail to appeal to each of the senses.

Anna Guest

Anna Guest is a native of New York City, where she has lived all her life—except for a year she spent writing in Mexico. She took a very long time to write "Beauty Is Truth," she has commented, because she felt the story had to be just right—sensitive, yet real. For the story was based upon a real person, a girl who had writing talent, as Jeanie does in the story. Guest further commented that the real-life Jeanie liked very much the story based on her character.

It's "no place"—but it's home.

in the inner city

Lucille Clifton

in the inner city
or
like we call it
home
5 we think a lot about uptown
and the silent nights
and the houses straight as
dead men
and the pastel lights
10 and we hang on to our no place
happy to be alive
and in the inner city
or
like we call it
15 home

Discussion

1. What two places are being contrasted here?

2. Suggest some specific details appropriate to "uptown" which might explain why the speaker describes it in each of these ways: (a) "silent nights"; (b) "pastel lights"; (c) "houses straight as / dead men."

3. (a) How do the speaker and others ("we") feel toward the inner city? (b) Why do you think the speaker refers to the inner city as "our no place"? (c) Suggest specific details for the inner city which contrast with those in 2 (a), (b), (c) and which might explain the speaker's feelings toward it.

4. (a) The speaker says they "think a lot about uptown." What do you suppose they think regarding it? (b) Where would the speaker rather be—in the inner city or uptown? Why?

Lucille Clifton 1936 •

The ability to win out over life's troubles is a theme expressed in much of Lucille Clifton's poetry. Her straightforward poems, pared to essential thoughts, often exhibit her vigorous, sometimes mocking humor, while they affirm the vitality of black life.

In addition to her poetry and fiction for adults, Clifton has written several books of poetry for young people in which she combines her strong voice as a poet with her warm love and understanding of youth. These books have been received with great enthusiasm, and she has received awards from the National Endowment for the Arts. She is currently poet-in-residence at Coppin State College in Baltimore, Maryland, where she lives with her husband and six children.

See **POINT OF VIEW** Handbook of Literary Terms

Casey Young is 12 years old when her father, Barney, lands in the hospital, and she is sent to live with her maternal grandmother—called Paw-Paw—in San Francisco's Chinatown. Casey's mother died when she was very young, and Barney has always been a bit of a drifter, full of hopes and dreams that never seem to work out; therefore, Casey knows next to nothing of her Chinese heritage. She feels lonely and out of place—unable to cope with the language or the people in this strange world. In this excerpt from Child of the Owl, *Casey finally finds some small part of what she has been searching for.*

My True Name

Laurence Yep

Monday afternoon my father called—collect. I sat up in bed, telling the operator it was okay. "How're you doing, Barney?"

"Fine, Casey. Listen, tell your grandmother that I'll send her the cash to pay for this call. I'm really sorry about having to do it collect. But I didn't want you to forget what my voice sounds like."

"As if I could forget." I lay back down on the bed. "Got all your postcards. You've really been doing some traveling. I tried writing you but my letters never seem to catch up with you. The post office keeps sending them back saying you've moved already."

"Yeah." He laughed, but it sounded like a forced laugh. Barney sounded real tired and real down. "I'm kinda hard to keep up with. So don't forget to tell your Paw-Paw that I won't stick her with the bill."

"It's okay, Barney. I still got some money left. I can use that."

"That's great," Barney said, relieved. "I don't want to have your Paw-Paw pay for everything."

I tucked the receiver between my chin and left shoulder so I could put my hands behind my head. "Don't worry about it, Barney. We've been getting along just great so I don't think she'd mind."

In the background I could hear the sound of a jukebox yodeling out some country tune and voices laughing just a little too loud. "So you been having fun in Chinatown?" he asked.

"Sure. I just wish you were here to show me around this place like you did at the park."

"You gotta live your own life, baby."

"I just wish I knew what that was." I hadn't meant to say anything, but it just came out.

"Huh?"

"I mean, I'm not much like my mother, am I?"

"I never wanted you to be," Barney said a little sharply. "Hey, what's going on up there? Is your Paw-Paw riding you about the way you are?"

"No. No. She's been great. Honest. She said I oughta be myself. All I meant was that I didn't think I was as much of a help to you as my mother."

"What would you know about that?" he demanded. "Let's just forget it, baby. It's in the past."

"But I can't forget, Barney. It's real important to me." My voice rose a little. "There's a difference between forgiving what happened and just forgetting. You can't run away from the past. I want to know what it means to be Chinese."

"I raised you to be an American." Barney sounded annoyed.

"Well, I'm a Chinese-American then," I argued.

"You said you're having a good time in Chinatown. Were you telling me the truth?"

"Not exactly." I wound the telephone cord around my index finger and then unwound it. "I'm getting along better than I did before, though."

"What's the matter? You too different than the others?"

"Kinda. But it's only going to be a few more months till summer, Barney. Then we'll be back together again just like always."

"I'll see what I can do about making it sooner, baby. I promise."

I clutched at the receiver. "Barney, don't do anything crazy. I can manage. Honest."

"I know you can, baby. You been carrying me all these years, so that's why I owe it to you to get you out of Chinatown as soon as I can." Barney paused. "Well, bye now."

"Barney—" I began but he had already hung up.

That Saturday I was sitting on the steps. Some of Paw-Paw's friends had had their social-security checks stolen right out of their mailboxes. The mailman wouldn't give me our mail because he didn't know me so I had to wait till he put all the mail in the boxes. Then I got out my key and lifted up the little door to our box and found the tan envelope with Paw-Paw's check and a plain white envelope as well that someone must have stuck in there since I got Friday's mail. I managed to pull at one loose corner of the envelope flap and rip it open. Inside was a five-dollar bill, no note. Just five dollars. I stood there puzzled for a while, but then I figured that this is what Barney must have meant when he said he'd see what he could do. I guess Barney must have one friend in San Francisco who would loan Barney the money and even bring it to me.

I tried to think of what to use the five dollars for. Finally, I decided it'd be nice to have a good Chinese dinner. Most of the time we made do without much meat because Paw-Paw could take a quarter pound of flank steak and cut it so thin that it seemed like you were getting a lot. She'd add that to vegetables and a clove of garlic and a piece of ginger—to kill off the bugs and germs in the vegetables—and fry all of it at high heat in oil, her face intent on the steam rising, and the oil hissing and crackling. Or she could take chicken and cut it into pieces and cook it in special sauces—like one she made out of soy sauce and anise and other herbs and spices—so that you wanted to put the gravy on the rice and eat that too. You wound up filling up on rice that way rather than on meat—but Paw-Paw always grumbled that her gravies were never as good as they used to be since the stores couldn't get things from the mainland. At any rate, I thought Paw-Paw would like part of a duck like she said once when we were walking back from the movies.

I went into Paw-Paw's favorite delicatessen at the upper end of Grant. It was actually a combination grocery store with fresh vegetables in crates set outside on the sidewalk. I walked down the row of crates, picking out some *bok choy* with long celerylike stems, broad leaves of a deep, almost bluish green, and little yellow flowers. The short-stemmed ones were the tenderest, Paw-Paw said. In a dry year, though, even the short stems would be tough for lack of water—or so Paw-Paw swore.

Then I went inside the store, where a counter occupied one corner. Behind the chest-high glass pane lay a row of steel pans heated by steam underneath. And each of the pans was filled with some dish: balls of ground fish and black, pungent mushrooms; cashew chicken with tender chicken breasts cut up into bite-size chunks and cashews cooked in oil so they were soft and button mushrooms and maybe baby corn—the kernels about the size of a pinhead and the whole cob as long and thick as my little finger. And skewered overhead would be slabs of barbecued spareribs waiting for the knife, or sometimes pieces of barbecued pork, their ends burnt black and tasting sweet and salty at the same time and the meat a bright red inside. Most of the time Paw-Paw just bought a little of the cheap things—stuff that she couldn't make herself or stuff that wasn't worth the bother of making for just two people.

At the moment there was only one clerk on duty, a tall, thin young man with pale skin and a round, impatient face. Paw-Paw always came to this place but she had always done the ordering—I'd just been along as a pack mule. And suddenly I realized that I didn't know much more than the names of the things. I just had to hope that he spoke some English.

A lady waddled up next to me—a fat, round lady, her hair cut short and curled tightly around her head. Her pasty jowls sagged and her buckteeth, one of which was gold, showed all the time. With her bulging shopping bags in either hand, she took up enough space for three people. The clerk ladled some sliced abalone and asparagus into a cardboard container. He dipped the ladle with a languid air—like you'd expect from some rich lady reaching into her box of chocolates. And when the clerk finished with the first customer, she started rattling off an order in Chinese.

"I think I was next," I said.

The clerk glanced at me and then at the lady, tapping the tray with one of the big spoons. With his other hand he picked up an open container from the ones stacked near him. The lady went on trying to order, waving her hand imperiously at the clerk.

I tapped her arm. "Excuse me, but I think I was next."

In a loud voice, the lady started to scold me—at least I think she did, but for all I knew she might have been reciting all the names in the Hong Kong telephone directory. Then she turned to the clerk and gave him her order again. This time he grunted and began to fill up the container for her. I suppose I should have just kept my mouth shut but it was the principle of the thing— her rudeness and the clerk's willingness to go along with her—that got me.

I reached over the steel shelf at the top of

the glass pane and grabbed at the clerk's arm.

"Hey, I was here before she was."

He only shrugged, pulling his arm free, and went on serving her.

At that moment a short, stocky, middle-aged man bustled over in a grease-stained tan smock. There was a little paper cap on his head and a toothpick dangled from between his teeth.

"What you want?" he asked. "I take care of you."

"I'd like half a roast duck."

"Oh-kay." He made the word sound like a song. He took a duck off a hook where it hung in the front window. Its juices had congealed on its fat, round bottom into small, white beads on the red-brown skin. He plopped that down on a cutting board to one side of the trays but still behind the glass pane. In one smooth motion he picked up a meat cleaver and brought it down with a solid meaty thwack that cut the duck's breast almost in half. Another heavy blow cut the lower part of the duck. Then he placed the cleaver along the neck and head and applied pressure gently with his fist on top of the blade, so that the bones crunched as he cut the rest of it in two. One half he laid to one side.

Jom ah? he asked.

"Excuse me?"

The young man snickered.

The man in the cap made chopping motions with his cleaver. "You want cut up?"

"Yes, please."

"How many pieces? Four? Eight?"

"Eight will be fine." I held up my fingers to be sure he understood.

It only took him a few expert cuts, the cleaver meeting the cutting board with loud *thunks* and spattering grease against the glass pane. Then he used the front of his cleaver—where the point would be on a knife—to scoop the duck into a cardboard container. On top of the pieces he ladled some juice and closed the flaps, saying something in Chinese.

I felt very self-conscious at that moment. And it didn't help any that the young man was snickering again. It must have seemed ridiculous to them that someone wouldn't know how to count out money or be able to pronounce *duck.* What I really felt like was a tourist.

"Excuse me?"

"That be one dollah and five cents," he said.

I'd made everything out to be ninety-five cents. But I figured he was adding on a dime because I couldn't speak Chinese. "It ought to be a dime less."

"Restaurant tax," the man said smoothly.

"My Paw-Paw said it was already figured into the price." I handed him the five dollars.

The young man rolled his eyes toward the ceiling while the middle-aged man muttered something. He went to a beat-up wooden cash register and banged the keys savagely. He slapped my change down on the little steel shelf on top of the glass pane. "All right. All right. I not charge sales tax then."

Well, I suppose the man had to save some face. I scooped the money into my hand and stuffed it into my pocket. "Thanks."

Still muttering to himself, the man slipped the container into a paper bag and handed it to me. I started for the street but the woman with the shopping bags was waiting for me. There was no way I could get past her. Between her bulk and her shopping bags, she filled the doorway.

"Excuse me," I said to her loudly, "I'd

like to get through."

But the woman started to shout at me.

I shouted right back at her. "I'd like to get through if you're finished."

But the woman didn't budge; she went on shouting—and not even looking at me. It was almost as if she were shouting at the world in general. Outside, people started turning their heads and even stopping to watch. I could feel the blood rushing to my face. I don't think I'd ever felt more embarrassed in my life—like one of those nightmares where you're suddenly naked in a crowd. I felt like the guilty person—not for demanding my rights but for being unable to speak Chinese so I could argue with the woman. I stood there stupidly.

At that moment the middle-aged clerk came out from behind the counter and took my arm, pulling me back into the store. "She like that. Doan mind her. Always shout. She f.o.b."

"What?"

"Fresh off the boat."

The young clerk leaned against the cash register, his arms folded, smirking broadly and enjoying the spectacle of the woman in the doorway.

The middle-aged clerk picked up an old towel and began wiping at the grease on the steel shelf. "Back in China," he explained, "all the time people they gotta push and push because things so crowded. They come over here. They doan understand they supposed wait their turn."

"Somebody ought to explain to her how things work over here," I said self-righteously.

"She go outside Chinatown, somebody have to. But in Chinatown why she need change?" The middle-aged man shrugged and I understood that I was the invader, the rude one, not her.

A lot of people lived in Chinatown because, like Paw-Paw, they wanted to. But there were a lot of people who would have liked to live away from Chinatown if they could only speak enough English. Since they couldn't, they were stuck here, paying high rents for tiny apartments, even though they might have been able to get apartments of the same size some blocks away—that's assuming that the landlords would be fair-minded and rent to Chinese, and more landlords were being fair nowadays. And those same Chinese couldn't get good-paying jobs for the same reason they couldn't move out of Chinatown so they wound up washing dishes and doing all the other dirty jobs in Chinatown and getting underpaid because they didn't even know what they ought to be earning.

Lucky for me a man in glasses came down one of the aisles. In his hands he had a clipboard of pink inventory sheets. He flipped one of them up and began studying his shelves, making check marks by the things that needed to be reordered. "She's blocking the doorway, Jack. Get rid of her."

He must have been the owner of the store because the middle-aged clerk immediately walked back to her. He shouted at her and for a moment it was fifty-fifty who could outshout the other but since the woman had already been shouting for five minutes and was getting hoarse, the clerk won. He repeated himself again loudly and pointed at her bags. The woman immediately twisted her head to look suspiciously in either direction and said something loud, not to me, but to the crowd who had gathered behind her. She glared around at them and then waddled forward in a slow, shuffling walk, taking nothing but small half steps, and all the while she twisted her head this way and that as if she expected trouble at any moment.

"What did you tell her?" I asked him.

"I tell her she better watch bags or someone take something while she busy talking." He wiped his hands on the towel as he walked around behind the counter.

It finally hit me that even though I looked Chinese and had learned some of the myths and a little bit of the language, I'd never really fit into Chinatown the way that my mother had. I couldn't even be like her in being Chinese.

Trying to spend the rest of the five dollars proved just as tough—when I went to the restaurant to order some chicken chow mein, the waiter couldn't understand me too well when I said it and he brought out a carton of that junk they feed to the tourists—you know, where the noodles are fried hard and crispy like potato chips— when what I wanted was the soft, wet kind the Chinese ate. And it took a little while arguing with the waiter before he went back and got what I wanted. As I was leaving I heard him use a phrase I'd heard Mr. Jeh use: "Native-born, no brains."

And I had more trouble when I went to get some *gai bow*—those are white buns about the size of my fist in which chicken and eggs and some pieces of barbecued pork are all cooked together. I ordered four of them and held up four fingers as well.

"Nothing else?" the owner asked.

"No, that's all."

"Okay, I get them." He went into the kitchen and I could hear the voice of a woman—it probably was his wife—rise above the clanging of pots and pans. I wasn't sure but I heard him say the Chinese word for *four* and I heard her say the word for *two*. He argued a little bit more and she said something in a sharp way. He came out looking very meek with a paper bag in his hand. "Sorry. All we got is two."

It was a small enough thing to happen and I don't mean to sound like a whiner but that day a lot of small things happened to me and they had built up inside, so that I felt like shouting as loudly as the woman and I was likely to suspect everyone. I took a chance and lied. "Just because I talk English doesn't mean I don't understand some Chinese. You've got plenty of them back there but you don't want to sell them to me unless I buy a lot of other stuff."

From the way his face flushed, I was sure I was right. He looked embarrassed and angry at the same time. "All we got is two I tell you and you're lucky to get these."

I should have known better than to call him a liar to his face. If I had asked him to count again or maybe told him I wanted them for my Paw-Paw, he might have given me what I wanted, but he needed some excuse. Now he wouldn't change his mind no matter what happened. I took the two and paid for them, feeling hot and frustrated inside and thinking that if I had ordered in Chinese, they might have given me what I wanted, or at least explained the situation to me. But to them I was an outsider.

Somehow Paw-Paw kept herself from laughing—how, I'm not sure. I know now that you order *bow* for brunch or lunch, *chow mein* for lunch, and rice and duck for dinner. It was a bit like serving up ham and eggs, a hamburger, and turkey with stuffing, all at the same time.

All Paw-Paw did when she saw the spread on the table was to stand in the middle of the room and stare. "Where did all this come from?"

So I proudly told her about the five dollars Barney had someone leave in our mailbox.

"You should have saved it," Paw-Paw scolded me good-naturedly.

"This is what Barney would have wanted." I held her coat while she slipped one arm out of a sleeve and then, half turning, slid her other arm free.

She sniffed appreciatively at the different dishes. "I was expecting leftovers." She sat down a little stiffly on her chair today because the cold damp had gotten to the rheumatism in her knees and elbows. "I can't remember when I had duck last." I brought in tea from the pot in the kitchen and set it down in the middle.

"Was it a long day at the shop?"

"Always the same. But the cloth they give us to work with gets shabbier and shabbier and some of the young ones, they don't take much care on the seams. I pity the person who buys one of the dresses they sew."

I dished some fluffy white rice into a rice bowl for Paw-Paw and then added some to a plate for myself. The steam rose from the rice, carrying a light, sweet scent. When I sat down on my stool, Paw-Paw shook her head. "Everything looks so good I don't know where to start."

"Don't just load up on rice now. *Hek soong.*" Meaning that she should eat from the side plates as well. Paw-Paw started to spoon a piece of neck onto her plate.

"No, come on, Paw-Paw." I used a serving spoon from another dish and put a meaty piece of breast on the small plate at her place.

Paw-Paw poked it with the serving spoon she had been using. "You take it."

"No, there's another meaty piece right there."

"That's the . . . the . . ." Paw-Paw hunted for the right word. "The bottom. It'll be mostly fat and that's what I like." Deftly she switched pieces. "The fat's where all the juices collect."

I picked at my piece. "You sure?"

"Of course."

I felt warm inside at being able to load the table this way with so much food. It's funny but I'd heard all those jokes about mothers who pile food onto people's plates and for the first time I felt I understood why they did that—not that I felt like getting into the hassle of cooking or wandering around in an apron; but it was nice just to be able to feed someone you liked. Only there was something incomplete about the dinner and it took me a moment to realize what it was.

So maybe I couldn't be much like my mother had been; maybe I couldn't even be as Chinese as her. But somehow I think she would have agreed with Paw-Paw when she told me to be myself. I think my mother would have liked me not for imitating her but for being what I was and that meant I couldn't turn my back on being Chinese—no matter what Barney had said.

I put down my fork and went back into the kitchen to get a pair of chopsticks and a bowl. When I got back to the table, I tilted up my plate so the rice slid into the bowl.

"You don't have to do that, you know," Paw-Paw said.

My shoulders sagged a little. "Will I look too stupid?"

"Oh, no, no," Paw-Paw said. "It's just that you should be able to eat in comfort."

"I know," I said, "but I want to learn."

"Well, then," Paw-Paw picked up her chopsticks. "You have to think of the chopsticks as two long fingers growing out of your hand. You hold the bottom chopstick between these fingers." She held up her hand so I could see the chopstick was near the first joints of her middle and fourth fingers and held there rigidly. "You keep this one straight. It's the top chopstick you move around." She held the other chopstick between the tips of her thumb and index finger and she showed me how easily she moved it around. "Don't let the parts above your hand cross over and don't squeeze things either. You don't have to press too hard. That's important to remember." To show me, she lifted up the piece of duck, slippery in its own juices, from her plate and then put it back down.

I tried to lift the piece of duck from my plate. On the fourth or fifth try, I managed to lift it halfway before it fell down. Dinner was going to take a long time.

"Very good." Paw-Paw beamed. She ladled some vegetables and sauce from another bowl on top of her rice. "Now you lift your rice bowl like this." She put her thumb on the top rim of the bowl and her fingers on the bottom rim of the little base of the bowl. "That way," she explained, "you don't really feel the heat of the bowl." She lifted it up toward her mouth in her left hand. "And you put the rice into your mouth." She angled the chopsticks at the tips so they were like a little paddle and with a shoveling motion, she pushed small amounts of rice into her mouth.

"I feel just like a kid again," I said apologetically. "I mean, I have to learn how to eat all over again." When I tried to use the chopsticks, I felt awkward. Paw-Paw did not laugh at me—even though dinner took twice as long as usual.

Afterwards, while we were doing the dishes, I glanced over at Paw-Paw, who wore an apron of green on a bright red background. "Paw-Paw, what's my name?"

"You know your name, girl."

"No, I mean my Chinese name."

"She came to me on her . . . let me see." Paw-Paw looked at the wall for a moment. "Yes, on her thirty-fifth birthday, to tell me the news. I was so surprised. And she told me, 'Mama, pick out the prettiest name you can. I won't pick out an American name until she has her Chinese name.' That's what she said."

"Well, what's my name?"

"*Cheun Meih,*" Paw-Paw said. When she said the words, they didn't sound like funny noises anymore. They sounded a little like singing. "It means Taste of Spring."

"Teach me how to say my name."

"Yes, of course." And we practiced it until I could sing my own name. My first name. My real name. My true name. □□

Discussion

1. (a) What qualities of Casey's personality do you learn from the things she tells about herself? (b) Do her actions and her treatment of other people support or contradict what she tells about herself? Explain.

2. What relationship has developed between Casey and Paw-Paw in the relatively short time Casey has lived with her?

3. (a) What are Casey's reasons for wanting to learn more about herself and her Chinese heritage? (b) What specific aspects of Chinese life does she learn about in this excerpt?

4. (a) Describe the fat lady's aggressive behavior. What reason does the clerk give for her behavior? (b) What moment of superiority over a "foreigner" does Casey allow herself? (c) What does Casey finally learn from this encounter? (d) What conclusions does she come to about Chinatown and the Chinese people there?

5. In traditional Chinese culture, "saving face"—not being caught in an embarrassing situation—is important. (a) Describe the two incidents in this excerpt that relate to saving face. (b) How might these incidents have been different if Casey had used a different approach in the first place?

6. (a) What amusing error does Casey make through her ignorance about Chinese food? (b) How does Paw-Paw react to Casey's attempts to learn about Chinese culture? (c) What con-clusions does Casey come to about herself as a Chinese-American?

7. Mention specific details and descriptions that might have been different if this story had been told from the point of view of one of these other characters: (a) the fat lady customer; (b) the middle-aged clerk; (c) Paw-Paw.

Vocabulary • Context

There are different kinds of context clues. Occasionally an author will tell directly—through an explanation or definition—what a word means. This is often done with foreign words that the author feels will be unfamiliar to the reader.

For example, when Casey picks out some *bok choy* (bok choi), the author first explains that it is in crates with fresh vegetables and then states that it has "long celerylike stems, broad leaves of a deep, almost bluish green, and little yellow flowers."

Each of the following Chinese words or phrases has similar explanations. Copy each on your paper, then find it in context in the selection. After the word, copy as much of the context as you need to explain what it means. Include indirect context clues as well if there are any present.

1. *"Jom ah?"* (jom ä)
2. *gai bow* (gā bou)
3. *chow mein* (chou mān)
4. *"Hek soong"* (hək sūng)
5. *Cheun Meih* (chyun mā′)

Extension • Speaking

Have you ever found yourself "the outsider" in a situation where you didn't know the language, the people, or the culture?

Describe for the class the situation and your reactions to it. What was the point of greatest misunderstanding? Did anyone offer help? Do you find it amusing now? What—if anything—did you learn from your experience?

Laurence Yep 1948 •

Laurence Yep was able to draw on his own experiences in writing *Child of the Owl,* the novel from which "My True Name" was taken, for he is a native of San Francisco and has known what it means to be an outsider. In his words: "I was raised in a black ghetto but commuted to a grammar school in Chinatown . . . so that I did not really meet White Culture until I went to high school. In a sense I have no one culture to call my own since I exist peripherally in several. However, in my writing I can create my own."

Which would you rather be?

Identity

Julio Noboa

Let them be as flowers,
always watered, fed, guarded, admired,
but harnessed to a pot of dirt.

I'd rather be a tall, ugly weed,
5 clinging on cliffs, like an eagle
wind-wavering above high, jagged rocks.

To have broken through the surface of stone,
to live, to feel exposed to the madness
of the vast, eternal sky.
10 To be swayed by the breezes of an ancient sea,
carrying my soul, my seed, beyond the mountains of time
or into the abyss of the bizarre.

I'd rather be unseen, and if
then shunned by everyone,
15 than to be a pleasant-smelling flower,
growing in clusters in the fertile valley,
where they're praised, handled, and plucked
by greedy, human hands.

I'd rather smell of musty, green stench
20 than of sweet, fragrant lilac.
If I could stand alone, strong and free,
I'd rather be a tall, ugly weed.

"Identity" by Julio Noboa, Jr. from *The Rican*, Journal of Contemporary Puerto Rican Thought, Spring, 1973. Reprinted by permission of the author.

Julio Noboa (hü′lē ō nə bō′ə).

Discussion

1. (a) Who is "them" in line 1? (b) What does "always watered, fed, guarded, admired, / but harnessed to a pot of dirt" suggest—in human terms—about the lives of these people?

2. Describe the kind of life the speaker is wishing for himself in lines 4–22. How does it contrast with the kind of life referred to in lines 1–3?

3. (a) In what sense might "madness" be a quality of the "vast, eternal sky" (lines 8–9)? (b) *Bizarre* means "strikingly odd; fantastic." How does the speaker seem to regard this abyss, or depth, into which he might be carried (line 12)? (c) Why might the human hands mentioned in line 18 be called "greedy"?

4. (a) Lines 21–22 suggest that the speaker wishes to be a weed because only that way can he achieve something else. What does the speaker *really* want? (b) Does the price he is willing to pay for what he wants seem to you too much? Explain your answer.

Julio Noboa, Jr. 1949 •

A native of the Bronx, New York, Julio Noboa now lives in Chicago, where he is studying educational anthropology and working as a leadership trainer with the Latino Institute.

A former editor on *The Rican, Journal of Contemporary Puerto Rican Thought,* Noboa writes poetry in both Spanish and English. His poems have been published in *The Rican* and in *Revista Chicano-Riqueña.* He reads his poetry for high-school and college classes in literature and the humanities and for poetry workshops. As a member of Los Otros Poetry Collective, he works with young people to develop their writing skills and to perform their works.

About "Identity," Noboa comments, "The whole poem is essentially a search for my individuality—finding myself as a person as opposed to being one of the crowd. It has to do with a sense of definition: what specific things make you a person unlike anybody else?"

3: The Outsider

CONTENT REVIEW

1. Each selection in this unit features a main character who is in one way or another an "outsider" to his or her environment. For each character listed below, first identify the way in which that character is an outsider in the selection, then explain how the character reacts to that environment—becomes part of it, remains a stranger to it—or what.

(a) Fiona Farmer in "Nancy."

(b) Richard Wright in "Hunger."

(c) Eileen and Ruth in "A Loud Sneer for Our Feathered Friends."

(d) The speaker in "Moving Camp Too Far."

(e) Casey Young in "My True Name."

(f) The speaker in "Identity."

2. Tone plays an important part in several selections in this unit. Find one or more selections that express each of the following tones. In each case what effect does the tone have on the selection?

(a) angry, scornful

(b) silly, ridiculous

(c) sad, regretful

(d) proud, firm

3. Point of view is a useful way to get information across to the reader, but it also limits the kind of information the reader will get. Explain how these selections would be different if they were written from different points of view:

(a) If Mary Mahoney were narrator in "A Loud Sneer," so she could tell "her side."

(b) If "Hunger" were written in the third person omniscient, so you could know the thoughts of Mrs. Wright.

(c) If "Sarah Cynthia Sylvia Stout" were written in the first person, so she could defend herself or explain her actions.

Unit 3, Test I
INTERPRETATION: NEW MATERIAL

Read the following poem, then on your paper write the answers to the questions. You may refer to the poem when necessary.

The Nomad Harvesters
Marie de L. Welch

The nomads had been the followers of flocks and herds,
Or the wilder men, the hunters, the raiders.
The harvesters had been the men of homes.

But ours is a land of nomad harvesters.
5 They till no ground, take no rest, are homed nowhere.
Travel with the warmth, rest in the warmth never;
Pick lettuce in the green season in the flats by the sea.
Lean, follow the ripening; homeless, send the harvest home;
Pick cherries in the amber valleys in tenderest summer.
10 Rest nowhere, share in no harvest;

Pick grapes in the red vineyards in the low blue hills.
Camp in the ditches at the edge of beauty.

They are a great band, they move in thousands;
Move and pause and move on.
15 They turn to the ripening, follow the peaks of seasons,
Gather the fruit and leave it and move on.
Ours is a land of nomad harvesters,
Men of no root, no ground, no house, no rest;
They follow the ripening, gather the ripeness,
20 Rest never, ripen never,
Move and pause and move on.

1. In the first stanza, the narrator contrasts two groups. These two groups are **(a)** followers and wild men; **(b)** hunters and raiders; **(c)** nomads and harvesters; **(d)** harvesters and men with homes.

2. Nomad harvesters are people who **(a)** harvest crops but have no permanent home; **(b)** follow flocks and herds; **(c)** farm the land and pay others to harvest the fruits and vegetables; **(d)** live in tents which they carry with them.

3. Which of the definitions that follow comes closest to defining *lean* as it is used in line 8? **(a)** bend or turn a little; **(b)** slant; **(c)** thin, not fat; **(d)** put in a leaning position.

4. In line 8 the harvester's situation is described as the opposite of what seems expected or appropriate. This is an example of **(a)** symbolism; **(b)** plot; **(c)** irony; **(d)** tone.

5. (a) What causes the harvesters to pause? **(b)** What causes them to move on?

6. The tone of this poem could be described as **(a)** light-hearted; **(b)** sorrowful; **(c)** humorous; **(d)** positive.

Unit 3, Test II
COMPOSITION

Choose any *one* of the following to write about.

1. In "Moving Camp Too Far," the speaker mourns the passing of his or her true heritage. The speaker of "in the inner city" stoutly defends his or her "home" and background; and in "My True Name" Casey tries to find out more about her heritage. With which person do you feel you have more in common? Write a few paragraphs on one of the following: **(a)** traditions that were once a part of your background but are no longer practiced by you and your family; **(b)** traditions you and your family carry on; **(c)** aspects of your heritage which you would want to know more about.

2. Imagine that ten years after the events described in "Nancy," Fiona and Darlene meet at a high-school social event. Describe this meeting—not only how the girls look and dress, but how they respond to each other. (You might try writing a dialogue between the two, and then have yourself and a classmate take parts and read this dialogue for the class.)

3. In "Beauty Is Truth," why was Jeanie's composition so successful? (Review page 173, especially Miss Lowy's comments in 173a, 2 and 173b, 7.) Try writing for your teacher and classmates a composition that fits those standards.

Courage comes in many ways—

taking dangerous chances to save a life;

giving up something for the good of others;

refusing to call it quits despite the odds;

accepting the challenge of what needs to be done.

Here are some people who have what it takes

to be called **HEROES**

She raced her pony right into the midst of the battle—and the enemy!

Where the Girl Saved Her Brother

Told by Strange Owl

Almost exactly a hundred years ago, in the summer of 1876, the two greatest battles between soldiers and Indians were fought on the plains of Montana. The first fight was called the Battle of the Rosebud. The second battle, which was fought a week later, was called the Battle of the Little Big Horn, where General Custer was defeated and killed. The Cheyennes[1] call the Battle of the Rosebud the fight *Where the Girl Saved Her Brother.* Let me tell you why.

But first let me explain what is meant when an Indian says, "I have counted coup." "Counting coup" is gaining war honors. The Indians think that it is easy to kill an enemy by shooting him from ambush. This brings no honor. It is not counting coup. But to ride up to an enemy, or walk up to him while he is still alive, unwounded and armed, and then to hit him with your feathered coup stick, or touch him with your hand, this brings honor and earns you eagle feathers. This is counting coup. To steal horses in a daring raid can also be counting coup. But one of the greatest honors is to be gained by dashing with your horse into the midst of your enemies to rescue a friend, surrounded and unhorsed, to take him up behind you and gallop out again, saving his life by risking your own. That is counting coup indeed, counting big coup.

1. **Cheyennes** (shi enz′), tribe of Algonquin Indians whose homeland originally was Minnesota.

Well, a hundred years ago, the white men wanted the Indians to go into prisons called "reservations," to give up their freedom to roam and hunt buffalo, to give up being Indians. Some gave in tamely and went to live behind the barbed wire of the agencies, but others did not.

Those who went to the reservations to live like white men were called "friendlies." Those who would not go were called "hostiles." They were not hostile, really. They did not want to fight. All they wanted was to be left alone to live the Indian way, which was a good way. But the soldiers would not let them. They decided to make a great

surround and catch all "hostiles," kill those who resisted, and bring the others back as prisoners to the agencies. Three columns of soldiers entered the last stretch of land left to the red man. They were led by Generals Crook, Custer, and Terry. Crook had the most men with him, about two thousand. He also had cannon and Indian scouts to guide him. At the Rosebud he met the united Sioux[2] and Cheyenne warriors.

The Indians had danced the sacred Sun Dance. The great Sioux chief Sitting Bull had been granted a vision telling him that the

_____
2. *Sioux* (sü), nation or confederation of tribes living on the plains of northern United States and southern Canada.

soldiers would be defeated. The warriors were in high spirits. Some men belonging to famous warrior societies had vowed to fight until they were killed, singing their death songs, throwing their lives away, as it was called. They painted their faces for war. They put on their finest outfits so that, if they were killed, their enemies should say, "This must have been a great fighter or chief. See how nobly he lies there."

The old chiefs instructed the young men how to act. The medicine men prepared the charms for the fighters, putting gopher dust on their hair, or painting their horses with hailstone designs. This was to render them invisible to their foes, or to make them bulletproof. Brave Wolf had the most admired medicine—a mounted hawk that he fastened to the back of his head. Brave Wolf always rode into battle blowing on his eagle-bone whistle—and once the fight started, the hawk came alive and whistled too.

Many proud tribes were there besides the Cheyenne—the Hunkpapa, the Minniconjou, the Oglala, the Burned Thighs, the Two Kettles[3]—and many famous chiefs and brave warriors—Two Moons, White Bull, Dirty Moccasins, Little Hawk, Yellow Eagle, Lame White Man. Among the Sioux was the great Crazy Horse, and Sitting Bull—their holy man, still weak from his flesh offerings made at the Sun Dance—and the fierce Rain-in-the-Face. Who can count them all, and what a fine sight they were!

Those who earned the right to wear war bonnets were singing, lifting them up. Three times they stopped in their singing, and the fourth time they put the bonnets on their heads, letting the streamers fly and trail behind them. How good it must have been to see this! What would I give to have been there!

Crazy Horse of the Oglala shouted his famous war cry, "A good day to die, and a good day to fight. Cowards to the rear, brave hearts—follow me!"

The fight started. Many brave deeds were done, many coups counted. The battle swayed to and fro. More than anybody else's, this was the Cheyenne's fight. This was their day. Among them was a brave young girl, Buffalo Calf Road Woman, who rode proudly at the side of her husband, Black Coyote. Her brother, Chief Comes-in-Sight, was in the battle too. She looked for him and at last saw him. His horse had been killed from under him. He was surrounded. Soldiers were aiming their rifles at him. Their white Crow[4] scouts circled around him, waiting for an opportunity to count cheap coups upon him. But he fought them with bravery and skill.

Buffalo Calf Road Woman uttered a shrill, high-pitched war cry. She raced her pony right into the midst of the battle, into the midst of the enemy. She made the spine-chilling, trilling, warbling sound of the Indian woman encouraging her man during a fight. Chief Comes-in-Sight jumped up on her horse behind his sister. Buffalo Calf Road Woman laughed with joy and with the excitement of battle. Buffalo Calf Road Woman sang while she was doing this. The soldiers were firing at her, and their Crow scouts were shooting arrows at her horse—but it moved too fast for her or Chief Comes-in-Sight to be hit. Then she turned her horse and raced up the hill from which the old chiefs and the medicine men watched the battle. The Sioux and Cheyenne saw what was being done. And then the white soldiers saw it too. They all stopped fighting

3. **the Hunkpapa** (hungk′pa′pə), **the Minniconjou** (min′i kon′-jü), **the Oglala** (ōg lä′lə), **the Burned Thighs, the Two Kettles,** all tribes of the Sioux.
4. **Crow** (krō), tribe formerly living in Montana; traditional enemies of the Cheyennes and Sioux.

and just looked at that brave girl saving her brother's life. The warriors raised their arms and set up a mighty shout—a long, trilling, undulating war cry that made one's hairs stand on end. And even some of the soldiers threw their caps in the air and shouted "Hurrah" in honor of Buffalo Calf Road Woman.

The battle was still young. Not many men had been killed on either side, but the white general was thinking, "If their women fight like this, what will their warriors be like? Even if I win, I will lose half my men." And so General Crook retreated a hundred miles or so. He was to have joined up with Custer, Old Yellow Hair, but when Custer had to fight the same Cheyennes and Sioux again a week later, Crook was far away and Custer's army was wiped out. So Buffalo Calf Road Woman in a way contributed to the winning of that famous battle too.

Many who saw what she had done thought that she had counted the biggest coup—not taking life but giving it. That is why the Indians call the Battle of the Rosebud *Where the Girl Saved Her Brother.*

The spot where Buffalo Calf Road Woman counted coup has long since been plowed under. A ranch now covers it. But the memory of her deed lives on—and will live on as long as there are Indians. This is not a fairy tale, but it is a legend. ☐☐

Discussion

1. (a) What does the narrator wish to emphasize by ending this account with the statement, "This is not a fairy tale, but it is a legend"? (b) Find evidence in the telling of the story that reveals the narrator's feelings of pride in the Cheyenne people.

2. Explain the difference between "counting coup," "counting cheap coup," and "counting the biggest coup."

3. (a) What circumstances led to the Battle of the Rosebud? (b) What impressions do you get of Buffalo Calf Road Woman during the battle? (c) What peril does she face as she enters the battle? (d) How did her deed affect military history, according to Strange Owl?

4. (a) What kind of hero does Buffalo Calf Road Woman represent? (b) Why is it important that the memory of her deed live on, as Strange Owl says it will?

Extension • Writing

You have been chosen to prepare a historical marker to commemorate the spot where Buffalo Calf Road Woman counted coup. Write a hundred words or less for the marker. What facts would you include? What illustration would be appropriate?

Richard Erdoes

Richard Erdoes, artist, photographer, and writer, first made contact with the Indians of the Southwest as an outgrowth of a painting assignment. Since then he has spent much time "listening to Indian friends telling the tales and legends of their people—stories told around a fire, drinking thick, black coffee and eating berry soup with frybread, or while driving in a car a hundred miles to a tribal pow-wow. . . ."

Erdoes explains that stories such as this one, told to him by Strange Owl, "are handed on from the older generation to the younger. It is all done by word of mouth—the art is in the telling, the pleasure in listening. Each speaker is an individualist telling the story in his own way. Some legends are sacred, and whoever relates them will make an effort to tell the story just as he heard it from his grandfather, in the same words if possible. . . . Some stories die because there is nobody left to tell them and nobody to remember. Luckily that does not happen very often."

It was maddening! He was stuck
only sixty feet from the mouth of the cave.
But if no one reached him, he would die there.

Caught in a Grip of Stone

Jack Markowitz

Hinckley Reservation, twenty miles south of Cleveland, is a unit of that city's Metropolitan Parks System. Its gentle landscape is typical of northeastern Ohio. In the fall, on weekends, thousands of families drive out "to see the leaves." Maple, oak, sour gum, and sassafras glow in every shade of gold and scarlet under towering green nets of Norway pine and spruce. Ripe walnuts in their green sacs fall on the blacktop with a gentle clunk.

Pleasant as Hinckley is to the eye, the great attraction it offers is Whipps Ledges —giant outcroppings of sandstone left by the last Ice Age.

Like a pile of giant gray bones the Ledges rear up in places one hundred feet above a wooded ravine. It takes rope and piton, and climbers of experience, to scale their steepest walls of bare stone—yet just a few yards away children and even older folks clamber over cracks and up gentler brushy slopes to the very top.

In the past, some eighty feet up on this tumble of earthbones, like a dark eye in the skull, stared Wild Cat Cave. The name was pure romance; actually its black interior harbored no wild animals of any kind.

On a certain autumn Tuesday, with no weekend crowds to hear him, Morris Baetzold was the cave's only living creature. He had it all to himself for twenty frantic minutes.

The easy way out was not for Morris. With two friends from the Methodist Children's Home of Berea, Ohio, he already had explored the safe part of the cave. Even little children were able to penetrate back to the "room" where (so went the popular legend) runaway slaves had been hidden before the Civil War. This was a space ten feet square and just high enough to allow the three boys—all fifteen years old—to sit up. It gave them a grand crawl of the flesh to snap off the flashlight and to make themselves sit in the utter dark and silence, breathless and oppressive as the grave.

The boys then crept out of the "room" single-file with Morris in the rear. They came to a stone slab on the right which, like a valve, blocked the crossing of the main and a side passage. Thirty-five feet ahead the cave exit shone wide as a door. The first two boys brushed off their jeans and leaped out into the sunlight.

Morris, however, lingered by the fallen slab. It was a massive piece of stone, about six feet square and two feet thick: it must have weighed tons. A thousand, maybe a million years ago, it had cracked out of the cave ceiling. Resting at an angle, the slab offered just two dark triangular openings into the side passage. The tighter of these was fifteen inches on a side, and right down on the cave's floor.

On sudden impulse Morris slithered in there, all five feet eight and 110 pounds of him. He had tried a few feet of the passage before. It intrigued him.

It was pitch dark behind the slab, and chilly—the constant 55 degrees of dead spaces in stone. But the passage was six feet high and a yard wide and Morris could stand in it. Too bad his pals had the flashlight!

Still, he wasn't scared. He wanted to do something strictly on his own. There was, he was convinced, another room down this passage, leading to a second exit: it seemed to him he had heard that somewhere— anyhow he felt sure of it. The thrill of finding it on this trip would be uniquely his.

And so Morris advanced, his hands carefully feeling along the cold stone walls as he went and his feet gingerly testing forward. It was not until he had made considerable progress that Morris Baetzold, at 11 A.M. on Tuesday, October 5, 1965, understood how much he had dared. By then, though, he was screaming for help.

His absence was discovered when his school bus was about to return to the children's home. Presently a search party returned to Wild Cat Cave. From a point below and to the left of a massive stone slab the earth seemed to have acquired the terrified voice of a boy.

"Don't worry, lad, we'll get you out!" teacher William Powell bellowed into the darkness.

A student with a flashlight squeezed behind the slab. The passage, it was observed, descended at a 15-degree angle, and its ceiling sloped down even more sharply. As a result, fifteen feet below and away from the slab, what started as a corridor narrowed down to a V-shaped fissure, a mere crack, about four and a half feet high. It was eighteen inches wide at the top, just half of that at the floor.

Ten feet in there—into the crack—on the bottom, lay Morris.

Caught in a "V" of stone, he was wedged tightly at his chest and hips. He had toppled on his side, trapping his right arm underneath him. His left leg wriggled toward his pals; his face was out of sight in the far darkness.

He had scratched with his left hand till his nails were broken and bleeding, but he could not reach any handhold by which to lift himself. He was as good as paralyzed. The movements he was able to make were squirmingly ineffective—except to wedge him deeper and tighter into the unrelenting stone.

Teacher Powell wasn't about to let any

other boy squeeze in there! Someone ran down a quarter-mile to the nearest road and flagged a park ranger. Within minutes an alarm was alerting both the police and volunteer firemen in Hinckley village two miles away.

Volunteer Bob Whitehead was among the first at the scene. Whitehead was wiry enough to worm behind the slab. But neither he nor any of the other volunteers could get into the tightest part of the fissure. That even a boy could—much less *would*—squeeze in there strained belief. One man muttered, "A kid has to want to get into that kind of mess."

The best the early volunteers could do was to poke a two-by-four wooden plank along the bottom of the fissure and try to raise the boy on this lever. But Morris was too far down and in. There was no fulcrum, no way to get leverage, though Whitehead and others sweated and grunted in the dim, bruising space behind the slab for some time.

They did, however, push a thin red hose as far in as possible towards Morris. Soon the hiss of compressed oxygen made the air more breathable.

Still, two and a half hours went by and the best help Bob Whitehead could stretch out to Morris was reassuring words. "We'll get you out," he said, "we're working on a lot of things. It's only a matter of time."

When he finally emerged for a break in the mid-afternoon sunlight, Whitehead blinked in amazement. A crowd!

An appeal was out for strong, small-bodied volunteers to help extract a 15-year-old boy from a cave. This message brought to Whipps Ledges hundreds of individual body types combined, as often as not, with some exotic notion of how best to achieve a rescue. The news media picked up the scent.

By 5 P.M., as thousands of commuters streamed out of Cleveland and Akron, their car radios told of a boy trapped, by then, for six hours.

That evening, as it happened, Hinckley's garden club ladies were to serve their annual dinner for the police and volunteer firemen. Some of the latter, astonished that "the kid hadn't been got out yet," stared blankly at the empty tables at the dinner and then drove out to Whipps Ledges. Everybody else seemed to be there.

The traffic of feet in the sandy bed of the cave entrance stirred up clouds of dust. It drifted back to the men laboring in the passage and even reached the wretched trapped boy, making him sneeze and cough. Police Chief Ronald Ciammachella finally had to order reporters, cameramen and scores of others getting in the way back— "Back!" They were roped off at fifty feet.

One skinny fireman was able to stretch far enough in to throw a lasso over Morris's lower left leg. But the boy wasn't wearing a belt and when the others back in the passage started hauling, Morris never moved. Only his pants did. The rope merely pulled on the trouser leg.

As the sunny day darkened into clear, chilly night, coffee and donut wagons appeared. Volunteers' wives brought heavy coats. Fires were lighted, blankets went around shoulders. On the darkening slope little groups talked gravely of the boy's danger.

But for hundreds the vivid fires, the roar of the power generator which illuminated the cave entrance up on the Ledges, the newsmen intoning solemnly to microphones and cameras: all this pulsed with the drama of a nationwide sensation unfolding. People wanted to be part of it. Only the cold of night, which would end with frost whitening the autumn brilliance, finally would drive the curious and the benignly useless back along the shrouded roads to home and TV set.

The struggle in the cave went on. Morris managed to catch a rope-end tossed to his left hand stretched behind him. But as the men hauled on the rope his hand was twisted behind his back and he had no strength to hold it.

Later, firemen extended a steel hook on a long pole. Morris caught the hook and inserted it in the collar of his simulated-leather jacket. When rescuers pulled on a rope attached to the hook, the boy seemed to rise slightly. Then his jacket tore and the hook ripped free, striking a spark off the stone wall.

Morris broke down. "You'll never get me out," he cried. "I'm gonna die here!"

Mr. and Mrs. Andrew Ulrich were watching the news on television in their home at North Royalton, a Cleveland suburb. Ulrich was a husky, round-faced man with a broken nose and a grin that almost pinched his eyes shut. He was a tool grinder at an automobile engine plant in the city. They had eight sons. Disciplined and sure of themselves, these kids might be able to help at the cave, Ulrich thought. His wife wasn't sure. The news reports made great mention of the variety of experts and gear already on hand. "We'd only get in their way," she said. And her husband agreed this made sense.

In fact, by then a Cleveland mining company was preparing to bring up a thirty-six-inch drilling rig. This could gouge a shaft twenty-five feet down from the top of the Ledges to a point somewhere in front of the trapped boy. But it would be used only as a last resort. Mysterious stresses web through a rock structure: hit one nerve of weakness and tons of rock might collapse.

The mining men urged that a trained cave rescue team be summoned from the National Speleological Society[1] in Washington. Fire Chief Paul Chodera got on the phone and by 3 A.M., famed spelunker[2] William Karas and his crew arrived by Air Force jet with a splendid assortment of ropes, straps and clamps . . . but no one skinny enough to reach Morris and hook the lad up.

A nurse from Akron tried. Five feet two and eighty-five pounds, with ropes slung to her belt, she strained to within two feet of the boy—and then dissolved in claustrophobic panic. She had to be pulled out.

It was a maddening situation. In actual walking distance this boy was no farther than sixty feet from the mouth of the cave! And so much help was on hand. There was a volunteer welder, able to fabricate any sort of metal hook or tool ordered; several carpenters rigging up devices of wood; a doctor from the town; the muscle power of any number of men; and cave experts who had pulled spelunkers and miners out of dozens of deeper, more complicated scrapes. If only this boy had fallen with his head toward, rather than away from, his rescuers. Or if he had more than one hand free. Or a belt on. Or even clothing sturdy enough to hold a hook. Somehow these disabilities and mischances had to be overcome.

"I guess we considered—at least talked about—a hundred different schemes during the night," Deputy Fire Chief Bob Mentzer recalls. Some were wildly impractical: to try to force the rock walls apart with jacks; to rig up the hardware of an overhead garage door and pick the boy up and out like a haunch of beef. There wasn't even a way to

---

1. **National Speleological** (spḗ/lē ə loj/ ə kəl) **Society,** organization dedicated to the study, exploration, and preservation of caves and related phenomena.
2. **spelunker** (spi lung/kər), person who explores and maps caves.

get food or drink to Morris. It was a disspiriting night, whose only comfort came in the brief periods the exhausted boy dozed off.

Next morning at 6:30 Andrew Ulrich turned his radio to the news. The boy in the cave was still trapped. Eighteen hours! It was like a slap in Ulrich's face.

Could his boys help? Michael, fifteen, and Gerald, twelve, were both small, sturdy fellows. An hour later he and his boys were clambering up to the cave at Whipps Ledges.

The "circus atmosphere," as he saw it— all the cameras, vehicles and crowds in what looked like almost a festive mood—repelled him. Quietly he asked to see someone in charge, but he was possibly the four or five hundredth man to ask that and for an hour or more no one paid much attention to him.

Some thought already had been given to using younger volunteers, but the authorities quailed at the risks. What was to keep an inexperienced kid from also getting trapped? But a certain modest firmness about Ulrich and his sons impressed the firemen and spelunker Karas. There was no bluff about these people. And if the father himself was volunteering the boys, well . . . .

The choice fell on Gerald, the younger. First Andrew Ulrich had to sign a release of liability.

Gerry Ulrich, a blond, cheerful boy, stood four feet eleven in his shoes and weighed eighty-two pounds. With two ropes running from straps around his chest and waist, he crept into the passage. His father, too chunky to get around the stone slab, watched from an opening, biting his lip.

Gerry made unprecedented progress. Able to stand nearly upright in the fissure, he got to within six inches of the trapped boy's foot. Morris's spirits leaped. "Is there anything I can do to help?" he begged. "Just tell me."

Then something happened which Gerry Ulrich, even years later, was at a loss to explain. He could not bring himself to lean down.

The boy blubbering on the floor, miserable in that dim, suffocating enclosure, looked like a snarled, smothering fish. Suddenly gasping for air, Gerry cried to be pulled out. Disgustedly the firemen hauled him back. That's what came of using a kid! But Andrew Ulrich gathered his boy up in a bear hug and held him tight till he grew calm again.

Andy wasn't daunted. "Why don't you try the other guy?" he said.

The "other guy" didn't talk much. Michael Victor Ulrich was blond and intense, with pale blue eyes. He studied what was happening with his lips drawn to a tight line above a small, firm chin. He had had some First Aid training as an Eagle Scout.[3] Normally 135 pounds, he would have been husky for his five feet seven, if he had not trained down to 120 to prepare for wrestling.

While Bill Karas was briefing him, Mike took off his jacket to reduce his bulk. That left him in a cotton shirt, trousers, shoes and socks. He had on a strong belt. To this, at his left side, a rope was tied. A nylon strap went around his chest and another rope trailed from that, under his left arm. But that wasn't all. Mike stowed a nylon strap and a metal clamp in his left trouser pocket. And one more strap went inside his shirt. He held the two long ropes that trailed back from him in his left hand, to keep them up out of the way. Plenty of hardware—now if he could keep it all straight and still move.

He started into the fissure. Two feet in, the ceiling drew so low and the side walls so

---

3. *Eagle Scout,* name given to signify the highest level of achievement in the Boy Scouts of America.

tight, he could neither stand nor stoop. So he began easing himself down toward his right side by pushing both hands against one wall and arching his back against the other. While changing handholds as he lowered himself, he would take a deep breath and lock himself in place between the walls.

The boy's self-control and patience impressed the men peering in after him. He finally worked himself down parallel to the floor of the fissure, his head lower than his feet, his right hand down—down at all times!—for support. He would *dive* in on top of Morris, but he wasn't going to rest on that squeezed floor, not for a minute. It was vital to stay out of that vise.

He progressed by emptying his lungs and simultaneously heaving himself up and ahead with his right hand—an inch, two inches at a time—then, with another deep breath, locking himself in place between the walls. Then heave and lock again. It was a weird kind of "swim," and torturously slow. At times, laying down the trailing ropes, he could find skimpy holds with his left hand, briefly taking some weight off his right. At no point was the fissure sufficiently wide to let him bring either hand between his body and the black, pressing walls.

It took Mike ten minutes to move eight feet. But at last he was looking down on Morris Baetzold's ankles.

From back in the passage men poked battery lamps into the fissure as far and as high as they could. There was no real help for it, though: Mike's position inevitably blocked most of the light. He would have to work on Morris in his own shadow.

It must be stressed that he could not use his right hand. That was needed strictly for support. He could only use his left, and that only by reaching over and past his own face and head. Still, little by little he was able to work Morris's trousers down, down, past the boy's knees.

Then Mike drew one of the straps Bill Karas had given him from his pocket and awkwardly passed the strap around Morris's left leg, three inches above the knee. Now the hard part: slipping the end of the strap through the buckle with just one hand. But he did it. And then he tightened the strap on Morris's leg.

All the while he talked to Morris, "It's only a matter of time and you'll be out," Mike said, unconsciously giving echo to words Morris had heard again and again for nearly twenty-four hours.

Back in the passage the men were breathlessly silent, too tense to realize how close the air had become, or how crowded the passage with grimy, weary bodies. Mike wiped the sweat from his eyes and dried his left hand on his shirt. Then he unhooked one rope from himself and passed about twelve inches of it through the strap above Morris's knee. Another tricky task: knotting the rope one-handed. Somehow he managed that, too, and then, as the final step, tightened the strap further as Karas had told him to.

For the first time in a full day, something concrete had been achieved—one tight strap around Morris Baetzold's knee, and a rope to pull on it.

That was that. It had taken Mike another ten minutes to work on Morris. His supporting right hand had put in plenty of service already and felt as though pierced by a swarm of hot and cold needles. But it had to stand up for another ten minutes of retreat from the fissure, a reverse "swim," coming out backwards. And it did. Mike did have to be helped to his feet, though. He was that cramped.

The men in the passage wasted no time. A crewman of Karas's picked up the rope from Morris's leg and leaned into the crack as far as a man could. He put the rope up across his shoulder—to provide some lift—and the others started hauling from behind him.

Morris Baetzold budged. Two inches. And no more!

They weren't *raising* the boy, that was the trouble. He had to be lifted up—UP—not just dragged in the bed of the fissure. If anything, he would wedge tighter. There had to be some way of getting elevation!

Bill Karas, looking almost ashamed, walked over to Mike Ulrich resting beside the stone slab. The kid was still massaging his arm. It must feel plenty cramped, Karas guessed. But look here, if Mike took a few minutes more to rest, did he think he could . . . ?

That was enough for Andy Ulrich. He had to step outside. After the suffocating suspense of the cave, daylight came as a shock. There was sunshine out there, blue sky, trees stirred by the wind! And people: hundreds of them among the brilliant foliage and the tumbled boulders of the slope, gazing up at the cave, waiting to cheer a life saved (or would they—depressing thought—be as morbidly satisfied by a life lost?).

How could it be that one life merited so much attention? Every week a thousand die on the roads and others unnumbered in hospitals, by illness, natural disaster, old age. These, however, are too many and past help. The heart cannot absorb such numbers: it stiffens to them. But one life on the razor's edge, able to fall either way, draws on the nerves of each of us. . . .

Back on top of Morris Baetzold's ankle, Mike Ulrich now knew better what had to be done. First he opened the strap on Morris's left thigh. Hauling on the rope had slid it down to the knee. Then Mike circled the strap around *both* of Morris's legs, three inches above the knees. The pulling rope stayed attached.

The critical question was whether there was something, some sort of projection, that could give the hauling rope some *lift*. With his left hand, Mike felt up along the rough rock wall. He put his hand up, over, across. Yes! There was an outcropping. No bigger than a fist, but it might do.

Mike pulled out the strap he had stowed in his shirt and with his left hand—and his *teeth*—he worked the strap's end through the buckle and drew it to an 8-inch loop. This he hung on the projecting rock. Now he took the metal clamp from his trouser pocket. It was shaped like a letter C. This he connected from the loop around the rock to the hauling rope. It would act as a pulley, providing an almost straight-up force on Morris's legs.

Mike's return squirm took another ten minutes. Once again he couldn't stand without help. He limped over beside the stone slab to stretch out.

The tension in the passage was all but unbearable. The men who would haul on the rope couldn't seem to get the sweat off their hands. They rubbed their pant legs. Should they give the rope a real jerk—or pull easy? "Easy, easy," Karas cautioned. And they started pulling. Nobody breathed. The rope tightened up over the leg of the C-clamp, tightened, tightened some more . . . .

Suddenly Morris Baetzold's hips swung up out of the wedge of rock. "It's working," he cried, "it's working!" He was able to pull his right arm out from under his body. He could use both hands! The men kept pulling till Morris's bare legs were almost up even with the loop around the projecting rock.

But something was wrong. Only the bot-

tom part of his body was moving. He was still wedged at the chest. It was as if his breastbone were hinged in the stone. Still stuck! Bill Karas looked down at the game boy resting by the stone slab. How could anyone ask him to volunteer even once more?

On his third trip into the fissure, Mike Ulrich once again worked with his left hand and teeth and made a slip loop in a second long rope. He pushed this loop out across Morris's free left hand and head. Then with groaning difficulty the trapped, exhausted boy inserted his newly-freed right arm up through the circle of rope and worked it down on his torso just below the shoulders.

Mike removed the C-clamp from the rope to Morris's legs and transferred it to the new rope at the shoulders. Object: to dislodge the upper part of Morris's body.

Once more Mike checked and tightened the other ropes and straps, he hoped for the last time. And then he made one more—this time, agonizing—return trip out of the fissure. A fourth would be just physically impossible.

This time the rescue team was taking no chances. Karas put every chip he had on the table. Through a hose extended on a long pole, a gallon of a slippery glycerine solution was dumped on Morris. Volunteer Curtis Peck, of Akron, then shoved a narrow greased board under the boy. They'd *lubricate* him out of there!

The men met resistance as they started hauling on the rope to Morris Baetzold's shoulders. "Pull," said Bill Karas, "pull!" Morris groaned as his chest and back scraped stone, but there was more joy than pain in it. He swung upward. His chest was free! No time to cheer yet. More timbers were stuffed in under the greased board beneath Morris. These would keep his body

from sagging while being drawn out. At all costs he had to be kept suspended where the fissure was a foot or more wide. And slowly, carefully, the men, no longer tired, pulled on the ropes and on the greased board.

It was 1:30 P.M., Wednesday, October 6, 1965, when Morris Baetzold, cramped, skinned, a great black bruise on his left cheek, and staring vacantly in shock, was brought again into the sunlight. Cameras and microphones floated at him out of a dazzling sky which hurt his eyes; police struggled and shouted to hold people away from his stretcher, while cheer after cheer rose up.

Six years later; another sunny October day; and a reporter went searching for the life that had been saved. Morris Baetzold recovered quickly in a hospital, but he left the Methodist Children's Home a year later. A friendly chaplain at the Home hadn't heard from him in some time. Possibly he would get in touch again, possibly not. That was how it was sometimes with boys from the Home.

At Hinckley Reservation the usual Sunday crowd was clambering over Whipps Ledges. But Wild Cat Cave ended in a solid wall. Within twenty-four hours of the rescue, on police orders, it had been dynamited and sealed forever.

In North Royalton, Mike Ulrich, newly home from a tour of duty in Germany with the Army, was planning marriage. He was still spare and tough, but no more talkative. "There was too much hassle about it. It happened a long time ago," he said. And it was all he would say.

His genial parents suggested, apologetically, that the front-page fame which had come to Mike at fifteen, the Boy Scout and press awards and honors from community groups, had pleased him at first, but ultimately repelled him. To be called "Mike the hero" by jocular classmates was less desirable than it sounds.

He had never even shown his fiancée what, for one of another temperament, would have been a prized possession. His mother had to dig it out dusty from behind a shelf full of knick-knacks and school mementoes.

It was a bronze medal three inches in diameter. On one side it bore the likeness of Andrew Carnegie[4] and the words, Carnegie Hero Fund, Established April 15th, 1904; and on the reverse, a motto beginning, "Greater love hath no man than this[5]. . . ." □□

---

4. *Andrew Carnegie* (1835–1919), U.S. steel manufacturer and philanthropist. (See also Notes and Comments on page 206.)
5. *"Greater . . . this."* The complete quotation is "Greater love hath no man than this, that a man lay down his life for his friends." (John 15:13)

Discussion

1. Contrast the description of Whipps Ledges and Wild Cat Cave with the description of Hinckley Reservation. What is the effect of this contrast?

2. (a) How does Morris get wedged in? (b) Why is his situation so serious?

3. (a)What attempts do the volunteer firemen make to rescue Morris? (b) After two and a half hours, what are the only positive results of all the rescue attempts? (c) What results do the public appeals for additional volunteers have?

4. (a) How does the description of each new attempt— from the fireman with the lasso to the nurse—add to the build-up of suspense? (b) Cite some of the reasons the narrator gives for stating finally (on page 199), "It was a maddening situation."

5. (a) Why does Andy Ulrich feel that his sons might be able to help? (b) Why do you think Gerry Ulrich asked to be pulled out when he was so close to the trapped boy? (c) Compare Andy Ulrich's reactions to Gerry's failure with those of the volunteer firemen.

6. (a) What impression of Mike Ulrich do you get from the narrator's descriptions? (b) What technique does Mike use to approach the trapped boy? (c) Would you call Mike's first effort a failure? Explain.

7. When Andy Ulrich steps outside the cave, he is shocked by the crowd waiting for news. Do you agree or disagree with the narrator's explanation for the spectators' intense interest? Why?

8. (a) Summarize what is accomplished by Mike Ulrich's second and third journeys into the fissure. (b) How is the waiting rescue team able to help?

9. (a) How do Mike's parents, six years later, explain their son's reluctance to discuss his heroism or to display his medal? (b) Do Mike's reactions seem understandable to you? How would you have behaved under similar circumstances?

Extension • Writing

You are the headline writer on a large Cleveland, Ohio, newspaper. A reporter is calling in stories about what is happening at the rescue site, Wild Cat Cave. Write an attention-getting headline, using at least 7, but no more than 10 words, for each of these stories:

1. Covering events that occurred during the first two and a half hours (198a,4).

2. Including events up to Morris's breakdown (199a,3).

3. Highlighting events up to the end of Gerry's attempt (200b,2).

4. Reporting events up through the freeing of Morris's legs (202b,5).

5. Covering events of the final rescue (204b,1).

Jack Markowitz

Jack Markowitz has made a career of journalism, from reporting to writing a daily business column, and has received several awards for excellence in reporting and writing. He works currently for the *Post-Gazette* in his native Pittsburgh, Pennsylvania. To do research for this and other accounts of heroism, Markowitz made use of the actual records of the Carnegie Hero Fund investigations. His book, *A Walk on the Crust of Hell,* tells these true stories and explores the motives that ordinary people have for their heroic actions.

notes and comments

The Carnegie Hero Fund

Carnegie Hero Fund Commission

Andrew Carnegie (1835–1919) was a U.S. iron and steel manufacturer who used part of his great wealth to help establish free public libraries and to aid educational institutions, scientific research, and other work for the public good. In 1904 he established the Carnegie Hero Fund Commission to give financial aid to persons injured while performing heroic lifesaving acts and also to the dependents of heroes who lost their lives on such occasions.

Each year the Commission awards medals in bronze, silver, or sometimes gold, and as much as $1,000 in cash, depending on the act of heroism. But deciding who is to receive an award is not at all a simple matter. Every day thousands of people find themselves in danger of losing their lives, and many are saved. What makes a particular act heroic?

The Commission assigns an investigator to each case reported to determine as exactly as possible what did take place. Most of these investigators have never actually seen anyone risk his or her life in such an act. Instead they must rely on facts—sometimes gathered months or even years after the event—such as descriptions of where the act took place, measurements, reports of weather conditions, etc. They also interview the rescuer and the person rescued, and eyewitnesses, if any can be found. The investigator must determine quite specifically whether or not the hero had risked his or her life—and knew it at the time.

The Hero Fund Commission then determines from the reports of the investigators whether each act warrants a Carnegie award.

While investigators are not supposed to try to reenact deeds of courage, still they frequently find themselves in unusual and hard-to-reach places doing remarkable things. In order to examine sites of rescue, investigators have gone to the top of a grain elevator by conveyor belt, to an Alaskan island by fishing boat over choppy seas, and into neighborhoods and countryside where they were not welcome as strangers.

Sometimes the investigator must use skillful interviewing to get the facts. Some people have to be tactfully drawn out. Rescuers sometimes feel a sense of guilt that they didn't accomplish more, or that too much is being made of what they did do. Some rescuers have been so modest that by withholding information they have effectively blocked any effort to honor them.

When they heard the whisper "Moses is back again,"
the daring handful of slaves tied up some ashcake and salt herring
in their bandannas and waited for the signal. . . .

from Harriet Tubman

Ann Petry

Along the eastern shore of Maryland, in
Dorchester County, in Caroline County, the
masters kept hearing whispers about the
man named Moses, who was running off
slaves. At first they did not believe in his
existence. The stories about him were fantastic, unbelievable. Yet they watched for
him. They offered rewards for his capture.

They never saw him. Now and then they
heard whispered rumors to the effect that he
was in the neighborhood. The woods were
searched. The roads were watched. There
was never anything to indicate his where-
abouts. But a few days afterward, a goodly
number of slaves would be gone from the
plantation. Neither the master nor the overseer had heard or seen anything unusual in
the quarter. Sometimes one or the other
would vaguely remember having heard a
whippoorwill call somewhere in the woods,
close by, late at night. Though it was the
wrong season for whippoorwills.

Sometimes the masters thought they had
heard the cry of a hoot owl, repeated, and
would remember having thought that the
intervals between the low moaning cry were
wrong, that it had been repeated four times
in succession instead of three. There was
never anything more than that to suggest

The Schomburg Collection, The New York Public Library

Adapted from *Harriet Tubman: Conductor on the Underground
Railroad,* by Ann Petry. Copyright 1955 by Ann Petry. Used with
the permission of the Thomas Y. Crowell Company and Russell
& Volkening, Inc.

that all was not well in the quarter. Yet when morning came, they invariably discovered that a group of the finest slaves had taken to their heels.

Unfortunately, the discovery was almost always made on a Sunday. Thus a whole day was lost before the machinery of pursuit could be set in motion. The posters offering rewards for the fugitives could not be printed until Monday. The men who made a living hunting for runaway slaves were out of reach, off in the woods with their dogs and their guns, in pursuit of four-footed game, or they were in camp meetings saying their prayers with their wives and families beside them.

Harriet Tubman could have told them that there was far more involved in this matter of running off slaves than signaling the would-be runaways by imitating the call of a whippoorwill, or a hoot owl, far more involved than a matter of waiting for a clear night when the North Star was visible.

In December, 1851, when she started out with the band of fugitives that she planned to take to Canada, she had been in the vicinity of the plantation for days, planning the trip, carefully selecting the slaves that she would take with her.

She had announced her arrival in the quarter by singing the forbidden spiritual— "Go down, Moses, 'way down to Egypt Land"—singing it softly outside the door of a slave cabin, late at night. The husky voice was beautiful even when it was barely more than a murmur borne on the wind.

Once she had made her presence known, word of her coming spread from cabin to cabin. The slaves whispered to each other, ear to mouth, mouth to ear, "Moses is here." "Moses has come." "Get ready. Moses is back again." The ones who had agreed to go North with her put ashcake and salt herring in an old bandanna, hastily tied it into a bundle, and then waited patiently for the signal that meant it was time to start.

There were eleven in this party, including one of her brothers and his wife. It was the largest group that she had ever conducted, but she was determined that more and more slaves should know what freedom was like.

She had to take them all the way to Canada. The Fugitive Slave Law[1] was no longer a great many incomprehensible words written down on the country's lawbooks. The new law had become a reality. It was Thomas Sims, a boy, picked up on the streets of Boston at night and shipped back to Georgia. It was Jerry and Shadrach, arrested and jailed with no warning.

She had never been in Canada. The route beyond Philadelphia was strange to her. But she could not let the runaways who accompanied her know this. As they walked along she told them stories of her own first flight, she kept painting vivid word pictures of what it would be like to be free.

But there were so many of them this time. She knew moments of doubt when she was half-afraid, and kept looking back over her shoulder, imagining that she heard the sound of pursuit. They would certainly be pursued. Eleven of them. Eleven thousand dollars' worth of flesh and bone and muscle that belonged to Maryland planters. If they were caught, the eleven runaways would be whipped and sold South, but she—she would probably be hanged.

They tried to sleep during the day but they never could wholly relax into sleep. She could tell by the positions they assumed, by their restless movements. And they walked

---

1. **Fugitive Slave Law.** Between 1793 and 1850, Congress enacted severe laws to provide for the return of escaped slaves. The Underground Railroad was largely a result of public distaste for these laws. Among other harsh measures, the law of 1850 imposed severe penalties upon anyone who helped a slave in his or her escape.

at night. Their progress was slow. It took them three nights of walking to reach the first stop. She had told them about the place where they would stay, promising warmth and good food, holding these things out to them as an incentive to keep going.

When she knocked on the door of a farmhouse, a place where she and her parties of runaways had always been welcome, always been given shelter and plenty to eat, there was no answer. She knocked again, softly. A voice from within said, "Who is it?" There was fear in the voice.

She knew instantly from the sound of the voice that there was something wrong. She said, "A friend with friends," the password on the Underground Railroad.

The door opened, slowly. The man who stood in the doorway looked at her coldly, looked with unconcealed astonishment and fear at the eleven disheveled runaways who were standing near her. Then he shouted, "Too many, too many. It's not safe. My place was searched last week. It's not safe!" and slammed the door in her face.

She turned away from the house, frowning. She had promised her passengers food and rest and warmth, and instead of that, there would be hunger and cold and more walking over the frozen ground. Somehow she would have to instill courage into these eleven people, most of them strangers, would have to feed them on hope and bright dreams of freedom instead of the fried pork and corn bread and milk she had promised them.

They stumbled along behind her, half-dead for sleep, and she urged them on, though she was as tired and as discouraged as they were. She had never been in Canada but she kept painting wondrous word pictures of what it would be like. She managed to dispel their fear of pursuit, so that they would not become hysterical, panic-stricken. Then she had to bring some of the fear back, so that they would stay awake and keep walking though they drooped with sleep.

Yet during the day, when they lay down deep in a thicket, they never really slept, because if a twig snapped or the wind sighed in the branches of a pine tree, they jumped to their feet, afraid of their own shadows, shivering and shaking. It was very cold, but they dared not make fires because someone would see the smoke and wonder about it.

She kept thinking, eleven of them. Eleven thousand dollars' worth of slaves. And she had to take them all the way to Canada. Sometimes she told them about Thomas Garrett, in Wilmington. She said he was their friend even though he did not know them. He was the friend of all fugitives. He called them God's poor. He was a Quaker[2] and his speech was a little different from that of other people. His clothing was different, too. He wore the wide-brimmed hat that the Quakers wear.

She said that he had thick white hair, soft, almost like a baby's, and the kindest eyes she had ever seen. He was a big man and strong, but he had never used his strength to harm anyone, always to help people. He would give all of them a new pair of shoes. Everybody. He always did. Once they reached his house in Wilmington, they would be safe. He would see to it that they were.

She described the house where he lived, told them about the store where he sold shoes. She said he kept a pail of milk and a loaf of bread in the drawer of his desk so that he would have food ready at hand for

---

2. **Quaker,** a member of a Christian group called the Society of Friends. The Quakers participated actively in the anti-slavery effort.

any of God's poor who should suddenly appear before him, fainting with hunger. There was a hidden room in the store. A whole wall swung open, and behind it was a room where he could hide fugitives. On the wall there were shelves filled with small boxes—boxes of shoes—so that you would never guess that the wall actually opened.

While she talked, she kept watching them. They did not believe her. She could tell by their expressions. They were thinking, New shoes, Thomas Garrett, Quaker, Wilmington—what foolishness was this? Who knew if she told the truth? Where was she taking them anyway?

That night they reached the next stop—a farm that belonged to a German. She made the runaways take shelter behind trees at the edge of the fields before she knocked at the door. She hesitated before she approached the door, thinking, suppose that he, too, should refuse shelter, suppose— Then she thought, Lord, I'm going to hold steady on to You and You've got to see me through—and knocked softly.

She heard the familiar guttural voice say, "Who's there?"

She answered quickly, "A friend with friends."

He opened the door and greeted her warmly. "How many this time?" he asked.

"Eleven," she said and waited, doubting, wondering.

He said, "Good. Bring them in."

He and his wife fed them in the lamplit kitchen, their faces glowing, as they offered food and more food, urging them to eat, saying there was plenty for everybody, have more milk, have more bread, have more meat.

They spent the night in the warm kitchen. They really slept, all that night and until dusk the next day. When they left, it was

with reluctance. They had all been warm and safe and well-fed. It was hard to exchange the security offered by that clean warm kitchen for the darkness and the cold of a December night. . . . Harriet had found it hard to leave the warmth and friendliness,

too. But she urged them on. For a while, as they walked, they seemed to carry in them a measure of contentment; some of the serenity and the cleanliness of that big warm kitchen lingered on inside them. But as they walked farther and farther away from the warmth and the light, the cold and the darkness entered into them. They fell silent, sullen, suspicious. She waited for the moment when some one of them would turn mutinous. It did not happen that night.

Two nights later she was aware that the

feet behind her were moving slower and slower. She heard the irritability in their voices, knew that soon someone would refuse to go on.

She started talking about William Still and the Philadelphia Vigilance Committee.[3] No one commented. No one asked any questions. She told them the story of William and Ellen Craft and how they escaped from Georgia. Ellen was so fair that she looked as though she were white, and so she dressed up in a man's clothing and she looked like a wealthy young planter. Her husband, William, who was dark, played the role of her slave. Thus they traveled from Macon, Georgia, to Philadelphia, riding on the trains, staying at the finest hotels. Ellen pretended to be very ill—her right arm was in a sling, and her right hand was bandaged, because she was supposed to have rheumatism. Thus she avoided having to sign the register at the hotels for she could not read or write. They finally arrived safely in Philadelphia, and then went on to Boston.

No one said anything. Not one of them seemed to have heard her.

She told them about Frederick Douglass,[4] the most famous of the escaped slaves, of his eloquence, of his magnificent appearance. Then she told them of her own first vain effort at running away, evoking the memory of that miserable life she had led as a child, reliving it for a moment in the telling.

But they had been tired too long, hungry too long, afraid too long, foot-sore too long. One of them suddenly cried out in despair, "Let me go back. It is better to be a slave than to suffer like this in order to be free."

She carried a gun with her on these trips. She had never used it—except as a threat. Now as she aimed it, she experienced a feeling of guilt, remembering that time, years ago, when she had prayed for the death of Edward Brodas, the Master, and then not too long afterward had heard that great wailing cry that came from the throats of the field hands, and knew from the sound that the Master was dead.

One of the runaways said, again, "Let me go back. Let me go back," and stood still, and then turned around and said, over his shoulder, "I am going back."

She lifted the gun, aimed it at the despairing slave. She said, "Go on with us or die." The husky low-pitched voice was grim.

He hesitated for a moment and then he joined the others. They started walking again. She tried to explain to them why none of them could go back to the plantation. If a runaway returned, he would turn traitor, the master and the overseer would force him to turn traitor. The returned slave would disclose the stopping places, the hiding places, the cornstacks they had used with the full knowledge of the owner of the farm, the name of the German farmer who had fed them and sheltered them. These people who had risked their own security to help runaways would be ruined, fined, imprisoned.

She said, "We got to go free or die. And freedom's not bought with dust."

This time she told them about the long agony of the Middle Passage[5] on the old slave ships, about the black horror of the holds, about the chains and the whips. They too knew these stories. But she wanted to remind them of the long hard way they had come, about the long hard way they had yet to go. She told them about Thomas Sims, the

---

3. **Philadelphia Vigilance Committee,** a group of citizens who guided slaves and helped pay their way to Canada.
4. **Frederick Douglass** (1817–1895), an ex-slave who became a leading figure in the anti-slavery movement through his eloquent lectures and abolitionist newspaper.
5. **Middle Passage,** the slaves' journey from Africa to America over the Atlantic Ocean.

boy picked up on the streets of Boston and sent back to Georgia. She said when they got him back to Savannah, got him in prison there, they whipped him until a doctor who was standing by watching said, "You will kill him if you strike him again!" His master said, "Let him die!"

Thus she forced them to go on. Sometimes she thought she had become nothing but a voice speaking in the darkness, cajoling, urging, threatening. Sometimes she told them things to make them laugh, sometimes she sang to them, and heard the eleven voices behind her blending softly with hers, and then she knew that for the moment all was well with them.

She gave the impression of being a short, muscular, indomitable woman who could never be defeated. Yet at any moment she was liable to be seized by one of those curious fits of sleep, which might last for a few minutes or for hours.[6]

Even on this trip, she suddenly fell asleep in the woods. The runaways, ragged, dirty, hungry, cold, did not steal the gun as they might have, and set off by themselves, or turn back. They sat on the ground near her and waited patiently until she awakened. They had come to trust her implicitly, totally. They, too, had come to believe her repeated statement, "We got to go free or die." She was leading them into freedom, and so they waited until she was ready to go on.

Finally, they reached Thomas Garrett's house in Wilmington, Delaware. Just as Harriet had promised, Garrett gave them all new shoes, and provided carriages to take them on to the next stop.

By slow stages they reached Philadelphia, where William Still hastily recorded their names, and the plantations whence they had come, and something of the life they had led in slavery. Then he carefully hid what he had written, for fear it might be discovered. In 1872 he published this record in book form and called it *The Underground Railroad*. In the foreword to his book he said: "While I knew the danger of keeping strict records, and while I did not then dream that in my day slavery would be blotted out, or that the time would come when I could publish these records, it used to afford me great satisfaction to take them down, fresh from the lips of fugitives on the way to freedom, and to preserve them as they had given them."

William Still, who was familiar with all the station stops on the Underground Railroad, supplied Harriet with money and sent her and her eleven fugitives on to Burlington, New Jersey.

Harriet felt safer now, though there were danger spots ahead. But the biggest part of her job was over. As they went farther and farther north, it grew colder; she was aware of the wind on the Jersey ferry and aware of the cold damp in New York. From New York they went on to Syracuse, where the temperature was even lower.

In Syracuse she met the Reverend J. W. Loguen, known as "Jarm" Loguen. This was the beginning of a lifelong friendship. Both Harriet and Jarm Loguen were to become friends and supporters of Old John Brown.[7]

From Syracuse they went north again, into a colder, snowier city—Rochester. Here they almost certainly stayed with Frederick Douglass, for he wrote in his autobiography:

"On one occasion I had eleven fugitives

---

6. *curious . . . hours.* At thirteen, Harriet Tubman nearly died from an accidental blow on her head. The resulting brain damage caused periodic sleeping seizures that troubled her throughout her life.
7. *Old John Brown* (1800–1859), a devoted abolitionist who tried to stir up a rebellion among the slaves. He was captured at Harpers Ferry, a town in West Virginia, when he attempted to raid a government arsenal there in 1859.

at the same time under my roof, and it was necessary for them to remain with me until I could collect sufficient money to get them to Canada. It was the largest number I ever had at any one time, and I had some difficulty in providing so many with food and shelter, but, as may well be imagined, they were not very fastidious in either direction, and were well content with very plain food, and a strip of carpet on the floor for a bed, or a place on the straw in the barn-loft."

Late in December, 1851, Harriet arrived in St. Catharines, Canada West (now Ontario), with the eleven fugitives. It had taken almost a month to complete this journey; most of the time had been spent getting out of Maryland.

That first winter in St. Catharines was a terrible one. Canada was a strange frozen land, snow everywhere, ice everywhere, and a bone-biting cold the like of which none of them had ever experienced before. Harriet rented a small frame house in the town and set to work to make a home. The fugitives boarded with her. They worked in the forests, felling trees, and so did she. Sometimes she took other jobs, cooking or cleaning house for people in the town. She cheered on these newly arrived fugitives, working herself, finding work for them, finding food for them, praying for them, sometimes begging for them.

Often she found herself thinking of the beauty of Maryland, the mellowness of the soil, the richness of the plant life there. The climate itself made for an ease of living that could never be duplicated in this bleak, barren countryside.

In spite of the severe cold, the hard work, she came to love St. Catharines, and the other towns and cities in Canada where black men lived. She discovered that freedom meant more than the right to change jobs at will, more than the right to keep the money that one earned. It was the right to vote and to sit on juries. It was the right to be elected to office. In Canada there were black men who were county officials and members of school boards. St. Catharines had a large colony of ex-slaves, and they owned their own homes, kept them neat and clean and in good repair. They lived in whatever part of town they chose and sent their children to the schools.

When spring came she decided that she would make this small Canadian city her home—as much as any place could be said to be home to a woman who traveled from Canada to the Eastern Shore of Maryland as often as she did.

In the spring of 1852, she went back to Cape May, New Jersey. She spent the summer there, cooking in a hotel. That fall she returned, as usual, to Dorchester County, and brought out nine more slaves, conducting them all the way to St. Catharines, in Canada West, to the bone-biting cold, the snow-covered forests—and freedom.

She continued to live in this fashion, spending the winter in Canada, and the spring and summer working in Cape May, New Jersey, or in Philadelphia. She made two trips a year into slave territory, one in the fall and another in the spring. She now had a definite crystallized purpose, and in carrying it out, her life fell into a pattern which remained unchanged for the next six years. □□

Discussion

1. (a) What exactly were the "station stops" of the Underground Railroad? **(b)** Why was "Underground Railroad" an accurate description of the system?

2. (a) Why was "Moses" an appropriate code name for Harriet Tubman? **(b)** Why do you think the spiritual "Go down, Moses" was forbidden?

3. (a) In what different ways did Harriet help the slaves find the will and courage to keep on? **(b)** Why couldn't she let a runaway return?

4. (a) What do you learn of Harriet Tubman's personality in the selection? **(b)** Which of Harriet Tubman's qualities do you consider heroic? Why? **(c)** In your opinion, should anyone else in the selection be called a hero or heroine? Why or why not?

5. (a) What did Harriet Tubman mean when she said "Freedom's not bought with dust"? **(b)** Do these words have application in the world today? Explain.

Vocabulary • Context

In the following sentences you should be able to determine from context clues the meaning of the italicized words. Read each sentence; then, from the words that follow, choose the one closest in meaning to the italicized word. Be sure you can pronounce and spell all the italicized words.

1. After nights of walking, and days of fitful sleeping on the cold ground, their clothes were dirty and *disheveled.*

Disheveled means **(a)** bright; **(b)** fresh; **(c)** untidy; **(d)** shrunken.

2. Harriet had told them about the place where they would stay, promising warmth, comfortable beds, and good food, holding these things out as an *incentive* to keep on.

Incentive means **(a)** motive; **(b)** warning; **(c)** agreement; **(d)** threat.

3. Despite hardship and difficulty, she was an *indomitable* woman.

Indomitable means **(a)** uneducated; **(b)** undefeatable; **(c)** penniless; **(d)** sick.

4. The runaways were not very *fastidious* about the quality of meals and shelter they received from Douglass, since they were used to sleeping on the ground and eating whatever they could find.

Fastidious means **(a)** grateful; **(b)** hard to please; **(c)** hasty; **(d)** interested.

5. Harriet spent a great deal of time patiently *cajoling* them into continuing the journey by promises of a better life.

Cajoling means **(a)** beating; **(b)** coaxing; **(c)** following; **(d)** explaining.

Ann Petry 1911 •

Ann Petry believes that it is impossible to understand the present—especially relations between people—without a knowledge of the past. She says:

"It seems to me that I have always been fascinated by American history—especially the period which encompasses the African slave trade, the ever increasing use of slaves in the South, the growing outcry for the abolition of slavery, and ends with the Civil War and the period of reconstruction.

"Slowly, over the years, I have become convinced that the most dramatic material available to the writer in this country is that which deals with the Negro, and his history in the United States. This material is rich, varied, and comparatively untouched, reaching back as it does to the seventeenth-century freedman or runaway slave or plantation hand, early ancestor of the mid-twentieth-century doctor or lawyer or schoolteacher.

"As for Harriet Tubman—I think she is the ideal heroine. When she is first seen, she is defenseless and much abused and slowly develops into a courageous woman with an impelling desire for freedom."

Today we can fly across oceans and continents in only a few hours.
How important can a flight be that lasted less than one minute?

The Campers at Kitty Hawk

John Dos Passos

On December seventeenth, nineteen hundred and three, Bishop Wright, of the United Brethren, onetime editor of the *Religious Telescope,* received in his frame house on Hawthorn Street in Dayton, Ohio, a telegram from his boys Wilbur and Orville who'd gotten it into their heads to spend their vacations in a little camp out on the dunes of the North Carolina coast tinkering with a homemade glider they'd knocked together themselves. The telegram read:

> SUCCESS FOUR FLIGHTS THURSDAY MORNING ALL AGAINST TWENTYONE-MILE WIND STARTED FROM LEVEL WITH EN-GINEPOWER ALONE AVERAGE SPEED THROUGH AIR THIRTY-ONE MILES LONGEST FIFTYSEVEN SECONDS INFORM PRESS HOME CHRISTMAS

The figures were a little wrong because the telegraph operator misread Orville's hasty penciled scrawl,
   but the fact remains
   that a couple of young bicycle mechanics from Dayton, Ohio,
   had designed, constructed, and flown
   for the first time ever a practical airplane.

After running the motor a few minutes to heat it up, I released the wire that held the machine to the track and the machine started forward into the wind. Wilbur ran at the side of the machine holding the wing to balance it on the track. Unlike the start on the fourteenth, made in a calm, the machine facing a twentyseven-mile wind started very slowly. . . . Wilbur was able to stay with it until it lifted from the track after a forty-foot run. One of the lifesaving men snapped the camera for us, taking a picture just as it reached the end of the track and the machine had risen to a height

From *The Big Money—The USA Trilogy* by John Dos Passos. Reprinted by permission of Elizabeth Dos Passos.
John Dos Passos (dōs päs′ōs)

*of about two feet. . . . The course of the flight up and down was extremely
erratic, partly due to the irregularities of the air, partly to lack of experience
in handling this machine. A sudden dart when a little over a hundred and
twenty feet from the point at which it rose in the air ended the flight. . . .
This flight lasted only twelve seconds, but it was nevertheless the first in the
history of the world in which a machine carrying a man had raised itself by
its own power into the air in full flight, had sailed forward without reduction
of speed, and had finally landed at a point as high as that from which it
started.*

A little later in the day the machine was caught in a gust of wind and
turned over and smashed, almost killing the coastguardsman who tried to
hold it down;
    it was too bad,
    but the Wright brothers were too happy to care;
    they'd proved that the thing flew.

*When these points had been definitely established, we at once packed
our goods and returned home, knowing that the age of the flyingmachine
had come at last.*

They were home for Christmas in Dayton, Ohio, where they'd been
born in the seventies of a family who had been settled west of the
Alleghenies since eighteen-fourteen; in Dayton, Ohio, where they'd been
to grammarschool and highschool and joined their father's church and
played baseball and hockey and worked out on the parallel bars and the
flying swing and sold newspapers and built themselves a printingpress out
of odds and ends from the junkheap and flown kites and tinkered with
mechanical contraptions and gone around town as boys doing odd jobs to
turn an honest penny.

The folks claimed it was the Bishop's bringing home a helicopter, a
fiftycent mechanical toy made of two fans worked by elastic bands that
was supposed to hover in the air, that had got his two youngest boys
hipped on the subject of flight

so that they stayed home instead of marrying the way the other
boys did, and puttered all day about the house picking up a living with
jobprinting,
    bicyclerepair work,
    sitting up late nights reading books on aerodynamics.
    Still they were sincere churchmembers, their bicycle business was
prosperous, a man could rely on their word. They were popular in
Dayton.
    In those days flyingmachines were the big laugh of all the cracker-

barrel philosophers. Langley's and Chanute's[1] unsuccessful experiments
had been jeered down with an I-told-you-so that rang from coast to coast.
The Wrights' big problem was to find a place secluded enough to carry on
their experiments without being the horselaugh of the countryside. Then
they had no money to spend;

     they were practical mechanics; when they needed anything they
built it themselves.

         They hit on Kitty Hawk,
     on the great dunes and sandy banks that stretch south toward
Hatteras seaward of Albemarle Sound,[2]
     a vast stretch of seabeach,

---

1. Langley's and Chanute's, Samuel P. Langley (1834–1906), pioneer in aeronautics, and Octave Chanute
(1832–1910), pioneer in glider experimentation.
2. Hatteras . . . Albemarle Sound. Cape Hatteras is east of Albemarle Sound, an inlet in the northeast
coast of North Carolina.

Bruce Roberts

empty except for a coastguard station, a few fishermen's shacks, and the swarms of mosquitoes and the ticks and chiggers in the crabgrass behind the dunes,

  and overhead the gulls and swooping terns, in the evening fish-hawks and cranes flapping across the saltmarshes, occasionally eagles

    that the Wright brothers followed soaring with their eyes
    as Leonardo[3] watched them centuries before,
    straining his sharp eyes to apprehend
    the laws of flight.

Four miles across the loose sand from the scattering of shacks, the Wright brothers built themselves a camp and a shed for their gliders. It was a long way to pack their groceries, their tools, anything they happened to need; in summer it was hot as blazes, the mosquitoes were bad;

---

3. **Leonardo,** Leonardo da Vinci (1452–1519), Italian artist and scientist who studied the principles of flight.

but they were alone there,

and they'd figured out that the loose sand was as soft as anything they could find to fall in.

There with a glider made of two planes and a tail in which they lay flat on their bellies and controlled the warp of the planes by shimmying their hips, taking off again and again all day from a big dune named Kill Devil Hill,

they learned to fly.

Once they'd managed to hover for a few seconds
and soar ever so slightly on a rising aircurrent,
they decided the time had come
to put a motor in their biplane.

Back in the shop in Dayton, Ohio, they built an airtunnel, which is their first great contribution to the science of flying, and tried out model planes in it.

They couldn't interest any builders of gasoline engines, so they had to build their own motor.

It worked; after that Christmas of nineteen-three the Wright brothers weren't doing it for fun any more; they gave up their bicycle business, got the use of a big old cowpasture belonging to the local banker for practice flights, spent all the time when they weren't working on their machine in promotion, worrying about patents, infringements, spies, trying to interest government officials, to make sense out of the smooth involved heartbreaking remarks of lawyers.

In two years they had a plane that would cover twentyfour miles at a stretch round and round the cowpasture.

People on the interurban car used to crane their necks out of the windows when they passed along the edge of the field, startled by the clattering pop-pop of the old Wright motor and the sight of the white biplane like a pair of ironingboards one on top of the other chugging along a good fifty feet in the air. The cows soon got used to it.

As the flights got longer,
the Wright brothers got backers,
engaged in lawsuits,
lay in their beds at night sleepless with the whine of phantom millions, worse than the mosquitoes at Kitty Hawk.

In nineteen-seven they went to Paris,
allowed themselves to be togged out in dress suits and silk hats,
learned to tip waiters,

talked with government experts, got used to gold braid and post-
ponements and Vandyke beards[4] and the outspread palms of politicos. For
amusement
      they played diabolo in the Tuileries Gardens.[5]

They gave publicized flights at Fort Myers, where they had their
first fatal crackup, St. Petersburg, Paris, Berlin; at Pau[6] they were all the
rage,
      such an attraction that the hotelkeeper
      wouldn't charge them for their room.
      Alfonso of Spain shook hands with them and was photographed
sitting in the machine.
      King Edward watched a flight,
      the Crown Prince insisted on being taken up,
      the rain of medals began.

They were congratulated by the Czar
and the King of Italy and the amateurs of sport, and the society
climbers and the papal titles,[7]
      and decorated by a society for universal peace.

Aeronautics became the sport of the day.
      The Wrights don't seem to have been very much impressed by the
upholstery and the braid and the gold medals and the parades of plush
horses;
      they remained practical mechanics
      and insisted on doing all their own work themselves,
      even to filling the gasolinetank.

In nineteen-eleven they were back on the dunes
      at Kitty Hawk with a new glider.
      Orville stayed up in the air for nine and a half minutes, which
remained a long time the record for motorless flight.
      The same year Wilbur died of typhoidfever in Dayton.
      In the rush of new names: Farman, Blériot, Curtiss, Ferber,
Esnault-Peltrie, Delagrange;[8]

---

4. **Vandyke beards,** small, pointed beards worn by European men at the turn of the century.
5. **diabolo** (dē ab′ə lō′) **in the Tuileries** (twē′lər ēz) **Gardens.** Diabolo is a game involving a top and a
string fastened to two sticks, so popular at the time that it was played by children and adults alike. The
Tuileries are formal public gardens in Paris, a fashionable promenade at the turn of the century.
6. **Fort Myer** (Washington, D.C.) . . . **St. Petersburg,** (Florida), **Paris** (France), **Berlin** (Germany) . . . **Pau**
(pō), a resort in the south of France.
7. **papal titles,** men who bear titles of nobility conferred by the Pope in his capacity as sovereign of the
Vatican.
8. **Farman . . . Delagrange,** all were pioneers in flying.

in the snorting impact of bombs and the whine and rattle of shrapnel and the sudden stutter of machineguns after the motor's been shut off overhead,

and we flatten into the mud

and make ourselves small cowering in the corners of ruined walls,

the Wright brothers passed out of the headlines;

but not even headlines or the bitter smear of newsprint or the choke of smokescreen and gas or chatter of brokers on the stockmarket or barking of phantom millions or oratory of brasshats laying wreaths on new monuments

can blur the memory

of the chilly December day

two shivering bicycle mechanics from Dayton, Ohio,

first felt their homemade contraption,

whittled out of hickory sticks,

gummed together with Arnstein's bicycle cement,

stretched with muslin they'd sewn on their sister's sewingmachine in their own backyard on Hawthorn Street in Dayton, Ohio,

soar into the air

above the dunes and the wide beach

at Kitty Hawk.

Discussion

1. **(a)** What overall impression of Wilbur and Orville Wright do you get from the selection? **(b)** Find expressions and descriptions in the selection that create this impression. **(c)** Were the Wright brothers' personalities changed by success? How can you tell?

2. There is little in the selection that is not factual. What details are included more to add color and interest than to tell the story?

3. Read the biography of John Dos Passos on this page. Then find in the selection examples of some of Dos Passos's "experiments in form." Explain the effect each of these has on the selection: **(a)** passages in poetry; **(b)** language appropriate to the characters; **(c)** use of italics; **(d)** words and sentences run together.

4. **(a)** In the section beginning "In the rush of new names" (221, line 31 to 222, line 7), the focus shifts from the Wright brothers. What is this section about? **(b)** Who is the "we" suddenly mentioned for the first time (222, line 4)? **(c)** What different images are contained all together in the section beginning "but not even headlines" (222, line 8)? **(d)** What effect did all these events have on the Wright brothers?

5. **(a)** What place in history do the Wright brothers hold, according to Dos Passos? **(b)** Does John Dos Passos seem to regard Wilbur and Orville Wright as heroes? How can you tell? **(c)** How well do the Wright brothers fit your own concept of a hero? Explain.

John Dos Passos
1896 • 1970

"Mostly *U.S.A.* is the speech of the people," John Dos Passos has said, and capturing the speech of the people is one thing he attempted to do in the many plays, novels, and historical works he wrote. He was referring not only to the country he came to know so well during the many trips he made with his parents when young; he was referring also to his novel, *U.S.A.* It is a remarkable work which tells the history of public moods and social changes during the early twentieth century, as experienced by several different characters—some real and some fictional. Dos Passos wanted to show, for one thing, how an individual is molded and changed by the society in which he or she lives. To get an effect of immediacy, he made some daring experiments in form, incorporating bits of autobiography and biography along with history—in the form of newspaper quotations, political speeches, popular songs, and the like. He wrote some passages in poetry, some in prose, and he wrote narrative passages as well as dialogue in the kind of language appropriate to the character he was treating. Dos Passos used many devices, also, to create emphasis: capital letters, italics, words and sentences run together, even the appearance of the type on the page. "The Campers at Kitty Hawk" is one of the numerous biographies of folk-heroes and public figures scattered throughout the three volumes of Dos Passos's novel.

The gun went off, and there was Cheryl—a hundred yards in front and running like a madwoman.

Being

Francene Sabin

Cary Herz

In 1967 a city-sponsored group called Youth in Action held a track meet at the Boys' High School field in Brooklyn, New York. Because she had nothing better to do that day, 13-year-old Cheryl Toussaint went to watch the meet. Sitting in the stands with her friends, Cheryl found it all very exciting: the speed of the sprinting girls, the yells and cheers of the spectators, the highly charged atmosphere of noise, tension, and fun.

Somebody

While the meet officials were arranging the order of final events, an "open" race for girls was announced. That meant that any girl present could come to the starting line and compete even if she didn't belong to a track team. Cheryl loved to run—on the street, in the schoolyard, or in the local playground—and she wanted to enter. Still, she hesitated. The girls she had been watching in the meet looked so fast. Cheryl's friends urged her to give it a try. "Go ahead, don't be chicken," they teased. And when one said, "I dare you," Cheryl accepted the challenge.

She was wearing a dress and a pair of sandals, hardly suitable clothing for a race, so a friend who was wearing sneakers swapped footgear with Cheryl. Of course, the fit wasn't exactly right, but it was the best available. Then another girl, who had changed into track shorts, lent her jeans to Cheryl. "Suited up" this way, Cheryl walked down to the starting line and waited for the race to begin.

"It was a hundred-yard dash," Cheryl remembered, "and I really didn't know what to do. I didn't even know how long a hundred yards was. I just stood at the line in someone's dungarees and someone else's sneakers. I didn't know how to start; I was standing straight up. Then the man said, 'Take your marks . . . Set . . . Go!' and I ran. I got second."

There were several qualifying heats being run, and Cheryl was told that the finals would be held in awhile. As she waited, Cheryl began to wonder whether she should enter the finals. "For some reason, I began to hurt right around my hip area, and I didn't understand it. So, I told my friends that I didn't think I'd run. They began the teasing routine again, saying that I was chicken and that I was copping out because I didn't think I was going to win, and that kind of thing. Well, that did it. I went back on the track, ran the final, and took fourth place. That wasn't bad, but the thing that got me was that the three girls ahead of me were all Atoms. I was so impressed with how fast they were that all I could think of was how I could join the team, too."

The Atoms Track Club of Brooklyn was an AAU (Amateur Athletic Union) team, made up of local girls who wanted to run competitively. There were many fine runners in the group, and it was beginning to develop into a real track power.

After the meet was over, Cheryl saw some Atoms runners doing exercises on the grass. Screwing up her courage, she walked over to them and asked how she could join the team. They told her that joining was easy: all she had to do was come to the practices every afternoon.

For a while, Cheryl went to Prospect

Park in Brooklyn for the Atoms' daily practice. But when no one paid much attention to her, she began to doubt herself and the results of her running. "I thought that because I was putting my whole heart into it, the coach should have done more than tell me to run laps, do exercises, or practice starts," she said.

Cheryl had no way of knowing that Atoms coach, Fred Thompson, always treated new team members this way. It was his way of testing their willingness to work. Realizing that the tough, time-consuming practice sessions were more than many girls would endure, he would watch them without their being aware of it. Then, if they stayed with it without any encouragement, he would be sure that they were ready for real coaching.

After two months as an Atom, Cheryl dropped out of the club. The memory of her one race, however, kept coming back to her—the pounding heart before the start, the wonderfully free feeling of running, the excitement of coming in ahead of others. So after six months away from the Atoms, Cheryl Toussaint returned to the club, this time to stay.

Those six months away from track had given the teenager time to think about herself, her attitude toward work, and her goals in life. Cheryl decided that she really cared about track, and she went out to the Prospect Park field ready to dig in and work, even if *nobody* paid any attention to her or praised her.

Fred Thompson had missed Cheryl during those six months, and had hoped she'd come back. He had sent a message to Cheryl, telling her she'd always be welcome. The coach hadn't pressed the issue, but he was very pleased when she did return.

The season for cross-country racing (long-distance races over all kinds of terrain) was just beginning, and Fred took the Atoms to a cross-country meet on Long Island, New York. That day Cheryl officially competed for the first time as an Atom, and neither she nor the coach ever forgot it.

"Cheryl had been back training with us for only about two weeks," Thompson recalled, "but I decided to enter her in a one-mile run, just to give her some competitive experience. Of course, she wasn't really in condition, and I knew it. So, I said to her before the race, 'Don't go out too fast, stay with the pack, and just try to finish.'

"Well, the gun went off, and before I knew it, Cheryl was a hundred yards in front of the whole field and running like a madwoman. I said to myself, 'My gosh, this kid is going to pass out!' But she just kept running. Then, with about a hundred yards to go, the oxygen debt[1] really hit her, and she just about collapsed. She fell down, then got up and started crawling on her hands and knees. It was unbelievable! She stood up, staggered some more, got about twenty yards from the finish line and fell again. She kept on going, crawling, still with nobody near her, and then right at the wire another girl caught up and won.

"Cheryl cried like a baby. I went over and picked her up, tried to comfort her, telling her that she had nothing to be ashamed of. But she just cried. I knew, at that moment, that this girl was going to be something special. I had never seen anything like that before in my whole life."

Until Fred Thompson came into her life, nobody had ever thought of Cheryl Toussaint as something special. Shortly after Cheryl's birth on December 16, 1952, her

---

1. *oxygen debt.* Cheryl's body was burning oxygen at a rate faster than her breathing could supply it, causing her muscles to lose their ability to respond.

parents separated and Cheryl went to live with her grandmother. Her home was a tenement flat in Bedford-Stuyvesant, Brooklyn . . . . In the crowded ghetto schools she attended, Cheryl slipped further and further behind grade level until, by junior high, she was classified as a "slow learner." It was humiliating to be placed in Corrective Reading and Corrective Math, to be kept out of regular classes, and to be forbidden to take the courses that would make her eligible for a good academic high school.

Then Cheryl joined the Atoms, and everything in her world, including school, took on new meaning. Fred Thompson assumed the role of the father she lacked at home, demanding that Cheryl do better, scolding her when she let up, praising her when she succeeded. "Freddy always encouraged me and all the girls to try for good grades," Cheryl explained. "He'd say, 'When those report cards come in, I want to see them!' and he really meant it. He made me feel that he was just as concerned with how I was doing in school as with my running. It was almost as if he were a parent—only having had so much education himself, he really knew what was going on. I couldn't tell him that a C was okay because the teacher had said so—he knew better. My mother and grandmother cared, and were concerned about my schooling, but Freddy knew what each grade meant. There was no snowing him."

With new motivation, Cheryl set to work. She begged the school authorities to let her take algebra, a foreign language, and more advanced English courses. The teachers seemed certain that Cheryl wouldn't be able to do the work, but she was insistent. Finally, they agreed to let her carry those subjects, in addition to her remedial classes, on a one-year trial. It was grueling, but Cheryl gave it everything she had and began to learn and do well.

"When I got my report card," Cheryl said, "not only did I feel good for myself in getting good grades, I felt proud having somebody else to show them to, somebody who really appreciated them. Freddy would say, 'Cheryl, that's darn good. Keep it up.' Then he started to talk about college."

. . .To Cheryl, Fred Thompson's mention of college sounded like a wild fairy tale. But she understood, as did all the Atoms, that Fred meant every word he said. He told them that if they were good enough, poverty would never stop them. For example, if they qualified for the Nationals, no matter where the competition was held, he'd see that they got there. An attorney at New York's Madison Square Garden, he would use his own salary, or borrow the money, or beg for it—but the Atoms never had to worry about how they would pay for track equipment, travel expenses, or entry fees.

Her part of the bargain, Cheryl learned, was to succeed in school (flunk and you were off the team) and to work doggedly on the track. And she stuck with the hard, two-hour practice every day. "When I first joined the team," Cheryl remembered, "it was plain exhausting. I'd come home after practice barely able to shower and eat; all I wanted to do was sleep. My grandmother was accustomed to the energetic, bouncy kid I had been, and here I was—collapsing.

"Even though it knocked me out, the running definitely helped me do better in school. I had to be very well scheduled. If I hadn't been running track every day, I'd have been at the nearest park, playing handball or softball, after school. But with those early-evening practices being so tiring, I knew I had to devote afternoons to homework if I wanted to graduate."

As her schoolwork improved, so did Cheryl's performance on the track. She loved the feeling of running and now, with coach Thompson's faith in her and her own new image of herself, she began turning in faster times and winning races. Cheryl had been running for only about a year when she qualified to compete in the U.S. trials for a place on the 1968 Olympic squad.

Looking back at that time, Cheryl later said, "I had been doing fairly well, but at that point I didn't think I was ready for the Olympics. It was enough of a thrill to know that I had made it to the trials. In a way, it was scary for me. I ran and did the best I could, coming in fifth, but I didn't make the Olympic team. I was a little disappointed, but I know now that if I had qualified for the team then, it might have been the ruination of me. Athletes can be thrown, and I've seen it happen to some when they advanced further than their emotional levels could cope with. Success too soon isn't always a good thing. Sometimes people aren't mentally ready for things, and I think I wasn't ready for the Olympics then."

Cheryl was ready to become an outstanding student, however. Fred Thompson had convinced her that she was college material and that with a little more effort she might earn a scholarship. With that goal firing her up even more, the "slow learner" was soon getting A's and zooming to the top of her class.

In June 1970 Cheryl graduated from Erasmus Hall High School in Brooklyn and received an academic scholarship to New York University.

"It might sound kind of boring," Cheryl said of her teen years, "because my life was a round of sleeping, eating, classes, running, studying, and more sleeping. But I was doing what I loved and what I wanted to do, and, anyway, there were those marvelous trips every year."

As one of America's top-ranked runners, Cheryl traveled to meets throughout the United States and Europe. The overseas trips gave her an opportunity to measure herself against foreign competition. Best of all, they gave her a chance to see new places, meet people from other countries, and learn through new experiences.

Running took Cheryl to Europe many times and to the U.S. Nationals year after year. Each trip was fun and each was a challenge, but they were only preparation for Cheryl's highest athletic priority—the Olympics.

The teenage runner made the Games the focus of her entire life, even to the extent of minoring in German at college so she would be able to communicate in Munich[2] in 1972. Only two things mattered—school and track. Being so dedicated didn't leave much free time for dating. While Cheryl went out with boys occasionally, she felt it was wrong to establish a serious relationship while she was in training.

"There was one boy," she said, "with whom I went to high school, and I saw him for about two years. But then, I was always so busy that I finally felt it wasn't fair to him or me. To go steady, I'd want to devote time to him, which would have meant taking time away from something else I'd like to do. So it just got to be a hassle. I had many male friends, but on a casual basis. When I wanted to go out, I'd call a friend and suggest something, and I'd feel free to say yes or no if someone called me. I liked it that way because I wasn't misleading anyone."

Although she had a less active social life

---

2. **Munich** (myü/nik), city in Germany, site of the 1972 Summer Olympics.

than many girls, Cheryl did not feel insecure about it—most of the time. She did, however, remember a time when it bothered her a lot. "I was about sixteen," she explained, "and going through a stage when I was always moaning that I wasn't going out enough, and that I always had to call off my dates. Looking back, I think I just couldn't differentiate between the important and the unimportant. Fortunately, I outgrew that!"

Fred Thompson encouraged Cheryl and all the Atoms to lead sensible, well-regulated lives and to take good care of their health. Cheryl always needed a lot of sleep and made sure she got enough. Weight was never a problem for her, as she naturally tended to be thin, but she tried to stick to solid foods and avoid sweets and excess starches.

"My only advice to Cheryl," Thompson said, "was to drink plenty of orange juice and stay with Grandma's food. That was what made her a healthy kid in the first place. Of course, when she was living in a college dormitory, Cheryl had to take care of herself. But by that time, she knew that the wrong foods or a lack of sleep would show in her running. She was too highly motivated to let that happen, so I never had to worry about her.". . .

Cheryl's sights were set on the 1972 Olympic team, and nothing was more important than that. Every meet counted, because every race was a rehearsal for the big one. During the indoor season in the winter of 1971-72, she was undefeated. She won the 440-yard dash at the Millrose Games, the 880-yard runs at the Maple Leaf Games in Canada and at the AAU Indoor Track and Field Championships, and the 800-meter run at the Olympic Invitational Track Meet. She was faster every time out, and everything seemed to be falling into place.

Then the outdoor season began, and

UPI

Cheryl had to run a time outdoors that would qualify her for the U.S. Olympic team. She began to press, and lost her concentration on the track. Coach Thompson tried to calm her, to reassure her that a good running time depended on good competition, and that she would make the team. Soon she had qualified as a runner on the metric mile[3] relay team. But she still hadn't qualified in her individual event, the 800 meters. And the summer was growing short.

Fred took Cheryl to Ohio, where there were to be two meets that would give her the opportunity to qualify. On the day of the first meet, Madeline Manning Jackson, the one woman who might have challenged Cheryl and made her run a fast time, came down ill. With nobody challenging her, Cheryl won the race, but her time still wasn't fast enough. At the second meet, Thompson was depending on Nancy Shafer, another top American runner, to push Cheryl to go all-out. But in the 95-degree heat on the day of the race, Nancy faded away, and from the first turn, Cheryl ran alone. Again she missed running a qualifying time.

Cheryl went to the Olympic training camp with just one last chance to make the team in an individual event. "On the day of the race," Fred Thompson recounted, "I sneaked in, so that Cheryl wouldn't see me. I hid behind a tree and watched her run. When she had done it, qualifying, I came out and she saw me. Well, we both cried and cried in relief. It was really down to the wire on that one."

Then she was off to Munich and the 1972 Olympics. Her first event was the 800-meter run, her specialty. In the qualifying heat, she followed Fred Thompson's advice never to fall farther back than third—with disastrous results. She failed to qualify and was out of competition for the medals. "If she'd been in

any other heat, my instructions would have been fine," Mr. Thompson said afterward. "But the girls in her heat went out so fast that Cheryl was thrown off her normal pace and didn't make it. It was my mistake, and I'll never stop blaming myself. If Cheryl had run her usual race, pacing her first quarter more slowly, she'd have made it to the semifinals and then, maybe, to the finals."

The night after the race, Thompson went looking for Cheryl in Olympic Village and found her in tears, broken-hearted at what she considered her failure. Fred consoled her, reminding her that she was the youngest one in the event, that her running career was just beginning, and that there would be another Olympics for her. Besides, the relay race was yet to come. Cheryl still had one more chance to win a medal.

On September 9, 1972, the first women's 4 × 400-meter relay[4] in Olympic history was set to be run. The U.S. team of Mabel Ferguson, Madeline Jackson, Cheryl Toussaint, and Kathy Hammond had to do well in their heat to qualify for the finals. Cheryl, running the third leg of the relay, waited to receive the baton from Madeline Jackson.

"I turned," Cheryl said, recreating the situation, "and reached for the stick. I was just starting to run with it when a girl from another team fell in front of me. My first reaction was to rear back, so I wouldn't trip over her—but you never stop. I dashed around her, only to have *another* runner step on the heel of my left shoe. Half my shoe was tied on tightly, but the other half was crushed under my heel. I thought, 'I can't believe it. Here I am in the Olympics, and my shoe is coming off!'

---

3. *metric mile,* a term used in swimming and track for 1500 meters, a distance 120 yards short of a regular mile.
4. *4 × 400-meter relay,* a 1600 meter race in which four runners on each team run 400 meters each.

"If I had stopped to pull it up, my teammates would have killed me, and I'd have felt awful because that was our opportunity to win a medal. So I just ran. I'd gone another ten yards or so when the shoe flew up in the air. I just kept running, dazed, wondering if my shoe had hit anyone, if the people in the stands and on TV could see my bare foot, and if they were asking what that girl was doing out there without a shoe.

"There had been two teams ahead of us when I got the stick; but somehow, before I knew it, I had passed their runners. Then I saw where I was and I felt stunned at getting there. All I'd been thinking was that my shoe had come off, that this was the Olympics, and that these things don't happen. But it did."

She may have done it the hard way—but she'd done it. Cheryl and her teammates had made it to the relay finals. "I was really confident," Cheryl said of the finals. "Nothing more could happen after that shoe thing. So when I received the baton pass, I just ran and ran until I couldn't run any more. We took second behind East Germany.

"Getting up on the victory stand with my teammates, I realized that I was going to come home from my first Olympics with a silver medal. Of course, I wish we had won, but that doesn't mean I wasn't thrilled by being up there. And, anyway, there was Montreal in 1976 to look forward to, and maybe a gold medal."

After the '72 Olympics, Cheryl came home and continued to concentrate on school and track. She graduated from college with a B+ average in 1974 and got a job with the Federal Reserve Bank in its management training program. And, at the same time, she started working toward the 1976 Olympics.

Cheryl collected many trophies and prizes in her running career, but the greatest reward track gave to the skinny girl from Bedford-Stuyvesant was a chance at a whole new life. For Cheryl, being one of Freddy's Atoms spelled the difference between being nobody and being somebody very special.

Fred Thompson might have known it all along, but Cheryl didn't realize just how special she was until February 5, 1970, when she set the first of her several world records. "It was in Toronto, Canada," she recalled, "at the Maple Leaf Invitational Indoor Games. I had never run the 600-yard event before in my life, but I felt prepared because I had been training well.

"There were so many girls in the event that it was split into two heats, both to count as finals. That meant you could win your heat and still lose the race if the girls in the other section had faster times. I was in the second section and my goal was to beat the time of the winner in the first heat.

"There were three and three-quarter laps to run in all, and, with about two laps left, I heard Freddy yelling, 'Go! Go! What are you waiting for?' And I went!

"I won my heat, then walked around the track to where Freddy and my teammates were waiting. It was funny, everybody was jumping up and down and smiling and reaching out to me. I looked at them and asked, 'Did I win?' What I meant was, did I beat the fastest time of the first heat? They just kept smiling. Then Freddy said, 'Look up at the clock.' So I looked and the clock read 1:22.2. I said, 'That's nice, I won.' Freddy just kept looking at me and said very calmly, 'I think it's a new world record.'

"I thought he was kidding, until they announced it over the loudspeaker. Then the tears came. I was so excited, and I couldn't believe it. I just could never imagine that *I* had really broken a world record—me, who'd never run a 600 before, who had never, never thought of myself as a world-record-holder. It was too much for me to understand. Freddy was overjoyed, and I was, too. I can't even express all the feelings I had. They told me to jog a victory lap, and I went around the track crying, with my mind in a total fog. At that moment, I felt as if I'd never be tired, as if I could run forever.

"That night, after I'd calmed down a little, I thought about it. Lots of people break world records, but *me*—wow! I thought about how lucky I was to be an Atom, and of all the things it had given me, and it was so wonderful." □□

Discussion

1. The following words might be used to characterize Cheryl Toussaint at various times in the selection: **(a)** humble; **(b)** insecure; **(c)** resolute; **(d)** grateful. Find incidents that reveal each of these character traits.

2. **(a)** Why doesn't Fred Thompson actively encourage Cheryl when she first attempts to join the Atoms? **(b)** Do you agree or disagree with his method? Why? **(c)** At what point does Fred Thompson realize that Cheryl is "something special"?

3. **(a)** In what areas is Fred Thompson most influential in guiding Cheryl? **(b)** On what occasion does the coach feel that he misguided her?

4. In what ways did running actually help Cheryl become an outstanding student?

5. **(a)** What was the "greatest reward" Cheryl received from track? **(b)** Is "Being Somebody" a better title for this story than "Running to Win"? Why or why not?

Extension • Speaking

You and your television camera crew are at the 1972 Olympics in Munich, Germany. Your assignment is to describe the women's 4 × 400-meter relay race—the first held in Olympic history. Concentrate on the final minutes of the race and include human-interest details that will appeal to your audience.

Francene Sabin

"Becoming a winner is never easy," comments Francene Sabin in her book, *Women Who Win*. "It takes an incredible amount of talent, determination, and just plain hard work for any young athlete to develop into a world-ranked competitor. . . .

"For some athletes, perfection is the name of the game. For others, winning is the only goal. And still others are motivated by the same drives that inspire great generals in combat, business tycoons in industry, explorers of land, sea, and space.

"But even with all their tal-ent and dedication, it is doubtful that these athletes could have made it to the top without the help of others. . . . Coach Fred Thompson guided Cheryl Toussaint to peaks of accomplishment far beyond her expectations, on and off the track. Speaking about the differences between male and female athletes, he said, 'Girls seem to get more emotionally involved in track than guys do. . . . For Cheryl and the other girls, this is the only thing they have, and they care. They have tremendous pride in themselves as individuals, and in their team. And competitive? I think girls are much more competitive than boys.'

"Coaches and parents can only help, however," continues Sabin. "Ultimately, winning is up to the individual herself. No amount of guidance from others will make a woman a champion unless she is willing and able to push her mind and body to the extreme limits. That's what separates the winners from all the others."

See **MOOD** Handbook of Literary Terms

*Somewhere in the depths of the
Pacific Ocean more than one life-and-death
drama was being enacted . . .*

The Pharmacist's Mate

Budd Schulberg

CHARACTERS: In the Wardroom

JIMMY BRUCE, *Pharmacist's Mate—the sea-
man in charge of the sick bay, or ship's
"hospital."*
LT. COMMANDER MILLER, *Captain ("Skip-
per") of the submarine.*
FLOYD HUDSON, *Executive Officer, or second
in command after Miller.*
TOMMY FORD, *Apprentice Seaman—the pa-
tient.*
SWEDE ENGSTRUM, *ship's cook.*
MIKE O'BRIEN, *Seaman.*
JEFF DAVISON, *a ship's officer.*
LEROY JOHNSON, *mess boy, or kitchen helper.*

Other Members of the Crew

BILL RIGGS, *Diving Officer—in charge of
controlling the depth of the submarine.*
WILLIAMS, *Quartermaster—in charge of the
ship's supplies and equipment.*
JOE FANELLI, *Seaman.*
GOODMAN, *Seaman.*
SONARMAN, *operator of the instrument using
sound to detect enemy ships.*
RADIOMAN, *the ship's radio operator.*
HELMSMAN, *stationed at the helm, or steer-
ing apparatus.*
YOUNG PETTY OFFICER, *a noncommissioned
officer.*

MESSENGER
FIRST ACEY-DEUCY PLAYER *and*
SECOND ACEY-DEUCY PLAYER, *both partici-
pants in a game using cards and dice.*

Also a chief of the watch, other petty officers, stand-by men, messengers, electricians, machinists, etc.

"The Pharmacist's Mate," a TV play by Budd Schulberg is
adapted from *Emergency at Sea* by George Weller, originally
published in *The Chicago Daily News*. Reprinted by permission
of Ad Schulberg and Harold Ober Associates, Inc.

1	Bow	6	Officers' Quarters
2	Hydroplanes	7	Chief's Room
3	Torpedo Rooms	8	Pump Room
4	Pantry	9	Control Room
5	Wardroom	10	Conning Tower

(Fade in[1] on view of the sea as seen in an enlarged circle through a submarine periscope. The sea is disturbed, boiling up. Dissolve to[2] interior view of conning tower. Present are the EXECUTIVE OFFICER *at the periscope, the* QUARTERMASTER, *working the periscope for him, the* HELMSMAN *and, off to the starboard side, the* SONARMAN. *The* EXECUTIVE OFFICER, LT. FLOYD HUDSON, *is in his late twenties, good-looking, tight-lipped, serious to the point of being disagreeable. He is walking the periscope around.[3])*

HUDSON *(turning from the periscope and addressing the* QUARTERMASTER*).* Down periscope, Williams.

WILLIAMS. Aye, aye, sir.

*(*HUDSON *goes to the squawk box[4] near the wheel. Close shot of* HUDSON.*)*

HUDSON *(into the squawk box).* Lt. Hudson in the conning tower. Lt. Hudson in the conning tower. Are you listening, Skipper?

VOICE OF SKIPPER *(on squawk box).* Go ahead, Hudson.

HUDSON. Still all clear. Nothing in sight.

---

1. *Fade in,* bring slowly into sight.
2. *Dissolve to,* change picture gradually.
3. *walking the periscope around,* turning the periscope to search for enemy ships or airplanes.
4. *squawk box,* communication system of ship.

11	Bridge	16	Engine Room
12	Periscope	17	Propeller
13	Galley	18	Rudder
14	Dinette	19	Stern
15	Crew's Quarters		

And it's all clear from the sonarman, too.

VOICE OF SKIPPER. Very well. Come up for a look every twenty minutes. And don't bother reporting again until you sight something.

HUDSON. Aye, aye, sir. *(Pause)* Ensign Riggs. Ensign Riggs, run at 90 feet until 1350 and then come back to periscope depth.[5]

(Cut to[6] control room, below the conning tower. Present are the diving officer, young, sandy-haired ENSIGN RIGGS; *the two planesmen, who operate the wheels that affect the angle and depth and control of the boat; men on the trim and air manifolds;[7] a chief of the watch,[8] and stand-by men and messengers.)*

RIGGS *(getting his order from the squawk box).* Aye, aye, Hudson.

(He turns to check the enormous depth-control gauge and addresses the planesmen.)

RIGGS. Five-degree down angle. Level off at 90.

5. *run at 90 feet . . . periscope depth,* keep the submarine 90 feet below the surface until 1:50 P.M. and then come up to the depth at which the periscope can be used for observation. Naval time is based on a twenty-four hour system; thus 1350 is 1:50 P.M.
6. *Cut to,* change picture to view of.
7. *the trim and air manifolds.* The trim manifold shifts water from some tanks to others to keep the boat level ("trim"); the air manifold blows water from tanks to level the boat when surfacing.
8. *chief of the watch,* man responsible during each four-hour period ("watch") the crewmen are on duty ("stand watch").

(One planesman nods and the giant wheel begins to turn. The depth-gauge needle drops. Cut back to conning tower.)

WILLIAMS *(standing near and addressing the youthful* HELMSMAN*).* Man, this is one night I wouldn't mind a little shore duty. Christmas Eve in Pearl.[9] *(Sighs)* Oughta be quite a brawl.

*(*LT. HUDSON, *behind him, overhears.)*

HUDSON. They didn't send us here to go to Christmas parties, Williams; they sent us to—

WILLIAMS *(rather tolerantly, with an old, wrinkled smile).* I know, I know, Lieutenant. If we can spot the enemy troopships and get a report back on their course, the islands fall into our hands like ripe apples. But Christmas Eve—a guy can dream, can't he?

HUDSON *(sharply, humorlessly).* Not when he's on watch. We can't slack off up here. We're out here to find them. They must be somewhere.

WILLIAMS *(dead-pan).* I'm sure they are, sir.

(New camera angle: HUDSON *turns to consult with* SONARMAN *in the background. In the foreground are* WILLIAMS *and the* HELMSMAN*.)*

HELMSMAN *(in a mumble).* Pretty serious fella—that new Exec.

WILLIAMS. Aw, he's just a little Academy-happy.[10] The Old Man[11] will straighten him out.

(Fade to corridor leading to galley, etc. The "Old Man" appears. He is in his early thirties, not as good-looking in a conventional way as the EXECUTIVE OFFICER*. Also in contrast to* LT. HUDSON, *he is relaxed, and underlying his control of every situation there is a current of good humor. He looks into the galley.* SWEDE, *the cook, big and easygoing, turns around with a wide grin. He looks*

much too rough to be an expert on fancy pastry; but just the same, he is. He works in shorts and he is bare to the waist, exhibiting some fancy tattooing.)*

SWEDE *(respectfully, but familiarly).* Cap'n.

MILLER. What've you got tonight, Swede?

SWEDE. Well, seein' it's Christmas, I thought I'd break out some steaks.

MILLER. And a cake?

SWEDE. Wait'll you see it. It's gonna have red and green lights that pop up and spell Merry Christmas.

MILLER *(grinning).* Good boy. You know what they say on a sub, Swede. Good chow is the skipper's secret weapon. What else is there to do on a pigboat but hunt and hide—and sleep and eat?

SWEDE. You can say that again, Cap'n. This is gonna be a rum cake that'll make 'em forget all about home cooking.

MILLER *(suddenly more serious).* I doubt that, Swede—even though you are the best cook I ever had aboard. *(Picking up something to munch on)* You know, when you get to be as old as I am, you learn something—to pick your cooks even more carefully than your gunnery officers.

(During the above conversation SWEDE *is not idle. He is kneading dough, checking his oven, etc. Now he takes some fried potatoes off the griddle.)*

SWEDE. Thanks, Cap'n. But if I had a little more room, I could really show you something.

MILLER *(picking up a potato slice).* That's how we all feel. But on a pigboat, you make do. Good luck with the cake, Swede. You better plan to serve it pretty early. I

---

9. Pearl, Pearl Harbor, the United States naval base in the Hawaiian Islands.
10. Academy-happy. Williams means that Hudson is over-proud of his training at the Naval Academy and his recent commission as an officer.
11. The Old Man, Miller, the commander of the ship.

doubt if we'll have much time for celebration after sundown.

SWEDE. Aye, aye, sir.

(COM. MILLER *goes on down the corridor toward the bow.* SWEDE *grins, picks up a plate of French fries, and turns toward the dinette next door. Cut to dinette.* SWEDE *enters, sets the plate down.*)

SWEDE. Free sample, fellers. Wrap your molars around these.

(*He exits. Half a dozen men are crowded into this dinette. A couple of petty officers are playing acey-deucy; another, a first-class gunner's mate[12]—squat, husky, tough-looking veteran submariner* O'BRIEN—*is kibitzing.* FANELLI, *a dark-haired young seaman, is trying to read a pocketbook while an apprentice seaman,* TOMMY FORD, *who hardly looks old enough to be away from home, is trying, in the midst of all this relaxed confusion, to write a letter.*)

FIRST ACEY-DEUCY PLAYER. Boy, I'll bet that girl of yours will be pining for you tonight—

SECOND ACEY-DEUCY PLAYER. Come on, play your cards. You haven't even got a girl.

FIRST PLAYER (*winking to the others*). Why should I? I c'n always take yours.

FANELLI. All right, knock it off, you guys. I'm trying to read.

O'BRIEN (*in a false soprano*). I'm trying to read.

(*Everyone except the letter writer laughs.*)

FANELLI (*putting the book down*). Christmas. At least on a CV[13] they'd have a tree . . . maybe a regular party with a band . . . and look at us . . . the only way we know it's Christmas is by short wave.

(*Camera centers on* TOMMY FORD *trying to write his letter. As he writes, he looks off meditatively, not hearing the adlib cracks, his mind thousands of miles away. While he*

goes on writing, we peek at his letter in an insert.*)

Dear Mom and Pop. Sure seems funny to be away from you for the first time on Christmas Eve. . . .

(*The pen pauses.*)

SECOND ACEY-DEUCY PLAYER. A year ago I was home-sweet-home, eating hot mince pie and then my girl came in and gave me this watch and when I turned it over it said—

EVERYONE (*except* TOMMY FORD *who continues to write*). To my dearest from his Bibsey.

SECOND ACEY-DEUCY PLAYER (*disgusted*). Aw, nothing's sacred around you guys.

O'BRIEN. That home-baked hot mince pie and a good ten-cent cigar after the turkey and your arm around the old lady's waist. (*Sighs*) Last Christmas I got so bloomin' sentimental about it I went down and got this little art job.

(*He rolls up his sleeve to show his powerful forearm. Close-up of tattoo on forearm showing "Mike" and "Kate" in a Christmas wreath. As he flexes his muscle, their heads go back and forth as in a kiss. Camera cuts back to group laughing.*)

ADLIB. What a man! (*Etc.*)

(*Close-up of* TOMMY FORD *ignoring the banter. Insert of letter.*)

Tonight I can just see the tree by the fireplace, and the kids and Mary Lou. . . .

O'BRIEN (*out of camera range*). You had him, if you'da rolled a six.

SECOND ACEY-DEUCY PLAYER (*out of camera range*). I know what they keep you around for, Obie—in case they run out of high-pressure air they've always got you.

---

12. **first-class gunner's mate,** a seaman having charge of weapons.
13. **CV,** aircraft carrier.

O'BRIEN *(out of camera range, flaring up).* Listen, Jackson, I was wearin' Dolphins[14] when you—

(In a wider camera angle TOMMY FORD *looks up, still oblivious of the group around him. The memory his words evoke makes it difficult for him to go on.)*

FANELLI, *(looking up from his book again).* Slow it down to two knots, you guys. You're racing your motors.

*(*TOMMY FORD *tries to go on writing, then stops as his hand goes to his right side; a small sound of pain escapes him. The others look up.)*

O'BRIEN *(sympathetically).* Whatsa matter, Tommy?

FORD. I dunno. I had a gut ache all night. Feels like a knife in there.

FIRST ACEY-DEUCY PLAYER. It's those biscuits we had last night. I tell ya that Swede is trying to poison us. It's sabotage, that's what it is.

O'BRIEN. Why don't you see the quack;[15] let him put you on the binnacle list.[16]

FORD *(talking with effort but trying to minimize the pain).* Aw, I guess I'll be all right. Maybe I did wolf too many of those biscuits down last night.

SECOND ACEY-DEUCY PLAYER. Whatta ya wanna bet the Swede worked in a cement factory before he got this job?

*(*TOMMY FORD *rubs his right side, obviously in distress, yet trying not to make too much of it.)*

O'BRIEN. No kidding, boy, I'd do something about that.

FORD. I did. I took some tablets the Chief[17] gave me this morning.

FIRST ACEY-DEUCY PLAYER. Oh, great. Just because the Chief knows how to doctor a Diesel,[18] he thinks he's a great medical man.

SECOND ACEY-DEUCY PLAYER. Well, he can't kill you any quicker than the quack—that's for sure.

(A MESSENGER *enters.)*

MESSENGER. Fanelli, Ford, O'Brien—five minutes and you're on watch, fellows.

(The MESSENGER *exits. The three he alerted rise and start toward the door.)*

FANELLI. Back to the salt mines, Tommy.

FORD *(trying to grin).* Right, Joe.

*(*O'BRIEN, *the veteran submariner, gunner's mate first-class, older than the others, puts his hand on* TOMMY FORD'S *shoulder.)*

O'BRIEN. That's a tough job on the planes,[19] kid. I wouldn't stand watch if I looked the way you do.

FORD. Aw, if I was back at the base I guess I'd see the doc. But out here, with something liable to happen any second—well, I c'n take it for four hours, and then I'll hit the sack.

O'BRIEN *(easily).* Know what I always say, lad? "Do what you're man enough to do."

(Cut to control room. In the background we can see TOMMY FORD *and* FANELLI *relieving the planesmen. In the foreground are* COM. MILLER, ENSIGN RIGGS, *and* LT. DAVISON, *a hulking, affable young Southerner.)*

MILLER. I'll be in the wardroom if you need me for anything, Riggs.

RIGGS. Yes, sir.

MILLER *(to* DAVISON*).* Come on, Jeff. I'll give you another chess lesson.

DAVISON. Chess? When we're practically up on the enemy beach?

---

14. *Dolphins,* insignia worn by officers and enlisted men on a submarine. A man wins his Dolphins only after finishing school and demonstrating that he knows the complete operation of the submarine.
15. *the quack,* a joking reference to a fake or incompetent doctor.
16. *binnacle list,* sick list.
17. *the Chief,* the chief petty officer, the highest rating among enlisted men.
18. *Diesel* (dē′zəl *or* dē′səl), the internal combustion engine used to run the submarine.
19. *the planes,* the wheels that affect the angle, depth, and control of the submarine. Ford is to serve as planesman for this watch.

MILLER *(smiling).* That's the time for chess.

(They start off toward the forward compartments. As they do so, they pass PHARMACIST'S MATE JIMMY BRUCE, *on his way aft.* MILLER *says, "Jimmy," and gives him an offhand salute, a habitual gesture.* JIMMY BRUCE *grins, mumbles a respectful "Cap'n," and we follow him as he continues on toward the rear compartments. Cut back to dinette as* JIMMY BRUCE *enters. He is a blond, wiry kid from Arkansas, about twenty-two years old. He has unruly hair and is cocky in an unobjectionable way, quick to grin. As soon as they see him, the* ACEY-DEUCY PLAYERS *set up a cross fire of banter that is apparently a stylized bit of by-play on the sub.)*

FIRST ACEY-DEUCY PLAYER. Hi ya, ducky.

BRUCE. Waddya mean, ducky?

FIRST ACEY-DEUCY PLAYER. The quack, quack, quack. *(They laugh.)*

SECOND ACEY-DEUCY PLAYER. How's everything back in Ar-*kan*sas?

BRUCE. It's not Ar-*kan*sas, it's—*(then realizing it is a rib)*—aw, why don't you guys get a new joke?

(He sits down and pulls out a comic book.)

FIRST ACEY-DEUCY PLAYER. Hey, quack, I got a hangnail that's painin' me somethin' awful.

SECOND ACEY-DEUCY PLAYER. Put 'im on the binnacle list so you c'n goldbrick[20] together.

BRUCE *(jovially).* Keep on callin' me quack and I'll cut that hangnail off—right up to here. *(He indicates the player's neck.)*

SECOND ACEY-DEUCY PLAYER. No kiddin', Brucie, how come you rate this soft job? The only noncombatant on the whole darn boat. Nothin' to do but sit around readin' comics.

BRUCE. Oh, sure. All I've got to do is stand regular watches like the rest of you, and doctor up you goof-offs on the side.

FIRST ACEY-DEUCY PLAYER. Listen to the boy. He never had it so good.

BRUCE *(grinning).* Sure, it's a breeze—as long as everyone stays in one piece around here.

(He settles down comfortably with his comic book; the ACEY-DEUCY PLAYERS *chatter up a little adlib on their game. Dissolve to periscope cutting through the rough sea. Then dissolve to conning tower.* EXECUTIVE OFFICER HUDSON *appears up the ladder from the control room, takes over the periscope lookout from the Chief, and peers intently at the sea and the sky. Cut to interior of control room.* TOMMY FORD *on the bow plane is perspiring from the effort to overcome his pain.)*

RIGGS. Mind your bubble,[21] Ford. Hold her to a half-degree down angle.

FORD *(through his teeth).* Aye, aye, sir.

(Shot of depth indicator. It is fluctuating, showing that the boat is in danger of broaching.[22] Close shot of RIGGS.)*

RIGGS *(observing the indicator).* Flood auxiliary from sea—one thousand pounds.

(Close shot of O'BRIEN *at trim manifold. He is opening the valve, and watching the gauge.)*

YOUNG PETTY OFFICER. Auxiliaries are flooding, sir.

(Close shot of air manifold.)

O'BRIEN. One thousand pounds flooded in auxiliary. Trim manifold secure.

(Wider angle shot of control room angled toward planes. ENSIGN RIGGS *comes up and looks over* TOMMY FORD'S *shoulder critically.)*

---

20. *goldbrick,* get out of work.
21. *bubble.* Above each plane is an instrument called a level; it is filled with a fluid in which a bubble rides. When the submarine is level, the bubble is dead center. It moves to indicate whether the boat is pointing up or down.
22. *broaching,* coming to the surface.

RIGGS. You've got a two-degree down angle. Come on, Ford, stay awake.

(TOMMY FORD *wipes the sweat from his forehead and, operating the plane automatically, adjusts the angle of the boat. Cut to wardroom.* COM. MILLER *has sat down to his game of chess with* LT. DAVISON. *To one side are charts which* MILLER *has been working on.*)

DAVISON (*in his slow drawl*). Chess. Sure never thought I'd learn to play a brainy game like chess.

MILLER (*with a slight smile, as he takes two of* DAVISON's *pawns with his knight*). What makes you think you've learned, Jeff?

DAVISON. Sure beats me how you figured that out, Skipper. I thought I had you trapped.

MILLER (*studying the board*). If you hope to skipper one of these boats some day, Jeff, this game can give you some pointers. A sub is like this king. Everything on the board is hunting you. And you can't use it to strike without fatally exposing yourself. (*He makes another move on the board and* DAVISON *winces.*) To stay alive, you always have to be at least two or three jumps ahead.

(*Over the squawk box in the corner we hear:*)

SQUAWK BOX. Wardroom, this is the conning tower, Lt. Hudson. Is the Captain there?

MILLER (*operating the squawk box*). What's the story, Floyd?

SQUAWK BOX. We've sighted smoke, sir. Maybe fifteen miles. Bearing 0–2–7.[23]

MILLER. Very well.

(*He rises and pushes the chessboard back, moving as quickly as possible in the cramped quarters.*)

DAVISON (*over the squawk box*). Okay, Hudson. The Skipper's on his way up.

(*Cut to conning tower.* HUDSON *is peering through the periscope again. The rough sea makes it difficult to maintain depth control.*)

WILLIAMS (*over the squawk box*). Mr. Hudson wants you to run at 55 feet.

SQUAWK BOX (RIGGS' *voice*). I need more speed.

(HUDSON *goes to the squawk box.*)

HUDSON. All right. But slow her down as soon as you can maintain trim at one-third speed.

SQUAWK BOX. Aye, aye, sir.

HUDSON. Down periscope.

(QUARTERMASTER WILLIAMS *begins to comply. Cut to control room,* ENSIGN RIGGS *at the squawk box.*)

RIGGS. All ahead two-thirds.

(*Cut to engine room: the engineman responds. Dissolve to exterior of submarine moving through water. Cut to conning tower as* COM. MILLER *appears up the ladder from the control room.*)

HUDSON. I think I have a destroyer bearing 0–3–5. And it looks like another one off our port bow. Hull down.[24]

MILLER. Very well. Let me have a look as soon as we get back to one-third.

(*After a pause, we hear over the squawk box:*)

RIGGS' VOICE. I can hold her at 55.

MILLER. Very well. Up periscope.

(WILLIAMS *raises the periscope. Meanwhile* MILLER *turns to the* SONARMAN.)

MILLER. Do you have the target bearing 0–3–5?

SONARMAN. Still all clear for me, sir.

MILLER. Keep searching in that quadrant. Let me know as soon as you pick them up. (*He turns and peers intently into the periscope. After a moment's study he speaks*

---

23. *Bearing 0-2-7.* Numbers are used to indicate the angle from which a ship is approaching.

24. *Hull down,* a submariner's expression meaning that the ship is so distant that only the mast and stacks are visible; the hull is invisible below the horizon.

with quiet satisfaction.) That looks like our little friends, all right. *(Studies them further)* We'll continue to close and track them at periscope depth until sundown. *(To* QUARTERMASTER WILLIAMS*)* What time is it, Williams?

WILLIAMS. 1317 hours, sir.

MILLER. Very well. Keep tracking their course and speed and at 1330 we'll surface to get off our report.

HUDSON. Aye, aye, sir. *(After a pause)* Sure wish we could take a crack at them now, Captain.

MILLER. So do I. But if our report brings our striking force[25] over in time to intercept them, that will more than make up for having to wait. *(MILLER returns to the periscope.)* Let's be very careful on these observations. We don't want some zoomy[26] to pick us up before we can accomplish this mission.

(The boat pitches upward, almost throwing them off balance.)

HUDSON *(on squawk box).* What's the matter down there? Can't you hold her at 55?

(Cut to control room. ENSIGN RIGGS *checks the depth gauge, which records 48, and then turns on* TOMMY FORD *who has been fighting collapse.)*

RIGGS *(angrily).* Come on, Ford. Watch that bubble.

FORD *(weakly).* Aye . . . aye, sir.

RIGGS. What's the matter with you today?

FORD. Sir, I'm not feeling well . . . there's something wrong. I . . .

RIGGS. Why didn't you say something right away so I could get you relieved?

FORD. Well, I—I thought I'd be all right, and . . . *(He clutches his side.)*

RIGGS *(turning to a stand-by planesman).* Goodman, relieve the stern planes. Depth 55. One-degree down angle. And don't let the waves suck you up.

*(*SEAMAN GOODMAN *moves in to take* FORD's *place. As* FORD *rises he is suddenly seized with excruciating pain and slumps to the deck.* ENSIGN RIGGS *and a stand-by messenger kneel beside him.* ENSIGN RIGGS *looks up at the chief of the watch.)*

RIGGS. Get Bruce. Have him report here right away.

*(*TOMMY FORD, *unconscious, writhes and groans.* RIGGS *rises and addresses the messenger and another stand-by.)*

RIGGS. Carry him in to my bunk.

*(*RIGGS *turns back to check the depth gauge. Cut to dinette.* JIMMY BRUCE *is reading his comic book. The acey-deucy game goes on.)*

SQUAWK BOX. Pharmacist's Mate Bruce. Pharmacist's Mate Bruce. Report to control room at once.

BRUCE *(pushing his comic book away reluctantly and rising).* Yeah, I got a cinch. All I have to do is sit down and one of you clumsy jokers is sure to bump his head on a hatchway. *(He folds his comic book into his pocket.)* I've been trying to finish "Li'l Abner" for three days!

FIRST ACEY-DEUCY PLAYER *(as* BRUCE *exits).* Don't worry, boy, you got lots of time. At the rate we're going, we'll still be out here next Christmas.

SECOND ACEY-DEUCY PLAYER *(calling after* BRUCE *in a mimicking voice).* Calling Dr. Kildare.[27] Calling Dr. Kildare. Emergency case of hiccoughs in the control room.

(The two men are laughing together at their wit as JIMMY BRUCE *hurries out. Cut to Chief's room.* JIMMY BRUCE *enters.* TOMMY FORD *is lying on the bunk, conscious but in terrible pain.)*

---

25. our striking force, nearby surface ships or aircraft which can attack the enemy destroyers.

26. zoomy, enemy aircraft.

27. Dr. Kildare, a fictional doctor, made famous by novels, movies, and, more recently, television.

BRUCE. Hello, Tommy. Let's have a look at you. *(He kneels at the bunk, feels* TOMMY FORD'S *head and sticks a thermometer in his mouth.* TOMMY FORD *screws his face up against the pain.* BRUCE *takes a hypodermic needle from his kit.)* This'll make you ride a little more comfortable. *(He shoots the morphine. Then he sits on the edge of the bunk and feels* TOMMY FORD'S *pulse. There is a tense silence. The water can be heard sloshing against the boat's sides.* TOMMY FORD *rolls his head as another spasm of pain seizes him.* JIMMY BRUCE *seems worried by the pulse.)*

BRUCE. How long has this been going on? *(*TOMMY FORD *tries to answer with the thermometer in his mouth.)* Hold it a second. I c'n never remember not to ask questions when I got that thing in their mouths. *(He removes the thermometer.)*

FORD *(speaking with great effort).* Since . . . yesterday.

*(*JIMMY BRUCE *studies the thermometer.)*

BRUCE. Why didn't you tell me right away?

FORD. I . . . I thought . . .

BRUCE. I'm the closest thing to a doctor they got on board, chum. Sometimes you fellas seem to forget that. *(Looks at the thermometer)* A hundred an'—*(He shakes his head.)*

*(*JIMMY BRUCE *returns to the bunk and presses his hand on* TOMMY FORD'S *abdomen.)*

BRUCE. Hurt there?

*(*TOMMY FORD *shakes his head.* JIMMY BRUCE *moves his hand and presses again.)*

BRUCE. There?

*(*TOMMY FORD *shakes his head.* JIMMY BRUCE *now presses the right lower abdomen.* TOMMY FORD *gives a tense cry of pain.* JIMMY BRUCE *maintains the pressure . . . and then suddenly releases it. The reaction on* TOMMY FORD *is even greater than it was before.)*

BRUCE. Mmmmmm-hmmmm. Mmmm-hmmmm. *(Then suddenly)* Take it easy a minute, kid. I better see the Skipper. *(He exists quickly.)*

(Cut to control room. COM. MILLER *is just coming down the ladder from the conning tower when* JIMMY BRUCE *appears.)*

BRUCE. Captain, c'n I talk to you a minute?

MILLER. Sure thing, son.

BRUCE. I just examined Tommy—Seaman Apprentice Ford. Looks to me like appendicitis—maybe acute.

MILLER. Any chance of holding out until we get back to port?

BRUCE. I don't see how, sir.

MILLER. Then what do you suggest, Jimmy?

BRUCE. Well, everything points to an immediate operation—if we had a surgeon on board.

MILLER. We never carry any *ifs* aboard these boats. *(Suddenly)* Don't suppose you were ever called upon to perform an appendectomy?

BRUCE *(taken aback).* Are you kidding? *(Catching himself)* I mean . . . no, sir. At Pearl, before I won my Dolphins, all the training I had was as a cardiographer.[28]

MILLER. Ever seen this operation performed?

BRUCE. Well, I . . . I wheeled a fellow in for one once. That's about as close as I ever came.

MILLER. Think you can do it?

BRUCE. I . . . I . . . well, I'd hate to say "yes" for sure and then foul it up.

MILLER. Jimmy, there's nothing in the book says a pharmacist's mate has to perform any duty for which he hasn't been specifically trained. So I'm not going to

---

28. *cardiographer* (kär/dē og/rə fər), a technician who operates a machine which registers the movements of the heart and who interprets the results.

order you to do this. I'm going to ask you to think it over for five minutes. *(Close on* BRUCE, *listening, as* MILLER *continues.)* If you say "yes" we'll give you all the cooperation possible. If you say "no," we'll give up our mission and see if we can't make it back to the tender[29] before—

BRUCE. Yes, sir, I understand.

(Medium shot, holding the two. JIMMY BRUCE *starts to turn away, obviously troubled.)*

MILLER. And Jimmy . . .

BRUCE *(turning around).* Yes, sir.

MILLER. Before we left the States, I had the opportunity of picking out every one of you men individually. For every one of you aboard there are at least ten others—almost as good. I didn't pick you for my pharmacist's mate because you happened to have a high rating as a technician—but because you impressed me as the kind of a man who could come through in emergencies.

*(*COM. MILLER'S *words seem to increase* JIMMY BRUCE'S *confidence.)*

BRUCE. Yes, sir.

*(*COM. MILLER *turns and starts toward the ladder, passing* ENSIGN RIGGS.)*

MILLER. How's she behaving, Bill?

RIGGS. This dirty weather's making her tough to handle. We nearly broached there a minute ago. *(He keeps his eye on the depth gauge while he is talking. Now, noticing that it is pointing a little too high, he acts promptly.)* Plane her down another five feet. . . .

*(*COM. MILLER *has started up to the conning tower. Cut to conning tower. As* MILLER appears, LT. HUDSON *is studying the chart.)*

HUDSON. Two more destroyers approximately twelve miles off the bow. Looks like the screen for the main force all right!

MILLER. That's fine. I—hope we don't have to lose 'em.

HUDSON. Lose 'em? Why should we if we keep closing in?

MILLER. That's the hitch. One of our seamen—young Ford—has appendicitis. Needs an operation pronto, according to Bruce. If he thinks he can do it, and I agree to let him go ahead, we'd have to get down for at least an hour.

HUDSON. An hour! They'll be out of sight by then. We may never pick up their trail again.

MILLER. I know. I know, Floyd. I suppose you're right . . . from a military standpoint. *(Close shot of the two men, favoring* MILLER*)* But, Floyd, one of these days you'll have your own command. Then you'll know a little more than you do now about the human side of this job. What makes these boats run? It's not the Diesels—they can always be replaced. It's the men—they aren't interchangeable. Not even young apprentice seamen like Tommy Ford.

(Close-up MILLER*)*

MILLER. It didn't take just months and months to train them and work them in as a team. It took years—all their lives—to develop into the kind of men who can stand the gaff of living on top of each other for fifty days at a time under constant danger without getting on each other's nerves.

(Medium shot favoring MILLER*)*

MILLER. No, Floyd, the life—even an outside chance to save the life—of one of my men still means more to me than the course and disposition of the whole enemy fleet.

---

29. *tender,* submarine tender, a boat having aboard all supplies to replenish fuel, food, and emergency medical facilities.

HUDSON. In an hour or two we could crack the secret of a major enemy movement—

MILLER. In another hour or two a nice kid from Chautauqua, Kansas, may be dead because his Skipper was afraid to take a chance.

HUDSON. But this kid, Bruce, if you don't mind my saying so, still seems pretty wet behind the ears. I can't see him performing any miracles.

MILLER. Floyd, I've seen my share of miracles aboard these boats. I've seen the big brave fellows cave in and I've seen panicky, half-grown kids suddenly find out they're men. Keep tracking 'em to the last possible moment. I'll send word up as soon as I decide.

(He starts down the ladder. Quick dissolve to corridor outside the Chief's room. As COM. MILLER *appears, coming forward from the control room,* JIMMY BRUCE *enters the corridor from the Chief's room, where the body of* TOMMY FORD *can be seen in the background.)*

MILLER. What's the story, Jimmy?

BRUCE. I'll take a crack at it.

MILLER. Good boy. Only now, for the record, I'm ordering you to do it. So, just in case we're unlucky and a bunch of second-guessing, top-brass medics[30] decide we could've waited, at a court martial three stripes on your arm look better than the crow.[31] *(*MILLER *forces a grin.)* Only I wouldn't have put this up to you if I wasn't dead sure you had it in you.

BRUCE *(a little shaky).* Thanks, Skipper. I just wish I was as sure as you are.

MILLER *(placing his hand on* JIMMY BRUCE'S *shoulder).* Better go in and see your patient. Put it up to him the same way I did you. This is a volunteer service. I want everybody to go in with his eyes open.

BRUCE *(his respect for the Skipper is obvious despite his conventional response).* Aye, aye, sir.

(He turns toward the Chief's room. Cut to Chief's room. As BRUCE *enters,* TOMMY FORD *looks up and forces a weak grin.)*

BRUCE. Tommy, there's no sense giving you a snow job. I'm gonna be level with you.

FORD. Okay, Jim.

BRUCE. If I just sit here picking my teeth and feeding you pills, I think you've had it.

FORD *(in a whisper).* Yeah, I know.

BRUCE. So the Skipper's giving me the green light to operate. It's a heck of a thing to tell you, but somehow I feel I've gotta say it—I'm not sure I know how. There's a chance that—*(He looks at* TOMMY FORD,

---

30. *top-brass medics,* doctors who hold high officer rank.
31. *at a court-martial . . . the crow,* if the matter comes before a Navy court, my three stripes as a lieutenant commander will carry more weight than your insignia as an enlisted man (the crow).

almost *begging.)* Well, it's plenty rugged either way. But I've gotta know if you think I should.

FORD. Whatever you say, Doc.

(JIMMY BRUCE straightens up.)

BRUCE. That's the first time anybody on this boat ever called me anything but *quack. (He rises.)* Rest easy, kid. It's a tough point but we're gonna get lucky and make it.

(TOMMY FORD, wincing, but forcing back any sound, makes a feeble but definite circle of approval with his thumb and forefinger. Dissolve to control room. COM. MILLER *talking into the general address system:)*

MILLER. Attention, all hands. We've got an emergency on our hands that calls for teamwork, and I want you all to know exactly what we're up against. We're going deeper so that Pharmacist's Mate Bruce can perform an appendectomy on Apprentice Seaman Ford.

(Wider angle of room as all listen intently.)

MILLER. I don't have to tell you what a ticklish job this is going to be. We'll have to keep her awful steady down there. Just a little better trim than we ever had before.

(Quick flashes of men in torpedo room, engine room, pump room, etc., listening.)

MILLER. Every one of you, wherever you're standing watch—the planesmen, you on the manifolds, you back there in the engine rooms—is going to be part of this thing. We've been in tough spots before and we've come through because each one of you knew that. So I've got a hunch you're all going to deliver this Christmas Eve for Tommy Ford and Jimmy Bruce. That is all. (MILLER *turns to* ENSIGN RIGGS.) Better check the pressure we've got in the boat. We'll need all the good air we can get because that ether's[32] going to smell things up. Take her to a

hundred feet. *(He turns away as* RIGGS *gives him an "Aye, aye, sir.")*

(Exterior of submarine as it noses down into the sea. Dissolve to the control room, discovering JIMMY BRUCE, *nervous but controlled;* COM. MILLER; LT. HUDSON; LT. DAVISON. *At the planes are* FANELLI *and* GOODMAN. *Keeping an eye on the bubble, the depth gauge, the Christmas tree,[33] etc., is the diving officer,* ENSIGN RIGGS. *At one of the manifolds is the chunky, tattooed veteran* O'BRIEN.)*

MILLER. Now, Jimmy, there's nothing in the book to cover this kind of deal. So we're going to stow rank and Navy regs.[34] From this point until the end of the operation, you're the boss. You pick your staff from any level you want—you tell us where you want us and what you want us to do.

(JIMMY BRUCE still seems uncertain about his authority. During this period he should seem to be groping his way toward the confidence and strength he will eventually assert.)

BRUCE. Aye, aye, sir. Can we have Tommy moved to the wardroom? See that he's made as comfortable as possible. And tell him I'll be with him as soon as I get everything squared away.

MILLER *(to* DAVISON). Get a detail and take care of that, Jeff.

BRUCE. Now for my chief assistant . . . *(He looks around.)* I don't want you to think I'm giving you the business, Skipper, but I think I'd pick you even if you were an apprentice striker.[35]

MILLER. Thanks, Jimmy. I wanted to be in

---

32. *ether,* a liquid formerly used as an anesthetic.
33. *the Christmas tree,* the board with red and green lights that controls the hydraulic system for the hull openings.
34. *we're going to stow rank and Navy regs,* we're going to disregard our official positions and Navy regulations governing relationships between people on different levels.
35. *an apprentice striker,* a sailor learning new and specific duties to get a petty officer's rating.

on every step of this thing. His life's in your hands, but I want there to be no doubt about the responsibility's being mine.

BRUCE. Now, I'm not sure exactly where to use him yet, but I'd like to have the Swede. He's one of those fellows who c'n do a little bit of everything, and also he's the luckiest gambler on the boat.

HUDSON. Sir, if I can butt in, don't you think it's a little more proper if all those in attendance were officers? After all—

MILLER (rather sharply). Hudson, a good officer knows when to pull rank, and when to stow it. And, I don't want to disillusion you, but the best men in the Navy aren't always the ones with the gold on their sleeves. Now send a messenger for Swede Engstrum.

HUDSON (silenced but obviously not convinced). Yes, sir.

BRUCE. Now for my nurse. (Looks around again) Lemme see, I'd like to have O'Brien.

(COM. MILLER crosses to RIGGS.)

MILLER. Have a stand-by take over the trim manifold. We want to use O'Brien.

RIGGS. Aye, aye, sir.

(He goes to O'BRIEN, taps him on the shoulder and points to the group around BRUCE. O'BRIEN—balding, bare-chested, and perspiring—joins the group.)

BRUCE. Obie, you're going to be a nurse.

O'BRIEN. A nurse!

BRUCE. Yeah. I won't say you're the prettiest nurse I ever saw—(O'BRIEN'S face wrinkles into a hard, likable grin)—but you're another guy I'd like to have around if things really get tough.

O'BRIEN (not at all maliciously). Okay, kid. If you c'n be a surgeon, I guess I c'n be a nurse.

BRUCE. Good deal, Pop. Now, let's see—an anesthetist. I want someone who's a real cool customer, and won't lose his head. (He nods to LT. HUDSON.) Lt. Hudson, I guess you'll fill the bill. I'll show you what I want when we get in there. Meanwhile, go check on the ether supply.

(LT. HUDSON hesitates, resenting being ordered around by a mere pharmacist's mate.)

BRUCE. Then I'd like Leroy Johnson—

HUDSON (stopping just as he's turning away). Johnson—the mess boy?

BRUCE. I know, Lieutenant, but his old man happens to be a doctor, and I figure . . .

MILLER (severely). That's all right, Jimmy. A surgeon doesn't need to know the rank or pedigree of his assistants. You're not handing out invitations to the Officers' Ball. You're picking men.

HUDSON (rebuked again, leaving). I'll check on that ether, Skipper.

BRUCE. Now lessee—we'll need a recorder—someone to make sure that everything that goes in, comes out.

(At this point LT. DAVISON has returned. SWEDE enters from left.)

BRUCE. I guess that'll be your job, Mr. Davison.

DAVISON. Aye, aye, Doc.

BRUCE. I've got a list of all the stuff we're going to need and, brother, it's rough. No ether cone, no antiseptic powder, no scalpel—in fact, no surgical instruments of any kind. (Shakes his head) They say one way to tell a submariner is the way he c'n open a bottle of beer with a fifty-cent piece. That's what we all gotta do now— get our noggins workin' on how t' make do.

SWEDE. I got some fine tea strainers in the galley. How about tryin' one of them for an ether cone?

BRUCE. I think ya got something there, Swede. Get on it. (As SWEDE starts off)

Oh, and while you're there, we're gonna need something for muscular retractors—that's to hold the wound open after I make the incision. I think maybe we c'n use some of your tablespoons, if we double 'em all the way back.

SWEDE *(heading back toward the control room).* Back in a flash, Doc.

BRUCE. Antiseptic powder. Well, why don't we just grind up some sulfanilamide tablets? Leroy, find as many as you can in the medicine chest and powderize 'em for me.

JOHNSON. Right, Jimmy. *(He starts off.)*

BRUCE. Then we'll need something to sterilize the instruments.

O'BRIEN. We could use the alcohol in the torpedoes.

BRUCE. Good deal.

(O'BRIEN hurries off.)

BRUCE. Then there's lights. We'll need a lot more'n we got in there. Maybe we can string some floods from the overhead.[36]

DAVISON. I'll get Chief Childs to put a couple of his electricians on that.

BRUCE. Check. Let's see, that takes care of just about everything except—except the scalpel. All I could find was an old scalpel blade without a handle.

MILLER. Could you hold it with a pair of pliers?

BRUCE. Kinda clumsy, Skipper. Wait a minute; I think I've got it—those hemostats we use for pinching blood vessels. Maybe one of the machinists could rig that up for me.

MILLER. Okay, I'll get somebody on it. You better go in and have a look at your patient.

BRUCE. Yes, Commander.

(COM. MILLER puts his hand on JIMMY BRUCE'S shoulder.)

MILLER. And remember what I told you, Jimmy. This deal is going to depend on you giving the orders. Until you get it all battened down, you're in command.

BRUCE *(suddenly).* Do you believe in God, sir?

MILLER *(seriously).* I certainly do, Jimmy. And I still believe He watches over all of us on earth.

BRUCE *(literally, with a deep sigh as he turns to enter the wardroom).* Boy, I just hope He doesn't have any trouble getting down here twenty fathoms below the surface.

(Close shot of LEROY JOHNSON pounding tablets to powder. Close shot of SWEDE stretching gauze over a strainer to form a homemade ether cone. Close shot of O'BRIEN draining alcohol from a torpedo. Close shot of machinist rigging the scalpel with a hemostat. Close shot of electricians in wardroom rigging overhead lights. Close shot of COM. MILLER bending the Monel-metal spoons into retractors. Close shot of JIMMY BRUCE in a corner of the wardroom, studying his handbook with a pencil in his hand. Cut to control room. Angle toward FANELLI and depth gauge, which is fluctuating. RIGGS enters to FANELLI.)

RIGGS. Watch that bubble, Fanelli. Hold her to one-half degree.

FANELLI. It's rough holding her against the swells, sir.

RIGGS. I know it. Do the best you can.

(Cut to conning tower. Close on SONARMAN, listening intently with earphones on. He turns to QUARTERMASTER WILLIAMS.)

SONARMAN. All clear on sound.

(Interior of wardroom. Close on clock showing time to be five minutes after two. Camera pans down to full shot[37] around table. Ready with the ether cans, behind TOMMY FORD'S

---

36. *string some floods from the overhead,* hang some floodlights from the ceiling.
37. *pans down to full shot,* moves down to include the whole group.

head, is LT. HUDSON. *Near him is* SWEDE, *who holds the improvised ether cone. At the side of the table facing the camera are* JIMMY BRUCE *and* COM. MILLER. *At the foot of the table is* O'BRIEN, *and sitting near him,* LT. DAVISON, *with medical books open and paper and pencil to record the movements of the operation. All these men wear white reversed pajama coats and their faces are covered by gauze masks, all except their eyes, which express tenseness and anxiety. In the taut silence we can hear, over the sound of the water washing the hull, the ticking of the clock.*

Cut to the pantry. Here LEROY JOHNSON *is stationed. He is placing the bent-double spoons into a pot of boiling water and is ready to pass them through the small sliding panel that leads directly into the wardroom. Cut to wardroom.)*

BRUCE *(his voice tight in his throat, the tone belying his attempts at confident words and manners).* Well, Tommy, I guess we're all set. In a minute or two we're gonna start feeding you the ether. You're not gonna feel a thing.

FORD *(in a hoarse whisper).* Listen, Jimmy, I don't wantcha to think I'm chicken or anything, but just in case, you know, if something goes wrong, I wantcha to go see my folks. Tell 'em . . . Tell 'em . . .

BRUCE *(embarrassed).* Aw, knock it off. You're gonna see your own folks. Pretty lucky guy, prob'ly get a fat sixty-day leave outa this deal.

FORD. Okay, Doc. But, just in case . . .

BRUCE. Sure . . . sure. . . . Now quit gabbin'. Think about something cheerful.

FORD *(to himself in a whisper).* I'll think about bein' home . . . Christmas Eve . . . Mary Lou . . .

(NOTE: *Through the above the trim of the submarine has been far from perfect. The*

boat has been pitching, not violently, but enough to be disturbing. SWEDE, *at* TOMMY FORD'S *head,* O'BRIEN, *at his feet, have been holding the patient in place on the table. Suddenly the submarine lurches upward.* TOMMY FORD *groans.)*

BRUCE *(on edge).* Whatsa matter with those guys? Don't they know what they're doin'?

(COM. MILLER'S *manner, in contrast to* JIMMY BRUCE'S, *is controlled and quieting.)*

MILLER. Easy, Jimmy. Let me see if I can straighten them out.

(He exits quickly. Cut to control room. The depth-gauge needle swings between 100 and 95. The planesmen are working the electrical. ENSIGN RIGGS *hovers over them.* COM. MILLER *enters.)*

MILLER. What's the trouble, Bill?

RIGGS. It's so rough down here that it's hard to maintain depth control. The two best men I've got are having trouble.

MILLER. Okay. Let's ease her down another fifty feet and see if it's any better. We'll never get this job done without perfect depth control.

RIGGS. Aye, aye, sir. We'll do the best we can. *(Slight smile)* And then we'll try to do even a little better than that.

(COM. MILLER *slaps* RIGGS *on the shoulder and turns back toward the wardroom.* RIGGS *turns to his men to give an order. Exterior of submarine as the boat noses down into a quieter layer. Interior of wardroom as the table becomes level at last. Everyone leaning in slightly toward* TOMMY FORD, *all faces washed out in the glare of the overhanging flood lights.)*

BRUCE *(in a strange, quiet voice).* That's better. Now if they can just hold like that. *(Pause)* Gloves.

(O'BRIEN *comes forward and holds them for* JIMMY BRUCE *while he sterilizes his hands in*

a ready bowl of alcohol. The fingers of the gloves are too long for JIMMY BRUCE'S small hands and the rubber ends are ludicrously limp.)

O'BRIEN. You look like Mickey Mouse, Doc.

(JIMMY BRUCE grins a little through his gauze, then turns back to the table and addresses SWEDE.)

BRUCE. Okay, Swede. I guess we're ready for your strainer. (SWEDE starts to lower it over TOMMY FORD'S mouth. JIMMY BRUCE turns to HUDSON.) Now, just like I told you, drop a little . . . easy . . . onto the strainer. (HUDSON appears to pour the ether too freely.) I said easy. We've only got five pounds. And when you figure all this pressure—

(COM. MILLER turns to the squawk box.)

MILLER. See if the pressure's built up again. If so, pump it back to one-tenth.

(Almost simultaneously, HUDSON has turned on BRUCE.)

HUDSON. Look, Bruce, I'm doing what I—

BRUCE (with a curt gesture). Pipe down. Watch him close. And remember— another drop—another—until the eyes begin to dilate. (To TOMMY FORD softly)

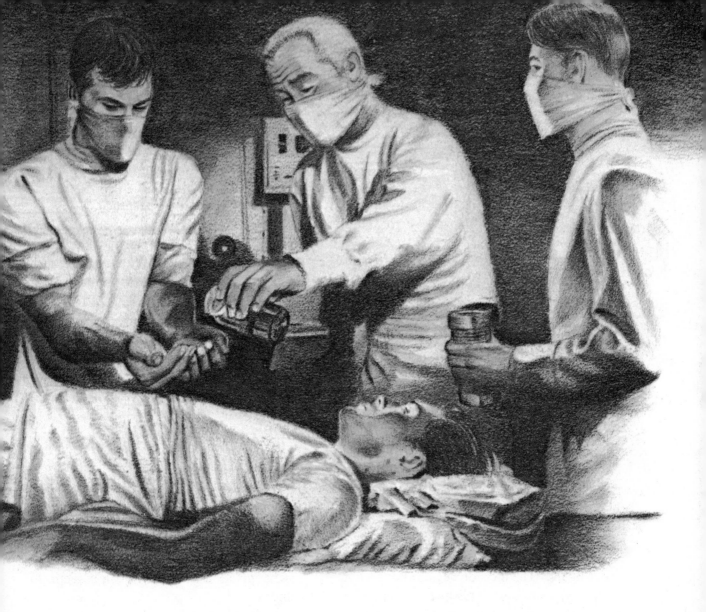

Now relax, Tommy—like you're sacking in[38] after a tough watch. Breathe deep. *(Takes a deep breath with him)* Attaboy. *(Close on* TOMMY FORD *breathing deeply, his eyes going vague. Angle on faces peering down at him slowly going out of focus. The ticking of the clock can be heard. Dissolve to control room. The gauge now shows nearly 150 feet.* FANELLI *and* GOODMAN, *the two planesmen, are obviously on edge to keep the boat steady.)*

RIGGS. That's it, fellows. Now, try to hold to a maximum of a half-degree down angle.

(Dissolve to wardroom. TOMMY FORD *is now unconscious. The clock on the wall shows twelve minutes after two.* JIMMY BRUCE *bends over his patient and studies his face. The silence is oppressive.* JIMMY BRUCE'S *face has begun to shine with perspiration under the lights.)*

BRUCE *(sounding jittery).* Well, I guess it's my move. *(He reaches out his hand.)* Scalpel.

*(*JOHNSON *removes scalpel from the improvised sterilizer and passes it through the*

---

38. *sacking in,* going to bed.

panel to O'BRIEN; O'BRIEN *takes the scalpel from* JOHNSON *and hands it across to* JIMMY BRUCE. JIMMY BRUCE *stares at it almost as if afraid of it. His hesitation is noticeable. He nods at* LT. DAVISON.)

BRUCE. Davison, before I make the incision, maybe you better check me out again to make sure. Read that page I got turned down.

DAVISON (*opening the handbook*). "When a hospital corpsman on duty on a ship that has no medical officer is confronted with a case of acute appendicitis, his judgment is put perhaps to its supreme test. . . . "

BRUCE (*impatiently*). Brother, you c'n say that again! But I mean further down where it's marked.

DAVISON. "In the case of appendectomies, it is the rare pharmacist's mate whose chances of proper diagnosis and successful operation are at all good. . . . "

BRUCE (*reacting angrily*). Hey, you pinhead, you're in the wrong book—the other big red one—*General Surgery.*

(DAVISON *picks up the other volume, already opened to the right page.*)

DAVISON. "The incision begins above a line between the anterior superior iliac spine and the umbilicus, about four centimeters medial to the anterior spine."

(*Close on* BRUCE *straining to understand.*)

DAVISON (*out of camera range*). "It extends downward and inward parallel to the fibers of the external oblique muscle and fascia. . . . "

(*Now the sweat is really standing out on* JIMMY BRUCE'S *face. He places his little finger on* TOMMY FORD'S *hip, the thumb on his umbilicus.*)

BRUCE (*muttering to himself in intense concentration*). Downward and inward . . . between the anterior superior iliac. . . .

(*Camera pans up and holds on clock ticking industriously. The minute hand moving slowly but at abnormal speed. We hear only* JIMMY BRUCE'S *staccato demands:*)

BRUCE. A spoon. . . .

DAVISON'S VOICE. One spoon.

BRUCE. Little more ether. . . .

(*Camera shoots through panel as* JOHNSON'S *hand, encased in white glove, passes instruments through to wardroom.*)

BRUCE. Those tweezers . . . sponge . . . scalpel . . . all right, quick—another spoon. . . .

(*Close on* DAVISON *recording insertion.*)

DAVISON. Spoon two.

BRUCE'S VOICE. Hemostat. . . .

(*Cut to control room medium close on* FANELLI *and* GOODMAN.)

FANELLI. Wonder how it's going?

(GOODMAN *turns to* ENSIGN RIGGS.)

GOODMAN. Any news yet, sir?

RIGGS (*shaking his head*). He's still hunting around. (*Checks gauge and bubble*) Nice work, boys. Hold her right there.

(*Back to wardroom.* JIMMY BRUCE'S *strained face reflects frustration and the dreadful possibility of failure.*)

BRUCE. Gee . . . this . . . oughta be the right place . . . but I . . . can't seem to find it.

(*Close on* HUDSON.)

HUDSON (*to* MILLER *in undertone*). What did I tell you? (*His eyes betray his lack of confidence in* BRUCE. *He looks at the clock.*)

MILLER (*with a firm warning gesture*). Shhh. . . .

(*Close on clock showing that twenty minutes have passed. Back to full shot of wardroom.*)

BRUCE. Sometimes these things aren't where they oughta be. Guess I'll hafta try the other side of the caecum. (*Pause*) Better widen the incision. (*He reaches his hand out.*) Scalpel.

(COM. MILLER *doesn't pass it quite quickly enough for* JIMMY BRUCE. *He snaps his fingers impatiently, his nerves in danger of cracking.*)

BRUCE. Come on, snap it up. I said the scalpel.

MILLER (*very quietly as he passes the scalpel to* BRUCE). Take it easy, son. You'll get there.

(COM. MILLER'S *manner seems to quiet* JIMMY BRUCE. *When he addresses* DAVISON *now, he sounds as though he has pulled himself together.*)

BRUCE. Hey, Davison, hold that picture up for me again.

(DAVISON *holds the open book up, right over* TOMMY FORD'S *prostrate figure.* JIMMY BRUCE *reads from it while he holds the scalpel poised over* TOMMY FORD'S *body, hidden from us by the sheet.*)

BRUCE (*reading slowly*). "To retract the muscle medially, the anterior and posterior sheaths are—" (TOMMY FORD *groans feebly.* JIMMY BRUCE *looks up at* LT. HUDSON. *Curtly.*) Come on—more ether.

HUDSON (*hesitating*). How long do you think this will take?

BRUCE (*flaring up*). How should I know? Y'think I do 'em every day?

HUDSON. But we have only four pounds left. If it takes you—

BRUCE. I don't want back talk. I want ether.

HUDSON. Back talk? What do you think you're—

MILLER (*breaking in*). Come on, Floyd, leave it up to the doc. Follow instructions.

HUDSON (*sullenly*). Yes, sir. (*He pours more ether onto the strainer* SWEDE *is holding.*)

BRUCE (*to* MILLER). Now, have a spoon ready, and I mean *ready.*

MILLER (*soothingly*). Okay, Doc. Okay.

(*Cut to control room. The men are silently,* tensely doing their jobs. RIGGS *glances at the clock. It shows half an hour has passed. Cut to conning tower. The* HELMSMAN *is sweating it out, too. He turns to check the time. Cut to dinette. The two* ACEY-DEUCY PLAYERS *are also involved, though the game still goes on.*)

FIRST PLAYER. It's taking a long time.

SECOND PLAYER. Come on, roll those bones.[39]

FIRST PLAYER (*taking a deep breath*). Get a load of that ether. What they tryin' t' do with it—asphyxiate all of us?

(*Back to wardroom. Somewhat drugged by the ether,* JIMMY BRUCE *runs his hand over his face.* COM. MILLER *watches him solicitously.*)

MILLER. Is the ether getting you, Doc?

BRUCE (*impatiently*). Nah, come on, let's get on with it. What's the next line, Davison?

DAVISON (*reading from the surgery book*). "Injury to the ilio . . . ilio. . . . "

BRUCE (*brusquely*). Ilioinguinal nerve.

DAVISON (*continuing*). "May result in paralysis. . . ."

(*Close on* DAVISON *reacting. Close on* BRUCE.)

BRUCE (*abruptly*). Okay, okay. On your toes everybody. Another spoon ready.

(*We feel from* BRUCE'S *eyes and the strain of his face the fearful pressure of this critical moment. Close shot of* SWEDE. *Close shot of* O'BRIEN. *Close shot of* JOHNSON. *All are watching tensely. Close on* BRUCE *who is sweating profusely, straining, then suddenly relieved.*)

BRUCE. Got around the nerve okay. (*He probes further. We can hear the ticking of the clock. Suddenly he looks up in triumph.*) I see it— No wonder I couldn't

---

39. *roll those bones,* roll those dice.

find it. All covered with adhesions and the tip is gangrenous.

(Group shot showing the response—relief—a momentary breather. Close on BRUCE.*)*

BRUCE *(all business now, and with more confidence).* All right, now, fast. Catgut.[40] Hemostat. Another retractor—

DAVISON. Catgut for first suture.

*(*DAVISON *looks up at clock. Close on clock showing two minutes before half past two. Dissolve. Close on clock, now showing nearly five past three. Camera pans down to full shot of wardroom. The room is full of foul ether vapors and* JIMMY BRUCE *shows signs of nervous exhaustion.)*

BRUCE *(to* MILLER*).* Come on . . . clamps . . . hold it open so I c'n. . . .

*(*TOMMY FORD *groans. Close on* TOMMY FORD.*)*

FORD *(stirring and groping up toward the surface of consciousness, hardly audible).* Oh . . .

(Close group shot at table.)

BRUCE *(anxiously).* More ether. He's coming out!

HUDSON. How much more do you think it's going to take?

BRUCE *(flaring up).* How many times must you ask me that? I'm trying my best. I—

HUDSON *(glancing at clock).* It's over an hour already. I just want to be sure we don't run out of ether before—

BRUCE *(facing him angrily).* If we do, Hudson, it'll be your fault and I'll— *(He seems almost ready to strike* HUDSON *who cuts in sharply.)*

HUDSON. Listen, Bruce, I don't care what you're doing. You're still an enlisted man and—

*(*COM. MILLER *takes control at this point in his authoritative, but very quiet, way.)*

MILLER. I think it's time to clear the air a little bit, fellows. Getting pretty foul in

here. *(Looks across at* SWEDE*)* Better get the blowers working, Swede.

*(*HUDSON *and* BRUCE *relax.* JIMMY BRUCE *goes back to work.)*

BRUCE *(snapping his fingers).* More catgut. Hemostat. Alcohol—

(Cut to dinette. The MESSENGER *who was seen previously kneeling over the fallen body of* TOMMY FORD *appears in the entrance way.)*

FIRST ACEY-DEUCY PLAYER. How's it going?

MESSENGER *(looking up).* They say he's got hold of a whole mess of appendix.

SECOND PLAYER. That's the *meso-appendix*—the little knob near the base.

FIRST PLAYER. Listen to the man—another quack!

(Cut to conning tower, angling toward HELMSMAN *and* WILLIAMS.*)*

HELMSMAN *(glancing up at clock).* What's taking so long?

WILLIAMS. What's the diff, long as he makes it?

(Medium close of SONARMAN, *listening intently as he moves his dial.)*

HELMSMAN. That stinkin' ether'll put us all under before he's through.

(Suddenly the SONARMAN *cocks his head, moves his dial slowly back and holds it. He listens more eagerly and signals* WILLIAMS.*)*

SONARMAN. Tell the Skipper I think I hear screws[41] bearing 0–3–9.

(Dissolve to wardroom. Close of BRUCE. *He has reached a delicate phase of the operation—the purse-string suture.)*

BRUCE *(hoarsely).* Okay. What's the next step?

DAVISON *(reading).* "The ends of the tied

---

40. *catgut,* used in surgical operations as thread to sew up (suture) a wound or cut.
41. *screws,* the propellers of a surface vessel.

purse-string suture are again tied over the stump of the mesoappendix. . . . "

BRUCE *(gritting his teeth)*. The ends of the—

(Suddenly they are interrupted by the squawk box.)

SQUAWK BOX *(voice of* QUARTERMASTER WILLIAMS*)*. Sound reports screws bearing 0–3–9, Skipper.

(Close on COM. MILLER, *reacting to this report of the presence of an enemy vessel. Wider angle of wardroom. The others also react to this new danger. They hesitate for a moment.)*

BRUCE *(to* O'BRIEN*)*. All right . . . more alcohol. . . . Let the Skipper worry about that.

(COM. MILLER goes to the squawk box.)

MILLER *(to squawk box)*. Let me know if they're closing. And get a turn count.[42]

(He turns back to the table and looks at BRUCE *questioningly.)*

BRUCE *(to himself)*. Oh, brother! If I make a mistake now.

SQUAWK BOX *(voice of* QUARTERMASTER WILLIAMS*)*. The screws are highspeed, Skipper. Still closing. Bearing 0–3–6.

(MILLER looks at JIMMY BRUCE.)

BRUCE. Go ahead, Skipper. I'll get Swede to relieve you. Better go fight your ship.

MILLER *(turns back to the squawk box)*. I'm on my way up to take charge of evasive action. Rig for silent running. Change course—right fifteen degrees rudder. *(He turns back to* JIMMY BRUCE, *puts his hand on his shoulder.)* Back as soon as I can shake this baby, Jimmy.

BRUCE *(so intent on what he is doing that he merely nods and goes on with his labors)*. Vaseline gauze. More catgut. . . .

(COM. MILLER exits. Cut to control room angled toward plane wheels. ENSIGN RIGGS *comes over to the planesmen.)*

RIGGS. Shift the bow and stern planes to hand power.

FANELLI *and* **GOODMAN.** Aye, aye, sir.

(While they attend to this, RIGGS *crosses back and gets on the squawk box.)*

RIGGS. Secure the I.C. motor generators.[43] Secure the blower and air conditioning.

(As COM. MILLER *appears on his way to the conning tower, the motors go off and the sudden quiet permits us to hear the water sloshing against the hull. Close on* FANELLI *and* GOODMAN. *Having to hold the planes with their own muscle power is a tremendous strain. Their arms tremble with the effort.)*

RIGGS. Hold her with everything you've got!

*(FANELLI *and* GOODMAN *can only nod as they put their strength against the wheels. Cut to interior of wardroom. The lights go out because of the cutting off of the generators.)*

BRUCE. Now what's the matter?

HUDSON. They've cut off the generators.

BRUCE *(cracking for a moment)*. Oh, brother, what a SNAFU![44] *(Then he takes hold again.)*

(There is a quick look between HUDSON *and* BRUCE, *nothing more.)*

HUDSON. We can finish up with the emergency lanterns.

BRUCE. Right. Break 'em out. No stinkin' subchaser's gonna foul up this operation.

*(HUDSON *stares at him a moment, impressed, then sets to work with the others. And* DAVISON, SWEDE, O'BRIEN, *and* HUDSON *grab the lanterns and rapidly set them up so that they throw a strange but adequate light on the operating table.)*

---

42. *a turn count,* a count of the rate of speed at which the propellers of the approaching ship are turning, to determine the speed of the vessel.
43. *Secure the I.C. motor generators,* shut off the internal combustion motor generators to cut down noise.
44. *SNAFU* (sna fü´), bad situation. The word *snafu* is derived from the initial letters of "situation normal—all fouled up."

BRUCE (*going back to his work*). Okay. We've almost got it now.

(*Cut to conning tower:* COM. MILLER *approaches the* SONARMAN. *The latter switches on the loud-speaker so* MILLER *and the audience can hear the sound of the approaching screws.*)

SONARMAN. Closing fast. Bearing 0–2–3.

MILLER (*to* WILLIAMS). We'll keep turning away from them—left rudder another ten degrees.

WILLIAMS. Aye, aye, sir.

SONARMAN (*calling out over the sound of the sonar*). Still closing, sir. Bearing 0–2–1.

MILLER. Very well.

(*Cut to control room.* FANELLI *and* GOODMAN *show perspiration on their faces as they strain to hold the boat steady. Cut to interior of dinette. The two* ACEY-DEUCY PLAYERS *are now silently sweating it out. One of them rattles the dice listlessly over and over. Cut to wardroom. With the ventilation system off, the effect of the ether fumes is overpowering.* JIMMY BRUCE *pauses and holds his head, seemingly overcome for a moment.*)

BRUCE. Oh, this ether.

(HUDSON'S *reaction is surprisingly sympathetic.*)

HUDSON. With those ventilators off, it's rough, kid. But at least it solves one thing for us—(*indicates the unconscious form of* TOMMY FORD)—it keeps him under. (*To* O'BRIEN) Try holding a little alcohol under his nose. That'll pep him up.

BRUCE (*looking at* HUDSON *warmly for the first time*). Thanks. (*Goes on with his work.*)

(*Cut to conning tower. Medium close at sonar table. The sound of the oncoming screws is considerably louder.*)

SONARMAN. Seem to be coming right for us, Skipper. Bearing 1–8–8.

MILLER (*to* WILLIAMS, *wearing earphones for silent running*). Right fifteen degrees rudder. We'll try to get on their course in the opposite direction.

(*Close on sonar apparatus as the sound of the screws grows louder. Cut to control room.* FANELLI *and* GOODMAN, *who can hear the approaching subchaser now, exchange a look of apprehension. Cut to dinette. The* ACEY-DEUCY PLAYERS *can hear it. They look at each other meaningfully. Back to wardroom.*)

BRUCE (*in a hoarse whisper*). Another drain. Alcohol. Have the needle ready.

(*The men in the wardroom too can hear the sound of the approaching enemy screws, but—except for a quick glance in the direction of the sound—all keep at their jobs. Cut to conning tower, close at sonar system. The sound of the enemy vessel is exceedingly loud now.*)

SONARMAN. Closing, closing. Gonna pass right over us.

MILLER (*in whisper to* QUARTERMASTER WILLIAMS). All stop.

(*Cut to control room. Now with all motors off,* FANELLI *and* GOODMAN *must strain harder than ever to hold the boat level. Their muscles stand out against the pressure of it.*)

RIGGS (*quietly*). Hang on! Hang on!

(*Cut to conning tower. The rumbling grows louder as the subchaser begins to pass over them. It sounds like an elevated railway. They all look up instinctively. Cut back to wardroom. The subchaser is passing over with a subway roar. Even* JIMMY BRUCE *is interrupted by the terrible proximity of the enemy. He looks up with anxious eyes. Then he takes hold again.*)

BRUCE. Okay, let's keep going. Every second counts now.

(*Reaction from* HUDSON—*increasingly impressed. Dissolve to interior of conning tower, close at sonar system. The sound indi-*

cates that the subchaser is now going away.)

SONARMAN *(suppressing a tendency to smile).* Screws now opening on one-eighty.[45]

MILLER *(relieved, turning to* WILLIAMS*).* All right. Make 50 R.P.M.'s[46] again. At 1540, if screws continue to open, return to normal running.

WILLIAMS *(also showing relief).* Aye, aye, sir.

MILLER *(to* SONARMAN*).* Report to me when it's all clear. *(He starts down the hatchway.)*

(Exterior of submarine underway, submerged. Dissolve to wardroom. Close on clock showing the time as 3:40.)

BRUCE'S VOICE. Ready . . . scalpel.

(Camera pulls back to full shot of everyone including COM. MILLER, *waiting tensely while* JIMMY BRUCE *goes in with scalpel off scene. He bends down over the body and probes with his other gloved hand. Close on* BRUCE *so that you cannot see what he is holding.)*

BRUCE *(triumphantly).* Well, there it is. Funny that a little thing like that c'n cause all this fuss. *(He snaps back into his job, clicking with efficiency and confidence now.)* All right now, let's get this thing battened down—sew Tommy back in one piece.

(Close shot favoring HUDSON. *He looks at* MILLER.*)*

HUDSON *(recalling* MILLER'S *words at the beginning; muttering them to himself).* "Panicky, half-grown kids suddenly find out they're men."

(MILLER just manages to overhear him and smiles.)

BRUCE *(to* HUDSON*).* What was that?

HUDSON. Nothing, Doc. Just talking to myself. Anything else you want me to do?

BRUCE. Just keep watching his eyes. We

don't want him to come out of this too soon.

HUDSON *(under his breath).* Aye, aye.

SQUAWK BOX. Conning tower reporting on sound. All clear. All clear.

(MILLER grins. Goes to squawk box.)

MILLER. Return to normal running. Get the

---

45. *Screws now opening on one-eighty.* The propellers of the subchaser are now going away from the stern.
46. *50 R.P.M.'s,* fifty revolutions per minute, or the submarine motor at low speed.

ventilators going. And bleed oxygen into the boat[47] so we can purify the air.

SQUAWK BOX. Aye, aye, sir. Oh, and Skipper, how's it going down there?

MILLER (cheerfully). Operation appendix is just about secured.

(He returns to the table. In a moment the lights come on. The ventilator starts. The men breathe in with relief. Cut to control room.)

RIGGS. Return bow and stern planes to normal power.

(SEAMEN FANELLI and GOODMAN grin and heave deep sighs of relief. Cut to interior of conning tower. Close on HELMSMAN, grinning. Cut to dinette. Close on ACEY-DEUCY PLAYERS, also grinning. Wardroom again.)

BRUCE (briskly). Okay, before this final suture—one last check to make sure we haven't left anything inside of Tommy.

DAVISON (checking his list). Hemostats— eight.

MILLER (counting the ones removed). Er . . . eight . . . check.

DAVISON. Gauze drains—five.

MILLER. Check.

DAVISON. Retractors, that is, spoons— three.

MILLER (counting them). Three. Check.

VOICE OF LEROY JOHNSON. Wait a minute! (They turn toward his voice in the pantry. Cut to pantry. JOHNSON bends down to talk through sliding door.) I handed out four spoons, and I want every one of my spoons back!

(Cut to wardroom. BRUCE reaches in out of the scene.)

BRUCE. Leroy, you're really on the ball. Here's your spoon!

(Everyone laughs and the tension is released.)

MILLER. Okay, Doc, soon as you give us the all clear, we'll surface and air out the boat, and see if we can't reestablish contact with our little friends.

(They turn back to finish the job. Dissolve to exterior of submarine surfacing. Then to interior of conning tower. Present, waiting with bursting lungs for the hatch to open, are all the principals at the operation. WILLIAMS throws open the hatch to the bridge. COM. MILLER, JIMMY BRUCE, SWEDE, O'BRIEN, LTS. HUDSON and DAVISON, and LEROY JOHNSON raise their faces to the open air, breathing luxuriously. HUDSON turns around and smiles at JIMMY BRUCE. We should have a feeling, without hitting it too hard, that this experience has mellowed him and brought him closer to the men.)

HUDSON (quietly). Nice work, Jimmy. I'm sorry I blew.

BRUCE. Aw, forget it, Mr. Hudson. You're a good man to have around.

HUDSON. Thanks, Jimmy. I feel the same way about you. (HUDSON relaxes slightly.)

SWEDE (suddenly lets out a wail of dismay). Oh, what I forgot!

O'BRIEN. Not another spoon?

SWEDE. My cake! My Christmas cake! It's been in the oven all this time! (He shoots down through the hatchway to the control room. Dissolve to galley.)

SWEDE (runs in, throws the oven door open and draws out his cake. It is burnt to ash. Half bitterly, half with humor). Serves me right for trying to get fancy on a pigboat. It happens every time.

(Back to conning tower with hatch to bridge open.)

MILLER. Well, Jimmy, I think you've got a Christmas present coming. I could have orders cut to send you home to college— pre-med. If ever I saw a great natural surgeon—

---

47. *bleed oxygen into the boat,* open the compressed-oxygen flasks in each compartment.

BRUCE. Me a surgeon? Are you kidding? I never want to go through anything like that again as long as I live. *(*MILLER, HUDSON, O'BRIEN, *and the others grin.)*

(The RADIOMAN *enters.)*

RADIOMAN. I got the report off, sir. Oh, and everybody back at the base is wishing us a Merry Christmas.

MILLER. That reminds me, men—we've been a little busy around here today or I would have said it sooner: Merry Christmas to all of you.

ADLIBS. Thanks, Skipper. Merry Christmas, sir.

(There is a general exchange of handshakes. BRUCE *and* HUDSON *shake, too, but casually, like the others.)*

MILLER *(all business again).* All right, men. Let's pull the plug[48] and get on with the job.

(Fade out.) ☐☐

---

48. **pull the plug**, dive.

Discussion

1. **(a)** What is the most immediate and important conflict in "The Pharmacist's Mate"? **(b)** What larger conflict are all these characters involved in, as well? **(c)** What effect does this larger conflict have upon the action within the submarine?

2. **(a)** What do you learn about Hudson's personality from his scene in the conning tower with Williams and the Helmsman (236a, lines 4–34)? **(b)** What do you learn of Miller's personality from his first scene with Swede (236a, line 35 to 237a, line 7)? **(c)** What do you learn of the other characters and of the general atmosphere on the submarine from the first two scenes in the dinette (237a, line 7 to 238b, line 22) and (239a, line 10 to 239b, line 10)?

3. Read "Emergency at Sea" (pages 260–261), the edited newspaper article on which this television play is based. **(a)** What is emphasized by calling the play "The Pharmacist's Mate"? **(b)** Explain how the fifth paragraph of the newspaper article was expanded in the play. What is the effect of this expansion?

4. **(a)** In paragraph 13 of the newspaper article, all the men serving in the wardroom were senior to the surgeon in both age and rank. How is this changed in the play? **(b)** Which character in the play most calls attention to the difference in rank among the men? **(c)** Is there more or less conflict in the play because of this difference? Explain.

5. In most plays you learn about the characters through dialogue and actions. **(a)** What are Commander Miller's outstanding qualities? **(b)** How are these qualities demonstrated?

6. **(a)** What sort of person is Jimmy Bruce when you first meet him? **(b)** Trace Bruce's development from the time he settles down with a comic book to his successful completion of the operation. **(c)** In what ways does he bear out the Skipper's statement, "I've seen panicky, half-grown kids suddenly find out they're men"?

7. Do any other characters change or grow during the course of the play? If so, explain that change or growth.

8. In your opinion, what is the point of greatest excitement in the play?

9. **(a)** Find evidences of humor in the play. **(b)** There is really no humor in the newspaper article. In your opinion, is the addition of humorous touches in the play desirable? Why or why not?

10. **(a)** Trace the changes in mood from scene to scene throughout the play. **(b)** What mood seems to prevail most strongly throughout?

Using context, structure, or your Glossary, answer the questions about each italicized word.

1. She proved to be extremely *competent* at repairing bicycles and was equally skilled at fixing tricycles, skates, and wagons.

(a) Can you get the meaning of *competent* from context? What does it mean?

(b) According to the Glossary, which syllable is accented in this word?

2. The two bolts on either side of the front wheel were *interchangeable.*

(a) What are the affixes in this word?

(b) Does either bolt fit either side of the wheel?

3. The ship hung motionless in forty *fathoms.*

(a) Which meaning of *fathom* in the Glossary is meant here? What part of speech is *fathom* in this sentence?

(b) How many feet are there in a fathom?

(c) What is the original meaning of *fathom?*

4. His pulse *fluctuated* widely during the operation.

(a) Did his pulse stay about the same, or did it vary?

notes and comments

George Weller

Emergency at Sea

They're giving him ether now," they said in the torpedo room.

"They've made the first cut. They're feeling around for it."

"They" were a group of anxious-faced men with their arms thrust into reversed white pajama coats. Gauze bandages hid all their expressions except the tensity in their eyes.

"It" was an acute appendix inside Dean Rector. The pains had become unendurable the day before, Rector's first birthday at sea. He was nineteen years old.

They were below the sea's surface. Above them were enemy waters crossed and recrossed by Japanese destroyers and transports.

The nearest surgeon competent to operate on Rector was thousands of miles away. There was just one way to prevent the appendix from bursting, and that was for the crew to operate.

And that's what they did.

The chief surgeon was a twenty-three-year-old pharmacist's mate. His name was Wheeler B. Lipes. He was classified as an electrocardiographer, but he'd seen Navy doctors take out one or two appendixes and thought he could do it.

There was difficulty about the ether. The crew did not know how long it would take to find the appendix. They didn't want the patient waking before they finished.

They decided to operate on the table in the officers' wardroom. The room was just long enough so that the patient's head and feet reached the two ends without hanging over.

First they got out a medical book and read up on the appendix. Everyone knew his role.

The cook provided the ether mask. It was an inverted tea-strainer, covered with gauze.

The "surgeon" had, as his staff, all men his senior in age and rank.

Before they carried Rector to the wardroom, the submarine captain asked Lipes to talk with the patient.

"Look, Dean, I never did anything like this before," Lipes said. "You don't have much chance to pull through anyhow. What do you say?"

"I know how it is, Doc."

It was the first time anybody had called Lipes "Doc." But there was in him, added to the

(b) How is the second syllable pronounced?

(c) What is the meaning of the Latin word from which *fluctuate* is derived?

5. After the storm, Gerry decided to try to *reestablish* contact with the pilot.

(a) What is the prefix in this word?

(b) Had Gerry been in contact with the pilot before the storm?

Budd Schulberg   1914 •

In adapting the news article below as a television play, Budd Schulberg was probably able to draw on his firsthand knowledge of Navy life, for he served in that branch of the armed forces during World War II and was commended for his gathering of photographic evidence of war crimes.

As a writer, Schulberg has become known for his hard-hitting realism. In his short stories, novels, plays, and screenplays, he has often exposed unpleasant truths about boxing, labor, politics, and Hollywood. For his original screenplay *On the Waterfront*, he won an Academy Award in 1954.

---

steadiness that goes with a submariner's profession, a new calmness.

The tools were laid out. They were far from perfect or complete for a major problem. The scalpel had no handle.

But submariners are used to "rigging" things. The machinist "rigged" a handle for the scalpel from a hemostat.

For an antiseptic agent, they ground sulfanilamide tablets into powder. In the cook's galley they found tablespoons. They bent these at right angles and made retractors with which to hold open the wound. Sterilizers? They milked alcohol from the torpedo mechanism and used it as well as boiling water.

The light in the wardroom was insufficient. They brought one of the big floods used for night loading and rigged it inside the wardroom's ceiling.

Rubber gloves were drawn upon the "Doc's" hands. The fingers were too long. The ends dribbled limply.

Rector wet his lips, glancing a side look at the tea-strainer ether mask. It was put down over his face. They waited for his pupils to dilate.

Lipes found the point where he intended to cut. It took him nearly twenty minutes to find the appendix.

Bulletins seeped back into the engine room and they kept the sub steady below a stormy sea.

The patient's face began to grimace.

"More ether," ordered the Doc.

There was hardly three-quarters of one can from the original five pounds left, but once again the tea-strainer was soaked in ether. The fumes made the operating staff giddy.

Suddenly came the moment when the Doc reached out his hand, pointing toward the needle threaded with catgut.

One by one the tablespoons were withdrawn and returned to the galley. It was the Skipper who noticed one spoon was missing. Lipes reached into the incision for the last time and withdrew the spoon and closed the incision.

At that moment the last can of ether went dry. It had taken the amateurs two and a half hours to perform a forty-five minute operation.

"It wasn't one of those 'snappy valve' appendixes," Lipes apologized as he felt the first handclasps upon his shoulder.

*Two very different enemies
in two very different conflicts—
how could old Mrs. Wang win
against either?*

The Old Demon

Pearl S. Buck

Old Mrs. Wang knew of course that there was a war. Everybody had known for a long time that there was war going on and that Japanese were killing Chinese. But still it was not real and no more than hearsay since none of the Wangs had been killed. The Village of Three Mile Wangs on the flat banks of the Yellow River, which was old Mrs. Wang's clan village, had never even seen a Japanese. This was how they came to be talking about Japanese at all.

It was evening and early summer, and after her supper Mrs. Wang had climbed the dike steps, as she did every day, to see how high the river had risen. She was much more afraid of the river than of the Japanese. She knew what the river would do. And one by one the villagers had followed her up the dike, and now they stood staring down at the malicious yellow water, curling along like a lot of snakes, and biting at the high dike banks.

"I never saw it as high as this so early," Mrs. Wang said. She sat down on a bamboo stool that her grandson, Little Pig, had brought for her, and spat into the water.

"It's worse than the Japanese, this old devil of a river," Little Pig said recklessly.

"Fool!" Mrs. Wang said quickly. "The river god will hear you. Talk about something else."

So they had gone on talking about the Japanese. . . . How, for instance, asked Wang, the baker, who was old Mrs. Wang's nephew twice removed, would they know the Japanese when they saw them?

Mrs. Wang at this point said positively, "You'll know them. I once saw a foreigner. He was taller than the eaves of my house and he had mud-colored hair and eyes the color of a fish's eyes. Anyone who does not look like us—that is a Japanese."

Everybody listened to her since she was the oldest woman in the village and whatever she said settled something.

Then Little Pig spoke up in his disconcerting way. "You can't see them, Grandmother. They hide up in the sky in airplanes."

Mrs. Wang did not answer immediately. Once she would have said positively, "I shall not believe in an airplane until I see it." But so many things had been true which she had not believed—the Empress, for instance, whom she had not believed dead, was dead. The Republic,[1] again, she had not believed in because she did not know what it was. She still did not know, but they had said for a long time there had been one. So now she merely stared quietly about the dike where they all sat around her. It was very pleasant and cool, and she felt nothing mattered if the river did not rise to flood.

"I don't believe in the Japanese," she said flatly.

They laughed at her a little, but no one spoke. Someone lit her pipe—it was Little Pig's wife, who was her favorite, and she smoked it.

"Sing, Little Pig!" someone called.

So Little Pig began to sing an old song in a high, quavering voice, and old Mrs. Wang listened and forgot the Japanese. The evening was beautiful, the sky so clear and still that the willows overhanging the dike were reflected even in the muddy water. Everything was at peace. The thirty-odd houses which made up the village straggled along beneath them. Nothing could break this peace. After all, the Japanese were only human beings.

"I doubt those airplanes," she said mildly to Little Pig when he stopped singing.

But without answering her, he went on to another song.

Year in and year out she had spent the summer evenings like this on the dike. The first time she was seventeen and a bride, and her husband had shouted to her to come out of the house and up the dike, and she had come, blushing and twisting her hands together, to hide among the women while the men roared at her and made jokes about her. All the same, they had liked her. "A pretty piece of meat in your bowl," they had said to her husband. "Feet a trifle big," he had answered deprecatingly. But she could see he was pleased, and so gradually her shyness went away.

He, poor man, had been drowned in a flood when he was still young. And it had taken her years to get him prayed out of Buddhist purgatory.[2] Finally she had grown tired of it, what with the child and the land all on her back, and so when the priest said coaxingly, "Another ten pieces of silver and he'll be out entirely," she asked, "What's he got in there yet?"

"Only his right hand," the priest said, encouraging her.

Well, then, her patience broke. Ten dollars! It would feed them for the winter. Besides, she had had to hire labor for her share of repairing the dike, too, so there would be no more floods.

"If it's only one hand, he can pull himself out," she said firmly.

She often wondered if he had, poor silly fellow. As like as not, she had often thought gloomily in the night, he was still lying there,

---

1. **The Republic.** For thousands of years China was an empire ruled by a succession of Emperors and Empresses. In 1912 the Republic of China was established, which lasted until 1949.
2. **Buddhist purgatory.** Buddhism as a religion held a position similar to Christianity in the Western World. Some forms of Buddhism teach of a heaven, hell, and purgatory where souls are purified.

waiting for her to do something about it. That was the sort of man he was. Well, some day, perhaps, when Little Pig's wife had had the first baby safely and she had a little extra, she might go back to finish him out of purgatory. There was no real hurry, though. . . .

"Grandmother, you must go in," Little Pig's wife's soft voice said. "There is a mist rising from the river now that the sun is gone."

"Yes, I suppose I must," old Mrs. Wang agreed. She gazed at the river a moment. That river—it was full of good and evil together. It would water the fields when it was curbed and checked, but then if an inch were allowed it, it crashed through like a roaring dragon. That was how her husband had been swept away—careless, he was, about his bit of the dike. He was always going to mend it, always going to pile more earth on top of it, and then in a night the river rose and broke through. He had run out

of the house, and she had climbed on the roof with the child and had saved herself and it while he was drowned. Well, they had pushed the river back again behind its dikes, and it had stayed there this time. Every day she herself walked up and down the length of the dike for which the village was responsible and examined it. The men laughed and said, "If anything is wrong with the dikes, Granny will tell us."

It had never occurred to any of them to move the village away from the river. The Wangs had lived there for generations, and some had always escaped the floods and had fought the river more fiercely than ever afterward.

Little Pig suddenly stopped singing.

"The moon is coming up!" he cried. "That's not good. Airplanes come out on moonlight nights."

"Where do you learn all this about airplanes?" old Mrs. Wang exclaimed. "It is tiresome to me," she added, so severely that

no one spoke. In this silence, leaning upon the arm of Little Pig's wife, she descended slowly the earthen steps which led down into the village, using her long pipe in the other hand as a walking stick. Behind her the villagers came down, one by one, to bed. No one moved before she did, but none stayed long after her.

And in her own bed at last, behind the blue cotton mosquito curtains which Little Pig's wife fastened securely, she fell peacefully asleep.

She had lain awake a little while thinking about the Japanese and wondering why they wanted to fight. Only very coarse persons wanted wars. In her mind she saw large coarse persons. If they came one must wheedle them, she thought, invite them to drink tea, and explain to them, reasonably—only why should they come to a peaceful farming village . . . ?

So she was not in the least prepared for Little Pig's wife screaming at her that the Japanese had come. She sat up in bed muttering, "The tea bowls—the tea—"

"Grandmother, there's no time!" Little Pig's wife screamed. "They're here—they're here!"

"Where?" old Mrs. Wang cried, now awake.

"In the sky!" Little Pig's wife wailed.

They had all run out at that, into the clear early dawn, and gazed up. There, like wild geese flying in autumn, were great birdlike shapes.

"But what are they?" old Mrs. Wang cried.

And then, like a silver egg dropping, something drifted straight down and fell at the far end of the village in a field. A fountain of earth flew up, and they all ran to see it. There was a hole thirty feet across, as big as a pond. They were so astonished they could not speak, and then, before anyone could say anything, another and another egg began to fall and everybody was running, running. . . .

Everybody, that is, but Mrs. Wang. When Little Pig's wife seized her hand to drag her along, old Mrs. Wang pulled away and sat down against the bank of the dike.

"I can't run," she remarked. "I haven't run in seventy years, since before my feet were bound.[3] You go on. Where's Little Pig?" She looked around. Little Pig was already gone. "Like his grandfather," she remarked, "always the first to run."

But Little Pig's wife would not leave her, not, that is, until old Mrs. Wang reminded her that it was her duty.

"If Little Pig is dead," she said, "then it is necessary that his son be born alive." And when the girl still hesitated, she struck at her gently with her pipe. "Go on—go on," she exclaimed.

So unwillingly, because now they could scarcely hear each other speak for the roar of the dipping planes, Little Pig's wife went on with the others.

By now, although only a few minutes had passed, the village was in ruins and the straw roofs and wooden beams were blazing. Everybody was gone. As they passed they had shrieked at old Mrs. Wang to come on, and she had called back pleasantly:

"I'm coming—I'm coming!"

But she did not go. She sat quite alone watching now what was an extraordinary spectacle. For soon other planes came, from where she did not know, but they attacked the first ones. The sun came up over the fields of ripening wheat, and in the clear summery air the planes wheeled and darted and spat at each other. When this was over, she thought, she would go back into the village and see if anything was left. Here and there a wall stood, supporting a roof. She could not see her own house from here. But

she was not unused to war. Once bandits had looted their village, and houses had been burned then, too. Well, now it had happened again. Burning houses one could see often, but not this darting silvery shining battle in the air. She understood none of it—not what those things were, nor how they stayed up in the sky. She simply sat, growing hungry, and watching.

"I'd like to see one close," she said aloud. And at that moment, as though in answer, one of them pointed suddenly downward, and, wheeling and twisting as though it were wounded, it fell head down in a field which Little Pig had ploughed only yesterday for soybeans. And in an instant the sky was empty again, and there was only this wounded thing on the ground and herself.

She hoisted herself carefully from the earth. At her age she need be afraid of nothing. She could, she decided, go and see what it was. So, leaning on her bamboo pipe, she made her way slowly across the fields. Behind her in the sudden stillness two or three village dogs appeared and followed, creeping close to her in their terror. When they drew near to the fallen plane, they barked furiously. Then she hit them with her pipe.

"Be quiet," she scolded, "there's already been noise enough to split my ears!"

She tapped the airplane.

"Metal," she told the dogs. "Silver, doubtless," she added. Melted up, it would make them all rich.

She walked around it, examining it closely. What made it fly? It seemed dead. Nothing moved or made a sound within it. Then, coming to the side to which it tipped, she

---

3. **before my feet were bound.** Among certain classes it was a custom to wrap the feet of a baby girl in tight bindings. The resulting deformity was considered attractive and further signified that she need not work.

saw a young man in it, slumped into a heap in a little seat. The dogs growled, but she struck at them again and they fell back.

"Are you dead?" she inquired politely.

The young man moved a little at her voice, but did not speak. She drew nearer and peered into the hole in which he sat. His side was bleeding.

"Wounded!" she exclaimed. She took his wrist. It was warm, but inert, and when she let it go, it dropped against the side of the hole. She stared at him. He had black hair and a dark skin like a Chinese and still he did not look like a Chinese.

"He must be a Southerner," she thought. Well, the chief thing was, he was alive.

"You had better come out," she remarked. "I'll put some herb plaster on your side."

The young man muttered something dully.

"What did you say?" she asked. But he did not say it again.

"I am still quite strong," she decided after a moment. So she reached in and seized him about the waist and pulled him out slowly, panting a good deal. Fortunately he was rather a little fellow and very light. When she had him on the ground, he seemed to find his feet; and he stood shakily and clung to her, and she held him up.

"Now if you can walk to my house," she said, "I'll see if it is there."

Then he said something, quite clearly. She listened and could not understand a word of it. She pulled away from him and stared.

"What's that?" she asked.

He pointed at the dogs. They were standing growling, their ruffs up. Then he spoke again, and as he spoke he crumpled to the ground. The dogs fell on him, so that she had to beat them off with her hands.

"Get away!" she shouted. "Who told *you* to kill him?"

And then, when they had slunk back, she heaved him somehow onto her back; and, trembling, half carrying, half pulling him, she dragged him to the ruined village and laid him in the street while she went to find her house, taking the dogs with her.

Her house was quite gone. She found the place easily enough. This was where it should be, opposite the water gate into the dike. She had always watched that gate herself. Miraculously it was not injured now, nor was the dike broken. It would be easy enough to rebuild the house. Only, for the present, it was gone.

So she went back to the young man. He was lying as she had left him, propped against the dike, panting and very pale. He had opened his coat and he had a little bag from which he was taking out strips of cloth and a bottle of something. And again he spoke, and again she understood nothing. Then he made signs and she saw it was water he wanted, so she took up a broken pot from one of many blown about the street, and, going up the dike, she filled it with river water and brought it down again and washed his wound, and she tore off the strips he made from the rolls of bandaging. He knew how to put the cloth over the gaping wound and he made signs to her, and she followed these signs. All the time he was trying to tell her something, but she could understand nothing.

"You must be from the South, sir," she said. It was easy to see he had education. He looked very clever. "I have heard your language is different from ours." She laughed a little to put him at his ease, but he only stared at her somberly with dull eyes. So she said brightly, "Now if I could find something for us to eat, it would be nice."

He did not answer. Indeed he lay back, panting still more heavily, and stared into space as though she had not spoken.

"You would be better with food," she went on. "And so would I," she added. She was beginning to feel unbearably hungry.

It occurred to her that in Wang, the baker's shop, there might be some bread. Even if it were dusty with fallen mortar, it would still be bread. She would go and see. But before she went she moved the soldier a little so that he lay in the edge of shadow cast by a willow tree that grew in the bank of the dike. Then she went to the baker's shop. The dogs were gone.

The baker's shop was, like everything else, in ruins. No one was there. At first she saw nothing but the mass of crumpled earthen walls. But then she remembered that the oven was just inside the door, and the door frame still stood erect, supporting one end of the roof. She stood in this frame, and, running her hand in underneath the fallen roof inside, she felt the wooden cover of the iron caldron. Under this there might be steamed bread. She worked her arm delicately and carefully in. It took quite a long time, but, even so, clouds of lime and dust almost choked her. Nevertheless she was right. She squeezed her hand under the cover and felt the firm smooth skin of the big steamed bread rolls, and one by one she drew out four.

"It's hard to kill an old thing like me," she remarked cheerfully to no one, and she began to eat one of the rolls as she walked back. If she had a bit of garlic and a bowl of tea—but one couldn't have everything in these times.

It was at this moment that she heard voices. When she came in sight of the soldier, she saw surrounding him a crowd of other soldiers, who had apparently come from nowhere. They were staring down at the wounded soldier, whose eyes were now closed.

"Where did you get this Japanese, Old Mother?" they shouted at her.

"What Japanese?" she asked, coming to them.

"This one!" they shouted.

"Is he a Japanese?" she cried in the greatest astonishment. "But he looks like us—his eyes are black, his skin—"

"Japanese!" one of them shouted at her.

"Well," she said quietly, "he dropped out of the sky."

"Give me that bread!" another shouted.

"Take it," she said, "all except this one for him."

"A Japanese monkey eat good bread?" the soldier shouted.

"I suppose he is hungry also," old Mrs. Wang replied. She began to dislike these men. But then, she had always disliked soldiers.

"I wish you would go away," she said. "What are you doing here? Our village has always been peaceful."

"It certainly looks very peaceful now," one of the men said, grinning, "as peaceful as a grave. Do you know who did that, Old Mother? The Japanese!"

"I suppose so," she agreed. Then she asked, "Why? That's what I don't understand."

"Why? Because they want our land, that's why!"

"Our land!" she repeated. "Why, they can't have our land!"

"Never!" they shouted.

But all this time while they were talking and chewing the bread they had divided among themselves, they were watching the eastern horizon.

"Why do you keep looking east?" old

Mrs. Wang now asked.

"The Japanese are coming from there," the man replied who had taken the bread.

"Are you running away from them?" she asked, surprised.

"There are only a handful of us," he said apologetically.

"We were left to guard a village—Pao An, in the county of—"

"I know that village," old Mrs. Wang interrupted. "You needn't tell me. I was a girl there. How is the old Pao who keeps the teashop in the main street? He's my brother."

"Everybody is dead there," the man replied. "The Japanese have taken it—a great army of men came with their foreign guns and tanks, so what could we do?"

"Of course, only run," she agreed. Nevertheless she felt dazed and sick. So he was dead, that one brother she had left! She was now the last of her father's family.

But the soldiers were straggling away again leaving her alone.

"They'll be coming, those little black dwarfs," they were saying. "We'd best go on."

Nevertheless, one lingered a moment, the one who had taken the bread, to stare down at the young wounded man, who lay with his eyes shut, not having moved at all.

"Is he dead?" he inquired. Then, before Mrs. Wang could answer, he pulled a short knife out of his belt. "Dead or not, I'll give him a punch or two with this—"

But old Mrs. Wang pushed his arm away.

"No, you won't," she said with authority. "If he is dead, then there is no use in sending him into purgatory all in pieces. I am a good Buddhist myself."

The man laughed. "Oh well, he is dead," he answered; and then, seeing his comrades already at a distance, he ran after them.

A Japanese, was he? Old Mrs. Wang, left alone with this inert figure, looked at him tentatively. He was very young, she could see, now that his eyes were closed. His hand, limp in unconsciousness, looked like a boy's hand, unformed and still growing. She felt his wrist but could discern no pulse. She leaned over him and held to his lips the half of her roll which she had not eaten.

"Eat," she said very loudly and distinctly. "Bread!"

But there was no answer. Evidently he was dead. He must have died while she was getting the bread out of the oven.

There was nothing to do then but to finish the bread herself. And when that was done, she wondered if she ought not to follow after Little Pig and his wife and all the villagers. The sun was mounting and it was growing hot. If she were going, she had better go. But first she would climb the dike and see what the direction was. They had gone straight west, and as far as eye could look westward was a great plain. She might even see a good-sized crowd miles away. Anyway, she could see the next village, and they might all be there.

So she climbed the dike slowly, getting very hot. There was a slight breeze on top of the dike and it felt good. She was shocked to see the river very near the top of the dike. Why, it had risen in the last hour!

"You old demon!" she said severely. Let the river god hear it if he liked. He was evil, that he was—so to threaten flood when there had been all this other trouble.

She stooped and bathed her cheeks and her wrists. The water was quite cold, as though with fresh rains somewhere. Then she stood up and gazed around her. To the west there was nothing except in the far distance the soldiers still half-running, and beyond them the blur of the next village, which stood on a long rise of ground. She had better set out for that village. Doubtless Little Pig and his wife were there waiting for her.

Just as she was about to climb down and start out, she saw something on the eastern horizon. It was at first only an immense cloud of dust. But, as she stared at it, very quickly it became a lot of black dots and shining spots. Then she saw what it was. It was a lot of men—an army. Instantly she knew what army.

"That's the Japanese," she thought. Yes, above them were the buzzing silver planes. They circled about, seeming to search for someone.

"I don't know who you're looking for," she muttered, "unless it's me and Little Pig and his wife. We're the only ones left. You've already killed my brother Pao."

She had almost forgotten that Pao was dead. Now she remembered it acutely. He had such a nice shop—always clean, and the tea good and the best meat dumplings to be had and the price always the same. Pao was a good man. Besides, what about his wife and his seven children? Doubtless they were all killed, too. Now these Japanese were looking for her. It occurred to her that on the dike she could easily be seen. So she clambered hastily down.

It was when she was about halfway down that she thought of the water gate. This old river—it had been a curse to them since time began. Why should it not make up a little now for all the wickedness it had done? It was plotting wickedness again, trying to steal over its banks. Well, why not? She wavered a moment. It was a pity, of course, that the young dead Japanese would be swept into the flood. He was a nice-looking boy, and she had saved him from being stabbed. It was not quite the same as saving

his life, of course, but still it was a little the same. If he had been alive, he would have been saved. She went over to him and tugged at him until he lay well near the top of the bank. Then she went down again.

She knew perfectly how to open the water gate. Any child knew how to open the sluice for crops. But she knew also how to swing open the whole gate. The question was, could she open it quickly enough to get out of the way?

"I'm only one old woman," she muttered. She hesitated a second more. Well, it would be a pity not to see what sort of a baby Little Pig's wife would have, but one could not see everything. She had seen a great deal in this life. There was an end to what one could see, anyway.

She glanced again to the east. There were the Japanese coming across the plain. They were a long clear line of black, dotted with thousands of glittering points. If she opened this gate, the impetuous water would roar toward them, rushing into the plains, rolling into a wide lake, drowning them, maybe. Certainly they could not keep marching nearer and nearer to her and to Little Pig and his wife who were waiting for her. Well, Little Pig and his wife—they would wonder about her—but they would never dream of this. It would make a good story—she would have enjoyed telling it.

She turned resolutely to the gate. Well, some people fought with airplanes and some with guns, but you could fight with a river, too, if it were a wicked one like this one. She wrenched out a huge wooden pin. It was slippery with silvery green moss. The rill of water burst into a strong jet. When she wrenched one more pin, the rest would give way themselves. She began pulling at it, and felt it slip a little from its hole.

"I might be able to get myself out of purgatory with this," she thought, "and maybe they'll let me have that old man of mine, too. What's a hand of his to all this? Then we'll—"

The pin slipped away suddenly, and the gate burst flat against her and knocked her breath away. She had only time to gasp, to the river:

"Come on, you old demon!"

Then she felt it seize her and lift her up to the sky. It was beneath her and around her. It rolled her joyfully hither and thither, and then, holding her close and enfolded, it went rushing against the enemy. ▢▢

Discussion

1. How is old Mrs. Wang regarded by the villagers?

2. Why does Mrs. Wang say she doubts the existence of the Japanese and airplanes?

3. What is her attitude toward each of the following, and why does she feel the way she does? **(a)** her husband and grandson; **(b)** warfare in general; **(c)** the bombing of the village; **(d)** death.

4. (a) Why does Mrs. Wang help the wounded soldier? **(b)** Describe her behavior toward him after she learns that he is Japanese.

5. (a) What are her motives in opening the water gate? **(b)** Since she had earlier shown kindness to the wounded Japanese, how can her flooding the village be consistent with her character?

6. (a) What has been the role of the river in the lives of the villagers? **(b)** How does the part the river plays in the conclusion of the story contrast with its earlier role?

7. Does Mrs. Wang triumph or suffer defeat in the end? Explain your answer.

Vocabulary • Structure

The Yellow River in "The Old Demon" is described as *malicious. Malicious* is a form of the word *malice*, which comes from the Latin word *malus*, meaning "poor" or "evil."

The prefix *mal-* is found in many English words. Read the sentences below and explain how the italicized word in each is related to "evil" or "poor" in meaning.

1. An unhappy patient accused Dr. Bache of *malpractice.*

2. The humane society was on hand to make certain that the animals were not *maltreated.*

3. My father told me to stop behaving like a *malcontent* and return to school.

4. We own a normal cat and a *maladjusted* poodle.

5. Throughout the world, millions of people suffer from *malnutrition.*

Pearl Buck   1892 • 1973

At one time Pearl Buck was as much at home in China as in America. Though born in West Virginia, she went to China with her missionary parents when she was only five months old. Her college years were spent back in the United States, but a few years later, Mrs. Buck returned to China to teach for five years.

Pearl Buck's first book appeared in 1930. A year later she published *The Good Earth,* a novel about China. A best-seller for nearly two years, *The Good Earth* was made into both a play and a movie, and has been translated into more than thirty languages. In 1938 she won the Nobel Prize in Literature.

4: Heroes

CONTENT REVIEW

1. The people in this unit exhibit different kinds of courage. Weigh the problems that they face and then decide which individuals, in your opinion, display courage because they are **(a)** persistent; **(b)** committed to a dangerous goal; **(c)** trained to accept and face hazards; **(d)** willing to accept unexpected challenges.

2. Which stories are the most suspenseful? What causes the suspense in each?

3. (a) Which selections in the unit are primarily factual? **(b)** Does the factual nature of any selection make it seem more or less interesting, in your opinion? Explain.

4. Which individual in any selection comes closest to your personal concept of a hero or heroine? Why?

Unit 4, Test I
INTERPRETATION: NEW MATERIAL

Read the following article, then on your paper answer the questions.

Nobody's Better Off Dead
Quentin Reynolds

In a veterans' hospital in New York lay a young Air Force pilot. His face was turned to the wall. He was bitter and angry. A plane crash had left his body paralyzed. He could not move from his neck down. He wanted to die.

He wouldn't even listen to the doctors. They spoke of a plan that might teach him to live with his handicap.

"Let's get Junius Kellogg to talk to him," one of the doctors said. "He's helped other men take hold of life again; maybe he can do it now. This young pilot was a college athlete. It should mean a lot to him to know that Junius once played basketball with the Harlem Globetrotters."

Six-foot nine-inch Junius Kellogg had been there for three years. He roomed with seven other men who, like him, were paralyzed. In that room Junius read the pilot's record. Then he wheeled himself down the corridor and into the young vet's room. But the pilot wasn't interested in what Junius had to say. "You're talking to a vegetable," he said.

"I was a vegetable myself," Kellogg laughed. "I was worse off than you."

"Stop wasting your time," the boy told him. "I'd be better off dead."

"Nobody's better off dead," Kellogg said sharply.

That was the first of many visits. The pilot began to look forward to seeing Kellogg. Kellogg has a soft voice. He spent his childhood in Virginia. Like so many big men, he was gentle. He took over the job of feeding the young man.

One day the pilot said: "I just found out who you are. Don't you miss playing basketball?"

"I'm too busy," Kellogg grinned. "I coach a wheel-chair basketball team. I exercise about five hours a day. I can't just lie in bed. My muscles must be made to work again. Why don't you get with this exercise deal like the rest of us?"

Four months later I saw the young pilot swinging on parallel bars. I saw him swimming in the pool. And I heard him laughing. Kellogg had started him on the road back.

As a young man, Junius Kellogg already had been tested more than most men are in a lifetime. He is the oldest of eleven children. His family was very poor. Even as a child he was big. When he went to high school, he found he was a natural athlete. He was a star in football, track, and basketball. He served for three and a half years in the army. Then he won a scholarship to a New York college.

By his senior year, Kellogg was among the country's top basketball stars. Offers began to come in for him to play for money after graduation.

One day a gambler offered him $1000 if he'd play poorly so his team would lose. Kellogg knew how unfair this would be. Such a deal would hurt honest players and the game itself. After asking for time to think it over, he went to his coach. College officials took Kellogg to the authorities.

Junius was asked to play along with the gamblers. He was to try to get more evidence. This would be a dangerous trick if the gamblers found out. He played his part well, though. The police were able to catch the leaders of the mob. The basketball scandals of 1951 hit the front pages.

Kellogg was praised by the newspapers. At his college he was a hero. When school was finished, he signed with the famous Harlem Globetrotters. He felt he could play for at least ten years. He would make more money each year. He also planned to study for a higher degree in physical education.

"I thought I had life licked," Kellogg says now. "Then the roof fell in on me."

On April 2, 1954, Kellogg and four friends were driving to a game. A tire blew, and the car turned over.

Five days later, Kellogg woke up in a hospital. His body was smashed, it seemed, beyond help. His friends were not badly hurt. Kellogg's neck was broken. His spinal cord was injured, too. To help him breathe, a hole was made in his windpipe. Then he could get air through a tube. Holes were also drilled in his head; put in them were tongs attached to weights. The weights were used to stretch his neck. Kellogg, in a state of coma nearly two weeks, didn't know about it.

When he finally came to, he found he had no feeling in his

arms or his legs, and he could not move them. But as he says now, "Every day a wonderful woman therapist came to work with me. She kept telling me, 'Move your thumb.' And darned if one day I didn't move it! That was a really big thrill for me. It was even better than scoring thirty-two points in one game!"

Months later Kellogg could feed himself and shave. At last he had gained enough strength to be sent to another veterans' hospital. Now he faced harder tasks. Before, he had been fighting just to stay alive. But this would begin a fight toward a *way* to live.

"I had a great worker called Brownie," Kellogg recalls. "He had me do exercises on a special table. I got so I could sit up without falling off. Often my hand would start to shake. 'Fight it!' Brownie would yell. 'Close your fist until it passes. Do you want to lie down all your life?'

"He kept at it for eight or nine hours a day. Sometimes I thought I hated him. Today I'm grateful."

It was a big day when Kellogg went to another class. Only his legs were helpless now. He could move his wheel chair around the hospital.

Next Brownie made him drop into the pool. He sank like a stone. When he came to the surface, he found he could still swim.

A few months later he met Saul Welger. Saul had been a polio victim since he was a small child. Saul was one of the stars of a wheel-chair basketball team. He played for Pan American Airways. Saul asked Kellogg to come over and watch his team practice. Kellogg had a friend drive him out there the next night.

Kellogg was amazed at what he saw. The Pan Am Jets shot baskets and moved around the floor in wheel chairs. All of these men held full-time jobs with Pan American. Kellogg found that there were about fifty such teams in the country.

In the fall of 1956 Kellogg was called to Pan Am. He was asked to take the place of their coach. "It's a job without pay," he was told. "But when you get in better shape, you may want to work for us."

"You got yourself a deal," Kellogg said. With him, the Pan Am Jets were a great team. They became about the best wheel-chair players in the country.

Kellogg drives a car. A gift, the car was made just for his use. He doesn't know who gave him the car. It came from someone who had read about Kellogg and wanted to do something to help him.

I drove to New Jersey with Kellogg one night. His team was playing the New Jersey Wheelers, a great team, too.

The game ended in an overtime win for the Jets, 46-45. As we went back to the hospital, I said, "That was one of the most exciting games I ever saw. Disability doesn't seem to bother your boys."

The big man laughed. "We've got a saying in some of our groups: 'Ability, not disability, is what counts.' That about sums it up."

I noticed that he didn't say anything about courage. But, I suppose, to a man like Junius Kellogg courage is something you take for granted. □□

1. The main purpose of the story about the young pilot is (a) to show why the pilot wanted to die; (b) to condemn flying; (c) to describe physical therapy; (d) to introduce Junius Kellogg.

2. When was Kellogg's honesty and moral courage tested?

3. How did Kellogg meet this challenge?

4. After the accident, Kellogg had to (a) learn how to move his arms and legs; (b) keep his body in good physical condition; (c) learn to live with his handicap; (d) all of these.

5. We can infer that at times Kellogg became discouraged because (a) he found he could still swim; (b) he sometimes felt hatred for Brownie; (c) he

was given a car; (d) during therapy he cried.

6. Which of the following words best describes the author's tone? (a) admiring; (b) indifferent; (c) sad; (d) angry.

Unit 4, Test II
COMPOSITION

Choose one of the following assignments to write about. Assume that you are writing for your classmates.

1. Below are four opinions on what makes a hero. Pick the opinion with which you most strongly agree and write a one-paragraph composition showing why you agree. Support your viewpoint with examples from the unit.

(a) Anyone who can face the problems of the modern world without trying to run away from them is worthy of the title *hero*.

(b) It is a mistake to believe that a hero today earns that title without the help of others. For every hero, there

are countless other people who worked in the background to make that heroism possible.

(c) To be a hero requires more courage than wisdom.

(d) A hero is not made accidentally. True heroes live according to heroic beliefs and principles. When such people get a chance to perform what we call an act of courage, they are really just behaving according to the rules they always live by.

2. Most daily newspapers carry one or more stories about acts of heroism. Look through a newspaper to find at least one such story, and in a short composition tell why you think the editor chose to print the story,

whether the act was truly heroic, and what you think made the "hero" act as he or she did.

3. Choose a real person who is considered by many to be a hero—a scientist, a religious leader, an athlete, a doctor, a political leader, an explorer, a soldier. The person need not be living now; you might choose someone from history. Find out all you can about that person by reading an encyclopedia, a biography, or an autobiography. Then assume that you have been asked to present an award for heroism to the person. Write a brief speech in which you tell why the award is being given.

"God of the Sea, I beg you, punish Ulysses for this.

Visit him with storm and shipwreck and sorceries.

Let him wander many years before he reaches home,

and when he gets there let him find himself forgotten,

unwanted, a stranger."

THE ADVENTURES OF ULYSSES

See **GLOSSARY OF PROPER NAMES** for "The Adventures of Ulysses" on pages 310–311 for pronunciation and identification of characters and places mentioned in the introduction below and in the selection following.

Introduction

The gods and goddesses of ancient Greece seem to us a peculiar lot. They established themselves after a long and terrible war which the brothers Zeus, Poseidon, and Hades waged against the race of older gods called the Titans. Once the Titans were finally overthrown, Zeus, Poseidon, and Hades drew lots to divide the earth among them. Zeus won the sky; Poseidon, the sea; and Hades, the underworld. From that time on, Zeus ruled the earth, along with his brothers, sisters, various spouses, and a few additional gods and goddesses, all of them making their home on Mount Olympus.

These Olympians were a quarrelsome family. They ruled the universe, but not peacefully. Though immortal, they nevertheless displayed the same range of emotions one finds among mortals—and often the same bad manners. Petty jealousies would often spring up between one god and goddess or another, and fights would follow. They played favorites among humans: to one they might give special powers, while they made life difficult for another. Since Olympians could influence events and determine mortals' fates, life on earth was largely unpredictable.

It was against this background that the Trojan War started—touched off by jealousy among the gods. Eris, the goddess of discord, was not invited to a feast. Angry at being snubbed, she threw into the banquet hall a golden apple on which were the words *For the Most Beautiful*. Three goddesses each immediately claimed the apple for her

own: Hera, wife of almighty Zeus; Athene, his daughter, goddess of both wisdom and battle; and Aphrodite, his daughter-in-law, goddess of love. The three appealed to Zeus to choose, but he knew better than to get involved in that argument. Instead, he advised them to go to the mountainside where young Prince Paris was tending his father's sheep. Paris, son of King Priam of Troy, was known for his fairness as a judge.

But the goddesses did not ask Paris to select the most beautiful among them; instead, they offered him bribes. From Hera came the offer to be ruler of Europe and Asia; from Athene, the chance to lead the Trojans to victory against the Greeks; from Aphrodite, the love of the most beautiful woman in the world. Paris gave Aphrodite the golden apple.

The woman who was most famous for her beauty was Helen, wife of King Menelaus of Sparta. Most of the kings and princes of Greece had wanted to marry her, in fact, and had come to Sparta bearing rich presents for King Tyndareus, Helen's father. Tyndareus was fearful of being accused of favoritism if he accepted the presents of any one suitor. If the rejected suitors took offense, they might wage war. Sensing the problem, King Ulysses of Ithaca offered Tyndareus a solution. Ulysses was well known for his cleverness, and so the king quickly accepted his advice. Tyndareus asked all the suitors solemnly to swear to defend and protect Helen and her chosen husband. Since each suitor hoped to be the one chosen, all of them swore to the oath. Then Tyndareus chose Menelaus to be Helen's groom, and appointed him king of Sparta as well. As reward for his advice, Ulysses asked to marry Penelope, Tyndareus's niece.

Guided by Aphrodite, Paris later arrived in Sparta. Menelaus treated him hospitably, as was the custom, but Menelaus was soon called away because of his father's death. Menelaus left Helen to rule in his absence.

Under Aphrodite's spell, Helen fell deeply in love with her visitor. She eloped with Paris, taking with her most of the palace treasures. Paris took her home with him to Troy, where his father, King Priam, found Helen so lovely he vowed to protect her and Paris and never to return her to Sparta.

Menelaus returned to find Helen gone. Hurt and angry, he called upon the kings and princes of all Greece to keep their vows and to help him. They responded, and eventually a thousand ships carrying troops sailed to Troy.

Troy, however, was a walled city, built for defense, and it was not easy to conquer. The war waged for ten years, with first one side, then the other, favored by the gods. Aphrodite, of course, sided with Paris and Troy; Hera—goddess of marriage—just as strongly opposed them. The rest of the gods and goddesses played their favorites as well, although Zeus remained neutral most of the time to avoid Hera's wrath.

After ten years the Greeks finally took Troy—through a trick. The clever Ulysses had built a huge wooden horse, the famous Trojan Horse, inside which warriors could hide. They left this horse outside the gates of Troy and sailed away—only to hide behind a nearby island. The Trojans assumed their foes had given up; nevertheless, they were puzzled by the enormous horse outside their gates. A Greek soldier, who had volunteered to remain behind and be captured, was brought before King Priam. He played his part well. He declared that both he and the horse were intended to be offerings to Athene, but that he had escaped. The horse had been built so large, the soldier claimed, to discourage the Trojans from carting it into their city. The Trojans were supposed to destroy the wooden offering and thereby bring the wrath of Athene upon themselves.

The scheme worked. The Trojans dragged the horse through the gates and into their city, thinking to win Athene's favor away from the Greeks. Then that night, the Greeks who had hidden in the horse, Ulysses included, climbed out through a trap door and threw wide the city gates. The remaining Greek soldiers, returned from hiding, stormed through the gates of Troy, set fire to buildings, and killed those who rushed out into the streets in confusion. By morning the city was in ruins. Helen was taken to Menelaus, who gladly received her back, and together they sailed home to Sparta.

When Ulysses had joined the Greek forces ten years earlier, he had been forced to leave behind in Ithaca his attractive and devoted wife, Penelope, and his young son, Telemachus. Throughout the war he had fought with courage, coolness, and—whenever necessary—cunning. His plan to take Troy had worked and had brought an end to the war. But Ulysses was weary of battle. He had begun to long increasingly for home. Ten years away from his wife, his son, and his native land seemed like an eternity.

In the story that follows, Ulysses begins his homeward journey, unaware of what the gods might yet have in store for him. □□

The Adventures of Ulysses

Bernard Evslin

Ships and Men

After Troy was burned, Ulysses sailed for home with three ships holding fifty men each.

Three thousand years ago ships were very different; through the years they have changed much more than the men who sail them.

These beaked warships used by the pirate kingdoms of the Middle Sea were like no vessels you have ever seen. Imagine a very long narrow rowboat with twenty oars on each side. The timbers of the bow curve sharply to a prow, and this prow grows longer and sharper, becomes in fact a long polished shaft tipped by a knife-edged brass spearhead. This was called the ram, the chief weapon of ancient warships.

In battle, the opposing ships spun about each other, swooping forward, twirling on their beams,[1] darting backward, their narrow hulls allowing them to backwater very swiftly. The object was to ram the enemy before he rammed you. And to ram first was the only defense, for the brass beak of the ramming ship sheared easily through the timbers of its victim, knocking a huge hole in the hull and sinking it before its men could jump overboard.

These warships were also equipped with sail and mast—used only for voyaging, never in battle—a square sail, and a short mast, held fast by oxhide stays. The sail was raised only for a fair wind, or could be tilted slightly for a quartering wind, but was useless against headwinds.

This meant that these ships were almost always at the mercy of the weather, and were often blown off course. Another thing that made them unfit for long voyages was the lack of cargo space. Only a few days' supply of food and water could be carried, leaving space for no other cargo. That is why these fighting ships tried to hug the coast and avoid the open sea.

Ulysses' problem was made worse by victory. When Troy was sacked, he and his men captured a huge booty—gold and jewels, silks, furs—and, after ten years of war, the men refused to leave any loot behind. This meant that each of his ships could carry food and water for a very few days.

This greed for treasure caused many of his troubles at first. But then troubles came so thick and fast that no one could tell what caused them; hardships were simply called bad luck, or the anger of the gods.

But bad luck makes good stories. □□

1. **twirling on their beams,** turning very quickly, as if the beam—the widest part of the ship—were a pivot.

The Ciconians

The voyage began peacefully. A fair north-east wind blew, filling the sails of the little fleet and pushing it steadily homeward. The wind freshened at night, and the three ships scudded along joyfully under a fat moon.

On the morning of the second day Ulysses saw a blue haze of smoke and a glint of white stone. He put in toward shore and saw a beautiful little town. The men stared in amazement at this city without walls, rich with green parks and grazing cattle, its people strolling about in white tunics. Ten years of war had made Ulysses' men as savage as wolves. Everyone not a shipmate was an enemy. To meet was to fight; property belonged to the winner.

Ulysses stood in the bow, shading his eyes with his hand, gazing at the city. A tough, crafty old warrior named Eurylochus stood beside him.

"We attack, do we not?" he asked. "The city lies there defenseless. We can take it without losing a man."

"Yes, it looks tempting," said Ulysses. "But the wind blows fair, and good fortune attends us. Perhaps it will spoil our luck to stop."

"But this fat little city has been thrown into our laps by the gods, too," said Eurylochus, "and they grow angry when men refuse their gifts. It would be bad luck *not* to attack."

Ulysses heard the fierce murmur of his men behind him, and felt their greed burning in his veins. He hailed the other ships and gave orders, and the three black-hulled vessels swerved toward shore and nosed into the harbor, swooping down upon the white city like wolves upon a sheepfold.

They landed on the beach. The townsfolk fled before them into the hills. Ulysses did not allow his men to pursue them, for there was no room on the ship for slaves. From house to house the armed men went, helping themselves to whatever they wanted. Afterward they piled the booty in great heaps upon the beach.

Then Ulysses had them round up a herd of the plump, swaying, crook-horned cattle, and offer ten bulls in sacrifice to the gods. Later they built huge bonfires on the beach, roasted the cattle, and had a great feast.

But while the looting and feasting was going on the men of the city had withdrawn into the hills and called together their kinsmen of the villages, the Ciconians, and began preparing for battle. They were skillful fighters, these men of the hills. They drove brass war chariots that had long blades attached to the wheels, and these blades whirled swiftly as the wheels turned, scything down the foe.

They gathered by the thousands, an overwhelming force, and stormed down out of the hills onto the beach. Ulysses' men were full of food and wine, unready to fight, but he had posted sentries, who raised a shout when they saw the Ciconians coming down from the hills in the moonlight. Ulysses raged among his men, slapping them with the flat of his sword, driving the fumes of wine out of their heads. His great racketing battle cry roused those he could not whip with his sword.

The men closed ranks and met the Ciconians at spearpoint. The Hellenes retreated slowly, leaving their treasure where it was heaped upon the beach and, keeping their line unbroken, made for their ships.

Ulysses chose two of his strongest men and bade them lift a thick timber upon their shoulders. He sat astride this timber, high enough to shoot his arrows over the heads of his men. He was the most skillful archer since Heracles. He aimed only at the chariot horses, and aimed not to kill, but to cripple, so that the horses fell in their traces, and their furious flailing and kicking broke the enemy's advance.

Thus the Hellenes were able to reach their ships and roll them into the water, leap into the rowers' benches, and row away. But eighteen men were left dead on the beach— six from each ship—and there was scarcely a man unwounded.

Eurylochus threw himself on his knees before Ulysses and said, "I advised you badly, O Chief. We have angered the gods. Perhaps, if you kill me, they will be appeased."

"Eighteen dead are enough for one night," said Ulysses. "Our luck has changed, but what has changed can change again. Rise, and go about your duties."

The ships had been handled roughly in the swift retreat from the Ciconian beach. Their hulls had been battered by axes and flung spears, and they had sprung small leaks. The wind had faded to a whisper, and the men were forced to row with water sloshing around their ankles. Ulysses saw that his ships were foundering, and that he would have to empty the holds. Food could not be spared, nor water; the only thing that could go was the treasure taken from Troy. The men groaned and tore at their beards as they saw the gold and jewels and bales of fur and silk being dropped overboard. But Ulysses cast over his own share of the treasure first—and his was the largest share—so the

men had to bite back their rage and keep on rowing.

As the necklaces, bracelets, rings, and brooches sank slowly, winking their jewels like drowned fires, a strange thing happened. A shoal of naiads—beautiful water nymphs—were drawn by the flash of the jewels. They dived after the bright baubles and swam alongside the ships, calling to the men, singing, tweaking the oars out of their hands, for they were sleek mischievous creatures who loved jewels and strangers. Some of them came riding dolphins, and in the splashing silver veils of spray the men thought they saw beautiful girls with fishtails. This is probably how the first report of mermaids arose.

Poseidon, God of the Sea, was wakened from sleep by the sound of this laughter. When he saw what was happening, his green beard bristled with rage, and he said to himself, "Can it be? Are these the warriors whom I helped in their siege of Troy? Is this their gratitude, trying to steal my naiads from me? I'll teach them manners."

He whistled across the horizon to his son, Aeolus, keeper of the winds, who twirled his staff and sent a northeast gale skipping across the sea. It pounced upon the little fleet and scattered the ships like twigs. Ulysses clung to the helm, trying to hold the kicking tiller, trying to shout over the wind. There was nothing to do but ship the mast[2] and let the wind take them.

And the wind, in one huge gust of fury, drove them around Cythera, the southernmost of their home islands, into the open waters of the southwest quarter of the Middle Sea, toward the hump of Africa called Libya. □□

---

2. **ship the mast.** The mast was short and could be *shipped,* or *unstepped*—that is, taken down—and sometimes was even carried off the ship for security.

Uncovering the Real Troy

One morning in 1873, Heinrich Schliemann (shlē′ män) was excavating a large mound of earth and stone called Hissarlik (hi sär lik′), in Turkey. As he carefully lifted a large copper shield he had just unearthed, he saw something gleaming underneath. He called his wife, Sophia, who was directing her own digging crew nearby. She joined him in the 28-foot trench, and together they lifted out piece after piece of one of the greatest treasures ever discovered—thousands of pieces of gold and silver jewelry, dishes, and household articles, in addition to pottery, tools, and weapons. To Heinrich Schliemann, this breathtaking find was the final proof that he had discovered Troy.

About 800 B.C. the Greek poet Homer wrote the two book-length poems called the *Iliad* (il′ē əd), the story of the Trojan War, and the *Odyssey* (od′ ə sē), of which "The Adventures of Ulysses" is a retelling. For centuries these poems, translated into many languages, have been read for enjoyment and for insight into ancient times. But few people seriously considered the poems as *history*. Some even claimed that Homer never existed—that the poems were really collections of songs made by many poets over the years.

Heinrich Schliemann first heard the stories as told by his father in their small village in Germany. The tales of adventure in ancient Greece inflamed his imagination as they had countless others'. But young Schliemann decided for himself that they were not just fanciful tales of a heroic age that never really existed, but that they were true—and that he was going to be the one to locate the long-lost city of Troy, and prove that the *Iliad* and the *Odyssey* had historical basis.

Schliemann was not trained as an archaeologist. Instead, he worked at a variety of jobs in Germany, Holland, Russia, and the United States, learning ten foreign languages and building a fortune. Finally, at the age of 47, with plenty of money to finance his own expeditions, he came to Greece to start digging, guided by his copy of the *Iliad*. There, he met and married Sophia. She was familiar with Homer, but she received her training as an archaeologist by working alongside her husband.

When the Schliemanns first announced their discovery of Troy, professional archaeologists mocked, or became angry. For Schliemann, in his eagerness to find treasures, had gone about his digging in a careless and unscientific way. He had destroyed layers of evidence not as spectacular as gold, but to the science of archaeology every bit as important. Furthermore, he had smuggled out of Turkey gold and other treasures belonging by agreement to that government.

Later expeditions uncovered not one, but nine separate cities on the same spot. Troy had been destroyed and rebuilt on its own ruins many times over, from 3000 B.C. to A.D. 400. Troy VII, the seventh layer from the bottom, was the Troy of Homer's heroes.

The Schliemanns and others after them excavated many other sites associated with ancient Greece. Such discoveries tell us a great deal about people who lived so long ago. Their weapons, tools, and household utensils fill in details of their lives which agree largely with Homer's descriptions, proving that the poet was far more accurate than supposed.

If Troy was real, are Ulysses and all the others likely to have been just characters in fiction? Schliemann also searched Ithaca, but found no traces of a dwelling grand enough to have been the palace of Ulysses and Penelope. Still, the search goes on—and who knows what next year might bring? After all, Troy was only a legend—until Heinrich and Sophia Schliemann proved otherwise.

The Lotus-Eaters

Now, at this time, the shore of Libya was known as "the land where Morpheus plays."

Who was Morpheus? He was a young god, son of Hypnos, God of Sleep, and nephew of Hades. It was his task to fly around the world, from nightfall to dawn, scattering sleep. His father, Hypnos, mixed the colors of sleep for him, making them dark and thick and sad.

"For," he said, "it is a little death you lay upon man each night, my son, to prepare him for the kingdom of death."

But his aunt, Persephone, sewed him a secret pocket, full of bright things, and said: "It is not death you scatter, but repose. Hang the walls of sleep with bright pictures, so that man may not know death before he dies."

These bright pictures were called dreams. And Morpheus became fascinated by the way a little corner of man's mind remained awake in sleep, and played with the colors he had hung, mixing them, pulling them apart, making new pictures. It seemed to him that these fantastic colored shadows the sleepers painted were the most beautiful, most puzzling things he had ever seen. And he wanted to know more about how they came to be.

He went to Persephone, and said, "I need a flower that makes sleep. It must be purple and black. But there should be one petal streaked with fire-red, the petal to make dreams."

Persephone smiled and moved her long white hand in the air. Between her fingers a flower blossomed. She gave it to him.

"Here it is, Morpheus. Black and purple like sleep, with one petal of fire-red for dreams. We will call it lotus."

Morpheus took the flower and planted it in Libya, where it is always summer. The flower grew in clusters, smelling deliciously of honey. The people ate nothing else. They slept all the time, except when they were gathering flowers. Morpheus watched over them, reading their dreams.

It was toward Lotusland that Ulysses and his men were blown by the gale. The wind fell while they were still offshore. The sky cleared, the sea calmed, a hot sun beat down. To Ulysses, dizzy with fatigue, weak with hunger, the sky and the water and the air between seemed to flow together in one hot blueness.

He shook his head, trying to shake away the hot blue haze, and growled to his men to unship the oars, and row toward land. The exhausted men bent to the oars, and the ships crawled over the fire-blue water. With their last strength they pulled the ships up on the beach, past the high-tide mark, and then lay down and went to sleep.

As they slept, the Lotus-eaters came out of the forest. Their arms were heaped with flowers, which they piled about the sleeping men in great blue and purple bouquets, so that they might have flowers to eat when they awoke, for these people were very gentle and hospitable.

The men awoke and smelled the warm honey smell of the flowers, and ate them in great handfuls—like honeycomb—and fell asleep again. Morpheus hovered over the sleeping men and read their dreams.

"These men have done terrible things," the god whispered to himself. "Their dreams are full of gold and blood and fire. Such sleep will not rest them."

And he mixed them some cool green and silver dreams of home. The nightmares faded. Wounded Trojans stopped screaming, Troy stopped burning; they saw their wives smile, heard their children laugh, saw the green wheat growing in their own fields. They dreamed of home, awoke and were hungry, ate the honeyed lotus flowers and fell into a deeper sleep.

Then Morpheus came to Ulysses who was stretched on the sand, a little apart from the rest. He studied his face—the wide grooved brow, the sunken eyes, the red hair, the jutting chin. And he said to himself, "This man is a hero. Terrible are his needs, sudden his deeds, and his dreams must be his own. I cannot help him."

So Morpheus mixed no colors for Ulysses' sleep, but let him dream his own dreams, and read them as they came. He hovered above the sleeping king and could not leave.

"What monsters he makes," he said to himself. "Look at that giant with the single eye in the middle of his forehead. And that terrible spider-woman with all those legs. . . . Ah, the things he dreams, this angry sleeper. What bloody mouths, what masts falling, sails ripping, what rocks and reefs, what shipwrecks . . . how many deaths?"

Ulysses awoke, choking, out of a terrible nightmare. It seemed to him that in his sleep he had seen the whole voyage laid out before him, had seen his ships sinking, his men drowning. Monsters had crowded about him, clutching, writhing. He sat up and looked about. His men lay asleep among heaped flowers. As he watched, one opened his eyes, raised himself on an elbow, took a handful of flowers, stuffed them into his mouth, and immediately fell asleep again.

Ulysses smelled the honey sweetness, and felt an overpowering hunger. He took some of the flowers and raised them to his mouth. As their fragrance grew stronger, he felt his eyelids drooping, and his arms grew heavy, and he thought, "It is these flowers that are making us sleep. Their scent alone brings sleep. I must not eat them."

But he could not put them down; his hand would not obey him. Exerting all the

bleak force of his will, he grasped his right hand with his left—as if it belonged to someone else—and one by one forced open his fingers and let the flowers fall.

Then he dragged himself to his feet and walked slowly into the sea. He went under and arose snorting. His head had cleared. But when he went up on the beach, the sweet fragrance rose like an ether and made him dizzy again.

"I must work swiftly," he said.

One by one he carried the sleeping men to the ships, and propped them on their benches. His strength was going. The honey smell was invading him, making him droop with sleep. He took his knife and, cutting sharp splinters of wood to prop open his eyelids, staggered back among the men. He worked furiously now, lifting them on his shoulders, carrying them two at a time, throwing them into the ships.

Finally, the beach was cleared. The men lolled sleeping upon the benches. Then, all by himself, using his last strength, he pushed the ships into the water. When the ships were afloat in the shallow water, he lashed one to another with rawhide line, his own ship in front. Then he raised his sail and took the helm.

The wind was blowing from the southwest. It filled his sail. The line grew taut; the file of ships moved away from Lotusland.

The men began to awake from their dreams of home, and found themselves upon the empty sea again. But the long sleep had rested them, and they took up their tasks with new strength.

Ulysses kept the helm, grim and unsmiling. For he knew that what he had seen painted on the walls of his sleep was meant to come true, and that he was sailing straight into a nightmare. ☐☐

See **FIGURATIVE LANGUAGE**
Handbook of Literary Terms

The Cyclops's Cave

After he had rescued his crew from Lotusland, Ulysses found that he was running from one trouble into another. They were still at sea, and there was no food for the fleet. The men were hungry and getting dangerous. Ulysses heard them grumbling: "He should have left us there in Lotusland. At least when you're asleep you don't know you're hungry. Why did he have to come and wake us up?" He knew that unless he found food for them very soon he would be facing a mutiny.

That part of the Aegean Sea was dotted with islands. On every one of them was a different kind of enemy. The last thing Ulysses wanted to do was to go ashore, but there was no other way of getting food. He made a landfall on a small mountainous island. He was very careful; he had the ships of the fleet moor offshore and selected twelve of his bravest men as a landing party.

They beached their skiff and struck inland. It was a wild hilly place, full of boulders, with very few trees. It seemed deserted. Then Ulysses glimpsed something moving across the valley, on the slope of a hill. He was too far off to see what they were, but he thought they must be goats since the hill was so steep. And if they were goats they had to be caught. So the men headed downhill, meaning to cross the valley and climb the slope.

Ulysses had no way of knowing it, but this was the very worst island in the entire sea on which the small party could have landed. For here lived the Cyclopes, huge savage creatures, tall as trees, each with one eye in the middle of his forehead. Once, long ago, they had lived in the bowels of Olympus, forging thunderbolts for Zeus. But he had punished them for some fault, exiling them to this island where they had forgotten all their smithcraft and did nothing but fight with each other for the herds of wild goats, trying to find enough food to fill their huge bellies. Best of all, they liked storms; storms meant shipwrecks. Shipwrecks meant sailors struggling in the sea, who could be plucked out and eaten raw; and the thing they loved best in the world was human flesh. The largest and the fiercest and the hungriest of all the Cyclopes on the island was one named Polyphemus. He kept constant vigil on his mountain, fair weather or foul. If he spotted a ship, and there was no storm to help, he would dive into the sea and swim underwater, coming up underneath the ship and overturning it. Then he would swim off with his pockets full of sailors.

On this day he could not believe his luck when he saw a boat actually landing on the beach, and thirteen meaty-looking sailors disembark, and begin to march toward his cave. But here they were, climbing out of the valley now, up the slope of the hill, right toward the cave. He realized they must be hunting his goats.

The door of the cave was an enormous slab of stone. He shoved this aside so that the cave stood invitingly open, casting a faint glow of firelight upon the dusk. Over the fire, on a great spit, eight goats were turning and roasting. The delicious savors of the cooking drifted from the cave. Polyphemus lay down behind a huge boulder and waited.

The men were halfway up the slope of the hill when they smelled the meat roasting. They broke into a run. Ulysses tried to restrain them, but they paid no heed—they were too hungry. They raced to the mouth of the cave and dashed in. Ulysses drew his sword and hurried after them. When he saw the huge fireplace and the eight goats spitted like sparrows, his heart sank because he knew that they had come into reach of something much larger than themselves. However, the men were giving no thought to anything but food; they flung themselves on the spit, and tore into the goat meat, smearing their hands and faces with sizzling fat, too hungry to feel pain as they crammed the hot meat into their mouths.

There was a loud rumbling sound; the cave darkened. Ulysses whirled around. He saw that the door had been closed. The far end of the cavern was too dark to see anything, but then—amazed, aghast—he saw what looked like a huge red lantern far above, coming closer. Then he saw the great shadow of a nose under it, and the gleam of teeth. He realized that the lantern was a great flaming eye. Then he saw the whole giant, tall as a tree, with huge fingers reaching out of the shadows, fingers bigger than baling hooks. They closed around two sailors and hauled them screaming into the air.

As Ulysses and his horrified men watched, the great hand bore the struggling little men to the giant's mouth. He ate them, still wriggling, the way a cat eats a grasshopper; he ate them clothes and all, growling over their raw bones.

The men had fallen to their knees and were whimpering like terrified children, but Ulysses stood there, sword in hand, his agile brain working more swiftly than it ever had.

"Greetings," he called. "May I know to whom we are indebted for such hospitality?"

The giant belched and spat buttons. "I am Polyphemus," he growled. "This is my cave, my mountain, and everything that comes here is mine. I do hope you can all stay to dinner. There are just enough of you to make a meal. Ho, ho. . . ." And he laughed a great, choking phlegmy laugh, swiftly lunged, and caught another sailor, whom he lifted into the air and held before his face.

"Wait!" cried Ulysses.

"What for?"

"You won't enjoy him that way. He is from Attica, where the olives grow. He was raised on olives and has a very delicate oily flavor. But to appreciate it, you must taste the wine of the country."

"Wine? What is wine?"

"It is a drink. Made from pressed grapes. Have you never drunk it?"

"We drink nothing but ox blood and buttermilk here."

"Ah, you do not know what you have missed, gentle Polyphemus. Meat-eaters, in particular, love wine. Here, try it for yourself."

Ulysses unslung from his belt a full flask of unwatered wine.[3] He gave it to the giant, who put it to his lips and gulped. He coughed violently, and stuck the sailor in a little niche high up in the cave wall, then leaned his great slab of a face toward Ulysses and said:

"What did you say this drink was?"

"Wine. A gift of the gods to man, to make women look better and food taste better. And now it is my gift to you."

"It's good, very good." He put the bottle to his lips and swallowed again. "You are very polite. What's your name?"

"My name? Why I am—nobody."

"Nobody. . . . Well, Nobody, I like you. You're a good fellow. And do you know what I'm going to do? I'm going to save you till last. Yes, I'll eat all your friends first, and give you extra time, that's what I'm going to do."

Ulysses looked up into the great eye and saw that it was redder than ever. It was all a swimming redness. He had given the monster, who had never drunk spirits before, undiluted wine. Surely it must make him sleepy. But was a gallon enough for that great gullet? Enough to put him to sleep—or would he want to eat again first?

"Eat 'em all up, Nobody—save you till later. Sleep a little first. Shall I? Won't try to run away, will you? No—you can't, can't open the door—too heavy, ha, ha. . . . You take a nap too, Nobody. I'll wake you for breakfast. Breakfast. . . ."

The great body crashed full-length on the cave floor, making the very walls of the mountain shake. Polyphemus lay on his back, snoring like a powersaw. The sailors were still on the floor, almost dead from fear.

"Up!" cried Ulysses. "Stand up like men! Do what must be done! Or you will be devoured like chickens."

He got them to their feet and drew them about him as he explained his plan.

"Listen now, and listen well, for we have no time. I made him drunk, but we cannot tell how long it will last."

Ulysses thrust his sword into the fire; they saw it glow white-hot.

"There are ten of us," he said. "Two of us have been eaten, and one of our friends is still unconscious up there on his shelf of rock. You four get on one side of his head, and the rest on the other side. When I give the word, lay hold of the ear on your side, each of you. And hang on, no matter how he

---

3. *unwatered wine.* Greek wine was made especially strong; it was the custom to dilute it with water before drinking.

thrashes, for I am going to put out his eye. And if I am to be sure of my stroke you must hold his head still. One stroke is all I will be allowed."

Then Ulysses rolled a boulder next to the giant's head and climbed on it, so that he was looking down into the eye. It was lidless and misted with sleep—big as a furnace door and glowing softly like a banked fire. Ulysses looked at his men. They had done what he said, broken into two parties, one group at each ear. He lifted his white-hot sword.

"Now!" he cried.

Driving down with both hands, and all the strength of his back and shoulders, and all his rage and all his fear, Ulysses stabbed the glowing spike into the giant's eye.

His sword jerked out of his hand as the head flailed upward, men pelted to the ground as they lost their hold. A huge screeching curdling bellow split the air.

"This way!" shouted Ulysses.

He motioned to his men, and they crawled on their bellies toward the far end of the cave where the herd of goats was tethered. They slipped into the herd and lay among the goats as the giant stomped about the cave, slapping the walls with great blows of his hands, picking up boulders and cracking them together in agony, splitting them to flinders, clutching his eye, a scorched hole now from which the brown blood jelled. He moaned and gibbered and bellowed in frightful pain; his groping hand found the sailor in the wall, and he tore him to pieces between his fingers. Ulysses could not even hear the man scream because the giant was bellowing so.

Now Ulysses saw that the Cyclops's wild stampeding was giving place to a plan. For now he was stamping on the floor in a regular pattern, trying to find and crush them beneath his feet. He stopped moaning and

listened. The sudden silence dazed the men with fear. They held their breath and tried to muffle the sound of their beating hearts; all the giant heard was the breathing of the goats. Then Ulysses saw him go to the mouth of the cave, and swing the great slab aside, and stand there. He realized just in time that the goats would rush outside, which is what the giant wanted, for then he could search the whole cave.

Ulysses whispered, "Quickly, swing under the bellies of the rams. Hurry, hurry!"

Luckily, they were giant goats and thus able to carry the men who had swung themselves under their bellies and were clinging to the wiry wool. Ulysses himself chose the largest ram. They moved toward the mouth of the cave, and crowded through. The Cyclops's hands came down and brushed across the goats' backs feeling for the men, but the animals were huddled too closely together for him to reach between and search under their bellies. So he let them pass through.

Now, the Cyclops rushed to the corner where the goats had been tethered, and stamped, searched, and roared through the whole cave again, bellowing with fury when he did not find them. The herd grazed on the slope of the hill beneath the cave. There was a full moon; it was almost as bright as day.

"Stay where you are," Ulysses whispered.

He heard a crashing, peered out, and saw great shadowy figures converging on the cave. He knew that the other Cyclopes of the island must have heard the noise and come to see. He heard the giant bellow.

The others called to him: "Who has done it? Who has blinded you?"

"Nobody. Nobody did it. Nobody blinded me."

"Ah, you have done it yourself. What a tragic accident."

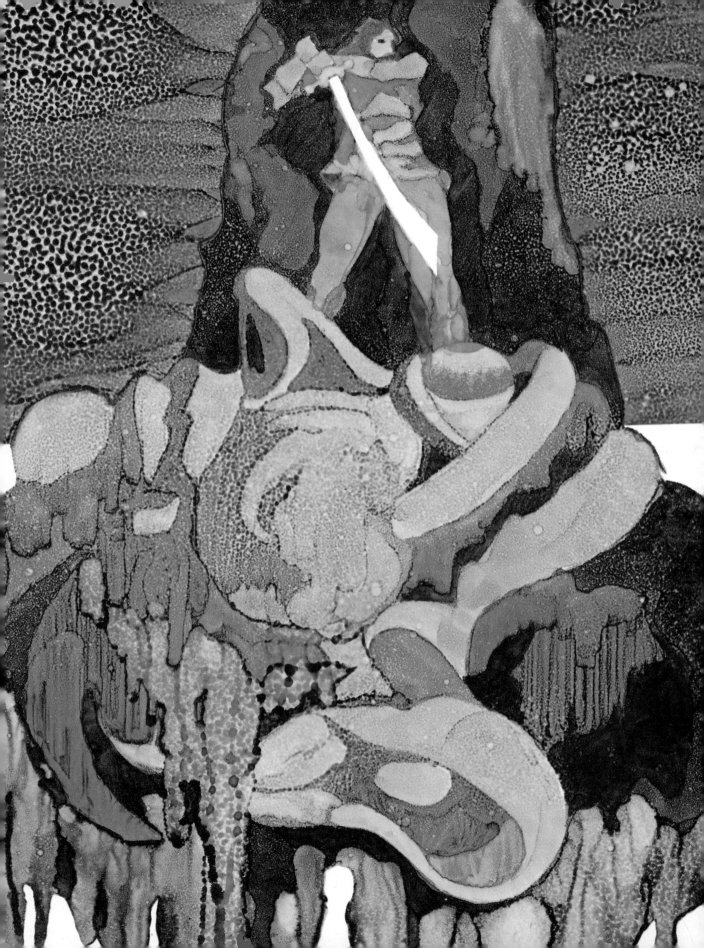

And they went back to their own caves.

"Now!" said Ulysses. "Follow me!"

He swung himself out from under the belly of the ram, and raced down the hill. The others raced after him. They were half-way across the valley when they heard great footsteps rushing after them, and Polyphemus bellowing nearer and nearer.

"He's coming!" cried Ulysses. "Run for your lives!"

They ran as they had never run before, but the giant could cover fifty yards at a stride. It was only because he could not see and kept bumping into trees and rocks that they were able to reach the skiff and push out on the silver water before Polyphemus burst out of the grove of trees and rushed onto the beach. They bent to the oars, and the boat scudded toward the fleet.

Polyphemus heard the dip of the oars and the groaning of the oarlocks, and, aiming at the sound, hurled huge boulders after them. They fell around the ship, but did not hit.

The skiff reached Ulysses' ship, and the sailors climbed aboard.

"Haul anchor, and away!" cried Ulysses. And then called to the Cyclops, "Poor fool! Poor blinded drunken gluttonous fool—if anyone else asks you, it is not Nobody, but Ulysses who has done this to you."

But he was to regret this final taunt. The gods honor courage, but punish pride.

Polyphemus, wild with rage, waded out chest-deep and hurled a last boulder, which hit mid-deck, almost sunk the ship, and killed most of the crew—among them seven of the nine men who had just escaped.

And Polyphemus prayed to Poseidon, "God of the Sea, I beg you, punish Ulysses for this. Visit him with storm and shipwreck and sorceries. Let him wander many years before he reaches home, and when he gets there let him find himself forgotten, unwanted, a stranger."

Poseidon heard this prayer, and made it all happen just that way. ☐☐

Vocabulary
Context, Dictionary

Good writing and effective storytelling may often be one and the same thing, and one way to tell a story effectively—to make it come alive for the reader—is to use vivid language.

A. The Cyclopes removed struggling sailors from the sea and ate them raw.

B. The Cyclopes plucked floundering sailors from the sea and devoured them raw.

Which sentence uses a verb that makes the Cyclopes seem hungrier, more cannibal-like, in their eating habits? Which sentence do you think uses more vivid action words?

In the next column are some words suggesting specific actions. If you are unfamiliar with any words, look up their meanings in the Glossary. Then rewrite each of the following sentences, substituting one or more of the words from the list for one or more words in each sentence to make the sentence more vivid.

pelted stampeded
scudded founder
drooped tweaked

1. As the prisoner and his guard pushed through the crowd, the people near the prisoner twisted his ears and those at a distance hit him with handfuls of small stones.

2. Blown by the northeast wind, the clouds moved across the sky above the plain where the frightened cattle ran.

3. When the man stopped rowing and leaned with exhaustion over the oars, the boat began to sink.

Keeper of the Winds

Now the black ships beat their way northward from the land of the Cyclopes. And Ulysses, ignorant of the mighty curse that the blind giant had fastened upon him, was beginning to hope that they might have fair sailing the rest of the way home. So impatient was he that he took the helm himself and kept it night and day although his sailors pleaded with him to take some rest. But he was wild with eagerness to get home to his wife, Penelope, to his young son Telemachus, and to the dear land of Ithaca that he had not seen for more than ten years now.

At the end of the third night, just as the first light was staining the sky, he saw something very strange—a wall of bronze, tall and wide, floating on the sea and blocking their way. At first he thought it was a trick of the light, and he rubbed his eyes and looked again. But there it was, a towering bright wall of beaten bronze.

"Well," he thought to himself, "it cannot stretch across the sea. There must be a way to get around it."

He began to sail along the wall as though it were the shore of an island, trying to find his way around. Finally, he came to a huge gate, and even as he gazed upon it in amazement, the gate swung open and the wind changed abruptly. The shrouds snapped, the sails bulged, the masts groaned, and all three ships of the fleet were blown through the gate, which immediately clanged shut behind them. Once within the wall, the wind fell off and Ulysses found his ship drifting toward a beautiful hilly island. Suddenly there was a great howling of wind. The sun was blown out like a candle. Darkness fell upon the waters. Ulysses felt the deck leap beneath him as the ship was lifted halfway out of the water by the ferocious gust and hurled through the blackness. He tried to shout, but the breath was torn from his mouth and he lost consciousness.

Ulysses had no way of knowing this, but the mischievous Poseidon had guided his ships to the island fortress of Aeolus, Keeper of the Winds. Ages before, when the world was very new, the gods had become fearful of the terrible strength of the winds, and had decided to tame them. So Zeus and Poseidon, working together, had floated an island upon the sea, and girdled it about with a mighty bronze wall. Then they set a mountain upon the island and hollowed out that mountain until it was a huge stone dungeon. Into this hollow mountain they stuffed the struggling winds, and appointed Aeolus as their jailer. And there the winds were held captive. Whenever the gods wanted to stir up a storm and needed a particular wind, they sent a message to Aeolus, who would draw his sword and stab the side of the mountain, making a hole big enough for the wind to fly through. If the north wind were wanted, he stabbed the north side of the mountain, its east slope for the east wind, and so on. When the storm was done, he would whistle the wind home, and the huge brawling gale, broken by its imprisonment, would crawl back whimpering to its hole.

Aeolus was an enormously fat demigod with a long wind-tangled beard and a red wind-beaten face. He loved to eat and drink, and fight, play games, and hear stories. Twelve children he had, six boys and six girls. He sent them out one by one, riding the back of the wind around the world, managing the weather for each month.

And it was in the great castle of Aeolus that Ulysses and his men found themselves when they awoke from their enchanted sleep. Invisible hands held torches for them, guided them to the baths, anointed them with oil, and gave them fresh clothing. Then the floating torches led them to the dining hall, where they were greeted by Aeolus and his twelve handsome children. A mighty banquet was laid before them, and they ate like starved men.

Then Aeolus said, "Strangers, you are my guests—uninvited—but guests all the same. By the look of you, you have had adventures and should have fine stories to tell. Yes, I love a tale full of fighting and blood and tricks, and if you have such to tell, then I shall entertain you royally. But if you are such men as sit dumb, glowering, unwilling to please, using your mouths only to stuff food into—then—well, then you are apt to find things less pleasant. You, Captain!" he roared, pointing at Ulysses. "You, sir—I take you for the leader of this somewhat motley crew. Do you have a story to tell?"

"For those who know how to listen, I have a tale to tell," said Ulysses.

"Your name?"

"Ulysses—of Ithaca."

"Mmm—yes," said Aeolus. "I seem to recognize that name—believe I heard it on Olympus while my uncles and aunts up there were quarreling about some little skirmish they had interested themselves in. Near Troy I think it was. . . . Yes-s-s. . . . Were you there?"

"I was there," said Ulysses. "I was there for ten years, dear host, and indeed took part in some of that petty skirmishing that will be spoken of by men who love courage when this bronze wall and this island, and you and yours, have vanished under the sea and have

been forgotten for a thousand years. I am Ulysses. My companions before Troy were Achilles, Menelaus, Agamemnon, mighty heroes all, and, in modesty, I was not least among them."

"Yes-s-s. . . ." said Aeolus. "You are bold enough. Too bold for your own good, perhaps. But you have caught my attention, Captain. I am listening. Tell on. . . ."

Then Ulysses told of the Trojan War; of the abduction of Helen, and the chase, and the great battles; the attacks, the retreats, the separate duels. He spoke of Achilles fighting Hector, and killing him with a spear thrust, of Paris ambushing Achilles; and, finally, how he himself had made a great hollow wooden horse and had the Greek armies pretend to leave, only to sneak back and hide in the belly of the horse. He told how the Trojans had dragged the horse within their gates, and how the Greek warriors had crept out at night and taken the city and slaughtered their enemies.

Aeolus shouted with laughter. His face blazed and his belly shook. "Ah, that's a trick after my own heart!" he cried. "You're a sharp one, you are. . . . I knew you had a foxy look about you. Wooden horse—ho ho! Tell more! Tell more!"

Then Ulysses told of his wanderings after the fall of Troy, of his adventure in Lotusland, and what had happened in the Cyclops's cave. And when Aeolus heard how he had outwitted Polyphemus and blinded his single eye, he struck the table with a mighty blow of his fist, and shouted, "Marvelous! A master stroke! By the gods, you are the bravest, craftiest warrior that has ever drunk my wine." He was especially pleased because he had always hated Polyphemus. He had no way of knowing, of course, that the blinded Cyclops had prayed to his father and had laid a curse on Ulysses, and that he, Aeolus, was being made the instrument of that curse. He did not know this, for the gods move in mysterious ways. And so he roared with laughter, and shouted, "You have pleased me, Ulysses. You have told me a brave tale, a tale full of blood and tricks. . . . And now I shall grant you any favor within my power. Speak out, Ulysses. Ask what you will."

"But one thing I seek, generous Aeolus," said Ulysses, "your help. I need your help in getting home. For it has been a long weary time since we saw our homes and our families. Our hearts thirst for the sight of Ithaca."

"No one can help you better than I," said Aeolus. "You sail on ships, and I am Keeper of the Winds. Come with me."

He led Ulysses out into the night. A hot orange moon rode low in the sky, and they could see without torches. Aeolus led him to the mountain, carrying his sword in one hand and a great leather bag in the other. He stabbed the side of the mountain. There was a rushing, sobbing sound; he clapped his leather bag over the hole, and Ulysses, amazed, saw the great bag flutter and fill. Aeolus held its neck closed, strode to the east face of the mountain, and stabbed again. As the east wind rushed out, he caught it in his sack. Then he stomped to the south slope and stabbed again, and caught the south wind in the sack. Now, very carefully, he wound a silver wire about the neck of the sack. It was full now, swollen, tugging at his arm like a huge leather balloon, trying to fly away.

He said, "In this bag are the north wind, the south wind, and the east wind. You must keep them prisoner. But if you wish to change course—if a pirate should chase you, say, or a sea monster, or if an adventure beckons, then you open the bag very carefully—you and you alone, Captain—and

whistle up the wind you wish, let just a breath of it out, close the bag quickly again, and tie it tight. For winds grow swiftly—that is their secret—and so they must be carefully guarded."

"I shall not change course," said Ulysses. "No matter what enemy threatens or what adventure beckons, I sail straight for Ithaca. I shall not open your bag of winds."

"Good," said Aeolus. "Then bind it to your mast, and guard it yourself, sword in hand; let none of your men approach, lest they open it unwittingly. In the meantime, I will send the gentle west wind to follow your ship and fill your sails and take you home."

"Thank you, great Aeolus, thank you, kindly keeper of the winds. I know now that the gods have answered my prayers, and I shall be able to cease this weary heartbreaking drifting over the face of the sea, having my men killed and eaten, my ships destroyed, and my hopes shattered. I will never cease thanking you, Aeolus, till the day I die."

"May that sad occasion be far off," said Aeolus politely. "Now, sir, much as I like your company, you had better gather your men and go. I shall be uneasy now until my winds return to me and I can shut them in the mountain again."

Ulysses returned to the castle and called together his men. Gladly they trooped down to the ships and went aboard. Ulysses bound the great leather sack to the mast and warned his crew that no man must touch it on pain of death. Then he himself stood with naked sword under the mast, guarding the sack.

"Up anchor!" he cried.

The west wind rolled off the mountain and filled their sails. The black ships slipped out of the harbor. Away from the island they sailed, away from the mountain and the castle, toward the wall of bronze. When they reached the wall, the great gate swung open and they sailed eastward over water oily with moonlight. Eastward they sailed for nine days and nine nights. In perfect weather they skimmed along, the west wind hovering behind them, keeping their sails full, pushing them steadily home.

And for nine nights and nine days, Ulysses did not sleep; he did not close his eyes or sheath his sword. He kept his station under the mast—food and drink were brought to him there—and never for an instant stopped guarding the sack.

Then, finally, on the morning of the ninth day, he heard the lookout cry, "Land Ho!" and strained his eyes to see. What he saw made his heart swell. Tears coursed down his face, but they were tears of joy. For he saw the dear familiar hills of home. He saw the brown fields of Ithaca, the twisted olive trees, and, as he watched, he saw them even more clearly, saw the white marble columns of his own castle on the cliff. And his men, watching, saw the smoke rising from their own chimneys.

When Ulysses saw the white columns of his palace, he knew that unless the west wind failed, they would be home in an hour, but the friendly wind blew steadily as ever. Ulysses heaved a great sigh. The terrible tension that had kept him awake for nine days and nights eased its grip. He raised his arms and yawned. Then he leaned against the mast and closed his eyes, just for a minute.

Two of the men, standing in the bow, saw him slump at the foot of the mast, fast asleep. Their eyes traveled up the mast to the great leather bag, plump as a balloon, straining against its bonds as the impatient winds wrestled inside. Then Poseidon, swimming invisibly alongside, clinked his golden armlets. The men heard the clinking, and thought it came from the bag.

One man said to the other: "Do you hear that? Those are coins, heavy golden coins, clinking against each other. There must be a fortune in that sack."

The other man said, "Yes, a fortune that should belong to all of us by rights. We shared the danger and should share the loot."

"It is true," said the first, "that he has always been generous. He shared the spoils of Troy."

"Yes, but that was then. Why does he not divide this great sack of treasure? Aeolus gave it to him, and we know how rich he is. Aeolus gave it to him as a guest gift, and he should share it with us."

"He never will. Whatever is in that bag, he does not mean for us to see it. Did you not observe how he has been guarding it all these nights and all these days, standing there always, eating and drinking where he stands, never sheathing his sword?"

"It is in his sheath now," said the second sailor. "And his eyes are closed. Look—he sleeps like a babe. I doubt that anything would wake him."

"What are you doing? What are you going to do with that knife? Are you out of your mind?"

"Yes—out of my mind with curiosity, out of my mind with gold fever, if you must know. Ulysses lies asleep. His sword sleeps in its sheath. And I mean to see what is in that bag."

"Wait, I'll help you. But you must give me half."

"Come then. . . ."

Swiftly and silently the two barefooted sailors padded to the mast, slashed the rope that bound the bag to the spar, and bore it away.

"Hurry—open it!"

"I can't. This wire's twisted in a strange knot. Perhaps a magic knot. It won't come out."

"Then we'll do it this way!" cried the sailor with the knife, and struck at the leather bag, slashing it open. He was immediately lifted off his feet and blown like a leaf off the deck and into the sea as the winds rushed howling out of the bag and began to chase each other around the ship. The winds screamed and jeered and laughed, growing, leaping, reveling in their freedom, roaring and squabbling, screeching around and around the ship. They fell on their gentle brother, the west wind, and cuffed him mercilessly until he fled; then they chased each other around the ship again, spinning it like a cork in a whirlpool.

Then, as they heard the far summoning whistle of the Keeper of the Winds—far, far to the west on the Aeolian Island—they snarled with rage and roared boisterously homeward, snatching the ships along with them, ripping their sails to shreds, snapping their masts like twigs, and hurling the splintered hulls westward over the boiling sea.

Ulysses awoke from his sleep to find the blue sky black with clouds and his home island dropping far astern, out of sight. He saw his crew flung about the deck like dolls, and the tattered sails and the broken spars, and he did not know whether he was awake or asleep—whether this was some nightmare of loss, or whether he was awake now and had slept before, dreaming a fair dream of home. Whichever it was, he began to understand that he was being made the plaything of great powers.

With the unleashed winds screaming behind him at gale force the trip back to where they had started took them only two days. And once again the black ships were hurled onto the island of the winds. Ulysses left his crew on the beach and went to the castle. He found Aeolus in his throne room, and stood before him, bruised, bloody, clothes torn, eyes like ashes.

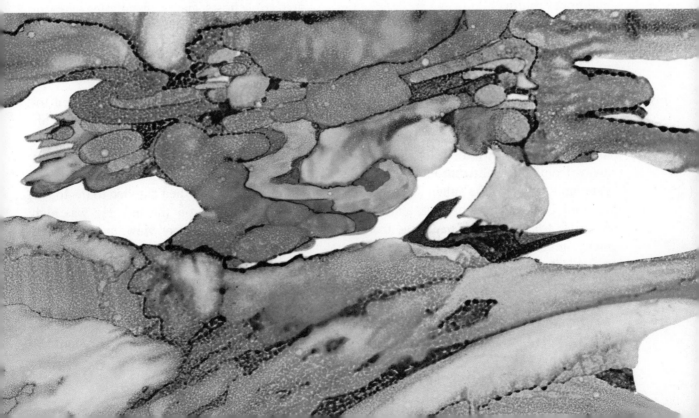

"What happened?" cried Aeolus. "Why have you come back?"

"I was betrayed," said Ulysses. "Betrayed by sleep—the most cruel sleep of my life—and then by a wicked foolish greedy crew who released the winds from the sack and let us be snatched back from happiness even as we saw the smoke rising from our own chimneys."

"I warned you," said Aeolus, "I warned you not to let anyone touch that bag."

"And you were right, a thousand times right!" cried Ulysses. "Be generous once again. You can heal my woes, you alone. Renew your gift. Lend me the west wind to bear me home again, and I swear to you that this time I shall do everything you bid."

"I can't help you," said Aeolus. "Whom the gods detest, no one can help. And they detest you, man—they hate you. What you call bad luck is their hatred, turning gifts into punishment, fair hopes into nightmares. And bad luck is very catching. So please go. Get on your ship and sail away from this island, and never return."

"Farewell," said Ulysses, and strode away.

He gathered his weary men and made them board again. The winds were pent in their mountain. The sea was sluggish. A heavy calm lay over the harbor. They had to row on their broken stumps of oars, crawling like beetles over the gray water. They rowed away from the island, through the bronze gate, and out upon the sullen sea.

And Ulysses, heartbroken, almost dead of grief, tried to hide his feelings from the men; he stood on deck, barking orders, making them mend sail, patch hull, rig new spars, and keep rowing. He took the helm himself and swung the tiller, pointing the bow eastward toward home, which once again, lay at the other end of the sea. ☐☐

See METAPHOR and SIMILE
Handbook of Literary Terms

Circe

Of the three crews, but one was left. Ulysses found himself with only forty-five men. He was determined to bring these men home safely, or die himself.

They were sailing northward again, and on the third day came in sight of land, low lying, heavily wooded, with a good sheltering harbor. Although they had met terrible treatment everywhere they had landed since leaving Troy, they were out of food, water was running low, and once again they would have to risk the perils of the land.

Ulysses was very cautious. He moored the ship off shore, and said to the crew:

"I shall go ashore myself—alone—to see what there is to see, and make sure there are no terrible hosts, giants, man-eating ogres, or secret sorceries. If I am not back by nightfall, Eurylochus will act as captain. Then he will decide whether to seek food and water here, or sail onward. Farewell."

He lowered a small boat and rowed toward the island, all alone. He beached his skiff and struck inland. The first thing he wanted to do was find out whether he was on an island, or the spur of a mainland. He climbed a low hill, then climbed to the top of a tree that grew on the hill. He was high enough now for a clear view, and he turned slowly, marking the flash of the sea on all sides. He knew that once again they had landed on an island and that the ship was their only means of escape if danger should strike.

Something caught his eye. He squinted

thoughtfully at what looked like a feather of smoke rising from a grove of trees. The trees were too thick for him to see through. He climbed down and picked his way carefully toward the smoke, trying to make as little noise as possible. He came to a stand of mighty trees—oak trees, thick and tall with glossy leaves. Glimmering through the trees he saw what looked like a small castle made of polished gray stone. He did not dare go near, for he heard strange howling sounds, a pack of dogs, perhaps, but different from any dogs he had ever heard. So he left the grove and made his way back toward the beach, thinking hard, trying to decide whether to sail away immediately or take a chance on the inhabitants being friendly. He did not like the sound of that howling. There was something in it that froze his marrow. He decided that he would not risk his men on the island, but that he would return to the ship, raise anchor, and sail away to seek food elsewhere.

Just then a tall white deer with mighty antlers stepped across his path. The great stag had a bearing proud as a king, and did not deign to run, but walked on haughtily as if he knew no one would dare to attack him. Unfortunately for the stag, however, Ulysses was too hungry to be impressed by any animal's own opinion of himself. The warrior raised his bronze spear and flung it with all the power of his knotted arm. It sang through the air, pierced the stag's body, and nailed him to a tree. The stag died standing up, still in his pride. He was a huge animal, so large that Ulysses feared he could not carry him back to the ship unaided. But then he remembered how hungry his men were, and he decided to try. He picked weeds and wove a rope which he twisted and twisted again until it was as strong as a ship's line. Then he bound the stag's legs together,

swung the great carcass up onto his back, and staggered off using his spear as a cane.

He was at the end of his strength when he reached the beach, and let the deer slip to the sand. He signaled to his men, who left the ship moored and came ashore on five small boats. They raised a mighty shout of joy when they saw the dead stag. All hands fell to. In a twinkling the deer was skinned and cut up. Fires were lighted, and the delicious smell of roasting meat drew the gulls to the beach, screaming and dipping, begging for scraps.

The men gorged themselves, then lay on the sand to sleep. Ulysses, himself, kept guard. All that night he stood watch, leaning on his spear, looking at the moon which hung in the sky like an orange, and paled as it climbed. As he watched, he turned things over in his mind, trying to decide what to do. While he was still bothered by the eerie howling of the mysterious animals at the castle, now, with his belly full, he felt less gloomy. The more he thought about it the wiser it seemed to explore the island thoroughly and try to determine whether it was a friendly place or not. For never before had he seen a deer so large. If there was one, there must be more; and with game like that the ship could be provisioned in a few days. Also the island was full of streams from which they could fill their dry casks with pure water.

"Yes," he said to himself, "perhaps our luck has changed. Perhaps the god that was playing with us so spitefully has found other amusements. Yes, we will explore this island, and see what there is to see."

Next morning he awakened his men and divided them into two groups, one led by himself, the other by Eurylochus. He said to Eurylochus, "There is a castle on this island. We must find out who lives there. If he be friendly, or not too strong a foe, we will stay here and hunt and lay in water until the hold be full; then we will depart. Now choose, Eurylochus. Would you rather stay here with your men and guard the ship while I visit the castle—or would you rather I keep the beach? Choose."

"O Ulysses," Eurylochus said. "I am sick of the sight of the sea. Even as my belly hungers for food, so do my eyes hunger for leaves and trees which might recall our dear Ithaca. And my foot longs to tread something more solid than a deck—a floor that does not pitch and toss and roll. Pray, gentle Ulysses, let me and my men try the castle."

"Go," said Ulysses. "May the gods go with you."

So Eurylochus and twenty-two men set out, while Ulysses guarded the ship. As the band of warriors approached the castle, they too heard a strange howling. Some of them drew their swords. Others notched arrows to their bowstrings. They pressed on, preparing to fight. They passed through the grove of oak trees, and came to where the trees thinned. Here the howling grew louder and wilder. Then, as they passed the last screen of trees and came to the courtyard of the shining gray castle, they saw an extraordinary sight—a pack of wolves and lions running together like dogs—racing about the courtyard, howling.

When they caught sight of the men, the animals turned and flung themselves upon the strangers, so swiftly that no man had time to use his weapon. The great beasts stood on their hind legs and put their forepaws on the men's shoulders, and fawned on them, and licked their faces. They voiced low muttering growling whines. Eurylochus, who stood half-embracing a huge tawny lion, said, "Men, it is most strange. For these fearsome beasts greet us as though we were lost friends. They seem to be trying to speak to us. And look—look—at their eyes! How intelligently they gleam, how sadly they gaze. Not like beasts' eyes at all."

"It is true," said one of the men. "But perhaps there is nothing to fear. Perhaps there is reason to take heart. For if wild beasts are so tame and friendly, then perhaps the master of the castle, whoever he is or whatever he is, will be friendly too, and welcome us, and give us good cheer."

"Come," said Eurylochus.

When they reached the castle gate, they stopped and listened. For they heard a woman singing in a lovely deep full-throated voice, so that without seeing the woman they knew she was beautiful.

Eurylochus said, "Men, you go into the castle and see what is to be seen. I will stay here, and make sure you are not surprised."

"What do you mean? You come with us. Listen to that. There can be no danger where there is such song."

"Yes, everything seems peaceful," said Eurylochus. "The wild animals are friendly. Instead of the clank of weapons, we hear a woman singing. And it may be peaceful. But something says to me, be careful, take heed. Go you, then. I stay on guard. If I am attacked, and you are unharmed, come to my aid. If anything happens to you, then I shall take word back to Ulysses."

So Eurylochus stood watch at the castle gate—sword in one hand, dagger in the other, bow slung across his back—and the rest of the men entered the castle. They followed the sound of singing through the rooms and out onto a sunny terrace. There sat a woman weaving. She sat at a huge loom, larger than they had ever seen, and wove a gorgeous tapestry. As she wove, she sang. The bright flax leaped through her fingers as if it were dancing to the music in her voice. The men stood and stared. The sun seemed to be trapped in her hair, so bright it was; she wore it long, falling to her waist. Her dress was as blue as the summer sky, matching her eyes. Her long white arms were bare to the shoulders. She stood up and greeted them. She was very tall. And the men, looking at her, and listening to her speak, began to believe that they were in the presence of a goddess.

She seemed to read thoughts too, for she said, "No, I am not a goddess. But I am descended from the Immortals. I am Circe, granddaughter of Helios, a sun-god, who married Perse, daughter of Oceanus. So what am I—wood nymph, sea nymph, something of both? Or something more? I can do simple magic and prophecy, weave certain homely enchantments and read dreams. But let us not speak of me, but of you, strangers. You are adventurers, I see, men of the sword, men of the black-prowed ships, the hawks of the sea. And you have come through sore, sad times, and seek a haven here on this western isle. So be it. I welcome you. For the sweetest spell Circe weaves is one called hospitality. I will have baths drawn for you, clean garments laid out. And when you are refreshed, you shall come and dine. For I love brave men and the tales they tell."

When the men had bathed and changed, Circe gave them each a red bowl. And into each bowl she put yellow food—a kind of porridge made of cheese, barley, honey, and wine plus a few secret things known only to herself. The odor that rose from the red bowls was more delicious than anything they had ever smelled before. And as each man ate he felt himself sinking into his hunger, *becoming* his hunger—lapping, panting, grunting, snuffling. Circe passed among them, smiling, filling the bowls again and

again. And the men, waiting for their bowls to be filled, looking about, seeing each other's face smeared with food, thought, "How strange. We're eating like pigs."

Even as the thought came, it became more true. For as Circe passed among them now she touched each one on the shoulder with a wand, saying: "Glut and swink, eat and drink, gobble food and guzzle wine. Too rude, I think, for humankind, quite right, I think, for *swine!*"

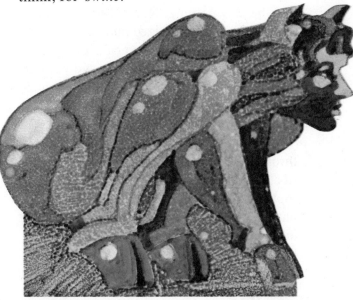

As she said these words in her lovely laughing voice, the men dwindled. Their noses grew wide and long, became snouts. Their hair hardened into bristles; their hands and feet became hooves, and they ran about on all fours, sobbing and snuffling, searching the floor for bones and crumbs. But all the time they cried real tears from their little red eyes, for they were pigs only in form; their minds remained unchanged, and they knew what was happening to them.

Circe kicked them away from the table. "To the sties!" she cried. She struck them with her wand, herding them out of the castle into a large sty. And there she flung them acorns and chestnuts and red berries, and watched them grubbing in the mud for the food she threw. She laughed a wild, hard, bright laugh, and went back into the castle.

While all this was happening, Eurylochus was waiting at the gate. When the men did not return he crept up to a bow slit in the castle wall and looked in. It was dark now. He saw the glimmer of torchlight, and the dim shape of a woman at a loom, weaving. He heard a voice singing, the same enchanting voice he had heard before. But of his men he saw nothing. Nor did he hear their voices. A great fear seized him. He raced off as fast as he could, hoping against hope that the beasts would not howl. The wolves and lions stood like statues, walked like shadows. Their eyes glittered with cold moonlight, but none of them uttered a sound.

He ran until the breath strangled in his throat, until his heart tried to crack out of his ribs, but he kept running, stumbling over roots, slipping on stones. He ran and ran until he reached the beach and fell swooning in Ulysses' arms. Then with his last breath he gasped out the story, told Ulysses of the lions and the wolves, of the woman singing in the castle, and how the men had gone in and not come out. And then he slipped into blackness.

Ulysses said to his men, "You hear the story Eurylochus tells. I must go to the castle and see what has happened to your companions. But there is no need for you to risk yourselves. You stay here. And if I do not return by sunfall tomorrow, then you must board the ship and sail away, for you will know that I am dead."

The men wept and pleaded with him not to go, but he said, "I have sworn an oath that I will never leave another man behind if there is any way I can prevent it. Farewell, dear friends."

It was dawn by the time he found himself among the oak trees near the castle. He heard the first faint howling of the animals in the courtyard. And as he walked through the rose and gray light, a figure started up before him—a slender youth in golden breastplates and golden hat with wings on it, holding a golden staff. Ulysses fell to his knees.

"Why do you kneel, venerable sir?" said the youth. "You are older than I, and a mighty warrior. You should not kneel."

"Ah, pardon," cried Ulysses. "I have sharp eyes for some things. Behind your youth—so fair—I see time itself stretching to the beginning of things. Behind your slenderness I sense the power of a god. Sweet youth, beautiful lad, I know you. You are Hermes, the swift one, the messenger god. I pray you have come with good tidings for me because I fear that I have offended the gods, or one of them anyway, and he has vowed vengeance upon me."

"It is true," said Hermes. "Somebody up there doesn't like you. Can't say who, not ethical, you know. But if you *should* suspect that he may have something to do with the management of sea matters, well, you're a good guesser, that's all."

"Poseidon . . . I have offended Poseidon," muttered Ulysses, "the terrible one, the earth-shaker."

"Well," said Hermes, "what do you expect? That unpleasant Cyclops whom you first blinded, then taunted is Poseidon's son, you know. Not a son to be proud of, but blood is thicker than water, as they say, even in the god of the sea. So Polyphemus tattled to his father, and asked him to do dreadful things to you, which, I'm afraid, he's been doing. Now, this castle you're going to is Circe's and she is a very dangerous person to meet—a sorceress, a doer of magical mischief. And she is waiting for you, Ulysses. She sits at her loom, weaving, waiting.

For you. She has already entertained your shipmates. Fed them. Watched them making pigs of themselves. And, finally, helped them on their way a bit. In brief, they are now in a sty, being fattened. And one day they will make a most excellent meal for someone not too fussy. Among Circe's guests are many peculiar feeders."

"Thunder and lightning!" cried Ulysses. "What can I do!"

"Listen and learn," said Hermes. "I have come to help you. Poseidon's wrath does not please all of us, you know. We gods have our moods, and they're not always kind, but somehow or other we must keep things balanced. And so I have come to help you. You must do exactly as I say, or nothing can help you. Now listen closely. First, take this."

He snapped his fingers and a flower appeared between them. It was white and heavily scented, with a black and yellow root. He gave it to Ulysses.

"It is called *moly*," he said. "It is magical. So long as you carry it, Circe's drugs will not work. You will go to the castle. She will greet you and feed you. You will eat the food which, to her amazement, will leave you unharmed. Then you will draw your sword and advance upon her as though you meant to kill her. Then she will see that you have certain powers, and will begin to plead with you. She will unveil enchantments more powerful than any she has yet used. Resist them you cannot, nor can any man, nor any god. Nor is there any counterspell that will work against such beauty. But if you wish to see your home again, if you wish to rescue your shipmates from the sty, you must resist her long enough to make her swear the great oath of the immortals—that she will not do you any harm as long as you are her guest. That is all I can do for you.

From now on, it is up to you. We shall be watching you with interest. Farewell."

The golden youth disappeared just as a ray of sunlight does when a cloud crosses the face of the sun. Ulysses shook his head, wondering whether he had really seen the god, or imagined him, but then he saw that he was still holding the curious flower, and he knew that Hermes had indeed been there. So he marched on toward the castle, through the pack of lions and wolves, who leaped about him, fawning, looking at him with their great intelligent eyes, and trying to warn him in their snarling, growling voices. He stroked their heads, and passed among them, and went into the castle.

And here, he found Circe, sitting at her loom, weaving and singing. She wore a white tunic now and a flame-colored scarf, and was as beautiful as the dawn. She stood up and greeted him, saying, "Welcome, stranger. I live here alone, and seldom see anyone, and almost never have guests. So you are triply welcome, great sea-stained warrior, for I know that you have seen battle and adventure and have tales to tell."

She drew him a warm perfumed bath, and her servants bathed and anointed him, and gave him clean garments to wear. When he came to her, she gave him a red bowl full of yellow food, and said, "Eat." The food smelled delicious; its fragrance was intoxicating. Ulysses felt that he wanted to plunge his face into it and grub it up like a pig, but he held the flower tightly, kept control of himself, and ate slowly. He did not quite finish the food.

"Delicious," he said. "Your own recipe?"

"Yes," she said. "Will you not finish?"

"I am not quite so hungry as I thought."

"Then, drink. Here's wine."

She turned her back to him as she poured

the wine, and he knew that she was casting a powder in it. He smiled to himself and drank off the wine, then said: "Delicious. Your own grapes?"

"You look weary, stranger," she said. "Sit and talk with me."

"Gladly," said Ulysses. "We have much to speak of, you and I. I'm something of a farmer myself. I breed cattle on my own little island of Ithaca, where I'm king—when I'm home. Won't you show me your livestock?"

"Livestock? I keep no cattle here."

"Oh, do you not? I fancied I heard pigs squealing out there. Must have been mistaken."

"Yes," said Circe. "Badly mistaken."

"But you do have interesting animals. I was much struck by the wolves and lions who course in a pack like dogs—very friendly for such savage beasts."

"I have taught them to be friendly," said Circe. "I am friendly myself, you see, and I like all the members of my household to share my goodwill."

"Their eyes," said Ulysses. "I was struck by their eyes—so big and sad and clever. You know, as I think of it, they looked like . . . human eyes."

"Did they?" said Circe. "Well—the eyes go last."

She came to him swiftly, raised her wand, touched him on the shoulder, and said: "Change, change, change! Turn, turn, turn!"

Nothing happened. Her eyes widened when she saw him sitting there, unchanged, sniffing at the flower he had taken from his tunic. He took the wand from her gently, and snapped it in two. Then drawing his sword he seized her by her long golden hair and forced her to her knees, pulling her head until her white throat was offered the blade

of the sword. Then he said, "You have not asked me my name. It is Ulysses. I am an unlucky man, but not altogether helpless. You have changed my men into pigs. Now I will change you into a corpse."

She did not flinch before the blade. Her great blue eyes looked into his. She took the sharp blade in her hand, stroked it gently, and said, "It is almost worth dying to be overcome by so mighty a warrior. But I think living might be interesting too, now that I have met you."

He tried to turn his head, but sank deeper into the blueness of her eyes.

"Yes, I am a sorceress," she murmured, "a wicked woman. But you are a sorcerer too, are you not? Changing me more than I have changed your men, for I changed only their bodies and you have changed my soul. It is no longer a wicked plotting soul, but soft and tender, full of love for you."

Her voice throbbed. He raised her to her feet, and said, "You are beautiful enough to turn any man into an animal. I will love you. But even before I am a man, I am a leader. My men are my responsibility. I must ask you to swear the great oath that you will not harm me when I am defenseless, that you will not wound me and suck away my blood as witches do, but will treat me honestly. And that, first of all, you will restore my men to their own forms, and let me take them with me when I am ready to leave."

"I will try to see that you are never ready," said Circe softly.

Circe kept her promise. The next morning she took Ulysses out to the sty and called the pigs. They came trotting up, snuffling and grunting. As they streamed past her, rushing to Ulysses, she touched each one on the shoulder with her wand. As she did so, each pig stood up, his hind legs grew longer, his front hooves became hands, his eyes grew, his nose shrank, his quills softened into hair, and he was his human self once more, only grown taller and younger.

The men crowded around Ulysses, shouting and laughing. He said to them: "Welcome, my friends. You have gone a short but ugly voyage to the animal state. And while you have returned—looking very well—it is clear that we are in a place of sorceries and must conduct ourselves with great care. Our enchanting hostess, Circe, has become so fond of our company that she insists we stay awhile. This, indeed, is the price of your release from hogdom. So you will now go down to your shipmates on the beach, and tell them what has happened. Ask them to secure the ship and then return here with you to the castle. It is another delay in our journey, but it is far better than what might have been. Go, then."

The men trooped happily down to the harbor and told the others what had happened. At first, Eurylochus protested. "How do I know," he said, "that you are not still under enchantment? How do I know that this is not some new trick of the sorceress to get us all into her power, turn us all to pigs, and keep us in the sty forever?"

But the other men paid no heed to his warning. They were eager to see the castle and the beautiful witch, to taste the delicious food, and enjoy all the luxuries their friends had described. So they obeyed Ulysses' commands. They dragged the ship up on the beach, beyond reach of the tide, unstepped its mast, then marched off laughing and singing toward the castle, carrying mast and oars and folded sail. Eurylochus followed, but he was afraid.

For some time, things went well. The men were treated as welcome guests. They feasted for hours each night in the great dining hall. And as they ate, they were entertained by minstrels singing, by acrobats, dancing bears, and dancing girls. During the day they swam in the ocean, hunted wild boar, threw the discus, had archery and spear-throwing contests, raced, jumped, and wrestled. Then as dusk drew in they returned to the castle for their warm perfumed baths and bowls of hot wine before the feasting began again.

As for Ulysses he found himself falling deeper under Circe's spell every day. Thoughts of home were dim now. He barely remembered his wife's face. Sometimes he would think of days gone by and wonder when he could shake off this enchantment and resume his voyage. Then she would look at him. And her eyes, like blue flame, burned these pictures out of his head. Then he could not rest until he was within the scent of her hair, the touch of her hand. And he would whimper impatiently like a dog dreaming, shake his head, and go to her.

"It is most curious," she said. "But I love you more than all my other husbands."

"In the name of heaven how many have you had?" he cried.

"Ah, don't say it like that. Not so many, when you consider. I have been a frequent widow, it is true. But, please understand, I am god-descended on both sides. I am immortal and cannot die. I have lived since the beginning of things."

"How many husbands have you buried, dear widow?"

"Buried? Why, none."

"I see. You cremate them."

"I do not let them die. I cannot bear dead things. Especially if they are things I have loved. Of all nature's transformations, death seems to me the most stupid. No, I do not let them die. I change them into animals, and they roam this beautiful island forevermore. And I see them every day and feed them

with my own hand."

"That explains those wolves and lions in the courtyard, I suppose."

"Ah, they are only the best, the cream, the mightiest warriors of ages gone. But I have had lesser husbands. They are now rabbits, squirrels, boars, cats, spiders, frogs, and monkeys. That little fellow there. . . ." She pointed to a silvery little ape who was prancing and gibbering on top of the bed-post. ". . . he who pelts you with walnut shells every night. He was very jealous, very busy and jealous, and still is. I picked their forms, you see, to match their dispositions. Is it not thoughtful of me?"

"Tell me," said Ulysses, "when I am used up, will I be good enough to join your select band of wolves and lions, or will I be something less? A toad, perhaps, or a snail?"

"A fox, undoubtedly," she said. "With your swiftness, and your cunning ways—oh, yes, a fox. A king of foxes." She stroked his beard. "But you are the only man who ever

withstood my spells," she said. "You are my conqueror, a unique hero. It is not your fate to stay with me. It is not my happy fate to arrange your last hours."

"Is it not?" said Ulysses.

"No," she said. "Unless you can wipe out of your mind all thoughts of home. Unless you can erase all dreams of battle and voyage, unless you can forget your men, and release me from my oath, and let them become animals, contented animals, then and then only, can you remain with me as husband forever. And I will give you of my immortality. Yes, that can be arranged. I know how. You will share my immortality and live days of sport and idleness and nights of love. And we will live together always, knowing no other, and we will never grow old."

"Can such a thing be?"

"Yes. But the decision is yours. I have sworn an oath, and cannot keep you against your will. If you choose, you can remain here with me, and make this island a paradise of pleasure. If not, you must resume your voyage, and encounter dangers more dreadful than any you have seen yet. You will watch friends dying before your eyes, have your own life imperiled a hundred times, be battered, bruised, torn, wave-tossed, all this, if you leave me. But it is for you to decide."

Ulysses stood up and strode to the edge of the terrace. From where he stood he could see the light dancing in a million hot little needles on the blue water. In the courtyard he saw the wolves and the lions. Beyond the courtyard, at the edge of the wood, he saw his men, happy looking, healthy, tanned; some were wrestling, some flinging spears, others drawing the bow. Circe had crossed to her loom and was weaving, weaving and singing. He remembered his wife. She also, at home in Ithaca, would sit and weave. But how different she looked. Her hair was no fleece of burning gold, but black. She was much smaller than Circe, and she did not sing.

"I have decided," he said. "I must go."

"Must you?"

"Yes."

"First let me tell you what the gods have decreed. If you sail away from this island, you cannot head for home. First you must go to the Land of the Dead."

"The Land of the Dead?" cried Ulysses. "No! No! It cannot be!"

"To the Land of the Dead. To Tartarus. This is the decree. You must go there with all your men. And there you must consult certain ghosts, of whom you will be told, and they will prophesy for you, and plan your homeward journey. And theirs is the route you must follow if you wish to see Ithaca again."

"The Land of the Dead, dark Tartarus, the realm of torment from which no mortal returns. Must I go there?"

"Unless you stay with me here, in peace, in luxury, in every pleasure but that of adventure."

"It cannot be," said Ulysses. "As you, beautiful sorceress, choose a form for your lovers that matches their natures, and which they must wear when they are no longer men, so the Fates, with their shears, have cut out my destiny.[4] It is danger, toil, battle, uncertainty. And, though I stop and refresh myself now and again, still must I resume my voyage, for that is my nature. And to fit my nature has fate cut the pattern of my days."

"Go quickly," said Circe. "Call your men and depart. For if you stay here any longer, I shall forget all duty. I shall break my oath and keep you here by force and never let you go. Quickly then, brave one, quickly!"

Ulysses summoned his men and led them down to the beach. They stepped the mast, rigged the sails, and sailed away. They caught a northwest puff. The sails filled and the black ship ran out of the harbor. Ulysses' face was wet with Circe's last tears and his heart was very heavy. But then spray dashed into his face with the old remembered bright shock, and he laughed.

The last sound the men heard as the ship threaded through the mouth of the harbor and ran for the open sea, was the howling of the lions and wolves who had followed them down to the beach. They stood now breast-deep in the surf, gazing after the white sail, crying their loneliness. □□

---

4. *the Fates . . . have cut out my destiny.* Human destiny was thought to be determined by three goddesses called the Fates. One spun the thread of life, the second measured it, and the third cut it.

THE VOYAGES

(FRANCE)

(SPAIN)

8
OCEAN STREAM
(ATLANTIC)

(NORTHERN AFRICA)

LEGEND
1 **Troy.** The site of the Trojan War is the beginning of Ulysses' journey home.
2 **The Ciconians.** Ulysses' men attempt to loot a rich city.
3 **Lotusland.** The god Morpheus gives sleep and dreams.
4 **Island of the Cyclopes.** Ulysses' men are trapped by the one-eyed giant Polyphemus.
5 **Aeolus.** The god of the winds offers Ulysses help.
6 **The Bag of Winds.** Ulysses' men release a terrible gale.
7 **Island of the Dawn.** Circe, the sorceress, turns men into beasts.
8 **Tartarus.** Ulysses seeks advice in the Land of the Dead.
9 **The Sirens.** Monsters sing to lure sailors to destruction.
10 **Scylla and Charybdis.** Ulysses tries to steer between a monster who eats sailors and a monster who creates a great whirlpool.
11 **Thrinacia.** The Sun Titan Hyperion demands revenge for the loss of his golden cattle.
12 **Storm at sea.** Ulysses is shipwrecked.
13 **Ogygia.** The sorceress Calypso offers Ulysses immortality.
14 **Ino.** The sea nymph lends Ulysses her magic veil.
15 **Phaeacia.** Nausicaa sings of heroes at a banquet in Ulysses' honor.
16 **Ithaca.** Ulysses arrives home—in disguise.

Glossary of Proper Names

Achilles (ə kil′ēz), Greek hero at the Trojan War.

Actaeon (ak tē′ən), hunter changed into a stag by the goddess Artemis and killed by his own hounds.

Aegean (i jē′ən) **Sea,** arm of the Mediterranean Sea between Greece and Turkey. See map.

Aeolian (ē ō′lē ən) **Island,** home of **Aeolus** (ē′ə ləs), god of the winds. See map.

Agamemnon (ag′ə mem′non), Menelaus's brother, leader of the Greeks in the Trojan War.

Agelaus (aj ə lā′əs), suitor for Penelope.

Ajax (ā′jaks), Greek hero at the Trojan War.

Alcinous (al sin′ō əs), king of Phaeacia, father of Nausicaa.

Amphitrite (am fi trī′tē), sea goddess, wife of Poseidon.

Anticleia (an ti klē′ə), mother of Ulysses.

Antinous (an tin′ō əs), suitor for Penelope.

Aphrodite (af′rə dī′tē), goddess of love and beauty.

Apollo (ə pol′ō), god of the sun, poetry, and music.

Arcadia (är kā′dē ə), mountain district in the south of ancient Greece.

Ares (er′ēz), god of war.

Arete (ə rē′tē), queen of Phaeacia, mother of Nausicaa.

Argo (är′gō), Ulysses' old, faithful hunting hound.

Artemis (är′tə mis), goddess of the chase, or hunt.

Athene (ə thē′nē), goddess of wisdom and battle.

Atlas (at′ləs), Titan who supports the heavens on his shoulders.

Attica (at′ə kə), district in southeast Greece.

Aulis (ô′lis), town on east coast of Greece.

Calypso (kə lip′sō), Titan sorceress who rules island of Ogygia.

Charybdis (kə rib′dis), monster who swallows the sea, causing a whirlpool.

Ciconian (si kō′nē ən), person from village near Troy where Ulysses first stops.

Cimmerian (sə mir′ē ən), one of people said to live in perpetual mists and darkness and to eat ship-wrecked sailors.

Circe (sėr′sē), sorceress who turns men into animals.

Cretan (krēt′n), person from **Crete** (krēt), Greek island southeast of mainland. See map.

Cyclops (sī′klops), *pl.* **Cyclopes** (sī klō′pēz), one of a race of one-eyed giants.

Cythera (si thir′ə), island in southern Greece.

Demeter (di mē′tər), goddess of agriculture.

Diomedes (dī′ə mē′dēz), Greek hero at the Trojan War.

Elpenor (el pē′nôr), sailor accidentally killed on voyage to Tartarus.

Elysian (i lizh′ən) **Fields,** place of bliss where heroes and good persons reside after death.

Eos (ē′os), goddess of the dawn.

Eris (er′is), goddess of strife and discord.

Ethiopian (ē′thē ō′pē ən), person from region in northeast Africa, south of Egypt.

Eumaeus (yü mē′əs), aged swineherd on Ithaca.

Euryalus (yü rī′ə ləs), young man of Phaeacia.

Eurycleia (yü ri klī′ə), Ulysses' faithful old nurse.

Eurylochus (yü ril′ō kəs), Ulysses' companion and second in command.

Eurymachus (yü rim′ə kəs), leader of the suitors for Penelope.

Fate (fāt), one of three goddesses who determine human destiny.

Fields of Asphodel (as′fə del), meadow where ghosts of heroes wander.

Gorgon (gôr′gən), monster with snakes for hair and a horrible face that turns people to stone.

Hades (hā′dēz), god of the lower world, the home of the dead.

Hector (hek′tər), Paris's elder brother, leader of the Trojan warriors.

Helen (hel′ən), wife of Menelaus, whose elopement with Paris caused the Trojan War.

Helios (hē′lē os), a sun god. Also called Hyperion.

Hellene (hel′ēn), a Greek; any one of Ulysses' men.

Hera (her′ə), wife of Zeus, queen of the gods, goddess of women and marriage.

Heracles (her′ə klēz), hero renowned for strength and courage. Also called Hercules (hėr′kyə lēz′).

a hat	i it	oi oil	ch child		a in about
ā age	ī ice	ou out	ng long		e in taken
ä far	o hot	u cup	sh she	ə	i in pencil
e let	ō open	ù put	th thin		o in lemon
ē equal	ô order	ü rule	ᴛʜ then		u in circus
ėr term			zh measure		

Hermes (hėr′mēz), god of travel, science, invention, and luck; messenger for the other gods.

Hyperion (hī pir′ē ən), Sun Titan, sometimes called Helios, whose chariot is the sun.

Hypnos (hip′nos), god of sleep.

Immortal (i môr′tl), any god or goddess; anyone who lives forever.

Ino (ī′nō), lesser sea goddess who rescues Ulysses.

Iros (ī′rəs), beggar in Ulysses' court.

Island of the Dawn, home of Circe. See map.

Ithaca (ith′ə kə), island west of Greece, home of Ulysses. See map.

Jasion (jā′zē ən), Titan lover of Demeter, crippled by Zeus.

Libya (lib′ē ə), part of northern Africa west of Egypt.

Menelaus (men′ə lā′əs), king of Sparta, husband of Helen.

Middle Sea, now called Mediterranean. See map.

Minos (mī′nəs), king and lawgiver of Crete who became a judge in the lower world.

Morpheus (môr′fē əs), god of dreams.

Naiad (nā′ad), lesser goddess guarding water.

Nausicaa (nô sik′ā ə), princess of Phaeacia who finds Ulysses and helps him.

Neoptolemus (nē op tol′ə məs), Greek hero, son of Achilles.

Nereid (nir′ē id), lesser sea goddess.

Nymph (nimf), lesser goddess of nature in seas, rivers, fountains, hills, trees, etc.

Ocean Stream, great stream supposed to surround all land. See map.

Oceanus (ō sē′ə nəs), god of the Ocean Stream.

Ogygia (ō jij′ē ə), island of Calypso. See map.

Olympus (ō lim′pəs), **Mount,** mountain in northeast Greece, home of the gods. See map.

Orion (ô rī′ən), famous hunter, killed by Artemis.

Paris (par′is), prince of Troy, whose elopement with Helen caused the Trojan War.

Penelope (pə nel′ə pē), wife of Ulysses, mother of Telemachus.

Perimedes (per i mē′dēz), one of Ulysses' crew.

Perse (pėr′sə), daughter of Oceanus, grandmother of Circe.

Persephone (pər sef′ə nē), goddess of the lower world, wife of Hades.

Phaeacia (fē ā′shə), island west of Greece, home of Nausicaa. See map.

Polyphemus (pol′ə fē′məs), Cyclops (one-eyed giant) whom Ulysses blinds.

Poseidon (pə sīd′n), god of the sea.

Priam (prī′əm), king of Troy.

Samos (sā′mos), Greek island in the Aegean Sea.

Scylla (sil′ə), monster who snatches sailors off ships and eats them.

Sicily (sis′ə lē), island near Italy. See map.

Siren (sī′rən), monster whose singing lures sailors to destruction on the rocks.

Sisyphus (sis′ə fəs), grandfather of Ulysses, condemned forever in the lower world to roll a heavy stone up a steep hill.

Sparta (spär′tə), city in Greece, home of Helen and Menelaus.

Styx (stiks), river in the lower world which souls of the dead must cross to reach Tartarus.

Tantalus (tan′tl əs), king punished in lower world by standing in water up to his chin under branches of fruit, yet unable to reach either.

Tartarus (tär′tər əs), the lower world; Hades.

Teiresias (tī rē′sē əs), famous blind prophet.

Telemachus (tə lem′ə kəs), prince of Ithaca, son of Ulysses and Penelope.

Thrinacia (thri nā′shə), island now called Sicily, home of Hyperion's golden cattle. See map.

Titan (tīt′n), one of family of giants who ruled the world before the gods of Olympus.

Trojan (trō′jən), person from **Troy** (troi), city in northwest Turkey, site of Trojan War. See map.

Tyndareus (tin der′ē əs), former king of Sparta, father of Helen.

Ulysses (yü lis′ēz), king of Ithaca, hero of the Trojan War.

Zeus (züs), god of the sky, ruler of gods and mortals.

The Land of the Dead

In those days men knew that the Ocean Stream was a huge river girdling the earth. Hades' kingdom, dark Tartarus, was presumed to be on the farther shore, over the edge of the visible world. But no one could be certain, for those who went there did not return.

Now it had been foretold by Circe that Ulysses would have to visit the Land of the Dead, and be advised by wise ghosts before he could resume his journey and find his way back to Ithaca. So he turned his bow westward; and a strong east wind caught his white sails and sent the ship skimming toward waters no ship had sailed before.

Night tumbled from the sky and set its blackness on the sea and would not lift. The ship sailed blindly. The men were clamped in a nameless grief. They could hardly bear the sound of their own voices, but spoke to each other in whispers. The night wore on and did not give way to dawn. There were no stars, no moon. They sailed westward and waited for dawn, but no crack of light appeared in the sky. The darkness would not lift.

Once again Ulysses lashed himself to the tiller, and stuck splinters of wood in his eye sockets to prop the weary lids. And, finally, after a week of night, a feeble light did curdle the sky—not a regular dawn, no joyous burst of sun, but a grudging milky grayness that floated down and thickened into fog. Still Ulysses did not dare to sleep, for day was no better than night; no man could see in the dense woolly folds of fog.

Still the east wind blew, pushing them westward through the curdling mist, and still Ulysses did not dare give over the helm. For he had heard that the westward rim of the world was always fog-girt, and was studded by murderously rocky islets, where dwelt the Cimmerians, who waited quietly in the fog for ships to crack upon their shores and deliver to them their natural food, shipwrecked sailors. Finally, Ulysses knew he could not keep awake any longer; yet he knew too that to give over the helm to anyone else meant almost certain death for them all. So he sent a sailor named Elpenor to climb the mast and try to see some distance ahead. No sooner had Elpenor reached the top of the mast than the ship yawed sharply. Ulysses lost his footing and stumbled against the mast.

No one saw Elpenor fall. The fog was too thick. But they heard his terrible scream turned into a choking gurgle. And they knew that he had been shaken from the mast and had fallen into the sea and been drowned. No sooner had his voice gone still than the fog thinned. They could see from one end of the ship to the other—the wet sails, the shining spar, each other's wasted faces. A white gull rose screaming and flew ahead of them.

"Follow that gull," said Ulysses. "He will lead us where we must go."

Then he stretched himself on the deck and went to sleep. Whereupon the crew began to whisper among themselves that the gull was the spirit of their shipmate, Elpenor, and that Ulysses had shaken him from the mast purposely, as you shake fruit from a tree, so that he might fall in the water and be drowned, giving them the white flight of his spirit to follow to Tartarus.

"He has murdered our shipmate," they whispered to each other, "as he will murder us all to gain his ends."

But they did not dare say it loud enough to awaken Ulysses.

All day they sailed, following the white flash of the gull, and when night came there were no stars and no moon, nothing but choking blackness. Ulysses took the helm again. But now the bow tipped forward and the stern arose, and the ship slipped through the water with a rushing rustling speed as if it were sailing downhill. The men clung to the shrouds, and wept and groaned, and pleaded with Ulysses to change course. But he answered them not at all. He planted his feet and gripped the tiller with all his strength, as the deck tilted and the ship slipped down, down. . . .

"Who has ever heard of the sea sloping?" he said to himself. "Truly this must be the waterway to the underworld, and we are the first keel to cut these fathoms. May the gods grant we cross them again going the other way."

There was a roaring of waters. The deck leveled. They sailed out of darkness as through a curtain, and found themselves in a strange place. The sea had narrowed to a river, the water was black, and the sky was black, curving downward like the inside of a bowl; the light was gray. Tall trees grew along the bank of the river—black poplars and white birches. And Ulysses knew that the black river was the Styx, and that he had sailed his ship into the Kingdom of the Dead.

There was no wind, but the sails remained strangely taut, and the ship floated easily into harbor, as if some invisible hand had taken the helm.

Ulysses bade his men disembark. He led them past a fringe of trees to a great meadow where black goats cropped black grass. He drew his sword and scraped out a shallow trench, then had his men cut the throats of two black goats and hold them over the trench until it was filled with blood. For it was ghosts he had come to counsel with, and ghosts, he knew, came only where they could find fresh blood to drink, hoping always to fill their dry veins.

The meadow was still. No birds sang. There was no shrill of insects; the goats did not bleat. The men were too frightened to breathe. Ulysses waited, leaning on his sword, gloomily watching the trench of blood. Then he heard a rustling, and saw the air thicken into spouts of steam. Steamy shapes separated, heads and shoulders of mist leaning over the trench to drink, growing more solid as they drank.

One raised its head and looked at him. He shuddered. It was his mother, Anticleia.

"Greetings, Mother. How do you fare?"

"Poorly, son. I am dead, dead, dead. I kept telling you I would die one day, but you never believed me. Now you see. But do you see? Say you see."

A thin tittering arose from the ghosts, and they spoke in steamy whispers.

"What are you doing here, man? You're still alive. Go and die properly and come back, and we will welcome you."

"Silence!" cried Ulysses. "I come for better counsel than this. I must find my way back to Ithaca past the mighty wrath of a god who reaches his strong hand and swirls the sea as a child does a mud puddle, dashing my poor twig of a ship from peril to grim peril. I need good counsel to get home. Where is the sage, Teiresias? Why is he not here to greet me?"

"Coming—coming—He is blind but he smells blood as far as any."

"Do not drink it all. Save some for him."

And Ulysses smote the ghosts with his sword, driving them back, whimpering, from the trench of blood.

But then, striding across the meadow, came certain ghosts in armor. Ulysses bowed low.

"Welcome, O Fox of War," cried the ghost of Achilles. "Tell me, do men remember me in Arcadia?"

"The gods have not allowed me to set foot upon our dear islands," said Ulysses. "But on whatever savage shore I am thrown there are those who know the name of great Achilles. Your fame outshines all warriors who have ever handled weapons. And your son, Neoptolemus, is a hero too."

"Thank you, Ulysses," said the ghost of Achilles. "Your words are fair and courteous, as always. Now, heed this: When you leave this place, you will sail past an island where you will hear the voices of maidens singing. And the sound of their singing will be sweeter than memories of home, and when your men hear them, their wits will be scattered, and they will wish to dive overboard and swim to shore. If they do, they will perish. For these maidens are a band of witch sisters—music-mad sisters—who lure sailors to the rocks so that they may flay them, and make drums of their skin and flutes of their bones. They are the Siren sisters. When you pass their shore, steer clear, steer clear."

"Thank you, great Achilles."

Next to Achilles stood a huge ghost staring at Ulysses out of empty eye sockets. He was a giant skeleton. He wore a cloak of stiffened blood and a red plume upon his skull. His spear and sword were made of bone too. He was Ajax.

"You tricked me, Ulysses," he said. "When great Achilles here fell on the field of battle, you claimed his golden armor by craft, when I should have had it, I . . . I . . . . You took the golden armor that my heart desired and drove me mad with rage,

so that I butchered cattle and captives, and then killed myself. I hate you, sly one, and have this bad news for you: If you ever do reach Ithaca, you will find your wife being courted by other men, your son a captive in your own castle, your substance devoured. This is my word to you, Ulysses. So you had simply better fall on your sword now where you stand, and save another trip to Hades."

"Thank you, great Ajax," said Ulysses. "I will remember what you have told me."

"I knew that Penelope was being wooed by other men in your absence," said Ulysses' mother. "I knew it well, but I would not speak evil of your wife, not I, not I. . . ."

"Thank you, Mother," said Ulysses.

Then came a ghost so new that his flesh had not quite turned to mist, but quivered on his bones like a pale jelly. He was Elpenor, who had fallen from the mast and had led them to Tartarus. When Ulysses saw who it was, he was taken by a great dread, and cried, "I did not push you, Elpenor. You fell. It was an accident, I swear."

"Nevertheless," said Elpenor, "my ghost will trouble you until you make my grave."

"How will I do that?"

"The first land you come to, build me a barrow and set thereon my oar. If you forget, I shall scratch at your windows and howl down your chimney and dance in your sleep."

"I will build your grave with my own hands," said Ulysses. "Have you any counsel for me?"

"Yes. Death has cleared my eyes, and I see things I would not have known. I see your ship now sailing in a narrow place between two huge rocks. Beneath the starboard rock is a cave, and in that cave squats Scylla, an unpleasant lady with twelve legs and six heads who cries with the voice of a new-born puppy. If you sail too near that

314   THE ADVENTURES OF ULYSSES

rock, she will seize six sailors to feed her six mouths—"

"Then I will steer away from Scylla—toward the other rock."

"Ah, but under the other rock lurks a strange thirsty monster named Charybdis whose habit it is to drink up a whole tide of water in one gulp, and then spit it out again, making a whirlpool of such terrible sucking force that any ship within its swirl must be destroyed."

"Monster to the right and monster to the left," cried Ulysses. "What can I do then?"

"You must keep to the middle way. But if you cannot—and indeed it will be very difficult, for you will be tacking against headwinds—then choose the right-hand rock where hungry Scylla squats. For it is better to lose six men than your ship and your entire crew."

"Thank you, courteous Elpenor," said Ulysses. "I will heed your words."

Then the air grew vaporous as the mob of ghosts shifted and swayed, making way for one who cleaved forward toward the trench of blood, and Ulysses recognized the one he was most eager to see, the blind woman-shaped ghost of Teiresias, sage of Thebes, expert at disasters, master of prophecy.

"Hail, venerable Teiresias," he cried, "all honor to you. I have journeyed far to make your acquaintance."

Teiresias came silently to the trench, knelt, and drank. He drank until the trench was empty and the misty bladder of his body was faintly pink.

"You honor me by your visit, Ulysses," he said. "Many men sought my counsel when I was alive, but you are the first client to make his way down here. You have heard these others tell you of certain petty dangers which you will do well to avoid, but I have a mighty thing to tell."

"Tell."

"Your next landfall will be Thrinacia, a large island which men shall one day call Sicily. Here the Sun Titan, Hyperion, pastures his herds of golden cattle. Your stores will have been eaten when you reach this place, and your men will be savage with hunger. But no matter how desperate for food they are, you must prevent them from stealing even one beef. If they do, they shall never see home again."

"I myself will guard the herds of the Sun Titan," said Ulysses, "and not one beef shall be taken. Thank you, wise Teiresias."

"Go now. Take your men aboard the ship, and go. Sail up the black river toward the upper air."

"But now that I am here and have come such a long and weary way to get here, may I not see some of the famous sights? May I not see Orion hunting, Minos judging? May I not dance with the heroes in the Fields of Asphodel? May I not see Tantalus thirsting, or my own grandfather, Sisyphus, rolling his eternal stone up the hill?"

"No," said Teiresias. "It is better that you go. You have been here too long already, I fear; too long exposed to these bone-bleaching airs. You may already be tainted with death, you and your men, making your fates too heavy for any ship to hold. Embark then. Sail up the black river. Do not look back. Remember our advice and forget our reproaches, and do not return until you are properly dead."

Ulysses ordered his men aboard. He put down the helm. There was still no wind. But the sails stretched taut, and the ship pushed upriver. Heeding the last words of the old sage, he did not look back, but he heard the voice of his mother calling, "Good-bye . . . good-bye . . ." until it grew faint as his own breath. ▢▢

The Sirens

In the first light of morning Ulysses awoke and called his crew about him.

"Men," he said. "Listen well, for your lives today hang upon what I am about to tell you. That large island to the west is Thrinacia, where we must make a landfall, for our provisions run low. But to get to the island we must pass through a narrow strait. And at the head of this strait is a rocky islet where dwell two sisters called Sirens, whose voices you must not hear. Now I shall guard you against their singing which would lure you to shipwreck, but first you must bind me to the mast. Tie me tightly, as though I were a dangerous captive. And no matter how I struggle, no matter what signals I make to you, *do not release me,* lest I follow their voices to destruction, taking you with me."

Thereupon Ulysses took a large lump of the beeswax which was used by the sail mender to slick his heavy thread, and kneaded it in his powerful hands until it became soft. Then he went to each man of the crew and plugged his ears with soft wax; he caulked their ears so tightly that they could hear nothing but the thin pulsing of their own blood.

Then he stood himself against the mast, and the men bound him about with rawhide, winding it tightly around his body, lashing him to the thick mast.

They had lowered the sail because ships cannot sail through a narrow strait unless there is a following wind, and now each man of the crew took his place at the great oars.

The polished blades whipped the sea into a froth of white water and the ship nosed toward the strait.

Ulysses had left his own ears unplugged because he had to remain in command of the ship and had need of his hearing. Every sound means something upon the sea. But when they drew near the rocky islet and he heard the first faint strains of the Sirens' singing, then he wished he had stopped his own ears too with wax. All his strength suddenly surged toward the sound of those magical voices. The very hair of his head seemed to be tugging at his scalp, trying to fly away. His eyeballs started out of his head.

For in those voices were the sounds that men love:

Happy sounds like bird railing, sleet hailing, milk pailing. . . .

Sad sounds like rain leaking, tree creaking, wind seeking. . . .

Autumn sounds like leaf tapping, fire snapping, river lapping. . . .

Quiet sounds like snow flaking, spider waking, heart breaking. . . .

It seemed to him then that the sun was burning him to a cinder as he stood. And the voices of the Sirens purled in a cool crystal pool upon their rock past the blue-hot flatness of the sea and its lacings of white-hot spume. It seemed to him he could actually see their voices deepening into a silvery cool pool, and that he must plunge into that pool or die a flaming death.

He was filled with such a fury of desire that he swelled his mighty muscles, burst the rawhide bonds like thread, and dashed for the rail.

But he had warned two of his strongest men—Perimedes and Eurylochus—to guard him close. They seized him before he could plunge into the water. He swept them aside as if they had been children. But they had held him long enough to give the crew time to swarm about him. He was overpowered—crushed by their numbers—and dragged back to the mast. This time he was bound with the mighty hawser that held the anchor.

The men returned to their rowing seats, unable to hear the voices because of the wax corking their ears. The ship swung about and headed for the strait again.

Louder now, and clearer, the tormenting voices came to Ulysses. Again he was aflame with a fury of desire. But try as he might he could not break the thick anchor line. He strained against it until he bled, but the line held.

The men bent to their oars and rowed more swiftly, for they saw the mast bending like a tall tree in a heavy wind, and they feared that Ulysses, in his fury, might snap it off short and dive, mast and all, into the water to get at the Sirens.

Now they were passing the rock, and Ulysses could see the singers. There were two of them. They sat on a heap of white bones—the bones of shipwrecked sailors—and sang more beautifully than senses could bear. But their appearance did not match their voices, for they were shaped like birds, huge birds, larger than eagles. They had feathers instead of hair, and their hands and feet were claws. But their faces were the faces of young girls.

When Ulysses saw them he was able to forget the sweetness of their voices because their look was so fearsome. He closed his eyes against the terrible sight of these bird-women perched on their heap of bones. But when he closed his eyes and could not see their ugliness, then their voices maddened him once again, and he felt himself straining against the bloody ropes. He forced himself to open his eyes and look upon the monsters, so that the terror of their bodies would blot the beauty of their voices.

But the men, who could only see, not hear the Sirens, were so appalled by their aspect that they swept their oars faster and faster, and the black ship scuttled past the rock. The Sirens' voices sounded fainter and fainter and finally died away.

When Perimedes and Eurylochus saw their captain's face lose its madness, they unbound him, and he signaled to the men to unstop their ears. For now he heard the whistling gurgle of a whirlpool, and he knew that they were approaching the narrowest part of the strait, and must pass between Scylla and Charybdis. □□

Scylla and Charybdis

Ulysses had been told in Tartarus of these two monsters that guard the narrow waterway leading to Thrinacia. Each of them hid beneath its own huge rock, which stood side by side and were separated only by the width of the strait at its narrowest point.

Charybdis dwelt in a cave beneath the left-hand rock. Once she had been a superbly beautiful naiad, daughter of Poseidon, and very loyal to her father in his endless feud with Zeus, Lord of Earth and Sky. She it was who rode the hungry tides after Poseidon had stirred up a storm, and led them onto the beaches, gobbling up whole villages, submerging fields, drowning forests, claiming them for the sea. She won so much land for her father's kingdom that Zeus became enraged and changed her into a monster, a huge bladder of a creature whose face was all mouth and whose arms and legs were flippers. And he penned her in the cave beneath the rock, saying, "Your hunger shall become thirst. As you once devoured land belonging to me, now you shall drink the tide thrice a day—swallow it and spit it forth again—and your name will be a curse to sailors forever."

And so it was. Thrice a day she burned with a terrible thirst, and stuck her head out of the cave and drank down the sea, shrinking the waters to a shallow stream, and then spat the water out again in a tremendous torrent, making a whirlpool near her rock in which no ship could live.

This was Charybdis. As for Scylla, who lived under the right-hand rock, she too had once been a beautiful naiad. Poseidon himself spied her swimming one day, and fell in love with her, and so provoked the jealousy of his wife, Amphitrite, that she cried, "I will make her the most hideous female that man or god ever fled from!"

Thereupon she changed Scylla into something that looked like a huge fleshy spider with twelve legs and six heads. She also implanted in her an insatiable hunger, a wild greed for human flesh. When any ship came within reach of her long tentacles, she would sweep the deck of sailors, and eat them.

Ulysses stood in the bow as the ship nosed slowly up the strait. The roaring of the waters grew louder and louder, and now he saw wild feathers of spume flying as Charybdis sucked down the tide and spat it back. He looked at the other rock. Scylla was not in sight. But he knew she was lurking underneath, ready to spring. He squinted, trying to measure distances. The only chance to come through unharmed, he saw, was to strike the middle way between the two rocks, just beyond the suction of the whirlpool, and just out of Scylla's reach. But to do this meant that the ship must not be allowed to swerve a foot from its exact course, for the middle way was no wider than the ship itself.

He took the helm, and bade his men keep a perfectly regular stroke. Then, considering further, he turned the helm over to Eurylochus, and put on his armor. Grasping sword and spear, he posted himself at the starboard rail.

"For," he said to himself, "there is no contending with the whirlpool. If we veer off our course it must be toward the other monster. I can fight any enemy I can see."

The men rowed very carefully, very

skillfully. Eurylochus chanted the stroke, and the black ship cut through the waters of the strait, keeping exactly to the middle way.

They were passing between the rocks now. They watched in amazement as the water fell away to their left, showing a shuddering flash of sea bed and gasping fish, and then roared back again with such force that the water was beaten into white froth. They felt their ship tremble.

"Well done!" cried Ulysses. "A few more strokes and we are through. Keep the way—the middle way!"

But, when measuring distance, he had been unable to reckon upon one thing. The ship was being rowed, and the great sweep oars projected far beyond the width of the hull. And Scylla, lurking underwater, seized two of the oars, and dragged the ship toward her.

Dumbfounded, Ulysses saw the polished shafts of the oars which had been dipping and flashing so regularly suddenly snap like twigs, and before he knew what was happening, the deck tilted violently. He was thrown against the rail and almost fell overboard.

He lay on the deck, scrambling for his sword. He saw tentacles arching over him; they were like the arms of an octopus, but ending in enormous human hands.

He found his sword, rose to his knees, and hacked at the tentacles. Too late. The hands had grasped six sailors, snatched them screaming through the air, and into the sea.

Ulysses had no time for fear. He had to do a number of things immediately. He roared to the crew to keep the ship on course lest it be swept into the whirlpool. Then he seized an oar himself and rowed on the starboard side where the oars had been broken.

From where he sat he could see Scylla's rock, could see her squatting at the door of her cave. He saw her plainly, stuffing the men into her six bloody mouths. He heard the shrieks of his men as they felt themselves being eaten alive.

He did not have time to weep, for he had to keep his crew rowing and tell the helmsman how to steer past the whirlpool.

They passed through the strait into open water. Full ahead lay Thrinacia with its wooded hills and long white beaches, the Isle of the Sun Titan, their next landfall. ☐☐

Vocabulary
Structure, Dictionary

Some compound words can be easily understood when you examine the words that make up the compound. *Heartbreak* can be divided into *heart* and *break,* and you understand the meaning. However, many compound words are not so easily analyzed. You can look at the parts of *sheepfold* and still not be certain of the meaning. Or the parts of a compound may prove misleading: a *swineherd* is not a herd of pigs but a person who herds pigs. When you are unsure whether the meaning suggested by the structure is the correct one, you must go to the Glossary or a dictionary.

Each sentence in the next column contains an italicized compound. Number your paper from one to four, and beside each number write (+) if you think the compound is used correctly and (0) if it is not. Be prepared to explain your choices.

1. During the rain the hill behind our house washed away, causing a *landfall* that left two inches of mud in our den.

2. Ira declared that his devotion to Terry began when she was his *shipmate* on a shrimp boat cruising the ocean.

3. Stan's test score showed the professor that Stan was *dumfounded* and should quit school.

4. Mother served the chicken on *breastplates* of antique china.

The Cattle of the Sun

Instead of landing on Thrinacia, as the crew expected, Ulysses dropped anchor and summoned his two underchiefs, Eurylochus and Perimedes, to take counsel.

He said, "You heard the warning of old Teiresias down in Tartarus. You heard him say that this island belongs to Hyperion, the Sun Titan, who uses it as a grazing land for his flocks. The warning was most dire: Whosoever of our crew harms these cattle in any way will bring swift doom upon himself, and will never see his home again."

"We all heard the warning," said Eurylochus, "and everyone will heed it."

"How can you be so sure?" said Ulysses. "If this voyage has taught you nothing else, it should have proved to you that there is nothing in the world so uncertain as man's intentions, especially his good ones. No, fair sirs, what I propose is that we change our plans about landing here and seek another island, one where death does not pasture."

"It will never do," said Eurylochus. "The men are exhausted. There is a south wind blowing now, which means we would have to row. We simply do not have the strength to hold the oars."

"Our stores are exhausted too," said Perimedes. "The food that Circe gave us is almost gone. The water kegs are empty. We must land here and let the men rest, and lay in fresh provisions."

"Very well," said Ulysses. "If it must be, it must be. But I am holding you two directly responsible for the safety of the sun-cattle. Post guards at night, and kill any man who

goes near these fatal herds."

Thereupon the anchor was raised, and the ship put into harbor. Ulysses did not moor the ship offshore, but had the men drag it up on the beach. He sent one party out in search of game, another to fill the water kegs, and a third to chop down pine trees. From the wood was pressed a fragrant black sap, which was boiled in a big iron pot. Then he had the men tar the ship from stem to stern, caulking each crack.

The hunting party returned, downhearted. There seemed to be no game on the island, they told Ulysses, only a few wild pigs, which they had shot, but no deer, no bear, no rabbits, no game birds. Just the pigs, and great herds of golden cattle.

The water party returned triumphantly, barrels full.

The men were so weary that Ulysses stood guard himself that night. Wrapped in his cloak, naked sword across his knees, he sat hunched near the driftwood fire, brooding into the flames.

"I cannot let them rest here," he said to himself. "If game is so scarce, they will be tempted to take the cattle. For hungry men the only law is hunger. No, we must put out again tomorrow and try to find another island."

The next morning he routed out the men. They grumbled terribly, but did not dare to disobey. However, they were not fated to embark. A strong south wind blew up, almost gale strength, blowing directly into the harbor. There was no sailing into the teeth of it, and it was much too strong to row against.

"Very well," said Ulysses, "scour the island for game again. We must wait until the wind drops."

He had thought it must blow itself out in a day or so, but it was not to be. For thirty days and thirty nights the south wind blew, and they could not leave the island. All the wild pigs had been killed. The men were desperately hungry. Ulysses used all his cunning to find food. He had the men fish in the sea, dig the beaches for shellfish and turtle eggs, search the woods for edible roots and berries. They tore the clinging limpets off rocks and shot gulls. A huge pot was kept boiling over the driftwood fire, and in it the men threw anything remotely edible—sea polyps, sea lilies, fish heads, sand crabs—vile broth. But most days they had nothing else. And they grew hungrier and hungrier.

For thirty days the strong south wind blew, keeping them beached. Finally, one night when Ulysses was asleep, Eurylochus secretly called the men together, and said, "Death comes to men in all sorts of ways. And however it comes, it is never welcome. But the worst of all deaths is to die of starvation. And to be forced to starve among herds of fat beef is a hellish torture that the gods reserve for the greatest criminals. So I say to you men that we must disregard the warning of that meddlesome ghost, Teiresias, and help ourselves to this cattle. We can do it now while Ulysses sleeps. And if indeed the Sun Titan is angered and seeks vengeance—well, at least we shall have had one more feast before dying."

It was agreed. They went immediately into the meadow. Now, Hyperion's cattle were the finest ever seen on earth. They were enormous, sleek, broad-backed, with crooked golden horns, and hides of beautiful dappled gold and white. And when the men came among them with their axes, they were not afraid, for no one had ever offered them any harm. They looked at the men with their great plum-colored eyes, whisked their tails, and continued grazing.

The axes rose and fell. Six fine cows were slaughtered. Because they knew they were committing an offense against the gods, the men were very careful to offer sacrifice. Upon a makeshift altar they placed the fat thighbones and burned them as offerings. They had no wine to pour upon the blazing meat as a libation, so they used water instead, chanting prayers as they watched the meat burn.

But the smell of the roasting flesh overcame their piety. They leaped upon the carcasses like wild beasts, ripped them apart with their hands, stuck the flesh on spits, and plunged them into the open fire.

Ulysses awoke from a dream of food. He sniffed the air and realized it was no dream, that the smell of roasting meat was real. He lifted his face to the sky, and said, "O mighty ones, it was unkind to let me fall into sleep. For now my men have done what they have been told they must not do."

He drew his sword and rushed off to the light of the fire.

But just then Zeus was hearing a more powerful plea. For the Sun Titan had been informed immediately by the quick spies that serve the gods, and now he was raging upon Olympus.

"O, Father Zeus," he cried, "I demand vengeance upon the comrades of Ulysses who have slaughtered my golden kine. If they are spared, I will withdraw my chariot from the sky.[5] No longer will I warm the treacherous earth, but will go to Hades and shine among the dead."

"I hear you, cousin," said Zeus, "and promise vengeance."

Ulysses dashed among the feasting crew, ready to cut them down even as they squatted there, eating.

"Wait," cried Eurylochus. "Hold your

---

5. *withdraw my chariot from the sky.* The sun was thought to be Hyperion's chariot, which he drove daily from horizon to horizon.

hand. These are not the Sun God's cattle. But six stags we found on the other side of the island."

"Stags?" roared Ulysses. "What kind of monstrous lie is this? You know there are no stags on this island."

"They were there," said Eurylochus. "And now they are here. Perhaps the gods relented, and sent them as food. Come, eat, dear friend, and do not invent misdeeds where none exist."

Ulysses allowed himself to be persuaded, and sat down among the men, and began to eat with ravenous speed. But then a strange thing happened. The spitted carcasses turning over the fire began to low and moo as though they were alive, one of the flayed hides crawled over the sand to Ulysses, and he saw that it was dappled gold and white, and knew he had been tricked.

Once again he seized his sword and rushed toward Eurylochus.

"Wait!" cried Eurylochus. "Do not blame me. We have not offended the gods by our trickery. For the south wind has fallen—see? The wind blows from the north now, and we can sail away. If the gods were angry, Ulysses, would they send us a fair wind?"

"To the ship!" shouted Ulysses. "We sail immediately."

The men gathered up the meat that was left, and followed Ulysses to the beached ship. They put logs under it and rolled it down to the sea. Here they unfurled the sail, and slid out of the harbor.

Night ran out and the fires of dawn burned in the sky. The men hurried about their tasks, delighted to be well fed and sailing again, after the starving month on Thrinacia.

But then Ulysses, observing the sky, saw a strange sight. The sun seemed to be frown-

ing. He saw that black clouds had massed in front of it. He heard a rustling noise, and looked off westward, where he saw the water ruffling darkly.

"Down sail!" he shouted. "Ship the mast!"

Too late. A wild west wind came hurtling across the water and pounced on the ship. There was no time to do anything. Both forestays snapped. The mast split and fell,

laying its white sail like a shroud over the ship. A lightning bolt flared from the blue sky and struck amidship. Great billows of choking yellow smoke arose. The heat was unbearable. Ulysses saw his men diving off the deck, garments and hair ablaze and hissing like cinders when they hit the water.

He was still shouting commands, trying to chop the sail free and fighting against the gale and fire. But he was all alone. Not one man was aboard. The ship fell apart beneath him. The ribs were torn from the keel. The ship was nothing but a mass of flaming timbers, and Ulysses swam among them. He held on to the mast, which had not burned. Pushing it before him, he swam out of the blazing wreckage. He found the keel floating free. The oxhide backstay was still tied to the head of the mast; with it he lashed mast and keel together into a kind of raft.

He looked about, trying to find someone to pull aboard. There was no one. He had no way of steering the raft, but had to go where the wind blew him. And now, to his dismay, he found the wind shifting again. It blew from the south, which meant that he would be pushed back toward the terrible strait.

All day he drifted, and all night. When dawn came, it brought with it a roaring sucking sound, and he saw that he was being drawn between Scylla and Charybdis. He felt the raft being pulled toward the whirl-pool. It was the very moment when Charybdis took her first drink of the day. She swallowed the tide, and held it in her great bladder of a belly. The raft spun like a leaf in the outer eddies of the huge suction, and Ulysses knew that when he reached the vortex of the whirlpool, he and the raft would be drawn to the bottom, and that he must drown.

He kept his footing on the raft until the very last moment, and just as it was pulled into the vortex, he leaped as high as he could upon the naked face of the rock, scrabbling for a handhold. He caught a clump of lichen, and clung with all his strength. He could climb no higher on the rock; it was too slippery for a foothold. All he could do was cling to the moss and pray that his strength would not give out. He was waiting for Charybdis to spit forth the tide again.

The long hours passed. His shoulders felt as though they were being torn apart by red-hot pincers. Finally he heard a great tumult of waters and saw it frothing out of the cave. The waves leaped toward his feet. And then he saw what he was waiting for— his raft came shooting up like a cork.

He dropped upon the timbers. Now he would have some hours of quiet water, he knew, before Charybdis drank again. So he kept to that side of the strait, holding as far from Scylla as he could, for he well remembered the terrible reach of her arms.

He passed safely beyond the rocks and out of the strait. For nine days he drifted under the burning sun, nine nights under the indifferent moon. With his knife he cut a long splinter from the timbers, and shaped it into a lance for spearing fish. He did not get any. Then he lay on his back, pretending to be dead, and gulls came to peck out his eyes. He caught them, and wrung their necks. He ate their flesh and drank their blood, and so stayed alive.

On the tenth day he found himself approaching another island.

He was very weak. The island grew dim as he looked at it. A black mist hid the land, which was odd because the sun was shining. Then the sky tilted, and the black mist covered him. □□

Calypso

When Ulysses awoke he found himself lying on a bed of sweet-smelling grass. The sun shone hotly, but he was in a pool of delicious cool shade under a poplar tree. He was still dizzy. The trees were swaying, and bright flowers danced upon the meadow. He closed his eyes, thinking, "I am dead then. The god that hunts me took pity and shortened my hard life, and I am now in the Elysian Fields."

A voice answered, "You have not died. You are not in the Elysian Fields. You have come home."

He opened his eyes again. A woman was bending over him. She was so tall that he knew she was no mortal woman, but nymph or naiad or demigoddess. She was clad in a short tunic of yellow and purple. Her hair was yellow, and long and thick.

"You are here with me," she said. "You have come home."

"Home? Is this Ithaca? Are you Penelope?"

"This is Ogygia, and I am Calypso."

He tried to sit up. He was too weak. "But Ithaca is my home," he said. "And Penelope is my wife."

"Home is where you dwell. And now you belong to me, because this island and everything on it is mine."

Ulysses went back to sleep. For he believed he was dreaming, and did not wish to wake up again and find himself on the raft. But when he awoke, he was still in his dream. He was strong enough now to sit up and look around. He was in a great grove hemmed by trees—alder and poplar and cypress. Across this meadow four streams ran, crossing each other, making a sound like soft laughter. The meadow was a carpet of wild flowers, violets, parsley, bluebells, daffodils, and cat-faced pansies. His bed had been made in front of a grotto, he saw. Over it a wild grapevine had been trained to fall like a curtain.

The vine curtain was pushed aside, and Calypso came out.

"You are awake," she cried, "and just in time for your wedding feast. The stag is roasted. The wine has been poured. No, don't move. You're still too weak. Let me help you, little husband."

She stooped and lifted him in her great white arms and carried him easily as though he were a child into the grotto, and set him before the hearth. A whole stag was spitted over the flame. The cave was carpeted with the skins of leopard and wolf and bear.

"Lovely and gracious goddess," said Ulysses, "tell me, please, how I came here. The last I remember I was on my raft, and then a blackness fell."

"I was watching for you," said Calypso. "I knew you would come, and I was waiting. Then your raft floated into sight. I saw you slump over and roll off the raft. And I changed you into a fish, for sharks live in this water and they are always hungry. As soon as I turned you into a fish, a gull stooped—and he would have had you—but I shot him with my arrow. Then I took my net and fished you out, restored you to your proper shape, fed you a broth of herbs, and let you sleep. That was your arrival, O man I have drawn from the sea. As for your departure, that will never be. Now eat your meat and drink your wine, for I like my husbands well fed."

Ulysses ate and drank, and felt his strength return.

"After all," he thought, "things could be worse. In fact they have been much worse. This may turn out to be quite a pleasant interlude. She is certainly beautiful, this Calypso. Rather large for my taste, and inclined to be bossy, I'm afraid. But who's perfect?"

He turned to her, smiling, and said, "You say you were waiting for me, watching for my raft. How did you know I would be coming?"

"I am one of the Titan brood," said Calypso. "Daughter of mighty Atlas, who stands upon the westward rim of the world bearing the sky upon his shoulders. We are the elder branch of the gods, we Titans. For us there is no before or after, only now, wherein all things are and always were and always will be. Time, you see, is a little arrangement man has made for himself to try to measure the immeasurable mystery of life. It does not really exist. So when we want to know anything that has happened in what you call 'before,' or what will happen in what you call 'after,' we simply shuffle the pictures and look at them."

"I don't think I understand."

"I have watched your whole voyage, Ulysses. All I have to do is poke the log in a certain way, and pictures form in the heart of the fire and burn there until I poke the log again. What would you like to see?"

"My wife, Penelope."

Calypso reached her long arm and poked the log. And in the heart of the flame Ulysses saw a woman, weaving.

"She looks older," he said.

"You have been away a long time. Only the immortals do not age. I was 2,300 years old yesterday. Look at me. Do you see any wrinkles?"

"Poor Penelope," said Ulysses.

"Don't pity her too much. She has plenty of company. She is presumed to be a widow, you know."

"Has she married again?"

"I weary of this picture. Would you like to see another?"

"My son, Telemachus."

She poked the fire again, and Ulysses saw the flickering image of a tall young man with red-gold hair. He held a spear in his hand and looked angry.

"How he has grown," murmured Ulysses. "He was a baby when I left. He is a young man now, and a fine one, is he not?"

"Looks like his father," said Calypso.

"He seems to be defying some enemy," said Ulysses. "What is happening?"

"He is trying to drive away his mother's suitors, who live in your castle now. She is quite popular—for an older woman. But then, of course, she has land and goods. A rich widow. You left her well provided, O sailor. She has many suitors, and cannot decide among them. Or perhaps she enjoys their courtship too much to decide. But your son is very proud of his father, whom he does not remember, and seeks to drive the suitors from your castle."

"I had better go home and help him," said Ulysses.

"Put that out of your mind. It simply will not happen. Forget Ithaca, Ulysses. You are a hero, a mighty hero, and heroes have many homes, and the last is always the best. Look at this. See some of your exploits. Like many warriors, you were too busy fighting to know what really happened."

She poked the log again and again, and a stream of pictures flowed through the fire. Ulysses saw himself standing on a rock in the Cyclops's cave, holding the white-hot sword above the great sleeping eye, prepar-

ing to stab it in. He saw himself wrestling with the leather bag of winds that Aeolus had given him; saw himself running with the wolves and lions who had been Circe's lovers in the dark courtyard of her castle. Then, sword in hand, he saw himself hacking at Scylla's tentacles as she reached across the tilting deck for his men. Going back he saw himself before his homeward voyage crouched in the black belly of the wooden horse he had made. Next, climbing out of that horse after it had been dragged into the city and racing with lifted sword to slaughter the sleeping Trojan warriors. And, as he watched and saw the old battles refought, the men who had been his friends, and the monstrous enemies he had overcome, his heart sang with pride, and a drunken warmth stronger than the fumes of wine rose to his head, drowning out all the pictures of home.

He stood up, and said, "Thank you for showing me myself, Calypso. I do seem to be a hero, don't I? And worthy to love a daughter of the Titans."

"Yes," said Calypso.

Now Calypso had amused herself with shipwrecked sailors before. But she was hard to please, and none of them had lasted very long. When she was tired of someone she would throw him back into the sea. If she were feeling goodnatured she would change him to gull or fish first. Indeed, the trees of the grove were filled with nesting sea birds—gull and heron and osprey and sand owls—who called to her at night, reproaching her.

"What is that clamor of birds?" said Ulysses.

"Just birds."

"Why do they shriek so?"

"They are angry at me for loving you. They were men once, like yourself."

"How did they get to be birds?"

"Oh, well, it's no very difficult transformation, when you know how. I thought they would be happier so."

"They don't sound very happy."

"They have jealous natures."

"You are not unlike Circe in some ways," said Ulysses. "You island goddesses are apt to be abrupt with your former friends. I've noticed this."

"It's a depressing topic, dear. Let's talk about me. Do you find me beautiful today?"

"More beautiful than yesterday, if that is possible. And no doubt will find you even lovelier tomorrow, since you have shown me the penalty of any inattention."

"Do not fear," said Calypso. "You are not like the others. You are bolder and have more imagination. You are a hero."

"Perhaps you could persuade your feath-ered friends to nest elsewhere? They make me nervous."

"Nothing easier. I shall simply tell them to depart. If they do not, I shall change them all to grasshoppers, all save one, who will eat the rest, and then die of overeating."

"Truly, you are wise and powerful, and fair beyond all women, mortal or immortal."

She smiled. "You have such an apt way of putting things," she said.

So Ulysses made himself at home on the island, and passed the time hunting game, and fishing the sea, and reveling with the beautiful Calypso. He was happy. Thoughts of home grew dim. The nymph taught him how to poke the magic log upon her hearth so that it would cast up fire pictures. And he sat by the hour on the great hearth, reading the flickering tapestry of days gone by and days to come. But she had instructed the log never to show him scenes of Ithaca, for she wished him not to be reminded of his home in any way, lest he be tempted to depart. But Ulysses was as crafty as she was, and after he had poked the log many times, asking it to show him what was happening on his island, and the log had cast up pictures of other times, other places, he realized that Calypso had laid a magic veto upon scenes of home. And this, instead of making him forget, made him more eager than ever to know what was happening to Telemachus and Penelope.

One day he went into the wood, snared a sea crow, and asked, "Can you speak?"

"Yes," said the crow.

"Were you once a man?"

"Once . . . once . . . at the time of your grandfather, Sisyphus. I was a clever man, a spy. That's why Calypso changed me into a crow when she grew weary of me, for of all creatures we are the best for spying and prying and tattling."

"Then you're the bird for me," cried Ulysses. "Listen, I wish you to fly to Ithaca. Go to my castle and see what is happening. Then come back and tell me."

"Why should I? What will you give me?"

"Your life."

"My life? I already have that."

"But not for long. Because if you refuse to do as I ask, I shall wring your neck."

"Hmmm," said the crow. "There is merit in your argument. Very well. I shall be your spy. Only don't let Calypso know. She'll catch me and feed me to the cat before I can report to you. I have a notion she'd like you to forget Ithaca."

"Fly away, little bird," said Ulysses, "and do what you have to do. I'll take care of things here."

The next day, at dusk, as he was returning from the hunt, he heard the crow calling from the depth of an oak tree.

"Greetings," said Ulysses. "Have you done what I asked?"

"I have flown to Ithaca," said the crow. "A rough journey by sea, but not really so far as the crow flies. I flew to your castle, and perched in an embrasure, and watched and watched. Briefly, your son is grieving, your wife is weaving, and your guests are *not* leaving."

"What does my wife weave?"

"Your shroud."

"Has she decided so soon that I am dead? I have been gone scarcely twenty years."

"She is faithful. But the suitors, who are brawling, ill-mannered young men, are pressing her to choose one of them for a husband. However, she refuses to choose until she finishes the shroud. And it has been three years aweaving, for each night she rips up the work she has done by day, so the shroud is never finished. But the suitors

grow impatient. They are demanding that she finish her weaving and choose a groom. Your son opposes them. And they threaten to kill him unless he steps aside."

"Thank you, crow," said Ulysses.

"What will you do now—try to escape?"

"Escape? I do not consider myself a captive, good bird. I shall simply inform Calypso that I intend to leave, and ask her to furnish transportation."

"You make it sound easy," said the crow. "Good luck."

And he flew away.

Ulysses went to Calypso in her grotto, and fell on his knees before her, and said, "Fair and gracious friend, you have made me happier than any man has a right to be, especially an unlucky one. But now I must ask you one last great favor."

Calypso frowned. "I don't like the sound of that," she said. "What do you mean 'last'? Why should I not go on doing you favors?"

"I must go home."

"This is your home."

"No. My home is Ithaca. Penelope is my wife. Telemachus is my son. I have enemies. They live in my castle and steal my goods. They wish to kill my son and take my wife. I am a king. I cannot tolerate insults. I must go home."

"Suppose you do go home, what then?"

"I will contend with my enemies. I will kill them or they will kill me."

"You kill them, say—then what?"

"Then I live, I rule. I don't know. I cannot read the future."

"I can. Look."

She poked the magic log. Fire pictures flared. Ulysses saw himself sitting on his throne. He was an old man. Penelope was there. She was an old woman.

"You will grow old . . . old. . . ." Calypso's voice murmured in his ear, unraveling in its rough purring way like raw silk. "Old . . . old. . . . You will live on memories. You will eat your heart out recalling old glories, old battles, old loves. Look . . . look into the fire."

"Is that me?"

"That's you, humping along in your old age among your hills, grown dry and cruel."

She tapped the log and the fire died.

"Do you still want to go back to Ithaca?" she said.

"Will my future be different if I stay here?"

"Certainly. If you stay with me, it will be entirely different. You will no longer be a mortal man. I will make you my eternal consort, make you immortal. You will not die or grow old. This will be your home, not only this island, but wherever the Titans rule."

"Never die, never grow old. It seems impossible."

"You are a man to whom impossible things happen," said Calypso. "Haven't you learned that by now?"

" 'Never' . . . ," said Ulysses. " 'Always' . . . . These are words I find hard to accept."

"Do not think you will be bored. I am expert at variety. I deal in transformations, you know."

"You are eloquent," said Ulysses. "And you need no eloquence, for your beauty speaks more than any words. Still, I cannot be immortal, never to die, never to grow old. What use is courage then?"

Calypso smiled at him. "Enough discussion for one night. You have time to decide. Take five or ten years. We are in no hurry, you and I."

"Five or ten years may seem little to an immortal," said Ulysses. "But I am still a man. It is a long time for me."

"That's just what I said," said Calypso. "It is better to be immortal. But, think it over."

The next morning, instead of hunting, Ulysses went to the other side of the island and built an altar of rocks and sacrificed to the gods. He poured a libation of unwatered wine, and raised his voice:

"O, great gods upon Olympus—thunder-wielding Zeus and wise Athene, earthshaking Poseidon, whom I have offended, golden Apollo—hear my prayer. For ten years I fought in Troy, and for ten more years have wandered the sea, been hounded from island to island, battered by storms, swallowed by tides. My ships have been wrecked, my men killed. But you have granted me life. Now, I pray you, take back the gift. Let me join my men in Tartarus. For if I cannot return home, if I have to be kept here as a prisoner of Calypso while my kingdom is looted, my son slain, and my wife stolen, then I do not wish to live. Allow me to go home, or strike me dead on the spot."

His prayer was carried to Olympus. Athene heard it. She went to Zeus, and asked him to call the gods into council. They met in the huge throne-room. As it happened, Poseidon was absent. He had ridden a tidal wave into Africa, where he had never been, and was visiting the Ethiopians.

Athene said, "O father Zeus, O brother gods, I wish to speak on behalf of Ulysses, who of all the mighty warriors we sent to Troy shows the most respect for our power, and the most belief in our justice. Ten years after leaving the bloody beaches of Troy he has still not reached home. He is penned now on an island by Calypso, daughter of Atlas, who uses all her Titanic enticements to keep him prisoner. This man's plight challenges our Justice. Let us help him now."

Zeus said, "I do not care to be called unjust. I am forgetful sometimes, perhaps, but then I have much to think of, many affairs to manage. And remember, please, my daughter, that this man has been traveling the sea, which belongs to my brother Poseidon, whom he has offended. Poseidon holds a heavy grudge, as you know; he does not forgive injuries. Ulysses would have been home years ago if he had not chosen to blind Polyphemus, who happens to be Poseidon's son."

"He has paid for that eye over and over again," cried Athene. "Many times its worth, I vow. And the earth-shaker is not here, as it happens. He is off shaking the earth of Africa, which has been too dry and peaceable for his tastes. Let us take advantage of his absence, and allow Ulysses to resume his voyage."

"Very well," said Zeus. "It shall be as you advise."

Thereupon he dispatched Hermes, the messenger god, to Ogygia. Hermes found Calypso on the beach singing a wild sea song, imitating now the voice of the wind, now the lisping scraping sound of waves on a shallow shore, weaving in the cry of heron and gull and osprey, tide suck and drowned moons. Now Hermes had invented pipe and lyre, and loved music. When he heard Calypso singing her wild sea song, he stood upon the bright air, ankle wings whirring, entranced. He hovered there, listening to her sing. Dolphins were drawn by her voice. They stood in the surf and danced on their tails.

She finished her song. Hermes landed lightly beside her.

"A beautiful song," he said.

"A sad song."

"All beautiful songs are sad."

"Yes. . . ."

"Why is that?"

"They are love songs. Women love men, and they go away. This is very sad."

"You know why I have come then?"

"Of course. What else would bring you here? The Olympians have looked down and seen me happy for a little while, and they have decreed that this must not be. They have sent you to take my love away."

"I am sorry, cousin. But it is fated that he find his way home."

"Fate . . . destiny . . . what are they but fancy words for the brutal decrees of Zeus. He is jealous, and that is the whole truth of it. He wants us all for himself. Don't deny it. When Eos, Goddess of Dawn, chose Orion for her lover, Zeus had his daughter, Artemis, slay him with her arrows. When Demeter, harvest wife, met Jasion in the ploughed fields, Zeus himself flung his bolt crippling him. It is always the same. He allowed Ulysses to be shipwrecked time and again. When I found him he was riding the timbers of his lost ship and was about to drown. So I took him here with me, and cherished him, and offered to make him immortal. And now Zeus suddenly remembers, after twenty years, that he must go home immediately, because it is ordained."

"You can't fight Zeus," said Hermes gently. "Why try?"

"What do you want me to do?"

"Permit Ulysses to make himself a raft. See that he has provisions. Then let him depart."

"So be it."

"Do not despair, sweet cousin. You are too beautiful for sorrow. There will be other storms, other shipwrecks, other sailors."

"Never another like him."

"Who knows?"

He kissed her on the cheek, and flew away. ☐☐

English Borrowings from Greek

What is your *Achilles' heel?* When Achilles was a baby, the story goes, his mother dipped him in the River Styx to make him safe from all mortal wounds. However, the heel she held him by was not touched by the magic waters, and so remained his one vulnerable spot. He was killed at Troy by being struck in that heel. And to this day, the band of tissue in your heel is known as your *Achilles' tendon.*

The term *Trojan Horse* still means something that betrays and destroys from within; if you're caught *between Scylla and Charybdis,* you still face two possible dangers.

Ulysses' adventures were first written down almost twenty-eight centuries ago, but the tales were being told or sung for unknown years before. In one form or another, they have excited listeners and readers for thousands of years.

Poetry, drama, stories, and films have been based on these tales. Paintings and sculpture have interpreted them. Modern artists continue to use these familiar scenes and characters.

Ancient Greece has influenced our culture greatly. About ten percent of our English words are borrowed from Greek or use Greek roots and affixes. But there are many more direct borrowings, such as saying "That's fate," when a situation cannot be helped. Here are some others:

Mount Olympus is an actual mountain in Greece, thought by the ancients to be the home of the gods. Nearby, contests in athletics, poetry, and music were held every four years in honor of Zeus. These Olympic Games were revived in modern times, with athletes from all over the world participating. The word *Olympian* means "majestic; like a god."

Hypnos was the Greek god of sleep, so it is not surprising that *hypnotism* was named after him. Throughout history, it has been a great problem of medicine to get a patient to relax or sleep so that treatment could be administered. Then in 1805 a narcotic drug was found that was a powerful painkiller and anesthetic. And since Morpheus was the god of dreams, *morphine* was named after him.

Atlas was one of the Titans—giants who ruled the earth before the gods of Olympus. (*Titanic* still means "gigantic; having great strength or power.") For his part in the War of the Gods, he was punished by having to support the heavens on his shoulders. A picture of Atlas was used in the 16th century for the cover of a collection of maps; such a book is still called an *atlas* today.

King Tantalus, as punishment for revealing some of Zeus's secrets, was made to stand in the underworld in water up to his chin, under branches laden with fruit. Every time Tantalus wanted to eat or drink, however, the fruit and the water would recede. To *tantalize* means to torment a person with things that can't be obtained.

Some names are still used in their original forms. Any handsome young man may be called an *Apollo;* any beautiful young woman, an *Aphrodite;* and any region of simple, quiet contentment, *Arcadia.* But some names are used in more general ways: *Spartan* means disciplined and brave, like the inhabitants of ancient Sparta; to *hector* is to bully someone, as Hector treated Achilles in the Trojan War; *herculean* describes the kind of strength and courage that Heracles had.

Nymph is sometimes applied to any graceful young woman, but it is used as well for certain insects in their stage of development between egg and adult form. And *siren,* besides meaning an attractive but dangerous woman, also means a loud, piercing whistle (usually a warning, unlike the Sirens' singing). No one is sure, however, how *Calypso* came to mean an improvised jazz song from the British West Indies.

Ino's Veil

In her generous way, Calypso went beyond what the gods had ordered, and provided Ulysses not with a raft, but with a beautiful tight little vessel, sturdy enough for a long voyage, and small enough for one man to sail.

But he would have done just as well with a raft, for his bad luck held. He was seventeen days out of Ogygia, scudding along happily, when Poseidon, on his way back from Africa, happened to notice the little ship.

The sea god scowled, and said, "Can that be Ulysses? I thought I had drowned him long ago. One of my meddlesome relatives up there must be shielding him, and I have a good notion who. Well, I'll give my owlish niece[6] a little work to do."

His scowl deepened, darkening the sun. He shook a storm out of his beard. The winds leaped, the water boiled. Ulysses felt the tiller being torn out of his hand. The boat spun like a chip. The sail ripped, the mast cracked, and Ulysses realized that his old enemy had found him again.

He clung to the splintered mast. Great waves broke over his head, and he swallowed the bitter water. He came up, gasping. The deck broke beneath him.

"Why am I fighting?" he thought. "Why don't I let myself drown?"

But he kept fighting by instinct. He pulled himself up onto a broken plank and clung there. Each boiling whitecap crested over him, and he was breathing more water

than air. His arms grew too weak to hold the plank, and he knew that the next wave must surely take him under.

However, there was a nereid near, named Ino, who hated Poseidon for an injury he had done her long before, and now she resolved to balk his vengeance. She swam to Ulysses' timber, and climbed on.

He was snorting and gasping and coughing. Then he saw that he was sharing his plank with a green-haired woman wearing a green veil.

"Welcome, beautiful Nereid," he said. "Are you she who serves Poseidon, ushering drowned men to those caverns beneath the sea where the white bones roll?"

"No, unhappy man," she said. "I am Ino . . . and I am no servant of the windy widowmaker. I would like to do him an injury by helping you. Take this veil. It cannot sink even in the stormiest sea. Strip off your garments, wrap yourself in the veil, and swim toward those mountains. If you are bold, and understand that you cannot drown, then you will be able to swim to the coast where you will be safe. After you land, fling the veil back into the sea, and it will find its way to me."

She unwound the green veil from her body, and gave it to him. Then she dived into the sea.

"Can I believe her?" thought Ulysses. "Perhaps it's just a trick to make me leave the pitiful safety of this timber. Oh, well, if I must drown, let me do it boldly."

He pulled off his wet clothes and wrapped himself in the green veil and plunged into the sea.

It was very strange. When he had been on the raft, the water had seemed death-

---

6. **owlish niece,** a reference to Athene, goddess of wisdom, whose symbol was the owl.

cold, heavy as iron, but now it seemed warm as a bath, and marvelously buoyant. He had been unable to knot the veil, but it clung closely to his body. When he began to swim he found himself slipping through the water like a fish.

"Forgive my suspicions, fair Ino," he cried. "Thank you . . . thank you. . . ."

For two days he swam, protected by Ino's veil, and on the morning of the third day he reached the coast of Phaeacia. But he could not find a place to come ashore, for it was a rocky coast, and the water swirled savagely among jagged boulders. So he was in great trouble again. While the veil could keep him from drowning, it could not prevent him from being broken against the rocks.

The current caught him and swept him in. With a mighty effort he grasped the first rock with both hands and clung there, groaning, as the rushing water tried to sweep him on. But he clung to the rock like a sea polyp, and the wave passed. Then the powerful back-tow caught him and pulled him off the rock and out to sea. He had gained nothing. His arms and chest were bleeding where great patches of skin had been scraped off against the rock.

He realized that the only thing he could do was try to swim along the coast until he found an open beach. So he swam and swam. The veil held him up, but he was dizzy from loss of blood. Nor had he eaten for two days. Finally, to his great joy, he saw a break in the reef. He swam toward it, and saw that it was the mouth of a river. Exerting his last strength, he swam into the river, struggled against the current, swimming past the shore where the river flowed among trees. Then he had no more strength. He was exhausted.

He staggered ashore, unwrapped the veil from his body, and cast it upon the river so that it would be borne back to Ino. When he tried to enter the wood, he could not take another step. He collapsed among the reeds. □□

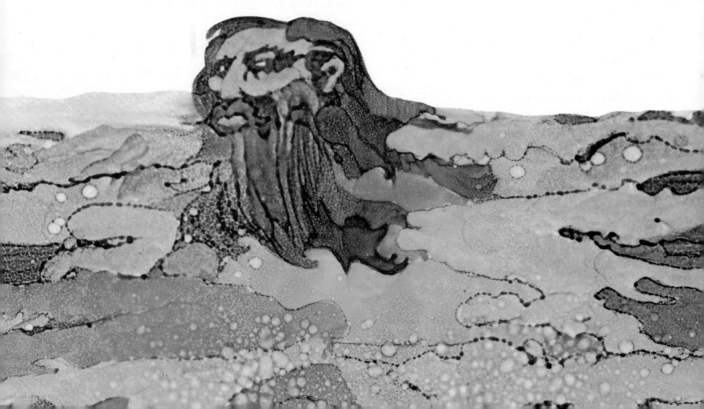

Nausicaa

In those days, girls did not find their own husbands, especially princesses. Their marriages were arranged by their parents, and it all seemed to work out as well as any other way. But Nausicaa, sixteen-year-old daughter of the King and Queen of Phaeacia, was hard to please, and had been turning down suitors for two years now. Her father, Alcinous, and her mother, Arete, were becoming impatient. There were several hot-tempered kings and princes who had made offers—for Nausicaa was very lovely—and Alcinous knew that if he kept turning them down he might find himself fighting several wars at once. He was a fine warrior, and enjoyed leading his great fleet into battle. Still, he preferred his wars one at a time.

He told the queen that Nausicaa would have to be forced to choose.

"I was very difficult to please, too," said Arete, "but I think you'll admit I married well. Perhaps she too knows in her heart that if she bides her time the gods will send a mighty man to be her husband."

The king smiled. Arete always knew the right thing to say to him. So the discussion ended for that day. Nevertheless, the queen knew that her husband was right, and that the girl would have to choose.

That night Nausicaa was visited by a dream. It seemed to her that the goddess Athene stood over her bed, tall and gray-eyed, and spoke to her, saying, "How can you have a wedding when all your clothes are dirty? Take them to the river tomorrow and wash them."

The goddess faded slowly until all that was left was the picture on her shield—a snake-haired girl.[7] And it seemed that the snakes writhed and hissed and tried to crawl off the shield to get at the dreamer. Nausicaa awoke, moaning. But she was a brave girl, and went right back to sleep and tried to dream the same dream again, so that she could learn more about the wedding. But the goddess did not return.

The next morning she went to her mother and told her of the dream.

"I don't understand it," she said. "What wedding?"

"Yours, perhaps," said Arete.

"Mine? With whom?"

"The gods speak in riddles. You know that. Especially when they visit us in dreams. So you must do the one clear thing she told you. Take your serving girls to the river, and wash your clothes. Perhaps, if you do that, the meaning will show itself."

Thereupon Nausicaa told her serving girls to gather all the laundry in the castle, and pile it in the mule cart. She also took food, a goatskin bottle of wine, and a golden flask of oil so that they could bathe in the river. Then they set off in the red cart, and the harness bells jingled as the mules trotted down the steep streets toward the river.

It was a sparkling morning. Nausicaa felt very happy as she drove the mules. They drove past the city walls, and down the hill, and along a road that ran through a wood until they came to the river.

They dumped the clothes in the water, and stamped on them, dancing and trampling and treading them clean. Then they dragged the clothes out, and pounded them on flat

---

7 **snake-haired girl.** The monsters called Gorgons had snakes in place of hair, and their look turned people to stone.

stones, afterward spreading them to dry in the hot sun.

They then flung off their garments and swam in the river, scrubbing each other and anointing themselves with oil.

"Well, you look clean enough to get married," cried Nausicaa. "But it's easier to wash than to wed, isn't it, girls?"

The maidens giggled wildly, and Nausicaa shouted with laughter. She was so drunk with sun and water that she felt she could run up the mountain and dance all day and night. It was impossible to sit still. She seized a leather ball from the cart, and flung it to one of her maids, who caught it and threw it back. Then the others joined in, and the girls frisked on the riverbank, tossing the ball back and forth.

Ulysses awoke from a deep sleep. He was still dazed, and could barely remember how he had gotten among the reeds. He peered out, saw the girls playing, and then shrank back, for he did not wish to be seen as he was, naked and bruised.

But Nausicaa threw the ball so hard that it sailed over the heads of the girls and fell near the clump of reeds where Ulysses was hiding. A girl ran to pick it up, then shrank back, screaming.

"A man!" she cried. "A man—all bloody and muddy."

Ulysses reached out and plucked a spray of leaves from a fallen olive branch, and came out of the reeds.

The girls saw a naked man holding a club. His shoulders were bleeding, his legs muddy, and his hair crusted with salt. They fled, screaming. But Nausicaa stood where she was, and waited for him.

Is this why Athene sent me here? she thought. Is this my husband, come out of the river? Is this what I am to take after all the beautiful young men I have refused? "Come back, you silly geese," she shouted to the girls. "Haven't you ever seen a man before?"

Then she turned to Ulysses, who had fallen to his knees before her.

"Speak, grimy stranger." she said, "Who are you, and what do you want?"

"Do not set your dogs upon me," said Ulysses. "I did not mean to surprise you in your glade."

"What talk is this? Are you out of your head?"

"Forgive me, but I know the fate of Actaeon, who came upon you in the wood. You turned him into a stag, and had your hounds tear him to pieces."

"Whom do you take me for?"

"Why you are Artemis, of course, Goddess of the Chase, maiden of the silver bow. I have heard poets praise your beauty, and I know you by your white arms. By your hair, and eyes, and the way you run—like light over water."

"Sorry to disappoint you, but I am not Artemis. I am Nausicaa. My father is king of this island. And I ask again—who are you?"

"An unlucky man."

"Where do you come from?"

"Strange places, princess. I am a sailor, hunted by a god who sends storms against me, wrecks my ships, kills my men. I come now from Ogygia, where I have been held captive by the Titaness, Calypso, who bound me with her spells. But as I was sailing away, a storm leaped out of the blue sky, smashing my boat. And I have been swimming in the sea for more than two days. I was dashed against the rocks of your coast, but managed to swim around it till I found this river. When I came ashore here, I had no strength to go farther, and fell where you found me."

"I suppose no one would look his best after spending two days in the sea and being beaten against rocks. You tell a good story, I'll say that for you. Why don't you bathe in the river now, and try to make yourself look human again. We can give you oil for anointing, and clean garments belonging to my brother. Then you can follow me to the castle and tell your story there."

"Thank you, sweet princess," said Ulysses.

He took the flask of oil, and went into the river and bathed and anointed himself. When he came out, he found clean garments waiting. The serving girls helped him dress, and combed out his tangled hair.

"Well," said Nausicaa, "you look much improved. I can believe you're some kind of chieftain now. Are you married?"

"Yes."

"Of course. You would have to be, at your age."

"I have not seen my wife for twenty years. She considers herself a widow."

"Has she remarried?"

"Perhaps. I do not know. Last I heard, she was being besieged by suitors."

"I am besieged by suitors too, but haven't found any I like well enough to marry."

As they spoke at the bank of the river, the serving girls had been piling the laundry into the mule cart.

"But I am thoughtless, keeping you here," said Nausicaa. "You need food and rest. You must come to the castle and finish your story there."

"The sight of your beauty is food and drink to me. And the sound of your voice makes me forget my weariness."

She laughed. "Are you courting me, stranger?"

"I am a homeless wanderer. I cannot court a princess. But I can praise her beauty."

"Come along to the castle. I want to introduce you to my father and mother. They are kind to strangers, very partial to brave men, and love to hear stories. And I want to hear more about you, too."

Now, that day, as it happened, King Alcinous had consulted an oracle, who prophesied, saying, "I see danger. I see a mountain blocking your harbor, destroying your commerce. I sense the cold wrath of the god of the sea."

"But the earth-shaker has always favored us," said the king. "He has showered blessings upon this island. Our fleets roam far, return laden. Why should he be angered now?"

"I do not know. It is not clear, it is not clear. But I say to you, O King, beware of strangers, shipwrecks, storytellers. Believe no tale, make no loan, suffer no harm."

"I don't understand."

"Neither do I. But there is no need to understand, only to obey."

The oracle departed, leaving the king very thoughtful.

Just at this time, Nausicaa was leading Ulysses into the courtyard of the castle. She bade her maids take him to the guest house.

"Wait till I send for you," she said. "Food will be brought, and wine."

She raced to her mother's chamber.

"Oh, Mother, Mother," she cried. "I'm so glad I obeyed the dream and went to the river to wash our clothes. What do you think I found there? A man, hiding in the reeds, naked and wounded. I soon set him right and brought him here. Such an interesting man."

"Brought him here? Here to the castle? Paraded a naked beggar through the streets for the whole town to see? My dear child, haven't you given them enough to gossip about?"

"He's no beggar, Mother. He's a sailor or a pirate or something. Such stories he tells.

Listen, he landed on an island once where men eat flowers that make them fall asleep and forget who they are. So they sleep all day and pick flowers all night, and are very happy. This man's crew went ashore and ate the flowers, and forgot who they were and didn't want to go back to the ship, just sleep. But he dragged them back anyway. I'd like to try those flowers, wouldn't you?"

"Who is this man? What's his name?"

"I don't know. He didn't tell me. It's a secret or something."

"Do you believe everything he tells you?"

"Oh, yes. He's not exactly handsome, but very strong-looking, you know. Too old though, much too old. And married, of course. But I don't think he gets along with his wife. You can see he has suffered. You can see by his eyes."

"Where is he now?"

"In the guest house. Don't you think we should have a banquet for him tonight? He's a distinguished visitor, isn't he—all those things he did?"

"We don't quite know what he is, do we, dear? I think I had better meet him myself first. Your father's in a funny mood. Met with the oracle today, and something went wrong, I think."

"Yes, yes, I want you to meet him before Father does. I want to know what you think. Shall I fetch him?"

"I'll send a servant, child. You are not to see him again until I find out more about him. Do you understand?"

"Oh, yes, find out, find out! Tell me everything he says."

Queen Arete spoke with Ulysses, and then went to her husband, the king, and told him of their visitor. She was amazed to see his face grow black with rage.

"By the gods," he cried. "These are foul tidings you bring. Only today the oracle warned against strangers, shipwrecks, and storytellers. And now you tell me our daughter has picked up some nameless ruffian who combines all three—a shipwrecked stranger telling wild tales. Precisely what is needed to draw upon us the wrath of the sea god. I shall sacrifice him to Poseidon, and there will be an end to it."

"You may not do that," said Arete.

"Who says 'may not' to me? I am king."

"Exactly why you may not. Because you are king. The man comes to you as a supplicant. He is under your protection. If you harm him, you will bring down upon yourself the wrath of all gods—not just one. That is the law of hospitality."

So the king ordered a great banquet that night to honor his guest. But certain young men of the court who were skilled at reading the king's moods knew that he was displeased, and decided to advance themselves in his favor by killing the stranger, and making it seem an accident.

"We will have games in the courtyard," said Euryalus their leader. "We will hurl discus and javelin, shoot with the bow, wrestle, and challenge him to take part. And, when he does, it may be that some unlucky throw of javelin, or misshot arrow, will rid us of his company. Or, perchance, if he wrestles, he will find his neck being broken. It looks to be a thick neck, but he has been long at sea and is unused to such exercises."

So the young men began to hold their contests in the courtyard. When Ulysses stopped to watch them, Euryalus stepped forth, and said, "There is good sport here, stranger, if you care to play."

"No, thank you," said Ulysses. "I'll just watch."

"Yes, of course," said Euryalus. "These games are somewhat dangerous. And one

can see that you are a man of prudence. But then, of course, you are rather old for such sports, aren't you?"

He laughed sneeringly, picked up the heavy discus, whirled, and threw. It sailed through the air and landed with a clatter far away. All the young men laughed and cheered.

"Where I come from," said Ulysses, "such little discs are given babies to teethe on. The grown men need a bit more to test them."

He strode over to a battle chariot, and broke off one of its wheels at the axle. It was a very heavy wheel, of oak bound with brass.

He hefted it, and said, "A little light, but it will do."

For he was filled with the wild rage that makes a man ten times stronger than he really is. He cradled the great wheel, whirled, and threw. It flew through the air, far past where the discus had landed, and thudded against the inner wall of the courtyard, knocking a hole in it. He turned to the others, who were paralyzed with amazement.

"Poor throw," he said. "But then, as you say, I'm rather old for such sport. However, since we are gathered here in this friendly fashion, let us play more games. If any of you would like to try me with sword or spear or dagger, or even a simple cudgel, let him step forth. Or, perchance, there is one who would prefer to wrestle?"

"That was well thrown, stranger," said Euryalus. "What is your name?"

"I do not choose to tell you my name, O athlete."

"You are not courteous."

"If you care to teach me manners, young sir, I offer again. Sword, spear, cudgel—any weapon you choose. Or no weapon at all except our hands."

"We are civilized here in Phaeacia," said Euryalus. "We do not fight with our guests. But I cannot understand why you refuse to tell us your name."

"A god hunts me. If I say my name, it may attract his notice."

The young men nodded. For this is what was believed at that time. But Euryalus ran to tell the king.

"I knew it," said Alcinous. "He carries a curse. He is the very man the oracle warned me against. I must get rid of him. But the law of hospitality forbids me to kill him under my roof. So tonight we entertain him at a banquet. But tomorrow he leaves this castle, and we shall find a way to see that he does not return."

"He is no weakling, this old sailor," said Euryalus. "He throws the discus almost as well as I."

Now, all this time, Nausicaa had been thinking about the stranger, and weaving a plan, for she was determined to find out who he was. She visited the old bard who had taught her to play the lyre, and whose task it was to sing for the guests at the royal feasts. She spoke and laughed with the old man and fed him undiluted wine until he lost his wits.

Then she locked him in the stable, where he fell fast asleep on a bundle of straw, and she departed with his lyre.

At the banquet that night, when the king called for the bard to sing his tales, Nausicaa said, "The old man is ill and cannot come. However, if you permit, I shall sing for your guests."

The king frowned. But Ulysses said, "This illness is a blessing, King. I think I should rather hear your black-haired daughter sing than the best bard who ever plucked a lyre."

The king nodded. Nausicaa smiled, and began to sing. She sang a tale of heroes. Of those who fought at Troy. She sang of fierce Achilles and mighty Ajax. Of Menelaus and his shattering war-cry. Of brave Diomedes, who fought with Ares himself when the war god came in his brazen chariot to help the Trojans.

She watched Ulysses narrowly as she sang. She saw his face soften, and his eyes grow dreamy, and she knew that he had been there, and that she was singing of his companions. But she still did not know his name.

Then she began to sing of that master of strategy, the great trickster, Ulysses. She sang of the wooden horse, and how the warriors hid inside while the Trojans debated outside, deciding what to do. Some of them wanted to chop it to pieces; others wished to take it to a cliff and push it off; still others wanted to bring it within the city as an offering to the gods—which, of course, was what Ulysses wanted them to do. She told of the men hiding in the belly of the horse, listening to their fate being debated, and of the fierce joy that flamed in their hearts when they heard the Trojans decide to drag the horse within the walls. And of how, in the blackness of the night, they came out of the horse, and how Ulysses led the charge.

She sang of him fighting there by the light of the burning houses, knee-deep in blood, and how he was invincible that night and carried everything before him.

And as she sang, she kept watching the stranger's face. She saw tears steal from between his clenched eyelids and roll down his cheeks. Amazed, the banqueters saw this hard-bitten sailor put his head in his hands and sob like a child.

He raised his streaming face, and said, "Forgive me, gracious king. But the wonderful voice of your daughter has touched my heart. For you must know that I am none other than Ulysses, of whom she sings."

A great uproar broke out. The young men cheered. The women wept. The king said, "My court is honored, Ulysses. Your deeds are known wherever men love courage. Now that I know who you are, I put all my power and goods at your disposal. Name any favor you wish, and it shall be yours."

Ulysses said, "O King, if I were the age I was twenty years ago when the ships were launched at Aulis, then the favor I would ask is your daughter's hand. For surely I have traveled the whole world over without seeing her like. I knew Helen whose beauty kindled men to that terrible war. I knew the beauties of the Trojan court whom we took captive and shared among us. And, during my wanderings I have had close acquaintance with certain enchantresses whose charms are more than human, namely Circe and Calypso. Yet never have I seen a girl so lovely, so witty, so courteous and kind as your young daughter. Alas, it cannot be. I am too old. I have a wife I must return to, and a kingdom, and there are sore trials I must undergo before I can win again what belongs to me. So all I ask of you, great king, is a ship to take me to Ithaca, where my wife waits, my enemies wait, my destiny waits."

Arete whispered to the king:

"Yes . . . yes . . . give him his ship tomorrow. I wish it could be tonight. See how your daughter looks at him; she is smitten to the heart. She is sick with love. Let him sail tomorrow. And be sure to keep watch at the wharf lest she stow away."

"It shall be as you say, mighty Ulysses," said the king. "Your ship will sail tomorrow."

So Ulysses departed the next day on a splendid ship manned by a picked crew, laden with rich goods the king had given him as hero gifts.

It is said that Athene drugged Poseidon's cup at the feast of the gods that night, so that he slept a heavy sleep and did not see that Ulysses was being borne to Ithaca. But Poseidon awoke in time to see the ship sailing back, and understood what had happened. In a rage he snatched Athene's Gorgonhead shield, the sight of which turns men to stone, and flashed it before the ship just as it was coming into port after having left Ulysses at his island. The ship and all its crew turned to stone, blocking the harbor, as the oracle had foretold.

It is said too that Nausicaa never accepted any of the young men who came a-wooing, announcing that she was wedded to song. She became the first woman bard, and traveled all the courts of the world singing her song of the heroes who fought at Troy, but especially of Ulysses and of his adventures among the terrible islands of the Middle Sea.

Some say that she finally came to the court of Ithaca to sing her song, and there she stayed. Others say that she fell in with a blind poet who took all her songs and wove them into one huge tapestry of song.

But it all happened too long ago to know the truth of it. ☐☐

Every occupation that people have shared throughout history has developed its own vocabulary. Because of the variety of Ulysses' adventures, we find in the tale words from many different occupations—sailing, farming, fighting (warfare), and manufacturing. All of the words listed at the right are taken from the story, and each has its origins in one of the four occupations mentioned above. Head your paper with these four occupational categories. Look up each word in the Glossary, determine in which category it belongs, and write the word under that column on your paper. Explain how you made your decisions.

fortress	armory
guild	launch
dungeon	smith
sty	moor
keel	besiege
bales	byre
buoyant	

Then be prepared to answer in class the following questions and to explain why you answered as you did.

1. Would you be more likely to find bales or bullets in an armory?

2. If there was no breeze, would the skipper of a sailboat launch or moor his boat?

3. Would a ship more likely remain buoyant if it had a hole in its sail or in its keel?

4. Would an army be more likely to besiege a fortress or a byre?

5. Would a dungeon be a suitable place for a guild to hold a meeting?

6. Would a smith be of much use in a sty?

The Return

Ulysses had landed on a lonely part of the shore. His enemies were in control of the island, and it was death to be seen. He stood on the empty beach and saw the Phaeacian ship depart. He was surrounded by wooden chests, leather bags, great bales—the treasure of gifts he had been given by Alcinous.

He looked about, at the beach and the cliff beyond, the wooded hills, the color of the sky. He was home after twenty years, but it did not seem like home. It seemed as strange and unfriendly as any of the perilous isles he had landed on during his long wanderings. And he knew that Ithaca would not be his again until he could know it as king, until he had slain his enemies and regained his throne.

His first care was to find a cave in the cliffside, and there stow all his treasure. He moved swiftly now; he had planned his first moves on his homeward trip. It had helped him keep his thoughts away from Nausicaa. He took off his rich cloak and helmet and breastplate, and hid them in the cave he had found, then laid his sword and spear beside them. He tore his tunic so that it hung in rags. He scooped up mud and smeared his face and arms and legs. Then he huddled his shoulders together and practiced a limping walk. Finally he was satisfied, and began to hump away along the cliff road, no longer a splendid warrior, but a feeble old beggar.

He made his way to the hut of his swineherd, Eumaeus, a man his own age, who had served him all his life, and whom he trusted. Everything was the same here, he saw. The pigs were rooting in the trampled earth. There were four lanky hounds who started from their sleep and barked as he came near.

A man came out of the hut, and silenced the dogs. Ulysses felt the tears well in his eyes. It was Eumaeus, but so old, so gray.

"What do you want?" said the swineherd.

"Food, good sir. Such scraps as you throw to the hogs. I am not proud, I am hungry."

"Are you a native of these parts?" said Eumaeus.

"No. I come from Crete."

"A long way for a beggar to come."

"I was not always a beggar. I was a sailor once . . . yes, and a captain of ships. I have seen better days."

"That's what all beggars say."

"Sometimes it's true. I once met a man from Ithaca, a mighty warrior, and the most generous man I have ever met. He gave me a good opinion of Ithaca. It is a place, I know, where the hungry and helpless are not spurned."

"I suppose this man you met was named Ulysses."

"Why, yes. How did you guess?"

"Because I have heard that tale so many times. Do you think you're the first beggar to come slinking around, pretending to have news of our king? Everyone knows that he vanished on his journey home from Troy. Beggars swarm all over us trying to get some supper by telling lies."

"Then you will give me no food?"

"I didn't say that. Even liars have to eat. Ulysses never turned a beggar away, and neither will I."

The swineherd fed Ulysses, and then let him rest by the fire. Ulysses pretended to sleep, but watched his host through half-closed eyes, and saw that the man was staring at him. He stretched and yawned.

"Are you sure you're a stranger to this island?" said Eumaeus. "Seems to me I've seen you before."

"No," said Ulysses. "You are mistaken. What shall I do now? Have I worn out my welcome, or may I sleep on your hearth tonight?"

"What will you do tomorrow?"

"Go to the castle and beg."

"You will not be welcome there."

"Why not? I will tell them how I met your king, and how kind he was to me. That should make them generous."

"It won't," said Eumaeus. "It will probably get you killed. Those who hold the castle now want to hear nothing about him—except the sure news of his death."

"How is that?"

"They hate him, because they do him harm. There are more than a hundred of them—rude brawling young princes from neighboring islands and thievish young nobles of this island. They dwell in his castle as if they had taken it after a siege and seek to marry his wife, Penelope, refusing to leave until she accepts one of them. They drink his wine, devour his stores, break up the furniture for firewood, roister all night, and sleep all day. Do you know how many hogs I have to bring them? Fifty a day. That is how gluttonous they are. My herds are shrinking fast, but they say they will kill me the first day I fail to bring them fifty hogs."

"I heard he had a grown son. Why does he not defend his father's goods?"

"He's helpless. There are too many of them."

"Is he at the castle now?"

"No one knows where he is. He slipped

away one night. Just as well. They were planning to kill him. The rumor is that he took ship and crew and went to seek his father. I hope he stays away. They will surely kill him if he returns."

"I go there tomorrow," said Ulysses. "It sounds like splendid begging. Such fiery young men are frequently generous, especially with other people's goods."

"You don't know them," said Eumaeus. "They are like wild beasts. But you cannot keep a fool from his folly. Go, if you must. In the meantime, sleep."

Now upon this night Telemachus was at sea, sailing toward Ithaca. He had found no news of his father and was coming home with a very heavy heart. He would have been even more distressed had he known that a party of wicked suitors was lying in wait for him aboard a swift ship full of fighting men. The ship was hidden in a cove, and the suitors meant to pounce upon him as he put into port.

But Athene saw this and made a plan. She went to Poseidon, and said, "I know you are angry with me, Uncle, for helping Ulysses. But now I wish to make it up to you. See, down there is a ship from Ithaca." She pointed to the suitors' vessel. "No doubt it holds friends of Ulysses, sailing out to meet their king. Why not do them a mischief?"

"Why not?" growled Poseidon.

And he wound a thick black mist about the suitors' ship so that it was impossible for the helmsman to see.

"Nevertheless," he said to Athene. "I still owe Ulysses himself a great mischief. I have not forgotten. In the meantime, let his friends suffer a bit."

The suitors' ship lay helpless in the mist, and Telemachus sailing past them, ignorant of danger, put into port and disembarked.

Athene then changed herself into a young swineherd, and hailed Telemachus on the beach:

"Greetings, my lord. I am sent by your servant, Eumaeus, to beg you to come to his hut before you go to the castle. He has important news to tell."

The lad set off, and Telemachus followed him toward the swineherd's hut.

Ulysses, dozing by the fire, heard a wild clamor of hounds outside, then a ringing young voice calling to them. He listened while the snarls turned to yaps of pleasure.

"It is my young master," cried Eumaeus, springing up. "Glory to the gods—he has come safely home."

Telemachus strode in. He was flushed from his walk. His face and arms were wet with the night fog, and his red-gold hair was webbed with tiny drops. To Ulysses he looked all aglitter, fledged by firelight, a golden lad. And Ulysses felt a shaft of wild joy pierce him like a spear, and for the first time he realized that he had come home.

But Telemachus was displeased to see the old beggar by the fire, for he wished to speak to Eumaeus privately to ask him how matters stood at the castle and whether it was safe for him to return.

"I do not wish to be discourteous, old man," he said, "but would you mind very much sleeping in the pig byre? You can keep quite warm there, and there are secret matters I wish to discuss."

"Be not wroth, my lord, that I have given this man hospitality," said Eumaeus. "He claims to have met your father once. A pitiful beggar's tale, no doubt, but it earned him a meal and a bed."

"Met my father? Where? When? Speak!"

But at the word "father," Ulysses could not endure it any longer. The voice of the young man saying that word destroyed all his strategies. The amazed Eumaeus saw the old beggar leap from his stool, lose his feebleness, grow wider, taller, and open his arms and draw the young man to him in a great bear hug.

"Dearest son," said the stranger, his voice broken with tears. "I am your father, Ulysses."

Telemachus thought he was being attacked, and tensed his muscles, ready to battle for his life. But when he heard these words and felt the old man's tears burning against his face, then his marrow melted, and he laid his head on his father's shoulder and wept.

Nor could the honest old swineherd say anything; his throat was choked with tears, too. Ulysses went to Eumaeus and embraced him, saying, "Faithful old friend, you have served me well. And if tomorrow brings victory, you will be well rewarded."

Then he turned to his son, and said, "The goddess herself must have led you here tonight. Now I can complete my plan. Tomorrow we strike our enemies."

"Tomorrow? Two men against a hundred? These are heavy odds, even for Ulysses."

"Not two men—four. There is Eumaeus here, who wields a good cudgel. There is the neatherd whom we can count on. And, no doubt, at the castle itself we will find a few more faithful servants. But it is not a question of numbers. We shall have surprise on our side. They think I am dead, remember, and that you are helpless. Now, this is the plan. You must go there in the morning, Telemachus, pretending great woe. Tell them you have learned on your journey that I am indeed dead, and that now you must advise your mother to take one of them in marriage. This will keep them from attacking you—for a while anyway—and will give us

the time we need. I shall come at dusk, just before the feasting begins."

"What of my mother? Shall I tell her that you are alive?"

"By no means."

"It is cruel not to."

"It will prove a kindness later. Bid her dress in her finest garments, and anoint herself, and be as pleasant as she can to the suitors, for this will help disarm them. Understand?"

"I understand."

"Now, mark this well. You will see me being insulted, humiliated, beaten perhaps. Do not lose your temper and be drawn into a quarrel before we are ready to fight. For I must provoke the suitors to test their mettle, and see where we should strike first."

Telemachus knelt in the firelight, and said, "Sire, I shall do as you bid. I don't see how we can overcome a hundred strong men, but to die fighting at your side will be a greater glory than anything a long life can bestow. Thank you, Father, for giving me this chance to share your fortune."

"You are my true son," said Ulysses, embracing the boy tenderly. "The words you have just spoken make up for the twenty years of you I have missed."

Eumaeus banked the fire, and they all lay down to sleep.

Ulysses came to the castle at dusk the next day and followed Eumaeus into the great banquet hall which was thronged with suitors. He humped along behind the swineherd, huddling his shoulders, and limping. The first thing he saw was a dog lying near a bench. By its curious golden brown color he recognized it as his own favorite hunting hound, Argo. It was twenty-one years old, incredibly old for a dog, and it was crippled and blind and full of fleas. But Telemachus had not allowed it to be killed because it had been his father's.

As Ulysses approached, the dog's raw stump of a tail began to thump joyously upon the floor. The tattered old ears raised. The hound staggered to his feet, let out one wild bark of welcome and leaped toward the beggar. Ulysses caught him in his arms. The dog licked his face, shivered, and died. Ulysses stood there holding the dead dog.

Then Antinous, one of the most arrogant of the suitors, who fancied himself a great jokester, strode up and said, "What are you going to do with that dead dog, man, eat him? Things aren't that bad. We have a few scraps to spare, even for a scurvy old wretch like you."

Ulysses said, "Thank you, master. I am grateful for your courtesy. I come from Crete, and—"

"Shut up!" said Antinous. "Don't tell me any sad stories. Now take that thing out and bury it."

"Yes, gracious sir. And I hope I have the honor of performing a like service for you one day."

"Oho," cried Antinous. "The churl has a tongue in his head. Well, well. . . ."

He seized a footstool and smashed it over Ulysses' back. Telemachus sprang forward, blazing with anger, but Eumaeus caught his arm.

"No," he whispered. "Hold your peace."

Ulysses bowed to Antinous, and said, "Forgive me, master. I meant but a jest. I go to bury the dog."

As soon as he left the room, they forgot all about him. They were agog with excitement about the news told by Telemachus, that Ulysses' death had been confirmed, and that Penelope would now choose one of them to wed. They crowded about Telemachus, shouting questions.

He said, "Gently, friends, gently. My mother will announce her choice during the course of the night. But first she desires that you feast and make merry."

The young men raised a great shout of joy, and the feasting began. Ulysses returned and went the round of the suitors, begging scraps of food. Finally he squatted near Eurymachus, a fierce young fellow whom he recognized to be their leader. Eurymachus scowled at him, but said nothing.

Into the banquet hall strode another beggar—a giant shaggy man. He was a former smith who had decided that it was easier to beg than to work at the forge. He was well liked by the suitors because he wheedled and flattered them, and ran their errands. He swaggered over to Ulysses and grasped him by the throat.

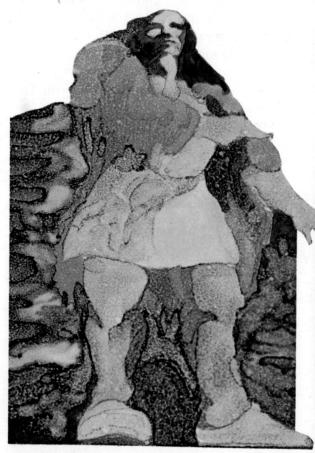

"Get out of here, you miserable cur," he said. "Any begging around here to do, I'll do it. I, Iros."

He raised his huge meaty fist and slammed it down toward Ulysses' head. But Ulysses, without thinking, butted the man in the stomach, knocking him back against the wall.

"Look at that," cried Eurymachus. "The old souse has a head like a goat. For shame, Iros, you ought to be able to squash him with your thumb."

"Exactly what I intend to do," said Iros, advancing on Ulysses.

"A fight! A fight!" cried the suitors. "A beggar-bout. Good sport."

They crowded around the beggars, leaving just space enough for them to move.

Ulysses thought quickly. He could not risk revealing himself for what he was, yet he had to get rid of the fellow. So he shrank into his rags, as though fearful, allowing Iros to approach. Then, as the great hands were reaching for him and the suitors were cheering and jeering, he swung his right arm, trying to measure the force of the blow exactly. His fist landed on the smith's chin. The suitors heard a dry cracking sound, as when you snap a chicken bone between your fingers, and they knew that their man's jaw was broken. He fell to the floor, unconscious, blood streaming from mouth and nose. Ulysses stooped and hoisted him over his shoulder and marched out of the banquet room, saying, "I'd better let him bleed outside. It will be less unpleasant for you gentlemen."

He draped the big man over a stile, and came back.

"Well struck, old bones," said Eurymachus. "You fight well for a beggar."

"A beggar?" said Ulysses. "What is a beggar, after all? One who asks for what he has not earned, who eats others' food, uses their goods? Is this not true? If so, young sir, I think you could become a member of our guild tomorrow."

Eurymachus carefully wiped the knife which he had been using to cut his meat, and held the point to Ulysses' throat.

"Your victory over that other piece of vermin seems to have given you big ideas," he said. "Let me warn you, old fool, if you say one word more to me that I find unfitting, I will cut you up into little pieces and feed you to the dogs. Do you understand?"

"I understand, master," said Ulysses. "I meant but a jest."

"The next jest will be your last," growled Eurymachus.

Telemachus stepped between them and said, "Beggar, come with me to my mother. She has heard that you are a voyager, and would question you about the places you have seen."

"What?" cried Eurymachus. "Take this stinking bundle of rags to your mother? She will have to burn incense for hours to remove the stench."

"You forget yourself, sir," said Telemachus. "You have not yet been accepted by my mother. She is still free to choose her own company."

Eurymachus played with his knife, glaring at Telemachus. He was angry enough to kill, but he did not wish to lose his chance with Penelope by stabbing her son. So he stepped aside, and let Telemachus lead the old beggar out of the hall.

"You have done well," whispered Ulysses. "Another second and I would have been at the cur's throat, and we would have been fighting before we were ready. Besides, it is time I spoke to your mother. She enters our plans now."

When he was alone with Penelope, he sat

with his face lowered. He did not wish to look at her. For her presence set up a great shuddering tenderness inside him, and he knew that he had to keep himself hard and cruel for the work that lay ahead.

"In this chamber, you are not a beggar, you are a guest," said Penelope. "So take your comfort, please. Be at ease here with me, and tell me your tidings. I understand you met my husband Ulysses once upon your voyages."

"Beautiful queen," said Ulysses. "I knew him well. Better than I have admitted. I am a Cretan. I was a soldier. When the war with Troy started I went as part of a free-booting band to sell our swords to the highest bidder. We took service with your husband, Ulysses, and I fought under his banner for many years. Now his deeds before Troy have become famous in the time that has passed since the city was destroyed. Bards sing them from court to court all over the lands of the Middle Sea. Let me tell you a little story, though, that has never been told.

"I lay with him in that famous wooden horse, you know. We crouched in the belly of the horse which was dragged into Troy and set before the altar as an offering to the gods. The Trojans were crowding around, looking at this marvelous wooden beast, wondering at it, for such a thing had never been seen. But Queen Helen knew the truth somehow and, being a mischief-loving lady always, tapped on the belly of the horse, imitating the voices of the heroes' wives. She did it so cunningly that they could have sworn they heard their own wives calling to them, and were about to leap out of the horse too soon, which would have been death.

"Now, Helen saved your voice till last. And when she imitated it, I heard Ulysses groan, felt him tremble. He alone was clever enough to know it was a trick, but your voice, even mimicked, struck him to the heart. And he had to mask his distress, and use all his force and authority to keep the others quiet. A tiny incident, madame, but it showed me how much he loved you."

Penelope said, "Truly, this is a story never told. And yet I think that of all the mighty deeds that are sung, I like this one best."

Her face was wet with tears. She took a bracelet from her wrist and threw it to him, saying, "Here is a gift. Small payment for such a tale."

"Thank you, Queen," said Ulysses. "My path crossed your husband's once again. My ship sailed past the Island of the Dawn. We had run out of water and were suffering from thirst, and there we saw a marvelous thing: A fountain of water springing out of the sea, pluming, and curling upon itself. We tasted it, and it was fresh, and we filled our water barrels. When I told about this in the next port, I learned how such a wonder had come to be. The enchantress, Circe, most beautiful of the daughters of the gods, had loved your husband and sought to keep him with her. But he told her that he must return to his wife, Penelope. After he left, she wept such tears of love as burned the salt out of the sea and turned it into a fountain of pure water."

Penelope took a necklace from her neck, and said, "I liked the first story better, but this is lovely, too."

Ulysses said, "Thank you, Queen. I have one thing more to tell. Your husband and I were talking one time around the watch fire on a night between battles, and he spoke, as soldiers speak, of home. He said that by the odds of war, he would probably leave you a widow. And, since you were beautiful, you would have many suitors, and would be hard put to decide. Then he said, 'I wish I could send her this advice: Let her take a man who can bend my bow. For that man alone will be strong enough to serve her as husband, and Ithaca as king.' "

"Did he say that—truly?"

"Truly."

"How can I ask them to try the bow? They will jeer at me. They may feel offended, and do terrible things."

"Disguise your intention. Tell them you cannot decide among such handsome charming suitors. And so you will let their own skill decide. They are to hold an archery contest, using the great bow of Ulysses, and he who shoots best to the mark will win you as wife. They cannot refuse such a challenge, their pride will not permit them to. Now, good night, lady. Thank you for your sweet company. I shall see you, perchance, when the bow is bent."

"Good night, old wanderer," said Penelope. "I shall never forget the comfort you have brought me."

As Ulysses was making his way through the dark hallway, something clutched his arm and hissed at him.

"Ulysses . . . Ulysses. . . . My master, my king . . . my baby . . . my lord. . . ."

He bent his head and saw that it was an old woman, and recognized his nurse, Eurycleia, who had known him from the day he was born, and who had tended him through his childhood.

"Dear little king," she wept. "You're back . . . you're back. I knew you would come. I told them you would."

Very gently he put his hand over her mouth, and whispered, "Silence. . . . No one must know, not even the queen. They will kill me if they find out. Silence . . . silence. . . ."

She nodded quickly, smiling with her sunken mouth, and shuffled away.

Ulysses lurked outside the banquet hall until he heard a great roar from the suitors, and knew that Penelope had come among them. He listened outside and heard her announce that she would choose the man, who, using her husband's great bow, would shoot best to the mark. He heard young men break into wild cheers. Then he hid himself as Telemachus, leading the suitors into the courtyard, began to set out torches for the shooting. Then it was that he slipped unnoticed into the castle and went to the armory where the weapons were kept. He put on a breastplate, and arranged his rags over it so that he looked as he had before. Then he went out into the courtyard.

All was ready for the contest. An avenue of torches burned, making it bright as day. In the path of light stood a row of battle-axes driven into the earth, their rings aligned. Each archer would attempt to shoot through those rings. Until now only Ulysses himself had been able to send an arrow through all twelve axe-rings.

Now, Penelope, followed by her servants, came down the stone steps carrying the great bow. She handed it to Telemachus, saying, "You, son, will see that the rules are observed." Then, standing tall and beautiful in the torchlight, she said, "I have given my word to choose as husband him who best shoots to the mark, using this bow. I shall retire to my chamber now, as is fitting, and my son will bring me the name of my next husband. Now, may the gods reward you according to your deserts."

She turned and went back into the castle. The noise fell. The young men grew very serious as they examined the great bow. It was larger than any they had ever seen, made of dark polished wood, stiffened by rhinoceros horn, and bound at the tips by golden wire. Its arrows were held in a bull-

hide quiver; their shafts were of polished ash, their heads of copper, and they were tailed with hawk feathers.

Ulysses squatted in the shadows and watched the suitors as they crowded around Telemachus, who was speaking.

"Who goes first? Will you try, sir?"

Telemachus handed the bow to a prince of Samos, a tall brawny man, and a skilled archer. He grasped the bow in his left hand and the dangling cord in his right, and tugged at the cord in the swift sure movement that is used to string a bow. But it did not bend. He could not make the cord reach from one end to the other. He put one end of the bow on the ground and grasped the other end and put forth all his strength. His back muscles glistened like oil in the torchlight. The bow bent a bit under the enormous pressure, and a low sighing sound came from the crowd, but when he tugged on the cord, the bow twisted in his hand as if it were a serpent, and leaped free. He staggered, and almost fell. An uneasy laugh arose. He looked wildly about, then stomped away, weeping with rage.

Telemachus picked up the bow, and said, "Next."

One by one they came; one by one they fell back. Not one of them could bend the bow. Finally, all had tried but Antinous and Eurymachus. Now Antinous was holding the bow.

He shook his head, and said, "It is too

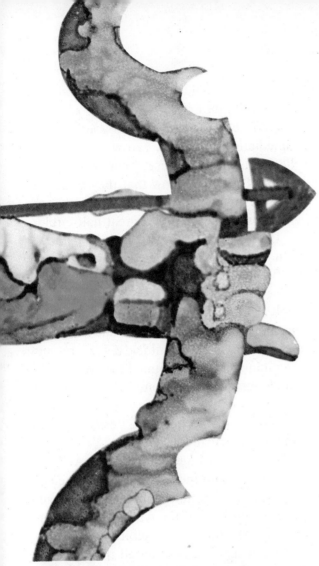

stiff; it cannot be bent. It has not been used for twenty years. It must be rubbed with tallow, and set by the fire to soften."

"Very well," said Telemachus.

He bade a servant rub the bow with tallow and set it near the fire. Ulysses kept out of sight. As they were waiting, Telemachus had a serving girl pass out horns of wine to the suitors. The men drank thirstily, but there was no laughter. They were sullen. Their hearts were ashen with hatred; they did not believe the bow could be softened. And Ulysses heard them muttering to each other that the whole thing was a trick.

Finally, Antinous called for the bow. He tried to string it. He could not.

"It cannot be done," he cried.

"No," said Eurymachus. "It cannot be done. I will not even try. This is a trick, another miserable deceitful trick. Shroud that is never woven, bow that cannot be bent, there is no end to this widow's cunning. I tell you she is making fools of us. She will not be taken unless she be taken by force."

A great shouting and clamor arose. The suitors pressed close about Telemachus, hemming him in so tightly he could not draw his sword.

"Stop!" shouted Ulysses.

He cried it with all his force, in the great bellowing clanging battle voice that had rung over spear shock and clash of sword to reach the ears of his men on so many fields before Troy. His great shout quelled the clamor. The amazed suitors turned to see the old beggar stride out of the shadows into the torchlight. He came among them, and grasped the bow, and said, "I pray you, sirs, let me try."

Antinous howled like a wolf and sprang toward Ulysses with drawn sword. But Telemachus stepped between them, and shoved Antinous back.

"My mother watches from her chamber window," he said. "Shall she see you as cowards, afraid to let an old beggar try what you cannot do? Do you think she would take any of you then?"

"Yes, let him try," said Eurymachus. "Let the cur have one last moment in which he pretends to be a man. And when he fails, as fail he must, then we'll chop his arms off at the shoulders so that he will never again be tempted to draw bow with his betters."

"Stand back," cried Telemachus. "Let him try."

The suitors fell back, their swords still drawn. Ulysses held the bow. He turned it lightly in his hands, delicately, tenderly, like a bard tuning his lyre. Then he took the cord and strung the bow with a quick turn of his wrist, and as the suitors watched, astounded, he held the bow from him and plucked the cord, making a deep vibrating harp note. Dumbfounded, they saw him reach into the quiver, draw forth an arrow, notch it, then bend the bow easily, powerfully, until the arrowhead rested in the circle of his fingers, just clearing the polished curve of the bow.

He stood there for a second, narrowing his eyes at the mark, then let the arrow fly. The cord twanged, the arrow sang through the air, and passed through the axe-rings, all twelve of them.

Then, paralyzed by amazement, they saw him calmly sling the quiver over his shoulder, and straighten up so that his breastplate gleamed through the rags. He stood tall and, throwing back his head, spoke to the heavens:

"So the dread ordeal ends, and I come to claim my own. Apollo, dear lord of the silver bow, archer-god, help me now to hit a mark no man has hit before."

"It is he!" cried Antinous. "Ulysses!"

He died, shouting. For Ulysses had notched another arrow, and this one caught Antinous full in the throat. He fell, spouting blood.

No suitor moved. They looked at the twitching body that had been Antinous, and felt a heavy sick fear, as if Apollo himself had come to loose his silver shaft among them.

Eurymachus found his tongue, and cried, "Pardon us, great Ulysses. We could not know you had returned. If we have done you evil, we will repay you, but hold your hand."

"Too late," said Ulysses. "Your evil can be repaid only by death. Now fight, or flee."

Then Eurymachus raised his sword and called to the suitors, "Up, men! Rouse your-

selves, or he will kill us all as we stand here. Let us kill him first."

And he rushed toward Ulysses, and fell immediately with an arrow through his chest. But he had roused them out of their torpor. They knew now that they must fight for their lives, and they charged across the yard toward Ulysses in a great half-circle.

Ulysses retreated slowly, filling the air with arrows, dropping a suitor with each shaft. But still they kept coming through the heaped dead. Now he darted backward suddenly, followed by Telemachus and Eumaeus, the swineherd, who had been protecting him with their shields. They ran into the dining hall and slammed the great portal, which immediately began to shake under the axe blows of the suitors.

"Overturn the benches," cried Ulysses. "Make a barricade."

The neatherd had joined them. And now Telemachus and the two men overturned the heavy wooden benches, making a barricade. They stood behind the wall of benches and watched the huge door splintering.

It fell. The suitors poured through. Now Ulysses shot the rest of his arrows so quickly that the dead bodies piled up in the doorway making a wall of flesh through which the suitors had to push their way.

His quiver was empty. Ulysses cast the bow aside, and took two javelins. But he did not throw. For the suitors were still too far away, and he had to be sure of killing each time he threw.

A suitor named Agelaus had taken charge now, and he motioned to his men, "Let fly your spears—first you, then you, then the rest. And after each cast of spears let us move closer to the benches."

The long spears hurtled past the rampart. One grazed Telemachus's shoulder, drawing blood. And Ulysses, seeing the blood of his son, lost the battle-coldness for which he was famous among warriors. For the first time he felt the wild hot curdling rage rising in him like wine, casting a mist of blood before his eyes. Without making a decision to move, he felt his legs carrying him toward the great hearth. There he knelt, and grasped the ring of the firestone—a huge slab of rock, large enough for a roasting ox. The suitors, charging toward the wall of benches, saw him rise like a vision of the past, like some Titan in the War of the Gods holding an enormous slab of rock over his head.

They saw their danger and tried to draw back, tried to scatter. But Ulysses had hurled the slab. It fell among the suitors and crushed them like beetles in their frail armor.

Only four of the suitors were left alive. Now Ulysses and Telemachus and the two servants were upon them—one to each and each killed his man. Then Ulysses and Te-lemachus raised a wild exultant yell. Dappled with blood, they turned to each other, and Ulysses embraced his son.

"Well struck," he said. Then, to Eumaeus, "Thank you, good friend. Now go tell your queen, Penelope, that the contest has been decided, and the winner claims her hand."

"Father," said Telemachus. "When I reach my full strength, shall I be able to bend the great bow?"

"Yes," said Ulysses. "I promise you. I will teach you everything you have to know. I have come home."

Penelope heard her son shouting. "Mother! Mother! It's Father! He's come home!"

Slowly she descended the great stairway and entered the throne-room. She looked at the man who had slain her suitors.

He arose and said, "I greet you, Penelope. I am Ulysses, your husband." □□

Discussion

Ships and Men (280)

1. (a) What about the design of Ulysses' ships suits them for waging war? **(b)** Why are they unsuitable for long sea voyages?

2. Explain what is meant by the statement "Ulysses' problem was made worse by victory."

The Ciconians (281–282)

1. (a) How does Eurylochus persuade Ulysses to attack the first town sighted? **(b)** How do Ulysses and his men show they have been affected by war?

2. How does Ulysses withdraw from the Ciconians without losing many men?

3. (a) What attracts the naiads to the ships? **(b)** What mistaken assumption does Poseidon make? How does he punish the men for it?

4. (a) By this point, what characteristics of Ulysses seem clear to you? **(b)** What characteristics of the gods have been demonstrated?

The Lotus-Eaters (285–287)

1. (a) How do first the lotus flowers and then Morpheus influence Ulysses' men? **(b)** How does Ulysses free himself and his men from Lotusland?

2. (a) Ulysses' dreams *foreshadow* (hint at) future events. Based on those dreams, what experiences appear to await him? **(b)** Ulysses seems to know his dreams will come true. Why, then, do you think he continues on his voyage?

The Cyclops's Cave
(287–292)

1. (a) Why do Ulysses and his men go ashore on the island of the Cyclopes? **(b)** How does Polyphemus trap them in his cave? **(c)** By what schemes does Ulysses escape from the cave with his men?

2. (a) How does Ulysses' final taunt bring further destruction? **(b)** What do the final two paragraphs tell you about the power of Poseidon and about Ulysses' future?

3. (a) List as many examples as you can find of *figurative language* used to describe Polyphemus. **(b)** Which descriptions seem especially fresh, original, and appropriate? Explain your choices.

Keeper of the Winds
(293–298)

1. (a) For what reason does Aeolus offer Ulysses any favor within his power? **(b)** What is the gift Aeolus gives, and what does he warn Ulysses about it?

2. (a) Describe the events that bring Ulysses back to the island of the winds. **(b)** Why does Aeolus refuse to aid him a second time?

Circe   (298–307)

1. (a) What precautions does Ulysses take when first landing on the island of Circe? **(b)** What is there in the behavior of the animals on the island that foreshadows what happens to the crewmen? **(c)** What happens to Eurylochus's men in Circe's castle? How is their fate appropriate?

2. (a) From Ulysses' encounter with Hermes, what impression do you get of how the gods treat each other? **(b)** What enables Ulysses to escape harm from Circe and to free his men from enchantment?

3. (a) Under what conditions might Ulysses become immortal? **(b)** What experiences await him if he leaves? **(c)** Why, then, does Ulysses go?

4. Circe says to Ulysses' crewmen, "You are . . . men of the black-prowed ships, the hawks of the sea." **(a)** What is Circe comparing to hawks in the above *metaphor?* **(b)** Do you think this comparison is an appropriate one? Why or why not?

5. "And her eyes, like blue flame, burned these pictures out of his head." **(a)** To what are Circe's eyes compared in the above description? **(b)** What helps you to identify this comparison as a *simile?* **(c)** Reread the paragraph (305b, 1) from which the above quote was taken. What effect do Circe's eyes have on Ulysses?

The Land of the Dead
(312–316)

1. (a) Describe the weather and water conditions on the way to Tartarus. **(b)** What do they suggest about the ship's destination? **(c)** What happens to Elpenor, and with what consequences for the others?

2. (a) Summarize the advice Ulysses receives from Achilles and the prophecy he receives from Ajax. **(b)** What forewarning does Ulysses receive from Teiresias?

3. Do the descriptions of Tartarus differ from what you might expect of "The Land of the Dead"? Explain.

4. Throughout the story, Ulysses reveals that he is a complex person. Cite incidents that show him to be **(a)** strong-willed and able to withstand temptation; **(b)** quick-witted; **(c)** cautious; **(d)** boastful; **(e)** courageous; **(f)** fated by the gods.

The Sirens   (317–318)

1. (a) What precautions does Ulysses take to avoid being shipwrecked by the Sirens? **(b)** How does their singing affect him?

2. How do Ulysses' men respond to the sight of the bird-women? Why?

Scylla and Charybdis (319–320)

1. (a) Under what circumstances were Charybdis and Scylla changed into monsters? **(b)** Why does Ulysses turn the helm over to Eurylochus?

2. (a) What has Ulysses been unable to reckon upon in measuring his distance? **(b)** What are the consequences for his crew?

The Cattle of the Sun (321–324)

1. Why, despite the warnings of Teiresias, do Ulysses and his men stop on the island of Thrinacia?

2. (a) How does Eurylochus persuade the men to kill the forbidden cattle? **(b)** What does Hyperion threaten to do if he does not get vengeance? **(c)** Describe Hyperion's vengeance.

Calypso (325–331)

1. (a) How does Calypso rescue Ulysses? **(b)** What does Ulysses learn about Ithaca and his future there if he returns? **(c)** In what two ways does he obtain this information?

2. Explain what Ulysses means by saying, "I cannot be immortal. . . . What use is courage then?"

3. Why does Calypso let Ulysses depart?

Ino's Veil (333–334)

1. After all he has been through, why does Ulysses—for the first time—think of giving up?

2. How does Ino help Ulysses?

Nausicaa (335–341)

1. Why is Nausicaa at the river where she discovers Ulysses?

2. (a) Why is King Alcinous hostile at first toward Ulysses? **(b)** How does Arete prevent him from sacrificing the stranger to Poseidon? **(c)** How does Ulysses demonstrate his abilities to the young men of the court?

3. (a) By what means does Nausicaa get Ulysses to reveal his identity? **(b)** How is Ulysses treated differently, once his identity is known? **(c)** Why is Arete now anxious for Ulysses to leave as soon as possible?

The Return (342–353)

1. (a) Upon arriving in Ithaca, why does Ulysses disguise himself as a beggar? **(b)** What does he learn from Eumaeus about matters at the castle?

2. (a) How does Telemachus figure in Ulysses' plan to get rid of his enemies? **(b)** How does Penelope participate unknowingly? **(c)** What final act does Ulysses keep for himself?

3. Discuss whether any character(s) might have behaved differently, to avoid bloodshed. Would different behavior be consistent with what you know about the characters? Explain.

4. Has "The Adventures of Ulysses" a happy ending? Explain.

Extension • Reading

"The Adventures of Ulysses" is taken from the book *Greeks Bearing Gifts* by Bernard Evslin (Four Winds Press, 1976), which also tells the story of the Trojan War and how the Greek warriors followed Ulysses' suggestion of using a wooden horse to capture Troy and win the war. If you have enjoyed the selection printed here, you will probably also enjoy reading the rest of the story, as well.

Tartarus is filled with the ghosts of characters from different stories and legends of ancient Greece. Ulysses mentions Orion, Minos, Tantalus, and Sisyphus, but cannot take the time to see them. You might enjoy reading the stories of these and other characters, which have been told and retold in many different forms.

Some of the most popular are these:

Greek Myths, by Olivia Coolidge (Houghton Mifflin, 1949)

Greek Gods and Heroes, by Robert Graves (Doubleday, 1960)

Heroes of Greece and Troy, by Roger Lancelyn Green (Walck, 1961)

The Golden Treasury of Myths and Legends, by Anne Terry White (Golden Press, 1959)

Extension • Writing

Calypso could cause pictures to form of the past, the present, or the future by poking the log in her hearth in a certain way. If Calypso offered you the opportunity to see one—and only one—picture, what would you choose?

Write a paragraph explaining your choice. Include details on what you might expect, or hope, to see.

One interesting characteristic of the gods as portrayed in the Greek myths is that they have their favorites among mortals whom they help and defend against the other gods when possible. Which of the Greek gods and goddesses would you most like to have on your side?

Write a paragraph in which you explain your choice. Be sure to tell what powers the particular god or goddess possesses that you feel would be of benefit to you.

Assume that you are a member of Ulysses' crew and that you have lived through the experience of having been turned into a pig by Circe. Write a letter to a friend or member of your family, describing how that event came about and detailing how you felt when it happened. Begin your letter, "Dear ____, You'll never guess what happened to me!"

Extension • Speaking

Circe turns people into animals that possess some of the qualities they had as humans. For example, she says she would have turned Ulysses into a fox because of his cunning and swiftness. What kind of animal would you become? Think of some of your most obvious qualities, then choose an animal that seems to express those or similar qualities. Explain to the class why you think your choice of animal is appropriate.

In exchange for Ulysses' "brave tale," the god Aeolus offers him any favor within his power. Suppose Aeolus were to offer you such a favor. To what use could you put Aeolus and his control over the winds? Can you think of an adventure in which the winds—or lack of them—would be useful? Explain to the class the favor you would ask of Aeolus.

5: The Adventures of Ulysses

CONTENT REVIEW

For each of the following statements, explain whether you *agree strongly* with the statement, *agree, have no opinion, disagree,* or *strongly disagree.* Be prepared to support your opinions with evidence from the selection, where appropriate.

1. Many times during his voyage, Ulysses might have avoided danger and so prevented the loss of more men.

2. Ulysses' crew is more a hindrance than a help to him in many of the situations they encounter.

3. Ulysses exhibits a few weaknesses that make him seem more human but sometimes cause him trouble.

4. Even though Circe does some evil things, she is basically loving and good.

5. Penelope's sacrifice—remaining faithful for twenty years to her absent husband—is too great.

6. It is for Penelope's own good that Ulysses uses her in his plan for revenge without taking her into his confidence.

7. Ulysses' homecoming is too filled with unjust revenge and bloodshed.

8. In "The Adventures of Ulysses" the gods are neither kind nor fair, but selfish and revengeful.

9. There is little or no humor in "The Adventures of Ulysses."

10. Because Ulysses is courageous and considerate toward his crew, I would be willing to risk my life to accompany him on a dangerous mission.

11. I would like to have Calypso reveal the past and the future to me.

12. If Circe offered me the chance to become immortal, I would take it.

Unit 5, Test I
INTERPRETATION: NEW MATERIAL

Read the poem below and on the next page. Then on your paper write the answers to the questions which follow.

An Ancient Gesture

Edna St. Vincent Millay

I thought, as I wiped my eyes on the corner of my apron:
Penelope did this too.
And more than once: you can't keep weaving all day
And undoing it all through the night;
5 Your arms get tired, and the back of your neck gets tight;

And along towards morning, when you think it will never be
    light,
And your husband has been gone, and you don't know
    where, for years,
Suddenly you burst into tears;
There is simply nothing else to do.

10 And I thought, as I wiped my eyes on the corner of my
    apron:
This is an ancient gesture, authentic,[1] antique,
In the very best tradition, classic, Greek;
Ulysses did this too.
But only as a gesture,—a gesture which implied
15 To the assembled throng that he was much too moved to
    speak.
He learned it from Penelope. . . .
Penelope, who really cried.

From *Collected Poems*, Harper & Row. Copyright 1954 by Norma Millay Ellis.

1. authentic (ô then′tik). 1. worthy of acceptance, trust, or belief; reliable. 2. coming from the source stated; not copied; real.

1. What is the gesture mentioned in the poem?

2. The word *ancient*, used to describe this gesture, implies that it is (a) for old people; (b) outdated; (c) wise; (d) very old.

3. According to the dictionary, *gesture* can mean: *(1)* a movement that expresses an emotion; *(2)* something said or done to impress or influence others. As the word is used in the poem, which definition applies to Penelope's gesture? to Ulysses'? Explain.

4. The speaker in the poem (a) disagrees with Penelope; (b) weaves and unravels; (c) refuses to do any work; (d) identifies with Penelope.

5. The act of weaving and unraveling could represent any act which is (a) futile; (b) tiring; (c) seemingly endless; (d) all of the above.

6. Why do you think that Ulysses' heroic deeds have not been mentioned in the poem?

7. Which words describe the mood of the poem? (a) dark foreboding; (b) bitter loneliness; (c) calm indifference; (d) lightheartedness.

8. Contrast the way Ulysses is reported to behave before the "assembled throng" in the poem with the way he behaves before Alcinous's court as Nausicaa sings of his deeds (pages 340–341 in "The Adventures of Ulysses"). (a) Is he emotionally moved in the story? in the poem? (b) Which words in the story and in the poem tell you so?

9. According to the poem Ulysses' display of emotion is not the genuine gesture that the assembled crowd thinks it is. The fact that we as readers know more about the genuineness of his gestures than his audience does is an example of **(a)** metaphor; **(b)** irony; **(c)** plot; **(d)** imagery.

10. Who, according to the poem, makes a gesture indicating emotion? **(a)** Ulysses; **(b)** Penelope; **(c)** the speaker; **(d)** all of the above.

11. The poem illustrates all of the following *except* **(a)** suffering; **(b)** deception; **(c)** emotion; **(d)** boastfulness.

12. The point of view in the poem is **(a)** first person; **(b)** third person; **(c)** both of the above; **(d)** neither of the above.

13. Cite two things the speaker and Penelope seem to have in common.

14. In calling her gesture "in the very best tradition," the speaker implies it **(a)** has happened many times before; **(b)** is a boring event; **(c)** is a yearly pose; **(d)** was a major decision.

Unit 5, Test II
COMPOSITION

Choose one of the following to write about.

1.   **Penelope**
Dorothy Parker

In the pathway of the sun,
    In the footsteps of the
                breeze,
Where the world and sky are
                one,
    He shall ride the silver seas,
5   He shall cut the glittering
                wave,
I shall sit at home, and rock;
Rise, to heed a neighbor's
                knock;
Brew my tea, and snip my
                thread;
Bleach the linen for my bed.
10   They will call him brave.

In this poem how does Penelope see Ulysses' experiences as compared with her own? Is her view realistic or biased? Would Ulysses agree with her? In a paragraph or two write what you think Ulysses' response to Penelope's words, as presented in this poem, would be.

2. There are several versions of what happened after Penelope and Ulysses were reunited. In one version, Penelope at first refuses to acknowledge Ulysses; then Athene casts a spell on him, making him a beautiful youth, and Penelope falls in love with him all over again. In a second version, Penelope never forgives Ulysses for having killed her beloved suitor, Antinous, and resumes weaving the shroud. In this version, Ulysses is killed by Telegonus (tə leg′ə nəs), his own son by Circe. Then Penelope and Telegonus are married. In the most common version, Penelope rejects Ulysses until he reveals secrets known by only the two of them, thus confirming his identity.

Summarize an ending to the story, using as many of the above events, or variations on them, as you think suitable. You will have to decide whether the ending is to be a happy one, and for which characters it is to be happy or tragic.

The possible and the impossible,

the not yet possible and the no longer possible—

all things come together where time and space meet

in the world of **YESTERDAY,**

TODAY,

TOMORROW

He was being offered riches, fame, love . . .
But to accept, he would have to disobey the king's command.

The Hundredth Dove

Jane Yolen

There once lived in the forest of old England a fowler named Hugh who supplied all the gamebirds for the high king's table.

The larger birds he hunted with a bow, and it was said of him that he never shot but that a bird fell, and sometimes two. But for the smaller birds that flocked like gray clouds over the forest, he used only a silken net he wove himself. This net was soft and fine and did not injure the birds though it held them fast. Then Hugh the fowler could pick and choose the plumpest of the doves for the high King's table and set the others free.

One day in early summer, Hugh was summoned to court and brought into the throne room.

Hugh bowed low, for it was not often that he was called into the king's own presence. And indeed he felt uncomfortable in the palace, as though caught in a stone cage.

"Rise, fowler, and listen," said the king. "In one week's time I am to be married." Then, turning with a smile to the woman who sat by him, the king held out her hand to the fowler.

The fowler stared up at her. She was neat as a bird, slim and fair, with black eyes. There was a quiet in her, but a restlessness too. He had never seen anyone so beautiful.

Hugh took the tiny hand offered him and put his lips to it, but he only dared to kiss the gold ring that glittered on her finger.

The king looked carefully at the fowler and saw how he trembled. It made the king smile. "See, my lady, how your beauty turns the head of even my fowler. And he is a man

who lives as solitary as a monk in his wooded cell."

The lady smiled and said nothing, but she drew her hand away from Hugh.

The king then turned again to the fowler. "In honor of my bride, the Lady Columba, whose name means dove and whose beauty is celebrated in all the world, I wish to serve one hundred of the birds at our wedding feast."

Lady Columba gasped and held up her hand. "Please do not serve them, sire."

But the king spoke to the fowler. "I have spoken. Do not fail me, fowler."

"As you command," said Hugh and he bowed again. He touched his hand to his tunic where his motto, *Servo*, "I serve," was sewn over the heart.

Then the fowler went back to the cottage deep in the forest where he lived.

There he took out the silken net and spread it upon the floor. Slowly he searched the net for snags and snarls and weakened threads. These he rewove with great care, sitting straight-backed at his wooden loom.

After a night and a day he was done. The net was as strong as his own stout heart. He laid the net down on the hearth and slept a dreamless sleep.

Before dawn Hugh set out into the forest clearing which only he knew. The trails he

"The Hundredth Dove" from *The Hundredth Dove and Other Tales* by Jane Yolen, original illustrations by David Palladini, as it first appeared in book form. First printed in *The Magazine of Fantasy and Science Fiction*, April 1977. Copyright © 1977, 1976 by Jane Yolen. Used with the permission of the Thomas Y. Crowell Company and Curtis Brown, Ltd.

followed were less than deer runs, for the fowler needed no paths to show him the way. He knew every tree, every stone in the forest as a lover knows the form of his beloved. And he served the forest easily as well as he served the high king.

The clearing was full of life; yet so silent did the fowler move, neither bird nor insect remarked his coming. He crouched at the edge, his brown and green clothes a part of the wood. Then he waited.

A long patience was his strength, and he waited the whole of the day, neither moving nor sleeping. At dusk the doves came, settling over the clearing like a gray mist. And when they were down and greedily feeding, Hugh leapt up and swung the net over the nearest ones in a single swift motion.

He counted twenty-one doves in his net, all but one gray-blue and meaty. The last was a dove that was slim, elegant, and white as milk. Yet even as Hugh watched, the white dove slipped through the silken strands that bound it and flew away into the darkening air.

Since Hugh was not the kind of hunter to curse his bad luck but rather praise his good, he gathered up the twenty and went home. He placed the doves in a large wooden cage whose bars he had carved out of white oak.

Then he looked at his net. There was not a single break in it, no way for the white dove to have escaped. Hugh thought long and hard about this, but at last he lay down to the cooing of the captured birds and slept.

In the morning the fowler was up at dawn. Again he crept to the forest clearing and waited, quieter than any stone, for the doves. And again he threw his net at dusk and caught twenty fat gray doves and the single white one.

But, as before, the white dove slipped through his net as easily as air.

The fowler carried the gray doves home and caged them with the rest. But his mind was filled with the sight of the white bird, slim and fair. He was determined to capture it.

For five days and nights it was the same except for this one thing: on the fifth night there were only nineteen gray doves in his net. He was short of the hundred by one. Yet he had taken all of the birds in the flock but the white dove.

Hugh looked into the hearthfire but he felt no warmth. He placed his hand upon the motto above his heart. "I swear by the king whom I serve and by the lady who will be his queen that I will capture that bird," he said. "I will bring the hundred doves to them. I shall not fail."

So the sixth day, well before dawn, the fowler arose. He checked the net one final time and saw it was tight. Then he was away to the clearing.

All that day Hugh sat at the clearing's

edge, still as a stone. The meadow was full of life. Songbirds sang that had never sung there before. Strange flowers grew and blossomed and died at his feet; yet he never looked at them. Animals that were once and were no longer came out of the forest shadows and passed him by: the hippocampus, the gryphon, and the silken swift unicorn.[1] But he never moved. It was for the white dove he waited, and at last she came.

In the quickening dark she floated down, feather light and luminous at the clearing's edge. Slowly she moved, eating and cooing and calling for her missing flock. She came in the end to where Hugh sat and began to feed at his feet.

He moved his hands once and the net was over her; then his hands were over her, too. The dove twisted and pecked, but he held her close, palms upon wings, fingers on neck.

When the white dove saw she could not move, she turned her bright black eyes on the fowler and spoke to him in a cooing woman's voice:

Master fowler, set me free,
Gold and silver I'll give thee.

"Neither gold nor silver tempt me," said Hugh. "*Servo* is my motto. I serve my master. And my master is the king."

Then the white dove spoke again:

Master fowler, set me free,
Fame and fortune follow thee.

But the fowler shook his head and held on tight. "After the king, I serve the forest," he said. "Fame and fortune are not masters here." He rose with the white dove in his hands and made ready to return to his house.

Then the bird shook itself all over and spoke for a third time. Its voice was low and beguiling:

Master fowler, free this dove,
The Queen will be your own true love.

For the first time, then, the fowler noticed the golden ring that glittered and shone on the dove's foot though night was almost on them. As if in a vision, he saw the Lady Columba again, slim and neat and fair. He heard her voice and felt her hand in his.

He began to tremble and his heart began to pulse madly. He felt a burning in his chest and limbs. Then he looked down at the dove and it seemed to be smiling at him, its black eyes glittering.

"*Servo,*" he cried out, his voice shaking and dead. "*Servo.*" He closed his eyes and twisted the dove's neck. Then he touched the motto on his tunic. He could feel the word *Servo* impress itself coldly on his fingertips. One quick rip and the motto was torn from his breast. He flung it to the meadow floor, put the limp dove in his pouch, and went through the forest to his home.

The next day the fowler brought the hundred doves—the ninety-nine live ones and the one dead—to the king's kitchen. But there was never a wedding. The Lady Columba came neither to the chapel nor the castle, and her name was never spoken of again in the kingdom.

The fowler gave up hunting and lived on berries and fruit the rest of his life. Every day he made his way to the clearing to throw out grain for the birds. Around his neck, from a chain, a gold ring glittered. And occasionally he would touch the spot on his tunic above his heart, which was shredded and torn.

But though songbirds and sparrows ate his grain, and swallows came at his calling, he never saw another dove. ☐☐

---

1. **hippocampus . . . unicorn,** mythical creatures. The *hippocampus* (hip′ə kam′pəs) has the front part of a horse and the tail of a fish; the *gryphon* (grif′ən) has the head and wings of an eagle and the body of a lion; and the *unicorn* (yü′nə kôrn) is like a horse, but has a single long horn on its forehead.

Discussion

1. (a) The fowler, Hugh, is said to serve two things. Who and what are they? (b) What does he wear as a sign of his service to one? (c) Give evidence to show Hugh takes pride in his work and has always done it well.

2. (a) What does the king command Hugh to do? Why? (b) How does the Lady Columba react?

3. (a) Why is Hugh so intent on catching the white dove? (b) How does the white dove apparently keep escaping? (c) How does Hugh finally catch it?

4. (a) What does the white dove offer Hugh as reward for setting it free? (b) What is the only offer that is a real temptation to him? (c) Why doesn't he accept that offer?

5. (a) Hugh keeps the other ninety-nine doves alive until he delivers them to the palace. Why do you suppose he kills the hundredth dove? (b) What clues are there in the story to the identity of that dove?

6. (a) How does he feel about his action? What tells you so? (b) In what sense(s) does the gold ring replace the motto Hugh once wore? (c) Suggest reasons why Hugh never sees another dove.

7. There are several elements in "The Hundredth Dove" that set it apart from realistic fiction. Explain how each of the following is used in this story: (a) language which is made to sound old-fashioned, or special in any other way; (b) fantastic plants and animals; (c) symbolic use of objects, colors, heat and cold, light and dark, etc.; (d) magic.

Vocabulary • Context

Use context to figure out meanings of the italicized words in the sentences below. Then choose from the list that follows the best definition for the italicized word and write the letter of that definition on your paper.

1. It was the *fowler* who supplied all the game birds for the king's table.

2. He touched his hand to his *tunic* where his motto was sewn over the heart.

3. He moved so silently that neither bird nor insect *remarked* his coming.

4. Although it was almost night, the *luminous* dove stood out against the dark forest.

5. The dove offered rewards in a voice so *beguiling* that the fowler trembled and almost let it go.

(a) pleasing or fascinating in order to trick or deceive
(b) appear dimly or vaguely as a threatening shape
(c) paid attention to
(d) person who hunts or catches wild birds
(e) man who gives up all worldly things and enters a monastery
(f) loose shirt, usually reaching to the knees
(g) loose, flowing trousers
(h) shining, full of light
(i) brand-new
(j) creating fear

Extension • Speaking

Mottos have been popular throughout history, and have been used by countries, political parties, families, and groups of people of various descriptions. For example, the official motto of the United States is "In God We Trust." Some other mottos have been "Strength from Unity"; "From Sea to Sea"; "All for One and One for All."

Perhaps you have one or more mottos on jackets, T-shirts, book bags, etc. Today it is possible to wear whatever motto happens to suit your mood on a particular day. But if you had to choose just one motto to represent what you stand for or believe in, what would that be?

Hugh's motto, *Servo*, was appropriate because he devoted his life to service—until the white dove. Tell the class what motto you choose for yourself and explain why it is appropriate to you.

Jabberwocky

Lewis Carroll

'Twas brillig, and the slithy toves
  Did gyre and gimble in the wabe;
All mimsy were the borogoves,
  And the mome raths outgrabe.

5 "Beware the Jabberwock, my son!
  The jaws that bite, the claws that catch!
Beware the Jubjub bird, and shun
  The frumious Bandersnatch!"

He took his vorpal sword in hand;
10 Long time the manxome foe he sought—
So rested he by the Tumtum tree,
  And stood awhile in thought.

And, as in uffish thought he stood,
  The Jabberwock, with eyes of flame,
15 Came whiffling through the tulgey wood,
  And burbled as it came!

One, two! One, two! And through and through
  The vorpal blade went snicker-snack!
He left it dead, and with its head
20 He went galumphing back.

"And hast thou slain the Jabberwock?
  Come to my arms, my beamish boy!
O frabjous day! Callooh! Callay!"
  He chortled in his joy.

25 'Twas brillig and the slithy toves
  Did gyre and gimble in the wabe;
All mimsy were the borogoves,
  And the mome raths outgrabe.

Lewis Carroll. *Through the Looking Glass*, 1871.

Discussion

1. Summarize the action described in the poem.

2. *Chortle,* coined by Lewis Carroll in "Jabberwocky," is now a perfectly acceptable word. It is a blend of *chuckle* and *snort.* **(a)** *Galumph* is another word that has been accepted into the language. Of what two words might it be a blend? (Check your guess in the Glossary.) **(b)** How would you explain the nonsense words not defined in the "Jabberwocky" glossary on page 367?

3. An unusual contrast is created when the words are nonsense and yet the tone is very formal. Point out as many places as you can find where old-fashioned, formal vocabulary or phrasing has been used.

4. (a) In addition to a pattern of end rhymes, the poem contains a number of *internal* rhymes—rhymes within a line. Find as many of these as you can. **(b)** In "Jabberwocky," the rhyme scheme can actually help you pronounce words that are unfamiliar to you because they were coined for this poem. Point out instances of nonsense words you can pronounce because they rhyme with real words.

5. Why do you suppose this nonsense poem has remained so popular throughout the years?

Not much information is given about the horrible monster, the Jabberwock. Make a "Wanted" poster of this creature. Include a drawing if you like. (If you can't draw, perhaps you could paste up a picture using parts of various animals cut from magazines, etc.) The information on your poster should include a general description of the Jabberwock, where it likes to hide, why it is dangerous, possible ways to trap it—and, of course, the reward you are offering.

Charles Lutwidge Dodgson, better known by his pen name of Lewis Carroll, was a mathematician. Yet there was another side to his nature for which he is remembered today.

Shy with adults, Dodgson felt more at home with young people. To amuse a little girl named Alice Liddell, Dodgson wrote a dream story called *Alice in Wonderland* and published it under the name Lewis Carroll. Suddenly famous, he wrote Alice into another story, *Through the Looking Glass*, in which she has a series of adventures on a giant chessboard.

These two books are Dodgson's best-known works.

Dodgson knew and loved poetry almost as much as he loved young people. During his time, English schoolchildren were often required to memorize poems that taught lessons; this memory work was supposed to teach them how to be good. Dodgson enjoyed rewriting the moral poems, changing them into nonsense. "Jabberwocky" is not based on a particular poem, but it is characteristic of its author's humor and imagination.

notes and comments

Glossary of Jabberwocky Terms

The following glossary of the invented words in "Jabberwocky" is compiled from ingenious definitions given by Humpty Dumpty in Lewis Carroll's *Through the Looking Glass.* The last definition is found in the *Preface* to *The Hunting of the Snark.*

Brillig, four o'clock in the afternoon—the time when you begin broiling things for dinner.
Slithy, both lithe (bending easily) and slimy. Humpty Dumpty calls *slithy* a portmanteau (pôrt-man′ tō) word because, like the suitcase of that name, there are two or more meanings packed up into one word.

Toves, animals something like badgers—they're something like lizards—and they're something like corkscrews. They make their nests under sundials; also they live on cheese.
Gyre, to go round and round like a gyroscope.
Gimble, to make holes like a gimlet.
Wabe, a grass-plot round a sundial; so called because it goes a long way before it, a long way behind it, and a long way beyond it on each side.
Mimsy, flimsy and miserable; another portmanteau word.
Borogove, a thin, shabby-looking bird with its feathers sticking out all around—

something like a live mop.
Mome. Humpty says that he is uncertain of the meaning of this word; but he thinks it's "short for *from home*—meaning that they'd lost their way."
Rath, a sort of green pig.
Outgrabe, past tense of *outgribe,* meaning to make a noise like something between bellowing and whistling, with a kind of sneeze in the middle.
Frumious, another portmanteau word meaning fuming and furious.

Enemies lurk in the garden,
and Death terrorizes the neighborhood
—until Rikki-tikki-tavi arrives.

Rikki-tikki-tavi

Rudyard Kipling

This is the story of the great war that Rikki-tikki-tavi[1] fought single-handed, through the bathrooms of the big bungalow in Segowlee cantonment.[2] Darzee[3] the Tailorbird helped him, and Chuchundra[4] the Muskrat, who never comes out into the middle of the floor, but always creeps round by the wall, gave him advice, but Rikki-tikki did the real fighting.

He was a mongoose, rather like a little cat in his fur and his tail, but quite like a weasel in his head and his habits. His eyes and the end of his restless nose were pink. He could scratch himself anywhere he pleased with any leg, front or back, that he chose to use. He could fluff up his tail till it looked like a bottle brush, and his war cry as he scuttled through the long grass was: *Rikk-tikk-tikki-tikki-tchk!*

One day, a high summer flood washed him out of the burrow where he lived with his father and mother, and carried him, kicking and clucking, down a roadside ditch. He found a little wisp of grass floating there, and clung to it till he lost his senses. When he revived, he was lying in the hot sun on the middle of a garden path, very draggled indeed, and a small boy was saying, "Here's a dead mongoose. Let's have a funeral."

"No," said his mother, "let's take him in and dry him. Perhaps he isn't really dead."

They took him into the house, and a big man picked him up between his finger and thumb and said he was not dead but half choked. So they wrapped him in cotton wool, and warmed him over a little fire, and he opened his eyes and sneezed.

"Rikki-tikki-tavi" from *The Jungle Book* by Rudyard Kipling. Reprinted by permission of Doubleday & Company, Inc., The National Trust and The Macmillan Co. of London & Basingstoke.

1. *Rikki-tikki-tavi* (rik′ē tik′ē tav′ē).
2. *Segowlee* (sə gou′li) ***cantonment*** (kan ton′mənt), the British military station at Segowlee, India.
3. *Darzee* (där zē′).
4. *Chuchundra* (chü chun′drə).

"Now," said the big man (he was an Englishman who had just moved into the bungalow), "don't frighten him, and we'll see what he'll do."

It is the hardest thing in the world to frighten a mongoose, because he is eaten up from nose to tail with curiosity. The motto of all the mongoose family is "Run and find out," and Rikki-tikki was a true mongoose. He looked at the cotton wool, decided that it was not good to eat, ran all around the table, sat up and put his fur in order, scratched himself, and jumped on the small boy's shoulder.

"Don't be frightened, Teddy," said his father. "That's his way of making friends."

"Ouch! He's tickling under my chin," said Teddy.

Rikki-tikki looked down between the boy's collar and neck, snuffed at his ear, and climbed down to the floor, where he sat rubbing his nose.

"Good gracious," said Teddy's mother, "and that's a wild creature! I suppose he's so tame because we've been kind to him."

"All mongooses are like that," said her husband. "If Teddy doesn't pick him up by the tail, or try to put him in a cage, he'll run in and out of the house all day long. Let's give him something to eat."

They gave him a little piece of raw meat. Rikki-tikki liked it immensely, and when it was finished he went out into the veranda and sat in the sunshine and fluffed up his fur to make it dry to the roots. Then he felt better.

"There are more things to find out about in this house," he said to himself, "than all my family could find out in all their lives. I shall certainly stay and find out."

He spent all that day roaming over the house. He nearly drowned himself in the bathtubs, put his nose into the ink on a writing table, and burned it on the end of the big man's cigar, for he climbed up in the big man's lap to see how writing was done. At nightfall he ran into Teddy's nursery to watch how kerosene lamps were lighted, and when Teddy went to bed Rikki-tikki climbed up too. But he was a restless companion, because he had to get up and attend to every noise all through the night, and find out what made it. Teddy's mother and father came in, the last thing, to look at their boy, and Rikki-tikki was awake on the pillow.

"I don't like that," said Teddy's mother. "He may bite the child."

"He'll do no such thing," said the father. "Teddy is safer with that little beast than if he had a bloodhound to watch him. If a snake came into the nursery now—"

But Teddy's mother wouldn't think of anything so awful.

Early in the morning Rikki-tikki came to early breakfast in the veranda riding on Teddy's shoulder, and they gave him banana and some boiled egg. He sat on all their laps one after the other, because every well-brought up mongoose always hopes to be a house mongoose some day and have rooms to run about in; and Rikki-tikki's mother (she used to live in the general's house at Segowlee) had carefully told Rikki what to do if ever he came across white men.

Then Rikki-tikki went out into the garden to see what was to be seen. It was a large garden, only half cultivated, with bushes, as big as summer houses, of Marshal Niel roses, lime and orange trees, clumps of bamboos, and thickets of high grass. Rikki-tikki licked his lips. "This is a splendid hunting ground," he said, and his tail grew bottle-brushy at the thought of it, and he scuttled up and down the garden, snuffing here and there till he heard very sorrowful voices in a thornbush. It was Darzee the

Tailorbird and his wife. They had made a beautiful nest by pulling two big leaves together and stitching them up the edges with fibers, and had filled the hollow with cotton and downy fluff. The nest swayed to and fro, as they sat on the rim and cried.

"What is the matter?" asked Rikki-tikki.

"We are very miserable," said Darzee. "One of our babies fell out of the nest yesterday and Nag[5] ate him."

"H'm," said Rikki-tikki, "that is very sad—but I am a stranger here. Who is Nag?"

Darzee and his wife only cowered down in the nest without answering, for from the thick grass at the foot of the bush there came a low hiss—a horrid cold sound that made Rikki-tikki jump back two clear feet. Then inch by inch out of the grass rose up the head and spread hood of Nag, the big black cobra, and he was five feet long from tongue to tail. When he had lifted one-third of himself clear of the ground, he stayed balancing to and fro exactly as a dandelion tuft balances in the wind, and he looked at Rikki-tikki with the wicked snake's eyes that never change their expression, whatever the snake may be thinking of.

"Who is Nag?" said he. "*I* am Nag. The great God Brahm[6] put his mark upon all our people, when the first cobra spread his hood to keep the sun off Brahm as he slept. Look, and be afraid!"

He spread out his hood more than ever, and Rikki-tikki saw the spectacle mark on the back of it that looks exactly like the eye part of a hook-and-eye fastening. He was afraid for the minute, but it is impossible for a mongoose to stay frightened for any length of time, and though Rikki-tikki had never met a live cobra before, his mother had fed him on dead ones, and he knew that all a grown mongoose's business in life was to fight and eat snakes. Nag knew that too and, at the bottom of his cold heart, he was afraid.

"Well," said Rikki-tikki, and his tail began to fluff up again, "marks or no marks, do you think it is right for you to eat fledglings out of a nest?"

Nag was thinking to himself, and watching the least little movement in the grass behind Rikki-tikki. He knew that mongooses in the garden meant death sooner or later for him and his family, but he wanted to get Rikki-tikki off his guard. So he dropped his head a little, and put it on one side.

"Let us talk," he said. "You eat eggs. Why should not I eat birds?"

"Behind you! Look behind you!" sang Darzee.

Rikki-tikki knew better than to waste time in staring. He jumped up in the air as high as he could go, and just under him whizzed by the head of Nagaina,[7] Nag's wicked wife. She had crept up behind him as he was talking, to make an end of him. He heard her savage hiss as the stroke missed. He came down almost across her back, and if he had been an old mongoose he would have known that then was the time to break her back with one bite; but he was afraid of the terrible lashing return stroke of the cobra. He bit, indeed, but did not bite long enough, and he jumped clear of the whisking tail, leaving Nagaina torn and angry.

"Wicked, wicked Darzee!" said Nag, lashing up as high as he could reach toward the nest in the thornbush. But Darzee had built it out of reach of snakes, and it only swayed to and fro.

Rikki-tikki felt his eyes growing red and hot (when a mongoose's eyes grow red, he is

---

5. **Nag** (näj).
6. **The Great God Brahm** (bräm), the supreme god of the Hindu religion, usually known as Brahma (brä′mə).
7. **Nagaina** (nä gān′ə).

angry), and he sat back on his tail and hind legs like a little kangaroo, and looked all round him, and chattered with rage. But Nag and Nagaina had disappeared into the grass. When a snake misses its stroke, it never says anything or gives any sign of what it means to do next. Rikki-tikki did not care to follow them, for he did not feel sure that he could manage two snakes at once. So he trotted off to the gravel path near the house, and sat down to think. It was a serious matter for him.

If you read the old books of natural history, you will find they say that when the mongoose fights the snake and happens to get bitten, he runs off and eats some herb that cures him. That is not true. The victory is only a matter of quickness of eye and quickness of foot—snake's blow against mongoose's jump—and as no eye can follow the motion of a snake's head when it strikes, this makes things much more wonderful than any magic herb. Rikki-tikki knew he was a young mongoose, and it made him all the more pleased to think that he had managed to escape a blow from behind.

It gave him confidence in himself, and when Teddy came running down the path, Rikki-tikki was ready to be petted. But just as Teddy was stooping, something wriggled a little in the dust, and a tiny voice said: "Be careful. I am Death!" It was Karait,[8] the dusty brown snakeling that lies for choice on the dusty earth; and his bite is as dangerous as the cobra's. But he is so small that nobody thinks of him, and so he does the more harm to people.

Rikki-tikki's eyes grew red again, and he danced up to Karait with the peculiar rocking, swaying motion that he had inherited from his family. It looks very funny, but it is so perfectly balanced a gait that you can fly off from it at any angle you please, and in dealing with snakes this is an advantage.

If Rikki-tikki had only known, he was doing a much more dangerous thing than fighting Nag, for Karait is so small, and can turn so quickly, that unless Rikki bit him close to the back of the head, he would get

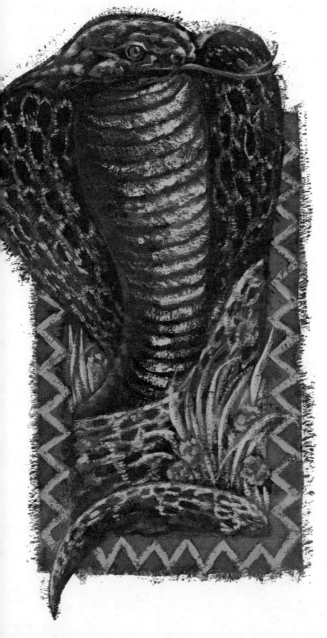

---

8. *Karait* (kä rīt′).

the return stroke in his eye or his lip. But Rikki did not know. His eyes were all red, and he rocked back and forth, looking for a good place to hold. Karait struck out. Rikki jumped sideways and tried to run in, but the wicked little dusty gray head lashed within a fraction of his shoulder, and he had to jump over the body, and the head followed his heels close.

Teddy shouted to the house: "Oh, look here! Our mongoose is killing a snake." And Rikki-tikki heard a scream from Teddy's mother. His father ran out with a stick, but by the time he came up, Karait had lunged out once too far, and Rikki-tikki had sprung, jumped on the snake's back, dropped his head far between his forelegs, bitten as high up the back as he could get hold, and rolled away.

That bite paralyzed Karait, and Rikki-tikki was just going to eat him up from the tail, after the custom of his family at dinner, when he remembered that a full meal makes a slow mongoose, and if he wanted all his strength and quickness ready, he must keep himself thin. He went away for a dust bath under the castor-oil bushes, while Teddy's father beat the dead Karait.

"What is the use of that?" thought Rikki-tikki. "I have settled it all."

And then Teddy's mother picked him up from the dust and hugged him, crying that he had saved Teddy from death, and Teddy's father said that he was a providence, and Teddy looked on with big scared eyes. Rikki-tikki was rather amused at all the fuss, which, of course, he did not understand. Teddy's mother might just as well have petted Teddy for playing in the dust. Rikki was thoroughly enjoying himself.

That night at dinner, walking to and fro among the wineglasses on the table, he might have stuffed himself three times over with nice things. But he remembered Nag and Nagaina, and though it was very pleasant to be patted and petted by Teddy's mother, and to sit on Teddy's shoulder, his eyes would get red from time to time, and he would go off into his long war cry of *"Rikk-tikk-tikki-tikki-tchk!"*

Teddy carried him off to bed and insisted on Rikki-tikki sleeping under his chin. Rikki-tikki was too well bred to bite or scratch, but as soon as Teddy was asleep he went off for his nightly walk round the house, and in the dark he ran up against Chuchundra the Muskrat creeping around by the wall. Chuchundra is a brokenhearted little beast. He whimpers and cheeps all the night, trying to make up his mind to run into the middle of the room. But he never gets there.

"Don't kill me," said Chuchundra, almost weeping. "Rikki-tikki, don't kill me!"

"Do you think a snake-killer kills muskrats?" said Rikki-tikki scornfully.

"Those who kill snakes get killed by snakes," said Chuchundra, more sorrowfully than ever. "And how am I to be sure that Nag won't mistake me for you some dark night?"

"There's not the least danger," said Rikki-tikki. "But Nag is in the garden, and I know you don't go there."

"My cousin Chua[9] the Rat told me—" said Chuchundra, and then he stopped.

"Told you what?"

"H'sh! Nag is everywhere, Rikki-tikki. You should have talked to Chua in the garden."

"I didn't—so you must tell me. Quick, Chuchundra, or I'll bite you!"

Chuchundra sat down and cried till the tears rolled off his whiskers. "I am a very

---

9. *Chua* (chü′ə).

poor man," he sobbed. "I never had spirit enough to run out into the middle of the room. H'sh! I mustn't tell you anything. Can't you *hear*, Rikki-tikki?"

Rikki-tikki listened. The house was as still as still, but he thought he could just catch the faintest *scratch-scratch* in the world—a noise as faint as that of a wasp walking on a windowpane—the dry scratch of a snake's scales on brick work.

"That's Nag or Nagaina," he said to himself, "and he is crawling into the bathroom sluice. You're right, Chuchundra; I should have talked to Chua."

He stole off to Teddy's bathroom, but there was nothing there, and then to Teddy's mother's bathroom. At the bottom of the smooth plaster wall there was a brick pulled out to make a sluice for the bath water, and as Rikki-tikki stole in by the masonry curb where the bath is put, he heard Nag and Nagaina whispering together outside in the moonlight.

"When the house is emptied of people," said Nagaina to her husband, "*he* will have to go away, and then the garden will be our own again. Go in quietly, and remember that the big man who killed Karait is the first one to bite. Then come out and tell me, and we will hunt for Rikki-tikki together."

"But are you sure that there is anything to be gained by killing the people?" said Nag.

"Everything. When there were no people in the bungalow, did we have any mongoose in the garden? So long as the bungalow is empty, we are king and queen of the garden; and remember that as soon as our eggs in the melon bed hatch (as they may tomorrow), our children will need room and quiet."

"I had not thought of that," said Nag. "I will go, but there is no need that we should hunt for Rikki-tikki afterwards. I will kill the big man and his wife, and the child if I can, and come away quietly. Then the bungalow will be empty, and Rikki-tikki will go."

Rikki-tikki tingled all over with rage and hatred at this, and then Nag's head came through the sluice, and his five feet of cold body followed it. Angry as he was, Rikki-tikki was very frightened as he saw the size of the big cobra. Nag coiled himself up, raised his head, and looked into the bathroom in the dark, and Rikki could see his eyes glitter.

"Now, if I kill him here, Nagaina will know; and if I fight him on the open floor, the odds are in his favor. What am I to do?" said Rikki-tikki-tavi.

Nag waved to and fro, and then Rikki-tikki heard him drinking from the biggest water jar that was used to fill the bath. "That is good," said the snake. "Now, when Karait was killed, the big man had a stick. He may have that stick still, but when he comes in to bathe in the morning he will not have a stick. I shall wait here till he comes. Nagaina—do you hear me?—I shall wait here in the cool till daytime."

There was no answer from outside, so Rikki-tikki knew Nagaina had gone away. Nag coiled himself down, coil by coil, round the bulge at the bottom of the water jar, and Rikki-tikki stayed still as death. After an hour he began to move, muscle by muscle, toward the jar. Nag was asleep, and Rikki-tikki looked at his big back, wondering which would be the best place for a good hold. "If I don't break his back at the first jump," said Rikki, "he can still fight. And if he fights—O Rikki!" He looked at the thickness of the neck below the hood, but that was too much for him; and a bite near the tail would only make Nag savage.

"It must be the head," he said at last; "the head above the hood. And, when I am once there, I must not let go."

Then he jumped. The head was lying a little clear of the water jar, under the curve of it; and, as his teeth met, Rikki braced his back against the bulge of the red earthenware to hold down the head. This gave him just one second's purchase, and he made the most of it. Then he was battered to and fro as a rat is shaken by a dog—to and fro on the floor, up and down, and around in great circles, but his eyes were red and he held on as the body cartwhipped over the floor, upsetting the tin dipper and the soap dish and the flesh brush, and banged against the tin side of the bath.

As he held he closed his jaws tighter and tighter, for he made sure he would be banged to death, and, for the honor of his family, he preferred to be found with his teeth locked. He was dizzy, aching, and felt shaken to pieces when something went off like a thunderclap just behind him. A hot wind knocked him senseless and red fire singed his fur. The big man had been wakened by the noise, and had fired both barrels of a shotgun into Nag just behind the hood.

Rikki-tikki held on with his eyes shut, for now he was quite sure he was dead. But the head did not move, and the big man picked him up and said, "It's the mongoose again, Alice. The little chap has saved *our* lives now."

Then Teddy's mother came in with a very white face, and saw what was left of Nag, and Rikki-tikki dragged himself to Teddy's bedroom and spent half the rest of the night shaking himself tenderly to find out whether he really was broken into forty pieces, as he fancied.

When morning came he was very stiff, but well pleased with his doings. "Now I have Nagaina to settle with, and she will be worse than five Nags, and there's no know-

ing when the eggs she spoke of will hatch. Goodness! I must go and see Darzee," he said.

Without waiting for breakfast, Rikki-tikki ran to the thornbush where Darzee was singing a song of triumph at the top of his voice. The news of Nag's death was all over the garden, for the sweeper had thrown the body on the rubbish heap.

"Oh, you stupid tuft of feathers!" said Rikki-tikki angrily. "Is this the time to sing?"

"Nag is dead—is dead—is dead!" sang Darzee. "The valiant Rikki-tikki caught him by the head and held fast. The big man brought the bang stick, and Nag fell in two pieces! He will never eat my babies again."

"All that's true enough. But where's Nagaina?" said Rikki-tikki, looking carefully round him.

"Nagaina came to the bathroom sluice and called for Nag," Darzee went on, "and Nag came out on the end of a stick—the sweeper picked him up on the end of a stick and threw him upon the rubbish heap. Let us sing about the great, the red-eyed Rikki-tikki!" And Darzee filled his throat and sang.

"If I could get up to your nest, I'd roll your babies out!" said Rikki-tikki. "You don't know when to do the right thing at the right time. You're safe enough in your nest there, but it's war for me, down here. Stop singing a minute, Darzee."

"For the great, the beautiful Rikki-tikki's sake I will stop," said Darzee. "What is it, O Killer of the terrible Nag?"

"Where is Nagaina, for the third time?"

"On the rubbish heap by the stables, mourning for Nag. Great is Rikki-tikki with the white teeth."

"Bother my white teeth! Have you ever heard where she keeps her eggs?"

"In the melon bed, on the end nearest the

wall, where the sun strikes nearly all day. She hid them there weeks ago."

"And you never thought it worthwhile to tell me? The end nearest the wall, you said?"

"Rikki-tikki, you are not going to eat her eggs?"

"Not eat exactly, no. Darzee, if you have a grain of sense you will fly off to the stables and pretend that your wing is broken, and let Nagaina chase you away to this bush. I must get to the melon bed, and if I went there now she'd see me."

Darzee was a feather-brained little fellow who could never hold more than one idea at a time in his head. And just because he knew that Nagaina's children were born in eggs like his own, he didn't think at first that it was fair to kill them. But his wife was a sensible bird, and she knew that cobra's eggs meant young cobras later on. So she flew off from the nest, and left Darzee to keep the babies warm, and continue his song about the death of Nag. Darzee was very like a man in some ways.

She fluttered in front of Nagaina by the rubbish heap and cried out, "Oh, my wing is broken! The boy in the house threw a stone at me and broke it." Then she fluttered more desperately than ever.

Nagaina lifted up her head and hissed. "You warned Rikki-tikki when I would have killed him. Indeed and truly, you've chosen a bad place to be lame in." And she moved toward Darzee's wife, slipping along over the dust.

"The boy broke it with a stone!" shrieked Darzee's wife.

"Well! It may be some consolation to you when you're dead to know that I shall settle accounts with the boy. My husband lies on the rubbish heap this morning, but before night the boy in the house will lie very still. What is the use of running away? I am sure to catch you. Little fool, look at me!"

Darzee's wife knew better than to do *that,* for a bird who looks at a snake's eyes gets so frightened that she cannot move. Darzee's wife fluttered on, piping sorrowfully, and never leaving the ground, and Nagaina quickened her pace.

Rikki-tikki heard them going up the path from the stables, and he raced for the end of the melon patch near the wall. There, in the warm litter above the melons, very cunningly hidden, he found twenty-five eggs, about the size of a bantam's eggs, but with whitish skins instead of shells.

"I was not a day too soon," he said, for he could see the baby cobras curled up inside the skin, and he knew that the minute they were hatched they could each kill a man or a mongoose. He bit off the tops of the eggs as fast as he could, taking care to crush the young cobras, and turned over the litter from time to time to see whether he had missed any. At last there were only three eggs left, and Rikki-tikki began to chuckle to himself, when he heard Darzee's wife screaming:

"Rikki-tikki, I led Nagaina toward the house, and she has gone into the veranda, and—oh, come quickly—she means killing!"

Rikki-tikki smashed two eggs, and tumbled backward down the melon bed with the third egg in his mouth, and scuttled to the veranda as hard as he could put foot to the ground. Teddy and his mother and father were there at early breakfast, but Rikki-tikki saw that they were not eating anything. They sat stone-still, and their faces were white. Nagaina was coiled up on the matting by Teddy's chair, within easy striking distance of Teddy's bare leg, and she was swaying to and fro, singing a song of triumph.

"Son of the big man that killed Nag," she

hissed, "stay still. I am not ready yet. Wait a little. Keep very still, all you three! If you move I strike, and if you do not move I strike. Oh, foolish people, who killed my Nag!"

Teddy's eyes were fixed on his father, and all his father could do was to whisper, "Sit still, Teddy. You mustn't move. Teddy, keep still."

Then Rikki-tikki came up and cried, "Turn round, Nagaina. Turn and fight!"

"All in good time," said she, without moving her eyes. "I will settle my account with *you* presently. Look at your friends, Rikki-tikki. They are still and white. They are afraid. They dare not move, and if you come a step nearer I strike."

"Look at your eggs," said Rikki-tikki, "in the melon bed near the wall. Go and look, Nagaina!"

The big snake turned half around, and saw the egg on the veranda. "Ah-h! Give it to me," she said.

Rikki-tikki put his paws one on each side of the egg, and his eyes were blood-red. "What price for a snake's egg? For a young cobra? For a young king cobra? For the last—the very last of the brood? The ants are eating all the others down by the melon bed."

Nagaina spun clear round, forgetting everything for the sake of the one egg. Rikki-tikki saw Teddy's father shoot out a big hand, catch Teddy by the shoulder, and drag him across the little table with the teacups, safe and out of reach of Nagaina.

"Tricked! Tricked! Tricked! *Rikk-tck-tck!*" chuckled Rikki-tikki. "The boy is safe, and it was I—I—I that caught Nag by the hood last night in the bathroom." Then he began to jump up and down, all four feet together, his head close to the floor. "He threw me to and fro, but he could not shake

me off. He was dead before the big man blew him in two. I did it! *Rikki-tikki-tck-tck!* Come then, Nagaina. Come and fight with me. You shall not be a widow long."

Nagaina saw that she had lost her chance of killing Teddy, and the egg lay between Rikki-tikki's paws. "Give me the egg, Rikki-tikki. Give me the last of my eggs, and I will go away and never come back," she said, lowering her hood.

"Yes, you will go away, and you will never come back. For you will go to the rubbish heap with Nag. Fight, widow! The big man has gone for his gun. Fight!"

Rikki-tikki was bounding all round Nagaina, keeping just out of reach of her stroke, his little eyes like hot coals. Nagaina gathered herself together and flung out at him. Rikki-tikki jumped up and backward. Again and again and again she struck, and each time her head came with a whack on the matting of the veranda and she gathered herself together like a watch spring. Then Rikki-tikki danced in a circle to get behind her, and Nagaina spun round to keep her head to his head, so that the rustle of her tail on the matting sounded like dry leaves blown along by the wind.

He had forgotten the egg. It still lay on the veranda, and Nagaina came nearer and nearer to it, till at last, while Rikki-tikki was drawing breath, she caught it in her mouth, turned to the veranda steps, and flew like an arrow down the path, with Rikki-tikki behind her. When the cobra runs for her life, she goes like a whiplash flicked across a horse's neck. Rikki-tikki knew that he must catch her, or all the trouble would begin again.

She headed straight for the long grass by the thornbush, and as he was running Rikki-tikki heard Darzee still singing his foolish little song of triumph. But Darzee's wife was

wiser. She flew off her nest as Nagaina came along, and flapped her wings about Nagaina's head. If Darzee had helped her they might have turned her, but Nagaina only lowered her hood and went on. Still, the instant's delay brought Rikki-tikki up to her, and as she plunged into the rathole where she and Nag used to live, his little white teeth were clenched on her tail, and he went down with her—and very few mongooses, however wise and old they may be, care to follow a cobra into its hole.

It was dark in the hole; and Rikki-tikki never knew when it might open out and give Nagaina room to turn and strike at him. He held on savagely, and stuck out his feet to act as brakes on the dark slope of the hot, moist earth.

Then the grass by the mouth of the hole stopped waving, and Darzee said, "It is all over with Rikki-tikki! We must sing his death song. Valiant Rikki-tikki is dead! For Nagaina will surely kill him underground."

So he sang a very mournful song that he made up on the spur of the minute, and just as he got to the most touching part, the grass quivered again, and Rikki-tikki, covered with dirt, dragged himself out of the hole leg by leg, licking his whiskers. Darzee stopped with a little shout. Rikki-tikki shook some of the dust out of his fur and sneezed. "It is all over," he said. "The widow will never come out again." And the red ants that live between the grass stems heard him, and began to troop down one after another to see if he had spoken the truth.

Rikki-tikki curled himself up in the grass and slept where he was—slept and slept till it was late in the afternoon, for he had done a hard day's work.

"Now," he said, when he awoke, "I will go back to the house. Tell the Coppersmith, Darzee, and he will tell the garden that Nagaina is dead."

The Coppersmith is a bird who makes a noise exactly like the beating of a little hammer on a copper pot. The reason he is always making it is because he is the town crier to every Indian garden, and tells all the news to everybody who cares to listen. As Rikki-tikki went up the path, he heard his "attention" notes like a tiny dinner gong, and then the steady *"Ding-dong-tock!* Nag is dead—*dong!* Nagaina is dead! *Ding-dong-tock!"* That set all the birds in the garden singing, and the frogs croaking, for Nag and Nagaina used to eat frogs as well as little birds.

When Rikki got to the house, Teddy and Teddy's mother (she looked very white still, for she had been fainting) and Teddy's father came out and almost cried over him; and that night he ate all that was given him till he could eat no more, and went to bed on Teddy's shoulder, where Teddy's mother saw him when she came to look late at night.

"He saved our lives and Teddy's life," she said to her husband. "Just think, he saved all our lives."

Rikki-tikki woke up with a jump, for the mongooses are light sleepers.

"Oh, it's you," said he. "What are you bothering for? All the cobras are dead. And if they weren't, I'm here."

Rikki-tikki had a right to be proud of himself. But he did not grow too proud, and he kept that garden as a mongoose should keep it, with tooth and jump and spring and bite, till never a cobra dared show its head inside the walls. ☐☐

Discussion

1. How does Rikki-tikki-tavi prove the family motto "Run and find out" fits him?

2. (a) Why do the snakes want to get rid of Teddy and his parents? (b) How does Rikki put an end to each of their plans?

3. When a reader is uncertain and anxious about the outcome, a story is said to contain *suspense*. (a) At what point in the story is suspense first aroused? (b) What is the moment of greatest suspense in the story?

4. (a) In 368b, 2, which gives a physical description of Rikki, to which of your senses do the images appeal? (b) Find images appealing to your sense of sound in the passages dealing with Nag and Nagaina (370a, 4 and 370b, 5). (c) In the scene describing the fight with Nag (374a, 1–2), which images appeal to physical feeling?

5. (a) What details in the story about the habits of animals seem to you to be factual? (b) "Darzee was very like a man in some ways," the story states. What human characteristics do Darzee, Rikki, and the other animals exhibit? (c) Review the Handbook article on *characterization* (page 532). What methods of characterization are used for the animals? for the humans? Find examples of each.

6. Read the biographical sketch of Rudyard Kipling on this page. Note that the animal tales Kipling wrote were similar to those he was told by his Indian nurses. What elements are there in "Rikki-tikki-tavi" to suggest that the tale is being told aloud to an audience?

7. Choose from the following words those that best describe the narrator's tone, and give reasons for your choice: *amused, cold, affectionate, critical, pitying, admiring, gloomy, ridiculing.*

Vocabulary • Dictionary

Because India was for many years a British colony, a number of Indian words have become common in English. For example, our word *bandanna* comes from a Hindi word for a dyeing process that involves tying the cloth in knots—what we call "tie-dyeing." A *bandanna* has come to mean, in English, a large scarf or handkerchief.

The words listed in the left-hand column below have all come to us from India. Match them with their original Indian meanings given at the right. Use the Glossary if necessary.

1. veranda	(a)	he robs
2. bungalow	(b)	leg + garment
3. cot		
4. shampoo	(c)	house
5. bangle	(d)	bracelet
6. cashmere	(e)	to press; knead
7. pajamas		
8. loot	(f)	bed frame
	(g)	porch
	(h)	area known for its goats

Rudyard Kipling
1865 • 1936

Born to English parents in Bombay, India, Rudyard Kipling spent his early childhood listening to his native nurses tell traditional tales of jungle animals. These entertaining tales were much like those Kipling himself wrote later.

Like most British children in foreign countries, he was sent to England for his schooling. When he returned to India at the age of seventeen, he began working on a newspaper. As a reporter, he traveled throughout the country and grew to know it as few outsiders do. Later, he set out to see the rest of the world, living in the United States for five years before settling permanently in England, where he continued his writing.

Today, Kipling is remembered throughout the world for his poems and tales of India. Of special interest are his *Just-So Stories, The Jungle Book,* and *The Second Jungle Book,* all of which deal with animals. *Kim,* an adventure story about an English orphan in India, and *Captains Courageous,* the story of a spoiled American boy on a fishing schooner, are also favorite reading.

Macavity: The Mystery Cat

T. S. Eliot

Macavity's a Mystery Cat: he's called the Hidden Paw—
For he's the master criminal who can defy the Law.
He's the bafflement of Scotland Yard, the Flying Squad's despair:[1]
For when they reach the scene of crime—*Macavity's not there!*

5 Macavity, Macavity, there's no one like Macavity,
He's broken every human law, he breaks the law of gravity.
His powers of levitation would make a fakir stare,[2]
And when you reach the scene of crime—*Macavity's not there!*
You may seek him in the basement, you may look up in the air—
10 But I tell you once and once again, *Macavity's not there!*

Macavity's a ginger cat, he's very tall and thin;
You would know him if you saw him, for his eyes are sunken in.
His brow is deeply lined with thought, his head is highly domed;
His coat is dusty from neglect, his whiskers are uncombed.
15 He sways his head from side to side, with movements like a snake;
And when you think he's half asleep, he's always wide awake.

Macavity, Macavity, there's no one like Macavity,
For he's a fiend in feline shape, a monster of depravity.

1. Scotland Yard . . . Flying Squad's despair. The Flying Squad, a group prepared to travel anywhere on short notice, is a section of the criminal investigation department of Scotland Yard, the headquarters of the London police.
2. His powers . . . would make a fakir stare. His ability to rise and float in the air *(levitate)* would surprise even a *fakir*, a Hindu religious man said to possess such powers.

Discussion

1. (a) Why is Macavity called "a mystery cat" (line 1)? **(b)** Why is it impossible to prosecute him for his deeds?

2. (a) What is suggested by calling Macavity "the Napoleon of Crime" (line 42)? **(b)** Point out details in the poem that suggest his importance as a criminal. **(c)** How do Macavity's crimes vary in degree of importance? Give examples.

3. What is the tone of the poem?

4. (a) Does this poem have a regular or a varied rhythm? **(b)** Pronounce the name *Macavity*. Which syllable do you stress the hardest? **(c)** Find and read lines which illustrate how the rhythm of the whole poem is the same as the rhythm of the name *Macavity*. **(d)** Discuss the way in which the rhythm or movement of the poem fits the overall tone.

You may meet him in a by-street, you may see him in the square—
20 But when a crime's discovered, then *Macavity's not there!*

He's outwardly respectable. (They say he cheats at cards.)
And his footprints are not found in any file of Scotland Yard's.
And when the larder's looted, or the jewel-case is rifled,
Or when the milk is missing, or another Peke's[3] been stifled,
25 Or the greenhouse glass is broken, and the trellis past repair—
Ay, there's the wonder of the thing! *Macavity's not there!*

And when the Foreign Office[4] finds a Treaty's gone astray,
Or the Admiralty[5] loses some plans and drawings by the way,
There may be a scrap of paper in the hall or on the stair—
30 But it's useless to investigate—*Macavity's not there!*
And when the loss has been disclosed, the Secret Service say:
"It *must* have been Macavity!"—but he's a mile away.
You'll be sure to find him resting, or a-licking of his thumbs,
Or engaged in doing complicated long division sums.

35 Macavity, Macavity, there's no one like Macavity,
There never was a cat of such deceitfulness and suavity.
He always has an alibi, and one or two to spare:
At whatever time the deed took place—MACAVITY WASN'T THERE!
And they say that all the Cats whose wicked deeds are widely known
40 (I might mention Mungojerrie, I might mention Griddlebone[6])
Are nothing more than agents for the Cat who all the time
Just controls their operations: the Napoleon[7] of Crime!

---

3. *Peke's.* A Pekingese is a tiny, Oriental breed of dog.
4. *Foreign Office,* the department of the government that deals with foreign affairs. It is comparable to the U.S. State Department.
5. *Admiralty,* the government department that handles commerce and shipping affairs.
6. *Mungojerrie, Griddlebone,* characters in *Old Possum's Book of Practical Cats,* in which "Macavity" is included.
7. *Napoleon* (nə pō′lē ən). Napoleon Bonaparte (1769–1821) was a French general who made himself emperor of France in 1804 and conquered a large part of Europe before being defeated at Waterloo in 1815.

Extension • Writing

T. S. Eliot 1888 • 1965

One of the mysteries about Macavity is how he always manages to have fled the scene of the crime before the police arrive. How *does* he do it? In one paragraph, write an explanation of how you think Macavity makes his getaways.

Both England and America claim a part in T. S. Eliot, perhaps the most influential twentieth-century poet in the English language. A quiet, reserved man, Eliot was born in St. Louis, Missouri. After making a brilliant record at Harvard, he moved to England, be-

came a British subject, and remained there for the rest of his life.

Much of Eliot's poetry is complex and intellectual, but "Macavity" comes from an amusing volume of poems, *Old Possum's Book of Practical Cats.*

See **STEREOTYPE** Handbook of Literary Terms

"She was horribly *good,"* began the bachelor,
and his little audience sat up in surprise.

The Storyteller

H. H. Munro

It was a hot afternoon, and the railway carriage was correspondingly sultry, and the next stop was at Templecombe, nearly an hour ahead. The occupants of the carriage were a small girl, and a smaller girl, and a small boy. An aunt belonging to the children occupied one corner seat, and the further corner seat on the opposite side was occupied by a bachelor who was a stranger to their party, but the small girls and the small boy emphatically occupied the compartment. Both the aunt and the children were conversational in a limited, persistent way, reminding one of the attentions of a housefly that refused to be discouraged. Most of the aunt's remarks seemed to begin with "Don't," and nearly all of the children's remarks began with "Why?" The bachelor said nothing out loud.

"Don't, Cyril, don't," exclaimed the aunt, as the small boy began smacking the cushions of the seat, producing a cloud of dust at each blow.

"Come and look out of the window," she added.

The child moved reluctantly to the window. "Why are those sheep being driven out of that field?" he asked.

"I expect they are being driven to another field where there is more grass," said the aunt weakly.

"But there is lots of grass in that field," protested the boy. "There's nothing else but grass there. Aunt, there's lots of grass in that field."

"Perhaps the grass in the other field is better," suggested the aunt fatuously.

"Why is it better?" came the swift, inevitable question.

"Oh, look at those cows!" exclaimed the aunt. Nearly every field along the line had contained cows or bullocks, but she spoke as though she were drawing attention to a rarity.

"Why is the grass in the other field better?" persisted Cyril.

The frown on the bachelor's face was deepening to a scowl. He was a hard, unsympathetic man, the aunt decided in her mind. She was utterly unable to come to any satisfactory decision about the grass in the other field.

The smaller girl created a diversion by beginning to recite "On the Road to Mandalay." She only knew the first line, but she put her limited knowledge to the fullest possible use. She repeated the line over and over again in a dreamy but resolute and very audible voice; it seemed to the bachelor as though someone had had a bet with her that she could not repeat the line aloud two thousand times without stopping. Whoever it was who had made the wager was likely to lose his bet.

"Come over here and listen to a story," said the aunt, when the bachelor had looked twice at her and once at the communication cord.[1]

The children moved listlessly toward the aunt's end of the carriage. Evidently her reputation as a storyteller did not rank high in their estimation.

In a low, confidential voice, interrupted at frequent intervals by loud, petulant questions from her listeners, she began an unenterprising and deplorably uninteresting story about a little girl who was good, and made friends with everyone on account of her goodness, and was finally saved from a mad bull by a number of rescuers who admired her moral character.

"Wouldn't they have saved her if she hadn't been good?" demanded the bigger of the small girls. It was exactly the question that the bachelor had wanted to ask.

"Well, yes," admitted the aunt lamely, "but I don't think they would have run quite so fast to her help if they had not liked her so much."

"It's the stupidest story I've ever heard," said the bigger of the small girls, with immense conviction.

"I didn't listen after the first bit, it was so stupid," said Cyril.

The smaller girl made no actual comment on the story, but she had long ago recommenced a murmured repetition of her favorite line.

"You don't seem to be a success as a storyteller," said the bachelor suddenly from his corner.

The aunt bristled in instant defense at this unexpected attack.

"It's a very difficult thing to tell stories that children can both understand and appreciate," she said stiffly.

"I don't agree with you," said the bachelor.

"Perhaps *you* would like to tell them a story," was the aunt's retort.

"Tell us a story," demanded the bigger of the small girls.

"Once upon a time," began the bachelor, "there was a little girl called Bertha, who was extraordinarily good."

The children's momentarily aroused interest began at once to flicker; all stories seemed dreadfully alike, no matter who told them.

"She did all that she was told, she was always truthful, she kept her clothes clean, ate milk puddings as though they were jam

---

1. **communication cord,** cord pulled to signal the engineer to stop the train in case of an emergency.

tarts, learned her lessons perfectly, and was polite in her manners."

"Was she pretty?" asked the bigger of the small girls.

"Not as pretty as any of you," said the bachelor. "But she was horribly good."

There was a wave of reaction in favor of the story; the word *horrible* in connection with goodness was a novelty that commended itself. It seemed to introduce a ring of truth that was absent from the aunt's tales of infant life.

"She was so good," continued the bachelor, "that she won several medals for goodness, which she always wore pinned onto her dress. There was a medal for obedience, another medal for punctuality, and a third for good behavior. They were large metal medals, and they clinked against one another as she walked. No other child in the town where she lived had as many as three medals, so everybody knew that she must be an extra good child."

"Horribly good," quoted Cyril.

"Everybody talked about her goodness, and the Prince of the country got to hear about it, and he said that as she was so very good she might be allowed once a week to walk in his park, which was just outside the town. It was a beautiful park, and no children were ever allowed in it, so it was a great honor for Bertha to be allowed to go there."

"Were there any sheep in the park?" demanded Cyril.

"No," said the bachelor, "there were no sheep."

"Why weren't there any sheep?" came the inevitable question arising out of that answer.

The aunt permitted herself a smile, which might almost have been described as a grin.

"There were no sheep in the park," said the bachelor, "because the Prince's mother had once had a dream that her son would either be killed by a sheep or else by a clock falling on him. For that reason the Prince never kept a sheep in his park or a clock in his palace."

The aunt suppressed a gasp of admiration.

"Was the Prince killed by a sheep or by a clock?" asked Cyril.

"He is still alive, so we can't tell whether the dream will come true," said the bachelor unconcernedly. "Anyway, there were no sheep in the park, but there were lots of little pigs running all over the place."

"What color were they?"

"Black with white faces, white with black spots, black all over, gray with white patches, and some were white all over."

The storyteller paused to let the full idea of the park's treasures sink into the children's imaginations; then he resumed:

"Bertha was rather sorry to find that there were no flowers in the park. She had promised her aunts, with tears in her eyes, that she would not pick any of the kind Prince's flowers, and she had meant to keep her promise, so of course it made her feel silly to find that there were no flowers to pick."

"Why weren't there any flowers?"

"Because the pigs had eaten them all," said the bachelor promptly. "The gardeners had told the Prince that you couldn't have pigs and flowers, so he decided to have pigs and no flowers."

There was a murmur of approval at the excellence of the Prince's decision; so many people would have decided the other way.

"There were lots of other delightful things in the park. There were ponds with gold and blue and green fish in them, and trees with beautiful parrots that said clever things at a moment's notice, and humming birds that hummed all the popular tunes of the day. Bertha walked up and down and enjoyed herself immensely, and thought to herself, 'If I were not so extraordinarily good I should not have been allowed to come into this beautiful park and enjoy all there is to be seen in it,' and her three medals clinked against one another as she walked and helped to remind her how very good she really was. Just then an enormous wolf came prowling into the park to see if it could catch a fat little pig for its supper.''

"What color was it?" asked the children, amid an immediate quickening of interest.

"Mud-color all over, with a black tongue and pale gray eyes that gleamed with unspeakable ferocity. The first thing that it saw in the park was Bertha; her pinafore was so spotlessly white and clean that it could be seen from a great distance. Bertha saw the wolf and saw that it was stealing toward her, and she began to wish that she had never been allowed to come into the park. She ran as hard as she could, and the wolf came after her with huge leaps and bounds. She managed to reach a shrubbery of myrtle bushes, and she hid herself in one of the thickest of the bushes. The wolf came sniffing among the branches, its black tongue lolling out of its mouth and its pale gray eyes glaring with rage. Bertha was terribly frightened, and thought to herself: 'If I had not been so extraordinarily good, I should have been safe in town at this moment.'

"However, the scent of the myrtle was so strong that the wolf could not sniff out where Bertha was hiding, and the bushes were so thick that he might have hunted about in them for a long time without catching sight of her; so he thought he might as well go off and catch a little pig instead. Bertha was trembling very much at having the wolf prowling and sniffing so near her,

and as she trembled the medal for obedience clinked against the medals for good conduct and punctuality. The wolf was just moving away when he heard the sound of the medals clinking and stopped to listen; they clinked again in a bush quite near him. He dashed into the bush, his pale gray eyes gleaming with ferocity and triumph, and dragged Bertha out and devoured her to the last morsel. All that was left of her were her shoes, bits of clothing, and the three medals for goodness.''

"Were any of the little pigs killed?"

"No, they all escaped."

"The story began badly," said the smaller of the two girls, "but it had a beautiful ending."

"It is the most beautiful story that I ever heard," said the bigger of the small girls, with immense decision.

"It is the *only* beautiful story I have ever heard," said Cyril.

A dissentient opinion came from the aunt.

"A most improper story to tell to young children! You have undermined the effect of years of careful teaching."

"At any rate," said the bachelor, collecting his belongings preparatory to leaving the carriage, "I kept them quiet for ten minutes, which was more than you were able to do."

"Unhappy woman!" he observed to himself as he walked down the platform of Templecombe station. "For the next six months or so those children will assail her in public with demands for an improper story!" □□

Discussion

1. Describe the setting and the circumstances that bring these people together.

2. (a) What sort of story does the aunt tell to keep the children quiet? **(b)** Discuss whether the aunt's story had a stereotyped plot and characters. How can you tell? **(c)** How do the children react to the aunt's story? Why?

3. (a) Why does the bachelor tell the children a story? **(b)** In the bachelor's story, is Bertha a stereotyped character? Explain. **(c)** What elements of a stereotyped plot are there in the bachelor's story? **(d)** What elements are there in the bachelor's story that appear to be deliberate violations of a stereotype?

4. (a) "The story began badly," says one girl, "but it had a beautiful ending." Why do the children think the bachelor's story began badly? **(b)** Why do they think it had a beautiful ending?

5. (a) While the bachelor is telling the story, how does the aunt regard his storytelling abilities? **(b)** How does she react to the end of the story? Why? **(c)** What does the aunt seem to believe the purpose of children's stories should be? Do you agree or disagree? Explain.

6. Discuss whether the bachelor actually is a good storyteller or not.

7. (a) Does the bachelor's story have any sort of moral, or lesson? If so, what is it? **(b)** How does Mark Twain's saying "The hardest thing to endure is a good example" apply to "The Storyteller"?

8. Do you find any elements of stereotypes in the bachelor, Cyril, the aunt, or the two girls? Explain.

Extension • Writing

In the beginning of the story, the bachelor says nothing out loud. What thoughts do you imagine are going through his mind, however? Is he amused by the children's behavior, or annoyed? How does he react to the aunt's story?

If the bachelor were keeping a journal of his experiences, how do you imagine he would describe this train ride? Write an entry from the bachelor's journal, an account of his thoughts and feelings during the trip. Write it in the first person ("I") as if you were the bachelor.

H. H. Munro   1870 • 1916

The bachelor in the train compartment who delights the children but confounds their aunt could almost be H(ector) H(ugh) Munro himself, one of the world's master storytellers. His tales, which often blend humor with an element of gruesomeness, and frequently contain characters who play tricks on each other, usually end in a surprising way.

"Saki," the name of a character who, in a twelfth-century Persian poem, carries wine to guests seated on the lawn, is Munro's pen name. Born in Burma, he was educated in England, and traveled throughout Europe. He published his first collection of short stories in 1904.

Do you know how to get to that special place . . . ?

Where the Sidewalk Ends

Shel Silverstein

There is a place where the sidewalk ends
And before the street begins,
And there the grass grows soft and white,
And there the sun burns crimson bright,
5 And there the moon-bird rests from his flight
To cool in the peppermint wind.

Let us leave this place where the smoke blows black
And the dark street winds and bends.
Past the pits where the asphalt flowers grow
10 We shall walk with a walk that is measured and slow,
And watch where the chalk-white arrows go
To the place where the sidewalk ends.

Yes we'll walk with a walk that is measured and slow,
And we'll go where the chalk-white arrows go,
15 For the children, they mark, and the children, they know
The place where the sidewalk ends.

Discussion

1. (a) What do you find in "this place" you are leaving? (b) What has caused these conditions?

2. In the "place where the sidewalk ends / And before the street begins," what is different about the grass, the sun, birds, and the wind?

3. What are the chalk-white arrows spoken of in stanzas 2 and 3?

4. (a) Who are the leaders to this special place where the sidewalk ends? (b) What do you think qualifies them as leaders?

5. What might the speaker be saying about our society today?

6. (a) Does the poem have a regular pattern of rhyme? If so, point it out. (b) Discuss whether the poem has a regular pattern of rhythm. (c) The poem speaks of walking in a certain way. Does the rhythm of the poem seem appropriate to this movement? Explain.

7. What do you think is the place "where the sidewalk ends"?

You're Imagining Things

Worlds of the Imagination—Oz, Wonderland, Tartarus, Never-Never Land, where the sidewalk ends, in the wabe, on the moon, twenty thousand leagues under the sea, aboard a starship—these worlds are too many to number. Imagination can transform a castle, a forest, a railway carriage, a biology lab—or your own backyard.

Human beings are capable of forming mental images of things not actually present—with wondrous consequences. Skyscrapers, airplanes, television—in fact, all of the developments of technology that make our modern world comfortable—were imagined in various forms long before the actual inventions. The Astronauts of Apollo II were the first men actually to set foot on the moon, but still they had lots of company. People imagined going to the moon and told stories about what they would find there for centuries before that actual first landing in July, 1969.

Imagination is a basic and natural human activity. When it is applied in one way—to technology—it can make truly amazing inventions possible. When it is applied in another way—to art—it can make the no-longer-possible or the not-yet-possible *seem* possible. It can create fantasy.

Animal fables, fairy tales, ghost stories, horror tales, and science fiction all have their place in fantasy. In fantasy, we can hear a magical dove speaking with the voice of the Lady Columba, we can share the thoughts and feelings of the mongoose, Rikki-tikki-tavi, we can beware the horrible monster called the Jabberwock—and cheer the hero who brings back its head.

Because fantasy is not "real," however, some people think it is not serious—even that it is childish. Yet, when you read a modern realistic story, or watch a television or movie dramatization, you generally do not remind yourself that the policewoman or the cowboy or even the space travelers are just actors speaking words written for them. For the time being you simply accept them. Not unless something goes wrong or something attracts your attention by not fitting in somehow, do you think about how real or unreal it is.

The same thing is true of literature in general, and the same thing is true of fantasy. While you are experiencing it, it *is* real. As a reader or viewer, you enter into a kind of cooperation with the writer or actors. Together you create another world altogether, a world with its own facts and its own rules. Sometimes these created worlds share a great deal with the world you live in outside the story. Sometimes they are strange and unusual in almost every aspect.

Perhaps fantasy has often been associated with small children because they seem more willing to accept a new set of rules for as long as the story lasts. But there is nothing childish about fantasy. Fantasy may be amusing, exciting, or frightening. Fantasy may include glorious adventures and happy endings, but it also may include grief and suffering and sometimes death.

Furthermore, fantasy can and often does concern itself with serious and important questions: What is intelligence? What different forms can communication between living things take on? What does it mean to be a human being? Do people have the right to use and perhaps destroy the animals and resources of this planet? What is the difference between life and death?

Through questions such as these, fantasy has the power to make us look at our own world with new eyes. We see reality differently—more freshly, and with more appreciation—after it has been enriched by fantasy.

Most people left the old man strictly alone—
and with good reason!

Get That Straight

Sabine R. Ulibarri

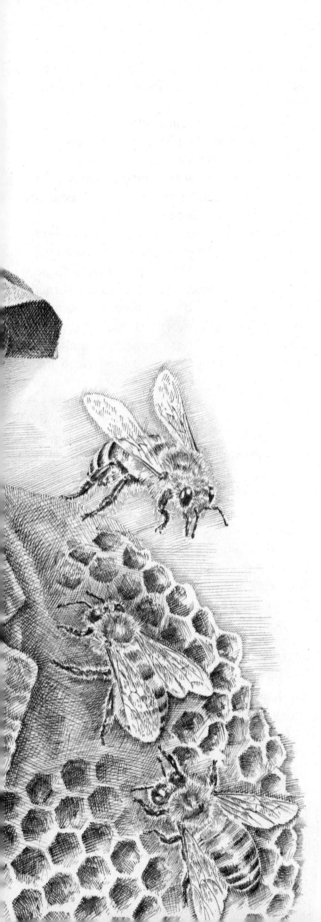

Don José Viejo[1] (Old Mister Joe) was more ancient than hunger. He was so tiny and so fragile that it hurt you to look at him. The sun or old age or knowledge of life had burned his skin till it was almost black. He shambled around town with his hat pulled down over his ears and his shoulders hunched foward, moving with tiny steps that reminded me of the hopping of birds. Everyone called him Don José Viejo.

On the street, loafers, louts, and children left him strictly alone. The old fellow was sharp and had a tongue of such razor-edged steel that several smart alecks had found themselves pinned to the wall and bleeding, the butt of the jokes and laughter of their companions, without even knowing how it happened. Everybody knew this. The old man knew it, too. He had open passage wherever he went.

I don't remember that he had any family. He lived alone in a miserable little hut that was cleaner than the bones of the desert. And he dressed fairly well—I don't know how. I remember that many times the old fellow invited me to his house and gave me meat pies, sugared cheese, jerky, and other things that the children of my time liked very much. Sometimes he told me stories of the old days, stories of Indians, of wild beasts in the forest, of cowboys.

On one occasion, he told me how he had fought a bear hand to hand. How, being so small, he had curled himself up under one arm of the monster so that the animal could neither crush nor bite him. How from underneath he had thrust his knife again and again

"Get That Straight" from *Tierra Amarilla: Stories of New Mexico* by Sabine R. Ulibarri, trans. by Thelma Campbell Nason, English translation copyrighted © 1971 by the University of New Mexico Press.

Sabine Ulibarri (ü lē bär′rē).

1. **Don José Viejo** (dôn hô se′ vē e′hô).

into the belly of the brute until it fell. A nine-year-old boy listening in open-mouthed amazement, I believed everything he told me. It was not necessary that he should prove his story. However, moved by some obscure impulse, Mister Joe took off his shirt and showed me his back. Today, after so many years, I still remember with frightening clarity the scars he bore. The claw marks, where the bear had torn away the living flesh, were indicated by several series of four irregular lines. It was a grillwork of scars. From that day on, I had an almost religious respect for Mister Joe.

Old Mister Joe used to come to my house every day, always carrying a little pail. My mother gave him a daily bucket of milk, for we had more than we needed. Perhaps it was because the old man was so kind to me, or because he had once been one of our shepherds, or simply because he was Mister Joe. I never knew why.

At that time we had a great many bees. The bee hives were on a bank beside the alfalfa field, because people said the best honey came from alfalfa blossoms. The hives could be clearly seen from the kitchen window. When the time came to gather the honey, the workmen put on two pairs of trousers, a jacket, and thick gloves. On their heads, they wore something like a bucket of woven wire. They looked like real monsters. A black cloud emerged as they uncovered the hives and buzzed about them all the time they were filling the buckets they carried. I watched them from a distance, very much impressed.

One winter a friend and I were out hunting birds with our slingshots. The ground was covered with frozen snow, so that we could walk on its surface. We found ourselves near the beehives. The idea occurred to us to go and eat some honey. I don't remember whether the big boxes were left out every winter or whether this was unusual.

When we got quite close, we stopped with some apprehension, for we knew very well what the bees could do. We discussed the situation for a while and decided that the bees must either be numbed by the cold or asleep, for everything was quiet.

I was the one who opened the box. Taking off the top, hearing the menacing buzz, and seeing the swarm were all one. Instantly the black, pointed cloud surged from the mouth of the hive and headed straight for the intruders, already in precipitate flight. The force of our pounding feet broke through the frozen snow which had supported us before, and we sank up to our belts. We kept running and struggling in despair, victims of a panic terror.

From time to time, I gave a quick glance over my shoulder without daring to take a good look. The sight of the thick black threat made me redouble my efforts. I don't know how long it took us to realize that the bees were not overtaking us. Perhaps it was when we fell exhausted in a drift.

We saw then that the mobile black cloud had descended and was lying motionless on the snow. When they came in contact with the cold air, the bees had become sluggish, then numb, and had finally fallen on the white, inhospitable surface.

We were a long time understanding what had happened and even longer in recognizing and admitting what a cruel thing we had done. There, scattered over the snow like raisins in rice, were the dead or dying bees. My first impulse was to gather them up and put them back into the hives, but it was obviously too late for that.

We did not say anything. We went back home in silence. Over the surface of the snow again. Honey, birds, and slings were forgotten. I did not look at my friend. He did not look at me. I suspect that it was because we both had something to hide. Out of the corner of my eye, I saw him dig at his eyes with the thick sleeve of his winter jacket. My wet cheeks were burning in the cold afternoon breeze.

Old Mister Joe visited the beehives, too. We used to see him pass with his little pail. He went to the hives, helped himself, and came back with the pail full. I am sure he did not have permission, but, as I said, the old fellow had, or assumed, special privileges. Since the loss was so insignificant, and since we would have given him the honey anyway, my father let him alone.

I already had a somewhat superstitious veneration for Mister Joe on account of his conquering bears and knowing so many unusual things. But the thing that astonished me most was that the bees did not sting him. I had seen him among the hives without any protection at all, tranquilly filling his pail while the dizzying swarm buzzed around his ears and the individual bees crawled over his hands and face. It seemed to me that he was talking to them. When his task was finished, he moved away with his birdlike step, absolutely calm.

This was a tremendous mystery for me. I used to wonder what quality of this man made it possible for him to face such terror and come out unscathed. This fact perplexed me even more than the business of the bear because I had had experience with bees. I speculated on the matter without ever reaching a solution. If I asked my father or the workmen, they would tell me that there are people like that. A statement which would tell me nothing at all.

One day when the old man came for milk, I was carried away by uncontrollable curiosity. Curbing the fear I had of him—as I have said the old fellow had an acid tongue—I decided to put the question to him.

"Listen, Don José, why don't the bees sting you?" I was very careful to omit the "Viejo."

"Well, boy, what do you think?"

"I don't know. I only know that they sting me and everybody else."

"I'd like to tell you, son. But it is a secret. Get that straight!"

"If you'll tell me, I won't tell anybody. I swear I won't. I'll swear on the Bible."

"Don't take holy things in vain, you bad-mannered brat!"

"Don't be mad, Don José. It is just that I wanted. . . . "

"All right, boy. But be very careful. . . . Do you really promise to keep the secret? You won't tell anyone, not even your father?"

"You can count on me, Don José." I felt very grown-up.

"Well, I'll tell you the truth. But I warn you that if you tell a single word of what I am going to say, the people of the valley will kill me. Then all the bees in the valley and the forest—and there are millions—will leave their hives and come down on Tierra Amarilla[2] like a fury to finish off all the people. Nothing will be left but bones. All that will happen because I am a bee. Get that straight!" His little eyes were dancing with glee.

"Don José Vie—I mean Don José. . . . " I had already repented of my action, but I did not know how to get out of the situation. The old man was off; there was no way to stop him.

"A long time ago, a fine, lively young

---

2. *Tierra Amarilla* (tyer′rä äm ä rē′yä).

fellow lived in a nearby town. There were two strange things about him. He was unusually fond of honey, and he loved bees. He liked them so much that he suffered a lot because men held them prisoners and stole their honey from them. Get that straight!

"The young man used to visit the bees and talk to them. Little by little he began to learn their language. They became great friends. He used to take them the most beautiful flowers from the garden, and they gave him the sweetest and richest honey anybody has ever seen.

"One day he took a notion to set his friends free. Get that straight! He began to whistle a strange melody, which the bees understood very well, and started out for the forest. The bees left their hives; they abandoned the alfalfa and the flowers and followed him, all humming the unusual melody that the young man was whistling. The world of men was filled with sound, shadow, and fear.

"The young man searched out the most hidden spot in the forest and there, in a tree which seemed suitable, he hived the bees. After that, he used to go from town to town whistling that same melody until there wasn't a single prisoner bee—get that!—in all this country. For many, many years there was no honey for toast nor for colds and coughs in the world of men.

"As you know, bees have a queen, the mother of all the bees. She is the biggest and most beautiful of them all. Well—now get this!—the queen fell in love with the young man. One day she settled on his lips and kissed him. So the young man became a bee and married the queen. And he died because the lovers of the queen must always die. Get that straight.

"That young man was my father. The queen bee was my mother. I was born in the forest among the bees. They brought me up. I am their brother. Get that straight! If you had looked closely, you would have seen the two little wings I have on my back. Look at me now and you will see that I look like a bee." And he was right!

"Now you understand why the bees don't sting me, why I talk to them. Now you'll understand the scars I have on my back. Bears are my worst enemies. They have followed me all my life. They want to suck my blood. They know what no man in the world knows—now get this!—that I do not have blood in my veins. They know that I am a bee and have honey instead."

The great bee rose from his perch. He picked up his bucket of milk. He fixed me with a beelike gaze.

"Remember, boy, what I told you. Not a single word! Get that straight!"

He went away with his tiny steps. I sat there trembling. I knew that Don José Viejo never lied. □□

Discussion

1. (a) How is Don José regarded by the villagers, in general? (b) What of the old man's speech and behavior causes them to regard him in this way? (c) How is he regarded by the narrator?

2. (a) How does Don José treat the narrator, in general? (b) What story does Don José tell about fighting a bear? (c) What proof does he offer that his story is true?

3. (a) What is remarkable about Don José's gathering honey? (b) How do the villagers explain Don José's apparent power over bees?

4. (a) What story does the narrator tell about the encounter he and a friend have with bees? (b) How does the narrator feel about bees after this encounter? (c) How does he feel about himself?

5. (a) Under what circumstances does Don José tell the narrator his story about bees? (b) What proof does he have of the truth of this story? (c) How much of this story does the narrator believe? Why?

6. (a) What does truth or falsehood have to do with telling a good story? (b) What do they have to do with the stories Don José tells the narrator? (c) Might Don José have had some further purpose in telling the story of why bees treat him as they do? Explain.

Vocabulary
Structure, Pronunciation, Dictionary

Copy the vocabulary words below on your paper. In column I, underline the prefix in each word. Underline the suffix in each word in Column II (you do not need to do anything about the spelling changes). Then underline with two lines the main accented or stressed syllable in each word. Be sure you know the meanings of all the words. Use your Glossary if you need help.

I.	II.
inhospitable	veneration
redouble	tranquilly
insignificant	apprehension
irregular	sluggish
unscathed	

Extension • Speaking

Don José Viejo told the story of the young man who freed bees by whistling a strange melody and having the bees follow him. This may remind you of another story in which a piped melody was followed by rats and then by children. In what ways are "The Pied Piper of Hamelin" and Don José Viejo's bee story alike? In what ways are they different?

Sabine Ulibarri

Isolated high in the northern mountains of New Mexico, the adobe town of Tierra Amarilla lies cradled in a valley. Here, Sabine Ulibarri spent his boyhood on his family's ranch, surrounded by traditions stretching back to when his ancestors entered New Mexico centuries ago with the Spanish soldiers and settlers. Later, he left to travel and study in Europe and Latin America. Today, he is a professor of Spanish literature at the University of New Mexico. He has written short stories, poetry, and biography.

At one time, Ulibarri fascinated his friends by telling them stories. Some of these listeners insisted he write these stories. "Get That Straight" is one of these stories found in the book *Tierra Amarilla*, named after his town. He has tried to write all the stories from his own viewpoint as a small boy.

A man can teach a robot about music,
but what can a robot teach a man about life?

Virtuoso

Herbert Goldstone

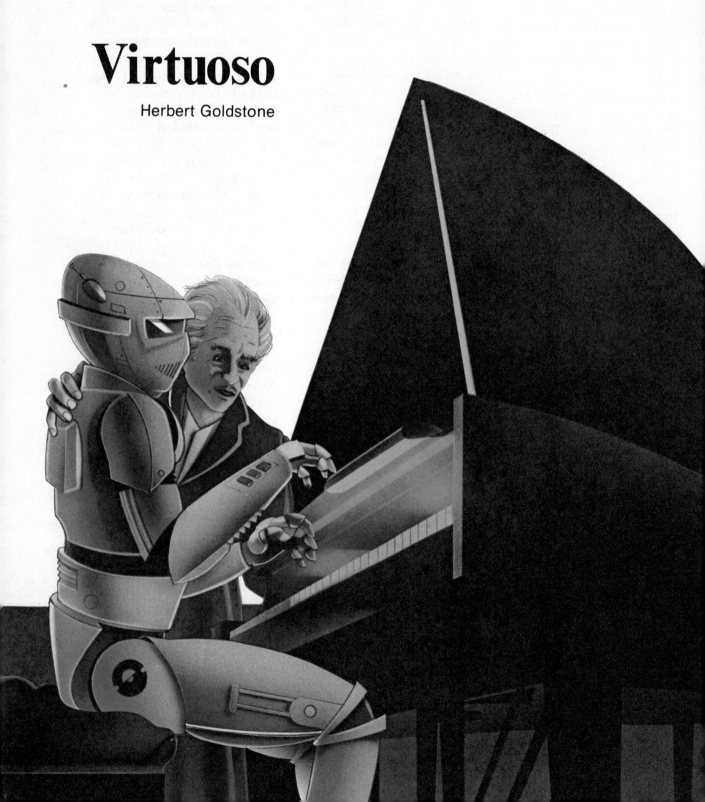

"Sir?"

The Maestro[1] continued to play, not looking up from the keys.

"Yes, Rollo?"

"Sir, I was wondering if you would explain this apparatus to me."

The Maestro stopped playing, his thin body stiffly relaxed on the bench. His long supple fingers floated off the keyboard.

"Apparatus?" He turned and smiled at the robot. "Do you mean the piano, Rollo?"

"This machine that produces varying sounds. I would like some information about it, its operation and purpose. It is not included in my reference data."

The Maestro lit a cigarette. He preferred to do it himself. One of his first orders to Rollo when the robot was delivered two days before had been to disregard his built-in instructions on the subject.

"I'd hardly call a piano a machine, Rollo," he smiled, "although technically you are correct. It is actually, I suppose, a machine designed to produce sounds of graduated pitch and tone, singly or in groups."

"I assimilated that much by observation," Rollo replied in a brassy baritone which no longer sent tiny tremors up the Maestro's spine. "Wires of different thickness and tautness struck by felt-covered hammers activated by manually operated levers arranged in a horizontal panel."

"A very cold-blooded description of one of man's nobler works," the Maestro remarked dryly. "You make Mozart and Chopin[2] mere laboratory technicians."

"Mozart? Chopin?" The duralloy sphere that was Rollo's head shone stark and featureless, its immediate surface unbroken but for twin vision lenses. "The terms are not included in my memory banks."

"No, not yours, Rollo," the Maestro said softly. "Mozart and Chopin are not for vacuum tubes and fuses and copper wire. They are for flesh and blood and human tears."

"I do not understand," Rollo droned.

"Well," the Maestro said, smoke curling lazily from his nostrils, "they are two of the humans who compose, or design successions of notes—varying sounds, that is, produced by the piano or by other instruments, machines that produce other types of sounds of fixed pitch and tone.

"Sometimes these instruments, as we call them, are played, or operated, individually: sometimes in groups—orchestras, as we refer to them—and the sounds blend together, they harmonize. That is, they have an orderly, mathematical relationship to each other which results in. . . ."

The Maestro threw up his hands.

"I never imagined," he chuckled, "that I would some day struggle so mightily, and so futilely, to explain music to a robot!"

"Music?"

"Yes, Rollo. The sounds produced by

"Virtuoso" by Herbert Goldstone. Reprinted by permission of the author.

1. **Maestro** (mī′strō), a master composer or teacher of music. [Italian]

2. **Mozart** (möt′särt) **and Chopin** (shō′pan), Wolfgang Amadeus Mozart (1756–1791), an Austrian composer, and Frederic Chopin (1810–1849), a Polish composer and pianist. Both are known for their keyboard compositions.

this machine and others of the same category are called music."

"What is the purpose of music, sir?"

"Purpose?"

The Maestro crushed the cigarette in an ash tray. He turned to the keyboard of the concert grand and flexed his fingers briefly.

"Listen, Rollo."

The wraithlike fingers glided and wove the opening bars of "Clair de Lune,"[3] slender and delicate as spider silk. Rollo stood rigid, the fluorescent light over the music rack casting a bluish jeweled sheen over his towering bulk, shimmering in the amber vision lenses.

The Maestro drew his hands back from the keys and the subtle thread of melody melted reluctantly into silence.

"Claude Debussy,"[4] the Maestro said. "One of our mechanics of an era long past. He designed that succession of tones many years ago. What do you think of it?"

Rollo did not answer at once.

"The sounds were well formed," he replied finally. "They did not jar my auditory senses as some do."

The Maestro laughed. "Rollo, you may not realize it, but you're a wonderful critic."

"This music, then," Rollo droned. "Its purpose is to give pleasure to humans?"

"Exactly," the Maestro said. "Sounds well formed, that do not jar the auditory senses as some do. Marvelous! It should be carved in marble over the entrance of New Carnegie Hall."[5]

"I do not understand. Why should my definition—?"

The Maestro waved a hand. "No matter, Rollo. No matter."

"Sir?"

"Yes, Rollo?"

"Those sheets of paper you sometimes place before you on the piano. They are the plans of the composer indicating which sounds are to be produced by the piano and in what order?"

"Just so. We call each sound a note; combinations of notes we call chords."

"Each dot, then, indicates a sound to be made?"

"Perfectly correct, my man of metal."

Rollo stared straight ahead. The Maestro felt a peculiar sense of wheels turning within that impregnable sphere.

"Sir, I have scanned my memory banks and find no specific or implied instructions against it. I should like to be taught how to produce these notes on the piano. I request that you feed the correlation between those dots and the levers of the panel into my memory banks."

The Maestro peered at him, amazed. A slow grin traveled across his face.

"Done!" he exclaimed. "It's been many years since pupils helped gray these ancient locks, but I have the feeling that you, Rollo, will prove a most fascinating student. To instill the Muse[6] into metal and machinery . . . I accept the challenge gladly!" He rose, touched the cool latent power of Rollo's arm.

"Sit down here, my Rolleindex Personal Robot, Model M-e. We shall start Beethoven[7] spinning in his grave—or make musical history."

More than an hour later the Maestro yawned and looked at his watch.

"It's late," he spoke into the end of the yawn. "These old eyes are not tireless like

<hr />

3. *"Clair de Lune"* (kler′ də lün′), a piano composition whose French title means "moonlight."
4. *Claude Debussy* (də byü′sē), French composer (1862–1918).
5. *Carnegie* (kär′nə gē) *Hall*, a historic and world-famous concert hall in New York City.
6. *the Muse* (myüz), one of the nine Greek goddesses of the fine arts and sciences. Here, the expression is extended to mean musical inspiration in general.
7. *Beethoven* (bā′tō vən), Ludwig van Beethoven (1770–1827), a German composer.

yours, my friend." He touched Rollo's shoulder. "You have the complete fundamentals of musical notation in your memory banks, Rollo. That's a good night's lesson, particularly when I recall how long it took me to acquire the same amount of information. Tomorrow we'll attempt to put those awesome fingers of yours to work."

He stretched. "I'm going to bed," he said. "Will you lock up and put out the lights?"

Rollo rose from the bench. "Yes, sir," he droned. "I have a request."

"What can I do for my star pupil?"

"May I attempt to create some sounds with the keyboard tonight? I will do so very softly so as not to disturb you."

"Tonight? Aren't you—?" Then the Maestro smiled. "You must pardon me, Rollo. It's still a bit difficult for me to realize that sleep has no meaning for you."

He hesitated, rubbing his chin. "Well, I suppose a good teacher should not discourage impatience to learn. All right, Rollo, but please be careful." He patted the polished mahogany. "This piano and I have been together for many years. I'd hate to see its teeth knocked out by those sledgehammer digits of yours. Lightly, my friend, very lightly."

"Yes, sir."

The Maestro fell asleep with a faint smile on his lips, dimly aware of the shy, tentative notes that Rollo was coaxing forth.

Then gray fog closed in and he was in that half-world where reality is dreamlike and dreams are real. It was soft and feathery and lavender clouds and sounds were rolling and washing across his mind in flowing waves.

Where? The mist drew back a bit and he was in red velvet and deep and the music swelled and broke over him.

He smiled.

My recording. Thank you, thank you, thank—

The Maestro snapped erect, threw the covers aside.

He sat on the edge of the bed, listening.

He groped for his robe in the darkness, shoved bony feet into his slippers.

He crept, trembling uncontrollably, to the door of his studio and stood there, thin and brittle in the robe.

The light over the music rack was an eerie island in the brown shadows of the studio. Rollo sat at the keyboard, prim, inhuman, rigid, twin lenses focused somewhere off into the shadows.

The massive feet working the pedals, arms and hands flashing and glinting—they were living entities, separate, somehow, from the machined perfection of his body.

The music rack was empty.

A copy of Beethoven's "Appassionata"[8] lay closed on the bench. It had been, the Maestro remembered, in a pile of sheet music on the piano.

Rollo was playing it.

He was creating it, breathing it, drawing it through silver flame.

Time became meaningless, suspended in midair.

The Maestro didn't realize he was weeping until Rollo finished the sonata.

The robot turned to look at the Maestro. "The sounds," he droned. "They pleased you?"

The Maestro's lips quivered. "Yes, Rollo," he replied at last. "They pleased me." He fought the lump in his throat.

He picked up the music in fingers that shook.

"This," he murmured. "Already?"

---

8. *"Appassionata"* (ä päs′yō nä′tä), a musical composition so nicknamed because of its feeling of passion, or strong emotion.

"It has been added to my store of data," Rollo replied. "I applied the principles you explained to me to these plans. It was not very difficult."

The Maestro swallowed as he tried to speak. "It was not very difficult. . . ." he repeated softly.

The old man sank down slowly onto the bench next to Rollo, stared silently at the robot as though seeing him for the first time.

Rollo got to his feet.

The Maestro let his fingers rest on the keys, strangely foreign now.

"Music!" he breathed. "I may have heard it that way in my soul. I know Beethoven did!"

He looked up at the robot, a growing excitement in his face.

"Rollo," he said, his voice straining to remain calm. "You and I have some work to do tomorrow on your memory banks."

Sleep did not come again that night.

He strode briskly into the studio the next morning. Rollo was vacuuming the carpet. The Maestro preferred carpets to the new dust-free plastics, which felt somehow profane to his feet.

The Maestro's house was, in fact, an oasis of anachronisms in a desert of contemporary antiseptic efficiency.

"Well, are you ready for work, Rollo?" he asked. "We have a lot to do, you and I. I have such plans for you, Rollo—great plans!"

Rollo, for once, did not reply.

"I have asked them all to come here this afternoon," the Maestro went on. "Conductors, concert pianists, composers, my manager. All the giants of music, Rollo. Wait until they hear you play."

Rollo switched off the vacuum and stood quietly.

"You'll play for them right here this afternoon." The Maestro's voice was high-pitched, breathless. "The 'Appassionata' again, I think. Yes, that's it. I must see their faces!

"Then we'll arrange a recital to introduce you to the public and the critics and then a major concert with one of the big orchestras. We'll have it telecast around the world, Rollo. It can be arranged.

"Think of it, Rollo, just think of it! The greatest piano virtuoso of all time . . . a robot! It's completely fantastic and completely wonderful. I feel like an explorer at the edge of a new world."

He walked feverishly back and forth.

"Then recordings, of course. My entire repertoire, Rollo, and more. So much more!"

"Sir?"

The Maestro's face shone as he looked up at him. "Yes, Rollo?"

"In my built-in instructions, I have the option of rejecting any action which I consider harmful to my owner," the robot's words were precise, carefully selected. "Last night you wept. That is one of the indications I am instructed to consider in making my decisions."

The Maestro gripped Rollo's thick, superbly molded arm.

"Rollo, you don't understand. That was for the moment. It was petty of me, childish!"

"I beg your pardon, sir, but I must refuse to approach the piano again."

The Maestro stared at him, unbelieving, pleading.

"Rollo, you can't! The world must hear you!"

"No, sir." The amber lenses almost seemed to soften.

"The piano is not a machine," that powerful inhuman voice droned. "To me, yes. I can translate the notes into sounds at a glance. From only a few I am able to grasp at once the composer's conception. It is easy for me."

Rollo towered magnificently over the Maestro's bent form.

"I can also grasp," the brassy monotone rolled through the studio, "that this . . . music is not for robots. It is for man. To me it is easy, yes . . . . It was not meant to be easy." □□

Discussion

1. (a) Why does the Maestro object when Rollo refers to the piano as a *machine* and an *apparatus?* **(b)** Why does he agree to teach Rollo about music?

2. (a) What are the Maestro's first reactions to hearing Rollo play? **(b)** Why does he weep? **(c)** Why do you think he wants Rollo to perform in public?

3. (a) Why does Rollo reject the Maestro's plan for him? **(b)** Is Rollo's refusal emotional or mechanical? Explain. **(c)** Read the article by Herbert Goldstone on this page. Do you think Rollo actually does manage to protect the Maestro's vanity by refusing to perform in public? Explain. **(d)** Can you think of any circumstances that might have allowed Rollo to play, and yet would not have gone against his built-in instructions? Discuss such circumstances.

4. Which of the following sentences best states the theme of the story? Give reasons for your choice. **(a)** Robots will be common objects in the future. **(b)** True art is the result of human pain and struggle. **(c)** Machines can produce greater art than humans can.

5. With which of the following statements about the theme do you agree most? Explain your reasons. **(a)** Fantasy is the only really successful way to present this theme. **(b)** The same theme might have been expressed in any number of ways, including fantasy. **(c)** The theme would have been better expressed by some means other than fantasy.

Extension • Speaking

When the Maestro weeps upon hearing Rollo play, the robot assumes the tears are an indication of possible harm to his owner. In keeping with his built-in instructions to reject actions that he considers harmful to his owner, Rollo refuses to continue playing. Would the Maestro agree with these built-in instructions? Do you agree? Can you think of circumstances where weeping might be an indication not of harm, but of good? Share with the class examples from your reading, from movies or television, or from personal experiences.

Herbert Goldstone

Of "Virtuoso," Herbert Goldstone says, "Originally, I toyed with the notion of a story about a famous concert pianist who had hurt his hands and tried to fake a performance by having records play off stage while he pretended to play at the keyboard. For one reason or another, it just didn't jell and, without warning, my old love for science fiction stepped in and took over. . . . The idea of a robot learning to play a piano and becoming an instant master just hit me and the story wrote itself. . . .

"Music is big in the Goldstone family, and I wrote with some amateurish familiarity with the subject. I'm not familiar with robots, but neither is anyone else, so I felt on safe grounds. That's one advantage to imaginative fiction. Nobody can argue with you.

"In a way, I was sorry the story ended the way it did. Rollo was understandably out to protect the Maestro's vanity, but it would have been great to see Rollo perform with the New York Philharmonic. Oh, well."

See **INFERENCES** Handbook of Literary Terms

He claimed people wanted
to watch him break his neck.
Was he right?

The Fallen Angel

Evan Hunter

He first came in one morning while I was making out the payroll for my small circus. We were pulling up stakes, ready to roll on to the next town, and I was bent over the books, writing down what I was paying everybody, and maybe that is why I did not hear the door open. When I looked up, this long, lanky fellow was standing there, and the door was shut tight behind him.

I looked at the door, and then I looked at him. He had a thin face with a narrow mustache, and black hair on his head that was sort of wild and sticking up in spots. He had brown eyes and a funny, twisted sort of mouth, with very white teeth which he was showing me at the moment.

"Mr. Mullins?" he asked.

"Yes," I said, because that is my name. Not Moon Mullins, which a lot of the fellows jokingly call me, but Anthony Mullins. And that is my real name, with no attempt to sound showmanlike; a good name, you will admit. "I am busy."

"I won't take much time," he said very softly. He walked over to the desk with a smooth, sideward step, as if he were on greased ball bearings.

"No matter how much time you will take," I said, "I am still busy."

"My name is Sam Angeli,"[1] he said.

"Pleased to meet you, Mr. Angeli," I told him. "My name is Anthony Mullins, and I am sorry you must be running along so quickly, but . . ."

"I'm a trapeze artist," he said.

"We already have three trapeze artists," I informed him, "and they are all excellent performers, and the budget does not call for . . ."

---

1. *Angeli* (anʹjə lē).

"They are not Sam Angeli," he said, smiling and touching his chest with his thumb.

"That is true," I answered. "They are, in alphabetical order: Sue Ellen Bradley, Edward the Great and Arthur Farnings."

"But not Sam Angeli," he repeated softly.

"No," I said. "It would be difficult to call them all Sam Angeli since they are not even related, and even if they were related, it is unlikely they would all have the same name—even if they were triplets, which they are not."

"*I* am Sam Angeli," he said.

"So I have gathered. But I already have three . . ."

"I'm better," he said flatly.

"I have never met a trapeze artist who was not better than any other trapeze artist in the world," I said.

"In my case it happens to be true," he said.

I nodded and said nothing. I chewed my cigar awhile and went back to my books, and when I looked up he was still standing there, smiling.

"Look, my friend," I said, "I am earnestly sorry there is no opening for you, but . . ."

"Why not watch me a little?"

"I am too busy."

"It'll take five minutes. Your big top is still standing. Just watch me up there for a few minutes, that's all."

"My friend, what would be the point? I already have . . ."

"You can take your books with you, Mr. Mullins; you won't be sorry."

I looked at him again, and he stared at me levelly, and he had a deep, almost blazing, way of staring that made me believe I would really not be sorry if I watched him perform. Besides, I could take the books with me.

"All right," I said, "but we're only wasting each other's time."

"I've got all the time in the world," he answered.

We went outside, and sure enough the big top was still standing, so I bawled out Warren for being so slow to get a show on the road, and then this Angeli and I went inside, and he looked up at the trapeze, and I very sarcastically said, "Is that high enough for you?"

He shrugged and looked up and said, "I've been higher, my friend. Much higher." He dropped his eyes to the ground then, and I saw that the net had already been taken up.

"This exhibition will have to be postponed," I informed him. "There is no net."

"I don't need a net," he answered.

"No?"

"No."

"Do you plan on breaking your neck under one of my tops? I am warning you that my insurance doesn't cover . . ."

"I won't break my neck," Angeli said. "Sit down."

I shrugged and sat down, thinking it was his neck and not mine. I opened the books on my lap and got to work, and he walked across the tent and started climbing up to the trapeze. I got involved with the figures, and finally he yelled, "Okay, you ready?"

"I'm ready," I said.

I looked up to where he was sitting on one trapeze, holding the bar of the other trapeze in his big hands.

"Here's the idea," he yelled down. He had to yell because he was a good hundred feet in the air. "I'll set the second trapeze swinging, and then I'll put the one I'm on in motion. Then I'll jump from one trapeze to the other one. Understand?"

"I understand," I yelled back. I'm a quiet man by nature, and I have never liked yelling.

Besides, he was about to do a very elementary trapeze routine, so there was nothing to get excited and yelling about.

He pushed out the second trapeze, and it swung away out in a nice clean arc, and then it came back and he shoved it out again and it went out farther and higher this time. He set his own trapeze in motion then, and both trapezes went swinging up there, back and forth, back and forth, higher and higher. He stood up on the bar and watched the second trapeze, timing himself, and then he shouted down, "I'll do a somersault to make it interesting."

"Go ahead," I said.

"Here I go," he said.

His trapeze came back and started forward, and the second trapeze reached the end of its arc and started back, and I saw him bend a little from the knees, calculating his timing, and then he leaped off, and his head ducked under, and he went into the somersault.

He did a nice clean roll, and then he stretched out his hands for the bar of the second trapeze, but the bar was nowhere near him. His fingers closed on air, and my eyes popped wide open as he sailed past the trapeze and then started a nose dive for the ground.

I jumped to my feet with my mouth open, remembering there was no net under him, and thinking of the mess he was going to make all over my tent. I watched him falling like a stone, and then I closed my eyes as he came closer to the ground. I clenched my fists and waited for the crash, and then the crash came, and there was a deathly silence in the tent afterward. I sighed and opened my eyes.

Sam Angeli got up and casually brushed the sawdust from his clothes. "How'd you like it?" he asked.

I stood stiff as a board and stared at him.

"How'd you like it?" he repeated.

"Dr. Lipsky!" I shouted. "Doc, come quick!"

"No need for a doctor," Angeli said, smiling and walking over to me. "How'd you like the fall?"

"The . . . the fall?"

"The fall," Angeli said, smiling. "Looked like the real McCoy, didn't it?"

"What do you mean?"

"Well, you don't think I missed that bar accidentally, do you? I mean, after all, that's a kid stunt."

"You fell on purpose?" I kept staring at him, but all his bones seemed to be in the right places, and there was no blood on him anywhere.

"Sure," he said. "My specialty. I figured it all out, Mr. Mullins. Do you know why people like to watch trapeze acts? Not because there's any skill or art attached. Oh, no." He smiled, and his eyes glowed, and I watched him, still amazed. "They like to watch because they are inherently evil, Mr. Mullins. They watch because they think that fool up there is going to fall and break his neck, and they want to be around when he does it." Angeli nodded. "So I figured it all out."

"You did?"

"I did. I figured if the customers wanted to see me fall, then I would fall. So I practiced falling."

"You did?"

"I did. First I fell out of bed, and then I fell from a first-story window, and then I fell off the roof. And then I took my biggest fall, the fall that . . . But I'm boring you. The point is, I can fall from any place now. In fact, that trapeze of yours is rather low."

"Rather low," I repeated softly.

"Yes."

"What's up?" Dr. Lipsky shouted, rushing into the tent, his shirttails trailing. "What happened, Moon?"

"Nothing," I said, wagging my head. "Nothing, Doc."

"Then why'd you . . . ?"

"I wanted to tell you," I said slowly, "that I've just hired a new trapeze artist."

We rolled on to the next town, and I introduced Angeli to my other trapeze artists: Sue Ellen, Farnings, and Edward the Great. I told them I wanted Angeli to have exclusive use of the tent that afternoon, and all afternoon I sat and watched him while he jumped for trapezes and missed and went flying down on his nose or his head or his back or whatever he landed on. I kept watching him when he landed, but the sawdust always came up around him like a big cloud, and I never could see what he did inside that cloud. All I know is that he got up every time, and he brushed himself off, and each time I went over to him and expected to find a hundred broken bones and maybe a fractured skull, but each time he just stood up with that handsome smile on his face as if he hadn't just fallen from away up there.

"This is amazing," I told him. "This is almost supernatural!"

"I know," he said.

"We'll start you tonight," I said, getting excited about it now. "Can you start tonight?"

"I can start any time," he said.

"Sam Angeli," I announced, spreading my hand across the air as if I were spelling it out in lights. "Sam An—" I paused and let my hand drop. "That's terrible," I said.

"I know," Angeli answered. "But I figured that out, too."

"What?"

"A name for me. I figured this all out."

"And what's the name?" I asked.

"The Fallen Angel," he said.

There wasn't much of a crowd that night. Sue Ellen, Farnings, and Edward the Great went up there and did their routines, but they were playing to cold fish, and you could have put all the applause they got into a sardine can. Except mine. Whenever I saw Sue Ellen, I clapped my heart out, and I never cared what the crowd was doing. I went out after Edward the Great wound up his act, and I said, "Ladeeeees and Gentulmennnn, it gives me great pleasure to introduce at this time, in his American première, for the first time in this country, the Fallen Angel!"

I don't know what I expected, but no one so much as batted an eyelid.

"You will note," I said, "that the nets are now being removed from beneath the trapezes, and that the trapezes are being raised to the uppermost portion of the tent. The Fallen Angel will perform at a height of one hundred and fifty feet above the ground, without benefit of a net, performing his death-defying feats of skill for your satisfaction."

The crowd murmured a little, but you could see they still weren't very excited about it all.

"And now," I shouted, "the Fallen Angel!"

Angeli came into the ring, long and thin, muscular in his red tights, the sequins shining so that they could almost blind you. He began climbing up to the bars, and everyone watched him, a little bored by now with all these trapeze acts. Angeli hopped aboard and then worked out a little, swinging to and fro, leaping from one trapeze to another, doing a few difficult stunts. He looked down to the band then, and Charlie started a roll on the drums, and I shouted into my megaphone, "And now, a blood-chilling, spine-tingling double somersault from one moving trapeze to another at one hundred and fifty feet above the ground—*without a net!*"

The crowd leaned forward a little, the way they always will when a snare drum starts rolling, and Angeli set the bars in motion, and then he tensed, with all the spotlights on him. The drum kept going, and then Angeli leaped into space, and he rolled over once, twice, and then his arms came out straight for the bar, and his hands clutched nothing, and he started to fall.

A woman screamed, and then they all were on their feet, a shocked roar leaping from four hundred throats all together. Angeli dropped and dropped and dropped, and women covered their eyes and screamed and brave men turned away, and then he hit the sawdust, and the cloud rolled up around him, and an *Ohhhhhhh* went up from the crowd. They kept standing, shocked, silent, like a bunch of pallbearers.

Then suddenly, casually, the Fallen Angel got to his feet and brushed off his red-sequined costume. He turned to the crowd and smiled a big, happy smile, and then he turned to face the other half of the tent, smiling again, extending his arms and hands to his public, almost as if he were silently saying, "My children! My nice children!"

The crowd cheered and whistled and shouted and stamped. Sue Ellen, standing next to me, sighed and said, "Tony, he's wonderful," and I heard her, and I heard the yells of "Encore!" out there, but I didn't bring Angeli out again that night. I tucked him away and then waited for the landslide.

The landslide came the next night. We were playing in a small town, but I think everyone who could walk turned out for the

show. They fidgeted through all the acts, crowding the tent, standing in the back, shoving and pushing. They were bored when my aerial artists went on, but the boredom was good because they were all waiting for the Fallen Angel, all waiting to see if the reports about him were true.

When I introduced him, there was no applause. There was only an awful hush. Angeli came out and climbed up to the bars and then began doing his tricks again, and everyone waited, having heard that he took his fall during the double somersault.

But Angeli was a supreme showman, and he realized that the value of his trick lay in its surprise element. So he didn't wait for the double somersault this time. He simply swung out one trapeze and then made a leap for it, right in the middle of his other routine

stunts, only this time he missed, and down he dropped with the crowd screaming to its feet.

A lot of people missed the fall, and that was the idea, because those same people came back the next night, and Angeli never did it the same way twice. He'd fall in the middle of his act, or at the end, or once he fell the first time he jumped for the trapeze. Another time he didn't fall at all during the act, and then, as he was coming down the ladder, he missed a rung and down he came, and the crowd screamed.

And Angeli would come to me after each performance and his eyes would glow, and he'd say, "Did you hear them, Tony? They want me to fall, they want me to break my neck!"

And maybe they did. Or maybe they

were just very happy to see him get up after he fell, safe and sound. Whatever it was, it was wonderful. Business was booming, and I began thinking of getting some new tops, and maybe a wild-animal act. I boosted everybody's salary, and I began taking a larger cut myself, and I was finally ready to ask Sue Ellen something I'd wanted to ask her for a long, long time. And Sam Angeli had made it all possible. I spoke to her alone one night, over by the stakes where the elephants were tied.

"Sue Ellen," I said, "there's something that's been on my mind for a long time now."

"What is it, Tony?" she said.

"Well, I'm just a small-time circus man, and I never had much money, you know, and so I never had the right. But things have picked up considerably, and . . ."

"Don't, Tony," she said.

I opened my eyes wide. "I beg your pardon, Sue Ellen?"

"Don't ask me. Maybe it could have been, and maybe it couldn't. But no more now, Tony. Not since I met Sam. He's everything I want, Tony; can you understand that?"

"I suppose," I said.

"I think I love him, Tony."

I nodded and said nothing.

"I'm awfully sorry," Sue Ellen said.

"If it makes you happy, honey . . ." I couldn't think of any way to finish it.

I started work in earnest. Maybe I should have fired Angeli on the spot, but you can't fire love, and that's what I was battling. So instead I worked harder, and I tried not to see Sue Ellen around all the time. I began to figure crowd reactions, and I realized the people would not hold still for my other aerial artists once they got wind of the Fallen Angel. So we worked Farnings and Edward (whose "Great" title we dropped) into one act, and we worked Sue Ellen into Angeli's act. Sue Ellen dressed up the act a lot, and it gave Angeli someone to kid around with up there, making his stunts before the fall more interesting.

Sue Ellen never did any of the fancy stuff. She just caught Angeli, or was caught by him—all stuff leading up to Angeli's spectacular fall. The beautiful part was that Sue Ellen never had to worry about timing. I mean, if she missed Angeli—so he fell. I thought about his fall a lot, and I tried to figure it out, but I never could, and after a while I stopped figuring. I never stopped thinking about Sue Ellen, though, and it hurt me awful to watch her looking at him with those eyes full of worship, but if she was happy, that was all that counted.

And then I began to get bigger ideas. Why fool around with a small-time circus? I wondered. Why not expand? Why not incorporate?

I got off a few letters to the biggest circuses I knew of. I told them what I had, and I told them the boy was under exclusive contract to me, and I told them he would triple attendance, and I told them I was interested in joining circuses, becoming partners sort of, with the understanding that the Fallen Angel would come along with me. I guess the word had got around by then because all the big-shot letters were very cordial and very nice, and they all asked me when they could get a look at Angeli because they would certainly be interested in incorporating my fine little outfit on a partnership basis if my boy were all I claimed him to be, sincerely yours.

I got off a few more letters, asking all the big shots to attend our regular Friday night performance so that they could judge the crowd reaction and see the Fallen Angel under actual working conditions. All my letters were answered with telegrams, and we set the ball rolling.

That Friday afternoon was pure bedlam. There's always a million things happening around a circus, anyway, but this Friday everything seemed to pile up at once. Like Fifi, our bareback rider, storming into the tent in her white ruffles.

"My horse!" she yelled, her brown eyes flashing. "My horse!"

"Is something wrong with him?" I asked.

"No, nothing's wrong with him," she screamed. "But something's wrong with José Esperanza,[2] and I'm going to wring his neck unless . . ."

"Now easy, honey," I said, "let us take it easy."

"I told him a bucket of *rye.* I did *not* say a bucket of oats. JuJu does not eat oats; he eats rye. And my safety and health and life depend on JuJu, and I will not have him eating some foul-smelling oats when I distinctly told José . . ."

"José!" I bellowed. "José Esperanza, come here."

José was a small Puerto Rican we'd picked up only recently. A nice young kid with big brown eyes and a small timid smile. He poked his head into the wagon and smiled, and then he saw Fifi and the smile dropped from his face.

"Is it true you gave JuJu oats, José, when you were told to give him rye?" I asked.

"Yes, *Señor,*"[3] José said, "that is true."

"But why, José? Why on earth . . ."

José lowered his head. "The horse, *Señor,* I like him. He is a nice horse. He is always good to me."

"What's that got to do with the bucket of rye?"

"*Señor,*" José said pleadingly, "I did not want to get the horse drunk."

"Drunk? Drunk?"

"Yes, *Señor,* a bucket of rye. Even for a horse, that is a lot of whiskey. I did not think . . ."

"Oh," Fifi wailed, "of all the—I'll feed the horse myself. I'll feed him myself. Never mind!"

She stormed out of the wagon, and José smiled sheepishly and said, "I did wrong, *Señor?*"

I shook my head, and José left, and when I turned around Sam Angeli was standing there. I hadn't heard him come in, and I wondered how long he'd been there, so I said, "A good kid, José."

"If you like good kids," Angeli answered.

"He'll go to heaven, that one," I said. "Mark my words."

Angeli smiled. "We'll see," he said. "I wanted to talk to you, Tony."

"Oh? What about?"

"About all these people coming tonight. The big shots, the ones coming to see me."

"What about them?"

"Nothing, Tony. But suppose—just suppose, mind you—suppose I don't fall?"

"What do you mean?" I said.

"Just that. Suppose I don't fall tonight?"

"That's silly," I said. "You have to fall."

"Do I? Where does it say I have to fall?"

"Your contract. You signed a . . ."

"The contract doesn't say anything about my having to fall, Tony. Not a word."

"Well . . . say, what is this? A holdup?"

"No. Nothing of the sort. I just got to thinking. If this works out tonight, Tony, you're going to be a big man. But what do I get out of it?"

---

2. *José Esperanza* (hô se′ es′pe rän′sä).
3. *Señor* (sā nyôr′), mister or sir. [Spanish]

"Do you want a salary boost? Is that it? O.K. You've got a salary boost. How's that?"

"I don't want a salary boost."

"What, then?"

"Something of very little importance. Something of no value whatever."

"What?" I said. "What is it?"

"Suppose we make a deal, Tony?" Angeli said. "Suppose we shake on it? If I fall tonight, I get this little something that I want."

"What's this little something that you want?"

"Is it a deal?"

"I have to know first."

"Well, let's forget it then," Angeli said.

"Now wait a minute, wait a minute. Is this 'thing'—Sue Ellen?"

Angeli smiled. "I don't have to make a deal to get her, Tony."

"Well, is it money?"

"No. This thing has no material value."

"Then why do you want it?"

"I collect them."

"And I've got one?"

"Yes."

"Well, what . . . ?"

"Is it a deal, or isn't it?"

"I don't know. I mean, this is a peculiar way to . . ."

"Believe me, this thing is of no material value to you. You won't even know it's gone. But if I go through with my fall tonight, all I ask is that you give it to me. A handshake will be binding as far as I'm concerned."

I shrugged. "All right, all right, a deal. Provided you haven't misrepresented this thing, whatever it is. Provided it's not of material value to me."

"I haven't misrepresented it. Shall we shake, Tony?"

He extended his hand, and I took it, and his eyes glowed, but his skin was very cold to the touch. I pulled my hand away.

"Now," I said, "what's this thing you want from me?"

Angeli smiled. "Your soul."

I was suddenly alone in the wagon. I looked around, but Angeli was gone, and then the door opened and Sue Ellen stepped in, and she looked very grave and very upset.

"I heard," she said. "Forgive me. I heard. I was listening outside. Tony, what are you going to do? What are *we* going to do?"

"Can it be?" I said. "Can it be, Sue Ellen? He looks just like you and me. How'd I get into this?"

"We've got to do something," Sue Ellen said. "Tony, we've got to stop him!"

We packed them in that night. They sat, and they stood, and they climbed all over the rafters; they were everywhere. And right down front, I sat with the big shots, and they all watched my small, unimportant show until it was time for the Fallen Angel to go on.

I got up and smiled weakly and said, "If you gentlemen will excuse me, I have to introduce the next act."

They all smiled back knowingly, and nodded their heads, and their gold stickpins and pinky rings winked at me, and they blew out expensive cigar smoke, and I was thinking, *Mullins, you can blow out expensive cigar smoke, too, but you won't have any soul left.*

I introduced the act, and I was surprised to see all my aerial artists run out onto the sawdust: Sue Ellen, Farnings, Edward and the Fallen Angel. I watched Angeli as he crossed one of the spotlights, and if I'd had any doubts they all vanished right then. Angeli cast no shadow on the sawdust.

I watched in amazement as the entire troupe went up the ladder to the trapezes. There was a smile on Angeli's face, but Sue Ellen and the rest had tight, set mouths.

They did a few stunts, and I watched the big shots, and it was plain they were not impressed at all by these routine aerial acrobatics. I signaled the band, according to schedule, and I shouted, "And now, ladies and gentlemen, the Fallen Angel in a death-defying, spine-tingling, bloodcurdling triple somersault at one hundred and fifty feet above the ground, *without a net!*"

Sue Ellen swung her trapeze out, and Angeli swung his, and then Sue Ellen dropped head downward and extended her hands, and Angeli swung back and forth, and the crowd held its breath, waiting for him to take his fall, and the big shots held their breaths, waiting for the same thing. Only I knew what would happen if he did take that fall. Only I knew about our agreement. Only I—and Sue Ellen, waiting up there for Angeli to jump.

Charlie started the roll on his snare, and then the roll stopped abruptly, and Angeli released his grip on the bar and he swung out into space, and over he went, once, twice, three times—and *slap.* Sue Ellen's hands clamped around his wrists, and she held on for dear life. I couldn't see Angeli's face from so far below, but he seemed to be struggling to get away. Sue Ellen held him for just an instant, just long enough for Edward to swing his trapeze into position.

She flipped Angeli out then, and over he went—and *wham.* Edward grabbed his ankles. Angeli flapped his arms and kicked his legs, trying to get free, but Edward—Edward the Great!—wouldn't drop him. Instead, he swung his trapeze back, and then gave Angeli a flip and Farnings grabbed Angeli's wrists.

Farnings flipped Angeli up, and Sue Ellen caught him, and then Sue Ellen swung her trapeze all the way back and tossed Angeli to Edward, and I began to get the idea of what was going on up there.

Edward tossed Angeli, and Farnings caught him, and then Farnings tossed him to Sue Ellen, and Sue Ellen tossed him right back again. Then Farnings climbed onto Sue Ellen's trapeze, and they both swung back to the platform.

Edward took a long swing, and then he tossed Angeli head over heels, right back to the platform, where Sue Ellen and Farnings grabbed him with four eager arms.

I was grinning all over by this time, and the crowd was booing at the top of its lungs. Who cared? The big shots were stirring restlessly, but they'd probably heard that Angeli sometimes fell coming down the ladder, and so they didn't leave their seats.

Only tonight, Angeli wasn't doing any falling coming down any ladder. Because Sue Ellen had one of his wrists and Farnings had one of his ankles, and one was behind him, and the other was ahead of him; and even if he pitched himself off into space, he wouldn't have gone far, not with the grips they had on both him and the ladder. I saw the big shots get up and throw away their cigars, and then everybody began booing as if they wanted to tear down the top with their voices. Angeli came over to me, and his face didn't hold a pleasant smile this time. His face was in rage, and it turned red, as if he would explode.

"You tricked me!" he screamed. "You tricked me!"

And all at once he wasn't there any more. □□

Discussion

1. (a) Who is the narrator in the story? **(b)** Cite lines in the first section of the story (through page 405b, 4) that are examples of the narrator's sense of humor. **(c)** With what tone of voice is the story narrated?

2. (a) Describe Sam Angeli's physical appearance. **(b)** Describe the way Angeli moves and the way he enters Mullins's office the first time the men meet. **(c)** What makes Mullins agree to watch Angeli perform?

3. (a) What is Sam Angeli's specialty as a trapeze artist? **(b)** What is his belief about why people watch trapeze acts? **(c)** What explanation does he give of how he developed his specialty? **(d)** Summarize the hints contained in this first section (through page 405b, 4), that Angeli is not what he pretends to be. **(e)** What further hints of Angeli's identity are given in the second section (through 406a, 2)?

4. (a) Why doesn't Angeli ever fall the same way twice? **(b)** Discuss how the reactions of the audience, the other performers, and the other circus owners seem to prove Angeli's theory of why people watch trapeze acts.

5. (a) Angeli bargains with Mullins on the afternoon before the big Friday night performance. What does Angeli offer to do for Mullins? **(b)** What does he want from Mullins in return? **(c)** How does Angeli trick Mullins into agreeing? **(d)** How does this episode change Mullins's and Sue Ellen's attitude toward Angeli? **(e)** At this point, who or what do they think Angeli is?

6. (a) In what way do Sue Ellen and the other trapeze artists cause Angeli to fail his part of the bargain? **(b)** Angeli accuses them of tricking him. Do you agree? **(c)** What do you think happens to Angeli at the end? **(d)** Who or what do you think Sam Angeli is?

7. Discuss in how many ways the title "The Fallen Angel" is appropriate to the story.

8. Consider questions 2–6 that you have answered above. Explain whether your answer to each question was **(a)** a fact, based on what someone said or did; **(b)** an inference, based on clues in the story; **(c)** a guess, based on your personal beliefs or feelings. For each inference, identify the hints or clues upon which you based your conclusion.

Extension • Reading

The idea of striking a bargain with the Devil has fascinated people for centuries, and has been the subject of innumerable stories, novels, plays, songs, operas, movies. In many of these, the Devil—in a variety of disguises—offers the main character something to exchange for his or her soul. Listed below are just a few examples.

The Devil's Bridge, a legend retold by Charles Scribner, Jr. (Charles Scribner's Sons, 1978).

A Book of Devils & Demons, by Ruth Manning-Sanders (E. P. Dutton, 1970).

The Year the Yankees Lost the Pennant, by Douglass Wallop (Norton, 1964).

The Devil and Daniel Webster, by Stephen Vincent Benét (Holt, Rinehart & Winston, 1937).

"Feathertop" in *Mosses from an Old Manse,* by Nathaniel Hawthorne.

Evan Hunter 1926 •

Evan Hunter has had a varied background of work: from selling lobsters to teaching in a high school. He is presently a fulltime writer and writes under the pen names of Hunt Collins and Ed McBain. His personal interests include skiing, snorkling, and making home movies.

The Monsters Are Due on Maple Street

Rod Serling

There is a fifth dimension beyond that which is known to man.
It is a dimension as vast as space, and as timeless as infinity.
It is the middle ground between light and shadow—
between science and superstition. And it lies between the pit
of man's fears and the summit of his knowledge.
This is the dimension of imagination.
It is an area which we call the Twilight Zone.

CHARACTERS:

Residents of Maple Street:

NARRATOR	DON MARTIN	SALLY, *Tommy's mother*
FIGURE ONE	STEVE BRAND	LES GOODMAN
FIGURE TWO	MYRA BRAND, *Steve's wife*	ETHEL GOODMAN, *Les's wife*
	PETE VAN HORN	MAN ONE
	CHARLIE	MAN TWO
	CHARLIE'S WIFE	WOMAN ONE
	TOMMY	

ACT ONE

(Fade in on shot of the night sky. The various heavenly bodies stand out in sharp, sparkling relief. The camera begins a slow pan[1] across the heavens until it passes the horizon and stops on a sign which reads "Maple Street." It is daytime. Then we see the street below. It is a quiet, tree-lined, small-town American street. The houses have front porches on which people sit and swing on gliders, talking across from house to house. STEVE BRAND is polishing his car, which is parked in front of his house. His neighbor, DON MARTIN, leans against the fender watching him. A Good Humor man riding a bicycle is just in the process of stopping to sell some ice cream to a couple of kids. Two women gossip on the front lawn. Another man is watering his lawn with a garden hose.

As we see these various activities, we hear the NARRATOR's voice.)

NARRATOR: Maple Street, U.S.A., late summer. A tree-lined little world of front porch gliders, hop scotch, the laughter of children, and the bell of an ice cream vendor.

(There is a pause and the camera moves over to a shot of the Good Humor man and two small boys who are standing alongside just buying ice cream.)

NARRATOR: At the sound of the roar and the flash of the light, it will be precisely six-forty-three P. M. on Maple Street.

(At this moment TOMMY, one of the two boys buying ice cream from the vendor, looks up to listen to a tremendous screeching roar from overhead. A flash of light plays on the faces of both boys and then moves down the street and disappears.

Various people leave their porches or stop what they are doing to stare up at the sky.

STEVE BRAND, the man who has been polishing his car, stands there transfixed, staring upwards. He looks at DON MARTIN, his neighbor from across the street.)

STEVE: What was that? A meteor?

DON: That's what it looked like. I didn't

---

1. **pan,** the television camera moves in order to get a wide view or to follow a moving object.

hear any crash though, did you?

STEVE: Nope. I didn't hear anything except a roar.

MYRA (from her porch): What was that?

STEVE (raising his voice and looking toward the porch): Guess it was a meteor, honey. Came awful close, didn't it?

MYRA: Too close for my money! Much too close.

(The camera pans across the various porches to people who stand there watching and talking in low conversing tones.)

NARRATOR: Maple Street. Six-forty-four P.M. on a late September evening. (A pause) Maple Street in the last calm and reflective moment . . . before the monsters came!

(The camera takes us across the porches again. A man is replacing a light bulb on a front porch. He gets down off his stool to flick the switch and finds that nothing happens.

Another man is working on an electric power mower. He plugs in the plug, flicks the switch of the mower off and on, but nothing happens.

Through a window we see a woman pushing her finger back and forth on the dial hook of a telephone. Her voice sounds far away.)

WOMAN ONE: Operator, operator, something's wrong on the phone, operator!

(MYRA BRAND comes out on the porch and calls to STEVE.)

MYRA (calling): Steve, the power's off. I had the soup on the stove and the stove just stopped working.

WOMAN ONE: Same thing over here. I can't get anybody on the phone either. The phone seems to be dead.

(We look down again on the street. Small, mildly disturbed voices creep up from below.)

VOICE ONE: Electricity's off.

VOICE TWO: Phone won't work.

VOICE THREE: Can't get a thing on the radio.

VOICE FOUR: My power mower won't move, won't work at all.

VOICE FIVE: Radio's gone dead!

(PETE VAN HORN, a tall, thin man, is seen standing in front of his house.)

PETE: I'll cut through the back yard . . . see if the power's still on, on Floral Street. I'll be right back!

(He walks past the side of his house and disappears into the back yard.

The camera pans down slowly until we are looking at ten or eleven people standing around the street and overflowing to the curb and sidewalk. In the background is STEVE BRAND'S car.)

STEVE: Doesn't make sense. Why should the power go off all of a sudden and the phone line?

DON: Maybe some kind of an electrical storm or something.

CHARLIE: That don't seem likely. Sky's just as blue as anything. Not a cloud. No lightning. No thunder. No nothing. How could it be a storm?

WOMAN ONE: I can't get a thing on the radio. Not even the portable.

(The people again murmur softly in wonderment.)

CHARLIE: Well, why don't you go downtown and check with the police, though they'll probably think we're crazy or something. A little power failure and right away we get all flustered and everything—

STEVE: It isn't just the power failure, Charlie. If it was, we'd still be able to get a broadcast on the portable.

(There is a murmur of reaction to this. STEVE looks from face to face and then over to his car.)

STEVE: I'll run downtown. We'll get this all straightened out.

(He walks over to the car, gets in, and turns the key.

Looking through the open car door, we see the crowd watching STEVE from the other side. He starts the engine. It turns over sluggishly and then stops dead. He tries it again, and this time he can't get it to turn over. Then very slowly he turns the key back to "off" and gets out of the car.

The people stare at STEVE. He stands for a moment by the car and then walks toward them.)

STEVE: I don't understand it. It was working fine before—

DON: Out of gas?

STEVE (shakes his head): I just had it filled up.

WOMAN ONE: What's it mean?

CHARLIE: It's just as if . . . as if everything had stopped. (Then he turns toward STEVE.) We'd better walk downtown.

(Another murmur of assent to this.)

STEVE: The two of us can go, Charlie. (He turns to look back at the car.) It couldn't be the meteor. A meteor couldn't do this.

(He and CHARLIE exchange a look. Then they start to walk away from the group.

TOMMY comes into view. He is a serious-faced young boy in spectacles. He stands halfway between the group and the two men who start to walk down the sidewalk.)

TOMMY: Mr. Brand . . . you'd better not!

STEVE: Why not?

TOMMY: They don't want you to.

(STEVE and CHARLIE exchange a grin and STEVE looks back toward the boy.)

STEVE: Who doesn't want us to?

TOMMY (jerks his head in the general direction of the distant horizon): Them!

STEVE: Them?

CHARLIE: Who are them?

TOMMY (intently): Whoever was in that thing that came by overhead.

(STEVE knits his brows for a moment, cocking his head questioningly. His voice is intense.)

STEVE: What?

TOMMY: Whoever was in that thing that came over. I don't think they want us to leave here.

(STEVE leaves CHARLIE, walks over to the boy, and puts his hand on the boy's shoulder. He forces his voice to remain gentle.)

STEVE: What do you mean? What are you talking about?

TOMMY: They don't want us to leave. That's why they shut everything off.

STEVE: What makes you say that? Whatever gave you that idea?

WOMAN ONE (from the crowd): Now isn't that the craziest thing you ever heard?

TOMMY (persistent but a little frightened): It's always that way, in every story I ever read about a ship landing from outer space.

WOMAN ONE (to the boy's mother, SALLY, who stands on the fringe of the crowd): From outer space yet! Sally, you better get that boy of yours up to bed. He's been reading too many comic books or seeing too many movies or something!

SALLY: Tommy, come over here and stop that kind of talk.

STEVE: Go ahead, Tommy. We'll be right back. And you'll see. That wasn't any ship or anything like it. That was just a . . . a meteor or something. Likely as not—(He turns to the group, now trying very hard to sound more optimistic than he feels.) No doubt it did have something to do with all this power failure and the rest of it. Meteors can do some crazy things. Like sunspots.

DON (picking up the cue): Sure. That's the kind of thing—like sunspots. They raise Cain with radio reception all over the world. And this thing being so close—why, there's no telling the sort of stuff it can do. *(He wets his lips, smiles nervously.)* Go ahead, Charlie. You and Steve go into town and see if that isn't what's causing it all.

(STEVE and CHARLIE walk away from the group down the sidewalk as the people watch silently.

TOMMY stares at them, biting his lips, and finally calls out again.)

TOMMY: Mr. Brand!

(The two men stop. TOMMY takes a step toward them.)

TOMMY: Mr. Brand . . . please don't leave here.

(STEVE and CHARLIE stop once again and turn toward the boy. In the crowd there is a murmur of irritation and concern, as if the boy's words—even though they didn't make sense—were bringing up fears that shouldn't be brought up.

TOMMY is partly frightened and partly defiant.)

TOMMY: You might not even be able to get to town. It was that way in the story. *Nobody* could leave. Nobody except—

STEVE: Except who?

TOMMY: Except the people they sent down ahead of them. They looked just like humans. And it wasn't until the ship landed that—*(The boy suddenly stops, conscious of the people staring at him and his mother and of the sudden hush of the crowd.)*

SALLY *(in a whisper, sensing the antagonism of the crowd):* Tommy, please son . . . honey, don't talk that way—

MAN ONE: That kid shouldn't talk that way . . . and we shouldn't stand here listening to him. Why this is the craziest thing I ever heard of. The kid tells us a comic book plot and here we stand listening—

(STEVE walks toward the camera, and stops beside the boy.)

STEVE: Go ahead, Tommy. What kind of story was this? What about the people they sent out ahead?

TOMMY: That was the way they prepared things for the landing. They sent four people. A mother and a father and two kids who looked just like humans . . . but they weren't.

(There is another silence as STEVE looks toward the crowd and then toward TOMMY. He wears a tight grin.)

STEVE: Well, I guess what we'd better do then is to run a check on the neighborhood and see which ones of us are really human.

(There is laughter at this, but it's a laughter that comes from a desperate attempt to lighten the atmosphere. The people look at one another in the middle of their laughter.)

CHARLIE *(rubs his jaw nervously):* I wonder if Floral Street's got the same deal we got. *(He looks past the houses.)* Where is Pete Van Horn anyway? Didn't he get back yet?

(Suddenly there is the sound of a car's engine starting to turn over.

We look across the street toward the driveway of LES GOODMAN's house. He is at the wheel trying to start the car.)

SALLY: Can you get started, Les?

(LES GOODMAN gets out of the car, shaking his head.)

LES: No dice.

(He walks toward the group. He stops suddenly as, behind him, the car engine starts up all by itself. LES whirls around to stare at it.

The car idles roughly, smoke coming from the exhaust, the frame shaking gently.

LES's eyes go wide, and he runs over to his car.

The people stare at the car.)

MAN ONE: He got the car started somehow.

He got *his* car started!

(The people continue to stare, caught up by this revelation and wildly frightened.)

WOMAN ONE: How come his car just up and started like that?

SALLY: All by itself. He wasn't anywheres near it. It started all by itself.

(DON MARTIN approaches the group, stops a few feet away to look toward LES'S car and then back toward the group.)

DON: And he never did come out to look at that thing that flew overhead. He wasn't even interested. *(He turns to the group, his face taut and serious.)* Why? Why didn't he come out with the rest of us to look?

CHARLIE: He always was an odd ball. Him and his whole family. Real odd ball.

DON: What do you say we ask him?

(The group start toward the house. In this brief fraction of a moment they take the first step toward a metamorphosis that changes people from a group into a mob. They begin to head purposefully across the street toward the house. STEVE stands in front of them. For a moment their fear almost turns their walk into a wild stampede, but STEVE'S voice, loud, incisive, and commanding, makes them stop.)

STEVE: Wait a minute . . . *wait a minute!* Let's not be a mob!

(The people stop, pause for a moment, and then much more quietly and slowly start to walk across the street.

  LES stands alone facing the people.)

LES: I just don't understand it. I tried to start it and it wouldn't start. You saw me. All of you saw me.

(And now, just as suddenly as the engine started, it stops, and there is a long silence that is gradually intruded upon by the frightened murmuring of the people.)

LES: I don't understand. I swear . . . I don't understand. What's happening?

DON: Maybe you better tell us. Nothing's working on this street. Nothing. No lights, no power, no radio. *(Then meaningfully)* Nothing except one car—*yours!*

(The people's murmuring becomes a loud chant filling the air with accusations and demands for action. Two of the men pass DON and head toward LES, who backs away from them against his car. He is cornered.)

LES: Wait a minute now. You keep your distance—all of you. So I've got a car that starts by itself—well, that's a freak thing—I admit it. But does that make me some kind of a criminal or something? I don't know why the car works—it just does!

(This stops the crowd momentarily and LES, still backing away, goes toward his front porch. He goes up the steps and then stops, facing the mob.)

LES: What's it all about, Steve?

STEVE *(quietly):* We're all on a monster kick, Les. Seems that the general impression holds that maybe one family isn't what we think they are. Monsters from outer space or something. Different from us. Fifth columnists[2] from the vast beyond. *(He chuckles.)* You know anybody that might fit that description around here on Maple Street?

LES: What is this, a gag? *(He looks around the group again.)* This a practical joke or something?

(Suddenly the car engine starts all by itself, runs for a moment, and stops. One woman begins to cry. The eyes of the crowd are cold and accusing.)

LES: Now that's supposed to incriminate me, huh? The car engine goes on and off

---

2. *fifth columnists,* people who engage in spying, sabotage, and other revolutionary activities within the borders of a nation.

and that really does it, doesn't it? *(He looks around the faces of the people.)* I just don't understand it . . . any more than any of you do! *(He wets his lips, looking from face to face.)* Look, you all know me. We've lived here five years. Right in this house. We're no different from any of the rest of you! We're no different at all. . . . Really . . . this whole thing is just . . . just weird—

WOMAN ONE: Well, if that's the case, Les Goodman, explain why—*(She stops suddenly, clamping her mouth shut.)*

LES *(softly):* Explain what?

STEVE *(interjecting):* Look, let's forget this—

CHARLIE *(overlapping him):* Go ahead, let her talk. What about it? Explain what?

WOMAN ONE *(a little reluctantly):* Well . . . sometimes I go to bed late at night. A couple of times . . . a couple of times I'd come out here on the porch and I'd see Mr. Goodman here in the wee hours of the morning standing out in front of his house . . . looking up at the sky. *(She looks around the circle of faces.)* That's right, looking up at the sky as if . . . as if he were waiting for something. *(A pause)* As if he were looking for something.

(There's a murmur of reaction from the crowd again as LES *backs away.)*

LES: She's crazy. Look, I can explain that. Please . . . I can really explain that . . . . She's making it up anyway. *(Then he shouts.)* I tell you she's making it up!

(He takes a step toward the crowd and they back away from him. He walks down the steps after them and they continue to back away. Suddenly he is left completely alone, and he looks like a man caught in the middle of a menacing circle as the scene slowly fades to black.)

ACT TWO

SCENE 1. *(Fade in on Maple Street at night. On the sidewalk, little knots of people stand around talking in low voices. At the end of each conversation they look toward* LES GOODMAN'S *house. From the various houses we can see candlelight but no electricity. The quiet which blankets the whole area is disturbed only by the almost whispered voices of the people standing around. In one group* CHARLIE *stands staring across at the* GOODMANS' *house. Two men stand across the street from it in almost sentry-like poses.)*

SALLY *(in a small, hesitant voice):* It just doesn't seem right, though, keeping watch on them. Why . . . he was right when he said he was one of our neighbors. Why, I've known Ethel Goodman ever since they moved in. We've been good friends—

CHARLIE: That don't prove a thing. Any guy who'd spend his time lookin' up at the sky early in the morning—well, there's something wrong with that kind of person. There's something that ain't legitimate. Maybe under normal circumstances we could let it go by, but these aren't normal circumstances. Why, look at this street! Nothin' but candles. Why, it's like goin' back into the Dark Ages or somethin'!

(STEVE walks down the steps of his porch, down the street to the GOODMANS' *house, and then stops at the foot of the steps.* LES *is standing there;* ETHEL GOODMAN *behind him is very frightened.)*

LES: Just stay right where you are, Steve. We don't want any trouble, but this time if anybody sets foot on my porch—that's what they're going to get—trouble!

STEVE: Look, Les—

LES: I've already explained to you people. I don't sleep very well at night sometimes. I get up and I take a walk and I look up at

the sky. I look at the stars!

ETHEL: That's exactly what he does. Why, this whole thing, it's . . . it's some kind of madness or something.

STEVE (nods grimly): That's exactly what it is—some kind of madness.

CHARLIE'S VOICE (shrill, from across the street): You best watch who you're seen with, Steve! Until we get this all straightened out, you ain't exactly above suspicion yourself.

STEVE (whirling around toward him): Or you, Charlie. Or any of us, it seems. From age eight on up!

WOMAN ONE: What I'd like to know is—what are we gonna do? Just stand around here all night?

CHARLIE: There's nothin' else we *can* do! (He turns back, looking toward STEVE and LES again.) One of 'em'll tip their hand. They *got* to.

STEVE (raising his voice): There's something you can do, Charlie. You can go home and keep your mouth shut. You can quit strutting around like a self-appointed hanging judge and just climb into bed and forget it.

CHARLIE: You sound real anxious to have that happen, Steve. I think we better keep our eye on you, too!

DON (as if he were taking the bit in his teeth, takes a hesitant step to the front): I think everything might as well come out now. (He turns toward STEVE.) Your wife's done plenty of talking, Steve, about how odd *you* are!

CHARLIE (picking this up, his eyes widening): Go ahead, tell us what she's said.

(STEVE walks toward them from across the street.)

STEVE: Go ahead, what's my wife said? Let's get it *all* out. Let's pick out every idiosyncrasy of every single man, woman, and child on the street. And then we might as well set up some kind of kangaroo court.[3] How about a firing squad at dawn, Charlie, so we can get rid of all the suspects. Narrow them down. Make it easier for you.

DON: There's no need gettin' so upset, Steve. It's just that . . . well . . . Myra's talked about how there's been plenty of nights you spent hours down in your basement workin' on some kind of radio or something. Well, none of us have ever *seen* that radio—

(By this time STEVE has reached the group. He stands there defiantly.)

CHARLIE: Go ahead, Steve. What kind of "radio set" you workin' on? I never seen it. Neither has anyone else. Who you talk to on that radio set? And who talks to you?

STEVE: I'm surprised at you, Charlie. How come you're so dense all of a sudden? (A pause) Who do I talk to? I talk to monsters from outer space. I talk to three-headed green men who fly over here in what look like meteors.

(MYRA BRAND steps down from the porch, bites her lip, calls out.)

MYRA: Steve! Steve, please. (Then looking around, frightened, she walks toward the group.) It's just a ham radio set, that's all. I bought him a book on it myself. It's just a ham radio set. A lot of people have them. I can show it to you. It's right down in the basement.

STEVE (whirls around toward her): Show them nothing! If they want to look inside our house—let them get a search warrant.

CHARLIE: Look, buddy, you can't afford to—

---

3. *kangaroo court,* term given to an unauthorized, on-the-spot mock trial in which heated emotion replaces reason and justice.

STEVE (interrupting him): Charlie, don't start telling me who's dangerous and who isn't and who's safe and who's a menace. (He turns to the group and shouts.) And you're with him, too—all of you! You're standing here all set to crucify—all set to find a scapegoat—all desperate to point some kind of a finger at a neighbor! Well now, look, friends, the only thing that's gonna happen is that we'll eat each other up alive—

(He stops abruptly as CHARLIE suddenly grabs his arm.)

CHARLIE (in a hushed voice): That's not the *only* thing that can happen to us.

(Down the street, a figure has suddenly materialized in the gloom, and in the silence we hear the clickety-clack of slow, measured footsteps on concrete as the figure walks slowly toward them. One of the women lets out a stifled cry. SALLY grabs her boy, as do a couple of other mothers.)

TOMMY (shouting, frightened): It's the monster! It's the monster!

(Another woman lets out a wail and the people fall back in a group staring toward the darkness and the approaching figure.

The people stand in the shadows watching. DON MARTIN joins them, carrying a shotgun. He holds it up.)

DON: We may need this.

STEVE: A shotgun? (He pulls it out of DON's hand.) No! Will anybody think a thought around here? Will you people wise up. What good would a shotgun do against—

(The dark figure continues to walk toward them as the people stand there, fearful, mothers clutching children, men standing in front of their wives.)

CHARLIE (pulling the gun from STEVE's hands): No more talk, Steve. You're going to talk us into a grave! You'd let whatev-

er's out there walk right over us, wouldn't yuh? Well, some of us won't!

(CHARLIE swings around, raises the gun, and suddenly pulls the trigger. The sound of the shot explodes in the stillness.

The figure suddenly lets out a small cry, stumbles forward onto his knees, and then falls forward on his face. DON, CHARLIE, and STEVE race forward to him. STEVE is there first and turns the man over. The crowd gathers around them.)

STEVE (slowly looks up): It's Pete Van Horn.

DON (in a hushed voice): Pete Van Horn! He was just gonna go over to the next block to see if the power was on—

WOMAN ONE: You killed him, Charlie. You shot him dead!

CHARLIE (looks around at the circle of faces, his eyes frightened, his face contorted): But . . . but I didn't know who he was. I certainly didn't know who he was. He comes walkin' out of the darkness—how am I supposed to know who he was? (He grabs STEVE.) Steve—you know why I shot! How was I supposed to know he wasn't a monster or something? (He grabs DON.) We're all scared of the same thing. I was just tryin' to . . . tryin' to protect my home, that's all! Look, all of you, that's all I was tryin' to do. (He looks down wildly at the body.) I didn't know it was somebody we knew! I didn't know—

(There's a sudden hush and then an intake of breath in the group. Across the street all the lights go on in one of the houses.)

WOMAN ONE (in a hushed voice): Charlie . . . Charlie . . . the lights just went on in your house. Why did the lights just go on?

DON: What about it, Charlie? How come you're the only one with lights now?

LES: That's what I'd like to know.

(A pause as they all stare toward CHARLIE.)

LES: You were so quick to kill, Charlie, and you were so quick to tell us who we had to be careful of. Well, maybe you *had* to kill. Maybe Pete there was trying to tell us something. Maybe he'd found out something and came back to tell us who there was amongst us we should watch out for—

(CHARLIE *backs away from the group, his eyes wide with fright.*)

CHARLIE: No . . . no . . . it's nothing of the sort! I don't know why the lights are on. I swear I don't. Somebody's pulling a gag or something.

(*He bumps against* STEVE *who grabs him and whirls him around.*)

STEVE: *A gag?* A gag? Charlie, there's a dead man on the sidewalk and you killed him! Does this thing look like a gag to you?

(CHARLIE *breaks away and screams as he runs toward his house.*)

CHARLIE: No! No! Please!

(*A man breaks away from the crowd to chase* CHARLIE.

As the man tackles him and lands on top of him, the other people start to run toward them. CHARLIE *gets up, breaks away from the other man's grasp, lands a couple of desperate punches that push the man aside. Then he forces his way, fighting, through the crowd and jumps up on his front porch.*

CHARLIE *is on his porch as a rock thrown from the group smashes a window beside him, the broken glass flying past him. A couple of pieces cut him. He stands there perspiring, rumpled, blood running down from a cut on the cheek. His wife breaks away from the group to throw herself into his arms. He buries his face against her. We can see the crowd converging on the porch.*)

VOICE ONE: It must have been him.

VOICE TWO: He's the one.

VOICE THREE: We got to get Charlie.

(*Another rock lands on the porch.* CHARLIE *pushes his wife behind him, facing the group.*)

CHARLIE: Look, look I swear to you . . . it isn't me . . . but I do know who it is . . . I swear to you, I do know who it is. I know who the monster is here. I know who it is that doesn't belong. I swear to you I know.

DON (*pushing his way to the front of the crowd*): All right, Charlie, let's hear it!

(CHARLIE'*s eyes dart around wildly.*)

CHARLIE: It's . . . it's . . .

MAN TWO (*screaming*): Go ahead, Charlie, tell us.

CHARLIE: It's . . . it's the kid. It's Tommy. He's the one!

(*There's a gasp from the crowd as we see* SALLY *holding the boy.* TOMMY *at first doesn't understand and then, realizing the eyes are all on him, buries his face against his mother.*)

SALLY (*backs away*): That's crazy! He's only a boy.

WOMAN ONE: But he knew! He was the only one who knew! He told us all about it. Well, how did he know? How *could* he have known?

(*Various people take this up and repeat the question.*)

VOICE ONE: How could he know?

VOICE TWO: Who told him?

VOICE THREE: Make the kid answer.

(*The crowd starts to converge around the mother, who grabs* TOMMY *and starts to run with him. The crowd starts to follow, at first walking fast, and then running after him.*

Suddenly CHARLIE'*s lights go off and the lights in other houses go on, then off.*)

MAN ONE (*shouting*): It isn't the kid . . . it's Bob Weaver's house.

WOMAN ONE: It isn't Bob Weaver's house, it's Don Martin's place.

CHARLIE: I tell you it's the kid.

DON: It's Charlie. He's the one.

(People shout, accuse, and scream as the lights go on and off. Then, slowly, in the middle of this nightmarish confusion of sight and sound the camera starts to pull away until once again we have reached the opening shot looking at the Maple Street sign from high above.)

SCENE 2. *(The camera continues to move away while gradually bringing into focus a field. We see the metal side of a spacecraft which sits shrouded in darkness. An open door throws out a beam of light from the illuminated interior. Two figures appear, silhouetted against the bright lights. We get only a vague feeling of form.)*

FIGURE ONE: Understand the procedure now? Just stop a few of their machines and radios and telephones and lawn mowers . . . throw them into darkness for a few hours, and then just sit back and watch the pattern.

FIGURE TWO: And this pattern is always the same?

FIGURE ONE: With few variations. They pick the most dangerous enemy they can find . . . and it's themselves. And all we need do is sit back . . . and watch.

FIGURE TWO: Then I take it this place . . . this Maple Street . . . is not unique.

FIGURE ONE *(shaking his head):* By no means. Their world is full of Maple Streets. And we'll go from one to the other and let them destroy themselves. One to the other . . . one to the other . . . one to the other—

SCENE 3. *(The camera pans up for a shot of the starry sky, and over this we hear the* NARRATOR's *voice.)*

NARRATOR: The tools of conquest do not necessarily come with bombs and explosions and fallout. There are weapons that are simply thoughts, attitudes, prejudices—to be found only in the minds of men. For the record, prejudices can kill and suspicion can destroy and a thoughtless, frightened search for a scapegoat has a fallout all its own for the children . . . and the children yet unborn. *(A pause)* And the pity of it is . . . that these things cannot be confined to . . . The Twilight Zone! *(Fade to black.)* □□

Discussion

1. **(a)** What is the setting of the play? **(b)** Name details that make this setting seem ordinary or commonplace. **(c)** Why is it important for the setting to be quite ordinary?

2. **(a)** What happening begins the action of the play? **(b)** How does Tommy affect the action? **(c)** Why does the group listen to Tommy?

3. Name in order the characters on whom the group's suspicion falls. For what reasons do the people accuse each of these characters?

4. What types of people do Steve and Charlie represent?

5. Reread the stage directions on 419a, 8 concerning the "metamorphosis that changes people from a group into a mob." **(a)** What is the difference between a group and a mob? **(b)** Do the people on Maple Street continue the metamorphosis into a mob? Explain.

6. Review the Handbook article on irony. **(a)** What is ironic about Charlie's being accused by his neighbors? **(b)** What is ironic about Charlie's accusing Tommy? What kind of irony is involved here? **(c)** What kind of irony is involved in Act II, Scene 2? Explain.

7. The play title is *The Monsters Are Due on Maple Street.* Who are the monsters?

8. What do you think will happen to the people on Maple Street? Support your answer with evidence from the play.

9. **(a)** In Act II, Scene 2, the figures discuss a "pattern." What is this pattern? **(b)** State what you think is the theme of the play. **(c)** Do you agree with this view of human nature? Why or why not?

10. **(a)** What elements of fantasy does the play include? **(b)** Is fantasy essential to the development of this particular theme? Why or why not?

11. Read the interview with Rod Serling on page 427. **(a)** Does the play illustrate his "awareness of human conflict"? Explain. **(b)** What examples from current television can you give to prove or disprove Serling's belief that television writers wield power and influence over their audiences?

Vocabulary • Structure

Study the structure of the italicized words in the sentences below, paying attention to the way prefixes and suffixes change the meanings of the roots. Then, on your paper, write a brief answer for each question.

1. If a ship on the horizon is *indistinct,* can you see it clearly?

2. If your father heads *purposefully* for the television set, can you tell that he has decided what he wants to watch?

3. If you see a magician *materialize* a rabbit, has the animal disappeared from your view?

4. If the actions of a friend are *inexplicable,* can you explain those actions?

5. If your little sister gazes with *wonderment* at the Christmas decorations in a downtown store, is she impressed with them?

6. If your baby brother has an *illogical* fear of the dark, can you comfort him with a reasonable explanation?

7. If you know your argument has *validity,* is it worth sticking by it and trying to defend it?

Questions Put to a Playwright

Mr. Serling, where do you get ideas for your television plays, and how do you prepare scripts?
I generally start with a rough theme or at least a semblance of a storyline. On occasion, I'll start with things as tenuous as a collection of interesting characters. Or, I might even start a script based on nothing more than an exciting title. If I'm doing a long and serious drama, I generally have a theme in mind. But if I'm dealing with something light, an interesting plot twist might trigger a story.

Generally, I write the whole script right from the top. But I write with an eye toward many, many rewrites. No writer ever writes the best he knows how the first time around.

Do you use personal background as a source for material?
Yes. I draw upon human and personal experiences, and I do so often because I write better when I'm dealing with a subject I know about. But in response to that age-old question as to whether a writer should limit himself to writing only of personal experiences—I don't subscribe to that. I think a good writer is an imaginative writer.

I do think, though, that when dealing with very special areas, the writer better be sure that he knows the language that exists within given professions and areas and times.

While writing, do you try to aim for a particular segment of the population?
No. I never do. I don't aim for any segment—any intellectual group or any particular type of people. I write the best I know how, for what I assume to be a generally bright and astute audience—one that is eye level to me in every respect. I think the writer who begins to tailor for a particular audience segment runs the risk of misreading who is listening to or reading him.

Do you think of yourself as simply a storyteller, or as a modern moralist, a social critic?
I'm all these things; all writers are. All writers are storytellers. All, in a sense, take a position of morality—at least a position which they assume to be a moral one. And all writers are indeed social critics.

Is there any common theme in your own writing?
I think you'll find that I have an awareness of human conflict—people fighting other people on many levels other than physical. I'm constantly aware of the combat that human beings enter into with themselves and others. Of the various themes, I've tried to attack prejudice more than any other social evil. I've always felt that prejudice is probably the most damaging, the most jeopardizing, most fruitless of the human frailties. I think prejudice is a waste, and its normal end is violence.

Do you feel that by your writing you wield power and influence attitudes?
Indeed I do. I know I wield power, and I know I influence attitudes just as any writer does. But no more than any other writer, and probably a lot less than many. A writer always influences his audience, motivates them, evokes some kind of reaction from them.

Is your work meant to be entertaining—or is entertainment secondary to intent?
Needless to say, I want to entertain. But I think there is a semantics problem here. You know, a very solid melodrama —one that is heavy and brutal and very commentative on the tragedy of the times—might still be entertaining. I think it harks back to your question about aiming at a particular audience segment. I have no preoccupation, no awareness, of whether or not I'm entertaining—again, I'm writing a story as honestly and as effectively as I know how. And, if in the process I do entertain, or simply titillate, or appeal to, or make laugh, or make weep, or make think, I've done my job.

6: Yesterday, Today, Tomorrow

CONTENT REVIEW

1. Which selections in this unit are set in the past? in the present? in the future?

2. Identify the fantastical elements in each of the following selections: **(a)** "The Hundredth Dove"; **(b)** "Get That Straight"; **(c)** "Where the Sidewalk Ends"; **(d)** "Virtuoso"; **(e)** *The Monsters Are Due on Maple Street.*

3. Several selections in this unit feature characters who get the better of their foes by outwitting them. Explain how this applies to characters in **(a)** "Rikki-tikki-tavi"; **(b)** "Macavity: the Mystery Cat"; **(c)** "The Fallen Angel."

4. "The Storyteller" and "Get That Straight" contain a story-within-the-story. **(a)** In each selection, who tells the story-within-the-story? **(b)** What prompts each story? **(c)** Briefly summarize the two stories. **(d)** What purpose might each narrator have in telling these stories?

5. Many characters in this unit make *inferences* and act upon them. Explain how these characters come to the following conclusions and what evidence or lack of evidence they have for making their inferences: **(a)** Hugh believes the white dove is the Lady Columba. **(b)** Nag and Nagaina are sure that by killing the humans they will drive the mongoose away. **(c)** Scotland Yard believes that the master criminal is Macavity. **(d)** The speaker in "Get That Straight" knows that Don José is telling the truth. **(e)** Rollo decides his playing the piano will be harmful to the Maestro. **(f)** Charlie believes that Pete Van Horn is the monster.

6. What characteristics should the *stereotyped* character of a king possess? Discuss your ideas with the class until you come to a general agreement. Do the same for stereotypes of a dragon–slaying hero, a criminal, a robot, the Devil, a creature from outer space. Then, explain to what extent examples of these character types in the unit fit or vary from the stereotypes you have agreed on.

Unit 6, Test I
INTERPRETATION: NEW MATERIAL

Read the following short story, and then on your paper answer the questions.

Key Item
Isaac Asimov

Jack Weaver came out of the vitals of Multivac looking utterly worn and disgusted.

From the stool, where the other maintained his own stolid watch, Todd Nemerson said, "Nothing?"

"Nothing," said Weaver. "Nothing, nothing, nothing. No one can find anything wrong with it."

"Except that it won't work, you mean."

Adapted from "Key Item," copyright 1968 by Mercury Press, Inc. in *Buy Jupiter and Other Stories* by Isaac Asimov. Used by permission of Doubleday & Company, Inc.

"You're no help sitting there!"

"I'm thinking."

"Thinking!"

Nemerson stirred impatiently on his stool. "Why not? There are six teams of computer technologists roaming around in the corridors of Multivac. They haven't come up with anything in three days. Can't you spare one person to think?"

"It's not a matter of thinking. We've got to look. Somewhere a relay is stuck."

"It's not that simple, Jack!"

"Who says it's simple. You know how many million relays we have there?"

"That doesn't matter. If it were just a relay, Multivac would have alternate circuits, devices for locating the flaw, and facilities to repair or replace the ailing part. The trouble is, Multivac won't only not answer the original question, it won't tell us what's wrong with it. —And meanwhile, there'll be panic in every city if we don't do something. The world's economy depends on Multivac, and everyone knows that."

"I know it, too. But what's there to do?"

"I told you, *think.* There must be something we're missing completely. Look, Jack, there isn't a computer bigwig in a hundred years who hasn't devoted himself to making Multivac more complicated. It can do so much now—it can even talk and listen. It's practically as complex as the human brain. We can't understand the human brain, so why should we understand Multivac?"

"Aw, come on. Next you'll be saying Multivac is human."

"Why not?" Nemerson grew absorbed and seemed to sink into himself. "Now that you mention it, why not? Could we tell if Multivac passed the thin dividing line where it stopped being a machine and started being human? *Is* there a dividing line, for that matter? If the brain is just more complex than Multivac, and we keep making Multivac more complex, isn't there a point where . . ." He mumbled down into silence.

Weaver said impatiently, "What are you driving at? Suppose Multivac were human. How would that help us find out why it isn't working?"

"For a human reason, maybe. Suppose *you* were asked the most probable price of wheat next summer and didn't answer. Why wouldn't you answer?"

"Because I wouldn't know. But Multivac would know! We've given it all the factors. It can analyze futures in weather, politics, and economics. We know it can. It's done it before."

"All right. Suppose I asked the question and you knew the answer but didn't tell me. Why not?"

Weaver snarled, "Because I had a brain tumor. Because I had

been knocked out. In other words, because my machinery was out of order. That's just what we're trying to find out about Multivac. We're looking for the place where its machinery is out of order, for the key item."

"Only you haven't found it." Nemerson got off his stool. "Listen, ask me the question Multivac stalled on."

"How? Shall I run the tape through you?"

"Come on, Jack. Give me the talk that goes along with it. You do talk to Multivac, don't you?"

"I've got to. Therapy."

Nemerson nodded. "Yes, that's the story. Therapy. That's the official story. We talk to it in order to pretend it's a human being so that we don't get neurotic over having a machine know so much more than we do. We turn a frightening metal monster into a protective father image."

"If you want to put it that way."

"Well, it's wrong and you know it. A computer as complex as Multivac *must* talk and listen to be efficient. Just putting in and taking out coded dots isn't sufficient. At a certain level of complexity, Multivac must be made to seem human because—it *is* human. Come on, Jack, ask me the question. I want to see my reaction to it."

Jack Weaver flushed. "This is silly."

"Come on, will you?"

It was a measure of Weaver's depression and desperation that he acceded. Half sullenly, he pretended to be feeding the program into Multivac, speaking as he did so in his usual manner. He commented on the latest information concerning farm unrest, talked about the new equations describing jet-stream contortions, lectured on the solar constant.

He began stiffly enough, but warmed to this task out of long habit, and when the last of the program was slammed home, he almost closed contact with a physical snap at Todd.

He ended briskly, "All right, now. Work that out and give us the answer pronto."

For a moment, having done, Jack Weaver stood there, nostrils flaring, as though he was feeling once more the excitement of throwing into action the most gigantic and glorious machine ever put together by the mind and hands of man.

Then he remembered and muttered, "All right. That's it."

Nemerson said, "At least I know now why *I* wouldn't answer, so let's try that on Multivac. Look, clear Multivac; make sure the investigators have their paws off it. Then run the program into it and let me do the talking. Just once."

Weaver shrugged and turned to Multivac's control wall, filled with its somber, unwinking dials and lights. Slowly he cleared it.

One by one he ordered the teams away.

Then, with a deep breath, he began once more feeding the program into Multivac. It was the twelfth time all told, the dozenth time. Somewhere a distant news commentator would spread the word that they were trying again. All over the world a Multivac-dependent people would be holding its collective breath.

Nemerson talked as Weaver fed the data silently. He talked diffidently, trying to remember what it was that Weaver had said, but waiting for the moment when the key item might be added.

Weaver was done and now a note of tension was in Nemerson's voice. He said, "All right, now, Multivac. Work that out and give us the answer."

He paused and added the key item. He said *"Please!"* And all over Multivac, the valves and relays went joyously to work. □□

1. The "official story" is that the men talk to the machine so that **(a)** they can think of it as a human being instead of a metal monster; **(b)** they can release some of their boredom and frustration; **(c)** they can learn more about it; **(d)** they can find out how much it knows.

2. "Key Item" is fantasy partly because **(a)** it takes place on another planet; **(b)** we do not know of any machines so complex that they have started being human; **(c)** Nemerson and Weaver look unlike any humans we know about; **(d)** as yet there are no computer technologists.

3. The plot of this story is advanced chiefly through **(a)** a description of what the characters are thinking; **(b)** the author's description of action; **(c)** the author's summary of a time lapse of several years; **(d)** dialogue.

4. The proof in the story that Multivac *is* human is that **(a)** it can analyze politics and weather; **(b)** it responds to commands; **(c)** it responds to kindness; **(d)** it takes on the physical characteristics of a person.

5. Which one of the following is *not* evident in this story? **(a)** conflict; **(b)** dialogue; **(c)** theme; **(d)** flashback.

Unit 6, Test II
COMPOSITION

Choose one of the following to write about.

1. One of your classmates says, "Fantasy is silly; it has nothing to do with the real world." Using one of the following selections try to convince your classmates in a short paper that fantasy is indeed related to life: "The Hundredth Dove," "Virtuoso," *The Monsters Are Due on Maple Street.*

2. The changing of animals into humans and humans into animals has always been a popular subject for writers. Discuss who is transformed in "Get That Straight" and "The Hundreth Dove" and what effect that transformation has on the main characters.

3. Many of the selections in this unit are about things that could not really happen but that we might wish could be. Think of something fantastic or magical that you wish might be and write about it as if it has already happened. You could begin your composition with "yesterday" or "last week." Describe the causes and the results of this fantastic or magical happening.

See something from an unusual vantage point—

like a roller coaster's front seat or inside a fish bowl.

Explore a range of feelings—

from joy in shared experience to pain in personal loss.

Take a closer look at the world around you—

a summer day's sunshine or patterns made by falling rai

Discover these and other

experiences in **POETRY**

See **CONNOTATION/DENOTATION** Handbook of Literary Terms

What is it like to be "kidnapped" by a poet?

Kidnap Poem

Nikki Giovanni

ever been kidnapped
by a poet
if i were a poet
i'd kidnap you
5 put you in my phrases and meter
you to jones beach
or maybe coney island
or maybe just to my house
lyric you in lilacs
10 dash you in the rain

blend into the beach
to complement my see
play the lyre for you
ode you with my love song
15 anything to win you
wrap you in the red Black green
show you off to mama
yeah if i were a poet i'd kid
nap you

"Kidnap Poem" by Nikki Giovanni from *Re: Creation* by Nikki Giovanni. Copyright © 1970, Broadside Press, Detroit, Michigan. Reprinted by permission.

Nikki Giovanni (ni′kē jō vä′nē)

Discussion

1. (a) What does the word "kidnap" mean? What connotations do you associate with the word? What are some of your feelings toward a person who would engage in kidnapping? **(b)** What does the title of the poem lead you to expect the poem will be about? What, instead, is the poem about? **(c)** Does the word "kidnap," as it is used in this poem, have the same connotations that it ordinarily has? Explain.

2. "Kidnap Poem" contains a number of terms associated with poetry—*meter, lyric,* and *ode,* for example. Consult the Glossary and find the usual definition for these terms. **(a)** How is Nikki Giovanni using the words in unusual ways? **(b)** Does her use of these words strengthen or weaken the poem? Explain.

3. A *pun* is the humorous use of a word to suggest not only its own meaning but also the meaning of another word or words with the same sound. **(a)** What two lines contain puns? **(b)** Are the puns appropriate to the feelings and thoughts being expressed? Explain.

4. In analyzing any poem, it is important that you do not confuse the speaker with the poet. The poet uses a speaker in the same way that a prose writer uses a narrator. In "Kidnap Poem" the speaker is not specifically identified. From evidence in the poem, however, what inferences, if any, might you make about the speaker's age, sex, race, geographic location, and education?

1. (a) Describe the steps the hunter has taken to "outwit" his prey. (b) What is the speaker's attitude toward the hunter's behavior? (c) How do you know?

2. (a) What is the *rhyme scheme* of "The Hunter"? (Read again the article on *rhyme* in the Handbook of Literary Terms for help with this question.) (b) Would the rhyme scheme for "The Hunter" be appropriate for a serious poem about the death of a child? Explain. (c) Is the rhythm of the poem—its measured movement or beat—fast or slow? (d) Would the same rhythm be suitable for a poem describing the actions of elderly people? Why or why not?

Ogden Nash   1902 • 1971

Ogden Nash poked fun at our way of life, our social customs, and at his own pet peeves. He used rhymes that were never meant to be and may never be again. He misspelled and mispronounced words to make them rhyme with others. He gleefully distorted meanings and invented new ones.

Nash held a variety of jobs, including work in advertising and publishing, before joining the staff of *The New Yorker* magazine. In 1931 he published his first volume of light verse, *Free Wheeling.* By 1935 he had become so successful that he was able to devote himself entirely to writing.

The Hunter

Ogden Nash

The hunter crouches in his blind
'Neath camouflage of every kind,
And conjures up a quacking noise
To lend allure to his decoys.
5 This grown-up man, with pluck and luck,
Is hoping to outwit a duck.

"The Hunter" from *Versus* by Ogden Nash. Copyright © 1947, 1949 by Ogden Nash. Reprinted by permission of Little, Brown and Company and Curtis Brown Ltd.

See **INVERSION** Handbook of Literary Terms

To a Dead Goldfish

O. B. Hardison, Jr.

Stirring with oars of filmy gold
The glassy tide that round him rolled,
He ruled two quarts of universe
And gave no subject ground to curse.

5 The snail in peace devoured the slime,
The seed toward heaven did greenly climb,
The fry disported in the deep,
Knowing their lord the watch did keep.

Splendid to see, upon his flanks
10 Grew golden scales in glittering ranks;
His gills were red, his belly white,
And from his regal eyes, a light

Appeared to stream. Serene, benign,
His sovereign touch would calm the brine,
15 And even unhallowed Tabby's claw
Recoiled from him in holy awe.

Still would he rule and swim, but Fate
(which must to all men soon or late)
Gave him the last and bitter cup:
20 Now see him floating, bottoms up.

Discussion

1. What are the "two quarts of universe" that the goldfish ruled?

2. (a) Trace the various ways in which the goldfish is compared to a ruler. **(b)** What kind of ruler was he?

3. (a) What impression do you get of the goldfish in the first four stanzas of the poem? **(b)** How is this impression altered in lines 17–20? **(c)** What tone does the poet give the poem through this complete reversal? **(d)** Does the rhyme scheme seem appropriate to the tone? Explain. **(e)** Does the poem have a theme, or is it simply meant to amuse? Explain.

4. A number of sentences are *inverted*, that is, words or phrases that would normally come after the subject and verb come before them. **(a)** Give examples of these *inversions*. **(b)** What purpose in the poem do you think they serve?

1. (a) On what grounds was the man who sold puppets and whistles arrested? **(b)** How did he behave when his turn came up in the courtroom? **(c)** What were the reactions of the people in the courtroom to his behavior?

2. The arrested man referred to himself as the monkey man, yet he had no monkey. Why might he have identified himself as he did?

3. (a) In the last line of the poem, "monkey business" can have two different meanings. What are they? **(b)** Is each meaning appropriate to the poem? Explain. **(c)** What, if anything, do you think the theme of the poem is?

4. (a) Of the following words, which best describes the tone of the poem: *sad, angry, joyous, matter-of-fact, regretful?* Explain. **(b)** Is the tone appropriate to the poem's sense, or meaning? Explain.

Victor Hernández Cruz

Victor Hernández Cruz was born in Puerto Rico and moved to the United States when he was four years old. He made his home in New York City until joining the English Department of the University of California at Berkeley. *Snaps,* his first collection of poetry, was published in 1968. His poems have appeared in numerous publications including *Evergreen Review* and *Journal of Black Poetry.*

Business

Victor Hernández Cruz

Don Arturo says:
There was a man
who sold puppets and whistles
for a living
5 He also played guitar
He used to go
to the shopping areas
and draw huge crowds
They bought his whistles
10 and puppets
They threw money into
his guitar
This was against the law
So he was arrested at
15 least three times a week
When his turn came up
in the courtroom
He took a puppet out
and put a show on
20 All the detectives
and court clerks
rolled on the floor
When he finished
they all bought puppets
25 and whistles from him
The judge got angry
and yelled:
What kind of business
is this
30 And the man said
I am the monkey man
and the
Monkey man sells
Monkey business.

From *Mainland*, by Victor Hernández Cruz. Copyright © 1973 by Victor Hernández Cruz. Reprinted by permission of Random House, Inc.

Victor Hernández (er nän′des) **Cruz** (krüs)

For heart-stopping excitement, there's nothing quite like . . .

The Contraption
May Swenson

Going up is pleasant. It tips your chin,
and you feel tall and free
as if in control of, and standing in
a chariot, hands feeling the frisky

5 reins. But, doubled in your seat,
knuckled to the fun-car's handrails,
you mount baby-buggied, cleat by cleat,
to that humped apogee your entrails

aren't ready for. Wind in your
10 ears, clouds in your eyes, it's easy
to define the prophetic jelly at your core
as joy. The landscape of amusement goes queasy

Mike Massaschi/STOCK, BOSTON

only when the gilded buckboard juts straight out
over undippered air. A jaw of horror will split
15 you? Not yet. The route
becomes a roaring trough for the next hill

hairpinning higher. You wish you had
the chance to count how many ups,
downs and switchbacks the mad
20 rattler, rearing its steel hoops, has. The divan hiccups

over a straightaway now, at mild speed.
Then you look: Jolly carousel and ferris wheel, far
years beneath, are cruel gears you can be emptied
into over the side of the hellish sled. Star-

25 beaded sky! (It feels better to look higher.) How
did the morning, the whole blue-and-white day
go by in what seems one swoop? You vow
to examine the contraption and its fairway,

measure the system of gruesome twists,
30 the queer dimensions, if ever you get down. Going
down is a dull road. Your fists
loosen, pretend no longer, knowing

they grip no stick of purpose. The final chutes are
unspectacular, slower repetitions of past
35 excitements. A used and vulgar car
shovels you home in a puzzling gloom. The vast

agitation faded in your bowels, you think
that from the ground you'll trace the rim
your coaster sped and crawled, the sink
40 and rise, the reason for its shape. Grim

darkness now. The ride
is complete. You are positioned for discovery, but,
your senses gone, you can't see the upper arching works.
        Wide
silence. Midnight. The carnival is shut.

Discussion

1. Who is the *you* in the poem?

2. (a) How does it feel to start upward in the contraption? (b) What does "baby-buggied" mean (line 7)? (c) What words in lines 9–12 indicate a thrilling ride is expected?

3. (a) How does it feel just before the first plunge downward (lines 12–14)? (b) What images in lines 15–17 show that the ride is fast and steep? (c) What is the "mad rattler" in lines 19–20? (d) Explain the use of hiccups in lines 20–21 to describe the motion of the contraption. (e) Why do the carousel and Ferris wheel (lines 22–24) bring to mind thoughts of gears?

4. What are the rider's feelings now that the ride is completed?

May Swenson 1919 •

May Swenson was born and educated in Utah. She has taught and given poetry readings at many American colleges, and has received several literary awards. Her poems, recognized for their imagery and unusual observations, have been recorded, set to music, and translated into German and Italian.

If you must travel late at night, beware of . . .

The Demon of the Gibbet[1]

Fitz-James O'Brien

There was no west, there was no east,
    No star abroad for eyes to see;
And Norman spurred his jaded beast
    Hard by the terrible gallows tree.

5 "O, Norman, haste across this waste—
    For something seems to follow me!"
"Cheer up, dear Maud, for, thanked be God,
    We nigh have passed the gallows tree!"

He kissed her lip: then—spur and whip
10   And fast they fled across the lea.
But vain the heel, and rowel steel—
    For something leaped from the gallows tree!

"Give me your cloak, your knightly cloak,
    That wrapped you oft beyond the sea!
15 *The wind is bold, my bones are old,*
    And I am cold on the gallows tree."

"O holy God! O dearest Maud,
    Quick, quick, some prayers—the best that be!
A bony hand my neck has spanned,
20   And tears my knightly cloak from me!"

"Give me your wine, the red, red wine,
    That in the flask hangs by your knee!
Ten summers burst on me accurst,
    And I'm athirst on the gallows tree!"

1. **Gibbet** (jib′it), an upright post
with a projecting arm at the top (in
this case, a branch projecting from
a tree), from which the bodies of
criminals were hung after execu-
tion.

25 "O Maud, my life, my loving wife!
       Have you no prayer to set us free?
   My belt unclasps—a demon grasps,
       And drags my wine flask from my knee!"

   "Give me your bride, your bonnie bride,
30   *That left her nest with you to flee!*
   O she hath flown to be my own,
       For I'm alone on the gallows tree!"

   "Cling closer, Maud, and trust in God!
       Cling close—Ah, heaven, she slips from me!"
35 A prayer, a groan, and he alone
       Rode on that night from the gallows tree.

Fitz-James O'Brien. *Dark of the Moon; Poems of Fantasy and the Macabre,*
August Derleth, ed. (Sauk City, Wis.: Arkham House), 1947.

Discussion

1. (a) What is the time of day in the first stanza? How do you know? (b) What is unusual about the weather? (c) What character is introduced? (d) What is he doing? (e) What is he near?

2. (a) What new character is introduced in the second stanza (lines 5–8)? (b) What concerns does she express? (c) What response does she receive?

3. (a) What is the relationship between the speakers in the second stanza? (b) Where in the poem do you learn this? (c) Across what kind of earth have they been riding? How do you know?

4. (a) Which words and phrases in the third stanza suggest Norman's efforts to make his horse hurry? (b) Why are his efforts termed "vain"?

5. (a) Who speaks in the lines set in italics? (b) What three things does he demand? (c) What are his reasons for wanting each thing? (d) How does he get each?

Extension • Writing

Assume you are Norman and you have just arrived at your hotel following the events described in "The Demon of the Gibbet." You take out a sheet of stationery to write home about what has happened. You begin, "Dear Mom and Dad: I have terrible news!" Finish the letter, telling your parents what happened, under what circumstances it happened, and how you feel about it.

Fitz-James O'Brien
1828 • 1862

Fitz-James O'Brien was born in County Limerick, Ireland. As a young man, he wasted his entire inheritance during four years in London and Paris. Broke when he arrived in New York in 1852, he soon established himself as a writer of essays, poems, stories and articles. When the Civil War began, he enlisted in the New York National Guard. He was wounded and died of tetanus shortly after having received special mention for gallantry at the Battle of Bloomery Gap.

The Builders

Sara Henderson Hay

I told them a thousand times if I told them once:
Stop fooling around, I said, with straw and sticks;
They won't hold up; you're taking an awful chance.
Brick is the stuff to build with, solid bricks.
5 You want to be impractical, go ahead.
But just remember, I told them; wait and see.
You're making a big mistake. Awright, I said,
But when the wolf comes, don't come running to me.

The funny thing is, they didn't. There they sat,
10 One in his crummy yellow shack, and one
Under his roof of twigs, and the wolf ate
Them, hair and hide. Well, what is done is done.
But I'd been willing to help them, all along,
If only they'd once admitted they were wrong.

Discussion

1. (a) Who is the speaker in this poem? (b) What is the first clue to his identity? (c) What story is he telling?

2. (a) What do the words "What is done is done" indicate about the speaker's attitude toward his brothers and toward what happened to them? (b) Why is he telling this story? (c) Does he succeed in his purpose? Explain.

3. Which of the following characteristics does the speaker reveal: (a) self-righteousness; (b) concern for others; (c) selfishness; (d) practicality; (e) guilt? Explain.

4. (a) According to the speaker, under what conditions would he have been willing to help his brothers? (b) Do you believe him? Explain.

5. (a) How does this version of the old story differ from the original? (b) What application might this version have to people? (c) Would you say the rhyme scheme of the poem is regular or irregular? Explain.

Extension • Writing

Assume that you are a newspaper reporter covering the slaying of the two pigs and the destruction of their homes. After examining what's left of the houses of stick and of straw, you interview the surviving brother. Write an account of your investigation. Begin your account, "Yesterday two pigs died unnecessarily."

Sara Henderson Hay 1906 •

Born in Pittsburgh, Sara Henderson Hay attended Brenau College and Columbia University. Subjects for her poetry are often provided by daily events and familiar scenes on which she sheds a special light. In *Story Hour,* she reconsiders fairy tales and legends as if their events and characters were real.

Vocabulary
Context, Dictionary

Often when you look up a word in the Glossary or a dictionary, you find not one but several definitions. You must then determine which of the definitions fits the word as it is used in the material you are reading. Sometimes a knowledge of parts of speech helps: if the word you are looking up is used as a noun, and two definitions—one for a noun and one for a verb—are given, you'll have no difficulty choosing the right one. But more often you will find several definitions for the same part of speech. Then you must go back to the context in which the word is used to see which definition best fits that context. Read the following sentence.

As the roller coaster climbed toward its *apogee*, George looked at the ground below and stifled a yell.

Now look up *apogee* in the Glossary. Of the two definitions given, which best fits the context of the sentence? What words or ideas in the sentence made you answer as you did? What made you eliminate the definition you did not use?

Read each sentence in the next column and look up the italicized word in the Glossary. On your paper write the definition you chose as the correct one for that context. Be prepared to read the sentences aloud and to explain why you chose the definition you did.

1. When she cleaned the aquarium, Monica had no trouble removing the big fish to a pail, but she worried about not catching all of the *fry.*

2. Harold's *benign* appearance hid the heart of a dictator.

3. Old and partially deaf, the *sovereign* was forced from her position by a much younger woman.

4. The family hoped that grandma's tumor would be *benign.*

5. Chores were divided so that Betty and Jolene would peel vegetables while Martin would *fry* the catch.

6. Tanya drilled a hole in the *sovereign* and attached it to her charm bracelet.

It Doesn't Have to Rhyme

Poems are what poets choose to make them, and they don't have to rhyme unless poets want them to. Because the earliest poems we learn are nursery rhymes and jingles (some of them from television), most of us first associate poetry with rhyme. But people identify poetry by many qualities, and much poetry has no rhyme at all.

Just as different kinds of games have their own rules, so different kinds of poems have theirs. You can't play any kind of game well unless you know the rules; poetry becomes more enjoyable when you understand what guidelines or patterns poets have imposed upon their creations.

Much poetry written before the twentieth century conformed to very strict rules, or *forms*. But modern poets sometimes decide that the meaning and emotion they want to express don't fit into a traditional form. In such cases, the poets are free to develop a new form to fit what they want to say.

Let's examine just a few of the many ways of putting a poem together. Poets can use rhyme to help create mood and melody:

> On either side the river lie
> Long fields of barley and of
>   rye,
> That clothe the world and
>   meet the sky;
> And through the field the
>   road runs by
> To many towered
>   Camelot
> > Tennyson, "The Lady of
> > Shalott"

Or if they wish, they may use words whose meaning and sound combine to establish a mood and create a melody:

> Season of mists and mellow
>   fruitfulness,
> Close bosom-friend of the
>   maturing sun . . .
> > Keats, "To Autumn"

They may use a very regular rhythm:

> By the shores of Gitche
>   Gumee
> By the shining Big-Sea-
>   Water
> Stood the wigwam of No-
>   komis,
> Daughter of the moon,
>   Nokomis.
> > Longfellow, "The Song
> > of Hiawatha"

Or an irregular rhythm:

> I saw in Louisiana a live-
>   oak growing
> All alone stood it and the
>   moss hung down from
>   the branches,
> Without any companion it
>   grew there uttering
>   joyous leaves of dark
>   green,
> And its look, rude, unbend-
>   ing, lusty, made me
>   think of myself . . .
> > Whitman, "I Saw in
> > Louisiana . . ."

They can use sounds to make a poem move slowly:

> Break, break, break
> On thy cold gray stones,
>   O Sea!
> > Tennyson, "Break,
> > break, break"

Or rapidly:

> And wretches hang that jury-
>   men may dine . . .
> > Pope, "The Rape of the
> > Lock"

Poets should use the sound patterns and rhythm and movement that are best suited to their subject matter. For example, a grief-stricken poet would not write:

> Grief is here, grief is there.
> Grief is round us everywhere.

Read the poem at the right to see if you can determine not only what kind of visits the poet, Vern Rutsala, is describing, but how he creates a mood and a melody:

Visits

Vern Rutsala

Strangers invade
the dim façades.
The cracked leather
flanks of suitcases
5 mutter like saddles.
Cousins test each other
on chinning bars
before their heights
are measured back to back.
10 And soon the houses change:

Daybeds convert
themselves obsequiously
to night duties.
Rooms are disarrayed:
15 Like weak triangles
metal coat hangers
on door knobs
ring the dim tunes
of all reunions.

Who are the visitors? How can you tell? Do they come often? What one word answers this question? What seems to be the speaker's feeling toward these visits? Explain.

There are no rhyming lines in "Visits," but Rutsala sets up definite sound patterns by repeating certain letters and letter combinations. Where is the *d* sound in *invade* (line 1) repeated? What words echo the vowel sound in *tunes* (line 18)? What other sound patterns are noticeable? Are the letter sounds in the poem light-sounding? If not, what are they? Are they in keeping with the speaker's attitude?

Does the poem have a regular or an irregular rhythm? Does the rhythm seem suitable to the poem? Why or why not? Try reading the poem aloud. Do the short lines make you read in a flowing manner or an abrupt one? Is the length of the lines in keeping with the visits? Explain.

Does the poem move rapidly or slowly? Which sounds do the most to influence the movement? Is the movement in keeping with the thought expressed in the poem?

In your opinion, has the poet used the rules appropriate to what he has to say?

In summary, poets should use the form that best fits their subject matter. They can use an existing set of rules or invent their own. Whichever they do, the poem should be based on careful repetition of rhythms and sounds; but the rhythm doesn't necessarily have to be regular, and the sound patterns don't necessarily have to be rhymes.

who knows if the moon's

E. E. Cummings

who knows if the moon's
a balloon,coming out of a keen city
in the sky—filled with pretty people?
(and if you and i should

5 get into it,if they
should take me and take you into their balloon,
why then
we'd go up higher with all the pretty people

than houses and steeples and clouds:
10 go sailing
away and away sailing into a keen
city which nobody's ever visited,where

always
      it's
15   Spring)and everyone's
in love and flowers pick themselves

Discussion

1. (a) Which of the following words apply to the speaker in the poem: *childish, childlike, cynical, imaginative, romantic?* Explain. **(b)** From what you have inferred about the speaker, describe what the "pretty people" might be like.

2. The speaker describes "a keen city which nobody's ever visited." **(a)** Do you think he considers this city "keen" *because* nobody has ever visited it? Why or why not? **(b)** Beyond not having had visitors, what is unusual about the city?

3. Parentheses can be used to set off material that qualifies, material that explains, or, as in an aside, material that establishes a more intimate relationship between a speaker and an audience. **(a)** Which of these purposes best explains the use of parentheses in the poem? Explain. **(b)** Read the lines enclosed in parentheses with vocal expression suitable for these emotions: **(1)** a wish (almost childlike) to adventure to a new place; **(2)** an it-doesn't-matter-much feeling; **(3)** a depressed feeling. Which interpretation seems most appropriate to the poem? Why?

4. (a) Would the poem be as appealing if more specific words were substituted for "pretty" and "keen"? Why or why not? **(b)** Would it be a better poem if a specific name, for example, Sue or Frank, were substituted for "you"? Explain.

How careless are you with words?

Words

Pauli Murray

We are spendthrifts with words,
We squander them,
Toss them like pennies in the air—
Arrogant words,
5 Angry words,
Cruel words,
Comradely words,
Shy words tiptoeing from mouth to ear.

But the slowly wrought words of love
10 And the thunderous words of heartbreak—
These we hoard.

Discussion

1. (a) What comparison is implied in lines 1–2? **(b)** How is this comparison reversed in lines 9–11? **(c)** Do these comparisons seem appropriate or farfetched? Explain.

2. (a) Look up the definition of "arrogant" in the Glossary; then, think of contexts in which some (or all) of these words might have an arrogant connotation: *sick, best, tired, stronger, you, I.* Why? **(b)** How would you explain the difference between "angry words" and "cruel words"? **(c)** Provide at least three "comradely words."

3. (a) Reread line 8 and try to visualize the image. Would *slipping* be as appropriate as *tiptoeing?* would *sneaking?* would *hiding?* Why or why not? **(b)** Would "slowly chiseled" be equally appropriate to "slowly wrought" in line 9? Explain.

Pauli Murray 1910 •

Pauli Murray's poems have appeared in *Common Ground, South Today,* and the *Saturday Review of Literature.* She has been represented in numerous anthologies including *American Negro Poetry.*

Born in Baltimore, Maryland, and educated in North Carolina, New York, and California, Ms. Murray is a part-time poet and full-time attorney-at-law.

Some pursuits involve a calculated risk!

Under the Mistletoe

Countee Cullen

I did not know she'd take it so,
    Or else I'd never dared;
Although the bliss was worth the blow,
I did not know she'd take it so.
5 She stood beneath the mistletoe
So long I thought she cared;
I did not know she'd take it so,
Or else I'd never dared.

"Under the Mistletoe" from *Copper Sun* by Countee Cullen. Copyright 1927 by Harper & Row, Publishers, Inc.; renewed 1955 by Ida M. Cullen. Reprinted by permission of the publisher.

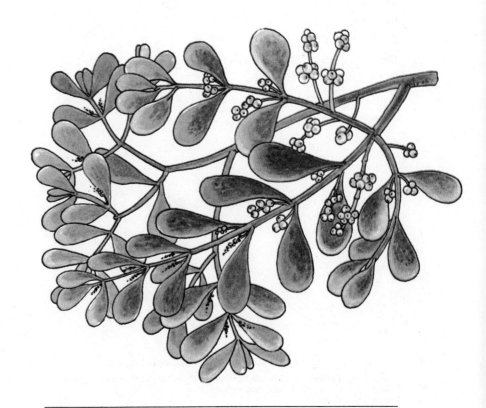

Discussion

1. (a) From what the speaker says, what do you infer has happened? **(b)** Do you think the speaker would be willing to undergo the same experience again? Explain.

2. (a) What examples of repetition can you find in the poem? **(b)** What might the repetition reveal about the state of the speaker's mind?

3. (a) Is the rhyme scheme of the poem regular or irregular? Explain. **(b)** Would you describe the rhythm or beat of the lines as familiar or unusual? Explain.

Countee Cullen
1903 • 1946

Though he wrote drama and prose as well as poetry, Countee Cullen is best remembered for his powerful lyrics, which explore the attitudes of people toward one another and the world about them, and reveal both the joyous and sorrowful aspects of the black American heritage.

Raised in New York City, Cullen attended New York University and Harvard. Considered one of the foremost lyric poets of this century, he once remarked about his poetry, "Most things I write I do for the sheer joy of music in them."

What would you shout if you were first to the top?

I Know That Feeling

Simon Ortiz

Tom, I think it was,
was telling Janice and Rosemary
about being a Mohawk[1]
and being an ironworker
5 on highsteel.
He said
that when they were finishing
the World Trade Center,[2]
he climbed all the way to the top—
10 he was the first one up there—
and he shouted at the top of his lungs,
"I'm an Indian."
I only heard
the story on a tape recorder,
15 but I know that feeling.

Discussion

1. **(a)** What is Tom's occupation? **(b)** What, according to the speaker, does Tom do one day on the job? **(c)** Would you describe Tom's actions as silly? dangerous? admirable? Why?

2. **(a)** What feeling do you think the speaker is referring to in line 15? **(b)** Have you ever experienced that same feeling? Explain.

Simon Ortiz

Simon Ortiz, an Acoma Pueblo Indian from New Mexico, has worked as a journalist, teacher, baker's helper, soldier, laborer, and public relations director among other things.

He does not recall ever deciding to become a poet, but he believes he may have been influenced as a young boy by an old relative who used to come to his home and tell stories.

With respect to his own writing, Ortiz has offered himself the following advice: "Pay attention to as many things as possible, note their detail, and breathe them into you. Don't worry about leaving some items out; you are only humble and among many parts and forms."

"I Know That Feeling" by Simon Ortiz from *Yardbird*, Vol. 3 published by Yardbird Publishing Co., Inc., 1974. Reprinted by permission.
Simon Ortiz (ôr tēs′)
1. *Mohawk*, member of a tribe of Iroquois Indians formerly living in central New York State.
2. *World Trade Center*, landmark in New York City and one of the tallest buildings in the United States.

Simon J. Ortiz. *The Man To Send Rain Clouds* edited by Kenneth Rosen. (New York: The Viking Press), 1974.

Portrait

Carolyn Rodgers

mama spent pennies
in uh gallon milk jug
saved pennies
fuh four babies
5 college educashuns

and when the babies
got bigger they would
secretly "borrow" mama's
pennies to buy candy

10 and pop cause mama
saved extras
fuh college educashuns
and pop and candy

was uh non-credit in bad teeth
15 mama pooled pennies
in uh gallon milk jug
Borden's by the way

and the babies went
to school cause mama saved
20 and spent and paid
fuh four babies

college educashuns
mama spent pennies
                    and nickels
25   and quarters
                    and dollars

and one life.
mama spent her life
in uh gallon milk jug
30 fuh four Black babies
college educashuns.

"Portrait" by Carolyn Rodgers from *Songs of a Blackbird* published by Third World Press. Reprinted by permission of the author.

1. Describe mama.

2. (a) Who do you think the speaker is? (b) What makes you think so? (c) How does the speaker feel about mama?

3. (a) What does the speaker mean by "uh non-credit in bad teeth"? (b) What is meant by "mama spent her life in uh gallon milk jug"?

4. What seems to be the purpose of using *uh* for *a, fuh* for *for, cause* for *because,* and *educashuns* for *educations?*

Carolyn Rodgers

Chicago-born Carolyn Rodgers describes her work as a love affair with words. She credits Gwendolyn Brooks, Pulitzer Prize-winning poet, with providing the encouragement she needed to quit her job as a counselor and language arts instructor and pursue a writing career full time.

Ms. Rodgers says that she writes the way she feels, wanting the reader to hear certain sounds. She often spells a word exactly the way it would be pronounced, so that the reader says as well as hears the sounds.

Old keepsakes—how do you measure their real worth?

Street Window

Carl Sandburg

The pawn-shop man knows hunger,
And how far hunger has eaten the heart
Of one who comes with an old keepsake.
Here are wedding rings and baby bracelets,
5 Scarf pins and shoe buckles, jeweled garters,
Old-fashioned knives with inlaid handles,
Watches of old gold and silver,
Old coins worn with finger-marks.
They tell stories.

Discussion

1. Explain the meaning of the first three lines.

2. (a) What kinds of things are brought to the pawnshop? **(b)** What might these things represent to the people who pawn them?

3. (a) What word besides *and* is used four times in the poem? **(b)** What reason might the poet have for repeating this word so many times?

4. (a) Do you tend to read the poem slowly or quickly? Why? **(b)** To what degree is the speed at which you read the poem appropriate to what the speaker is saying? Explain.

Extension • Writing

Assume that you desperately need money. What, of everything you own, would you least like to sell? Write a short paper that begins, "Of all my possessions, I would never like to part with. . ." Develop your paper with details: you might tell how you obtained this possession, what use you have made of it, why it has become precious to you, what plans you have for its future.

Carl Sandburg 1878 • 1967

Because his family was poor, Carl Sandburg left school at thirteen to drive a milk truck. While still in his teens he traveled around the country in box-cars, making friends with hoboes and working when he needed money. Later he worked his way through college, did some traveling—this time as a salesman—and finally took a job in Chicago. That city and its people are the subject of some of his best poems.

Sandburg's talents were not limited to poetry: he was a noted collector of folklore who did much to popularize folk music and who won recognition as a historian with his six-volume biography of Lincoln.

Are you like the people described in this poem?

The Forecast

Dan Jaffe

Perhaps our age has driven us indoors.
We sprawl in the semi-darkness, dreaming sometimes
Of a vague world spinning in the wind.
But we have snapped our locks, pulled down our
     shades,
5 Taken all precautions. We shall not be disturbed.
If the earth shakes, it will be on a screen;
And if the prairie wind spills down our streets
And covers us with leaves, the weatherman will tell us.

From *Prairie Schooner* published by the University of Nebraska Press. Copyright © 1964 by Dan Jaffe. Reprinted by permission of the author.

Jay King

Discussion

1. (a) What is the meaning of "our age" (line 1)? (b) In what ways might "our age" influence our activities?

2. (a) What kind of forecast is the speaker describing? (b) By what means will we receive it? (c) What has it replaced in our lives?

3. (a) What is the speaker's attitude toward the kind of life described in the poem? How can you tell? (b) Is the speaker at all optimistic about the people who have snapped their locks and pulled down their shades? Explain.

Extension • Writing

Assume that you have it within your power to shut off all television sets forever. Before deciding whether to use this power, you should consider the consequences of eliminating television entirely. How would your life differ? What changes might occur within your family? How would society behave differently? (For example, would professional football remain as important as it now is? Might people read more? visit more? sleep more? Would they know as much about the world they inhabit?)

Write a paper that begins "I have decided to eliminate (or decided against eliminating) television entirely." Support your position with a number of reasons that your classmates will regard as both specific and sound.

Read the groups of sentences below. Then on your paper answer the questions that follow. If necessary, use the Glossary or a dictionary to check any words you are unsure of.

1. Grandmother knew that if she gave Jimmy the money, he would squander it no matter how badly his family needed food.

2. Grandmother knew that if she gave Jimmy the money, he would hoard it no matter how badly his family needed food.

a. In sentence 1, what does Grandmother think Jimmy will do with the money?

b. In sentence 2, what does Grandmother think Jimmy will do with the money?

3. Jenny made a red lacquer box with a beautifully inlaid cover.

4. Jenny made a blue lacquer box with a beautifully painted cover.

c. For which of the boxes would Jenny have had to cut into the cover?

d. For which of the boxes would Jenny have had to use small pieces of wood, metal, or other material?

5. His parents worried that David was turning into a miser.

6. His parents worried that David was turning into a spendthrift.

e. In which situation—that described in sentence 5 or that described in 6—would David be likely to have a lot of money saved?

It Says a Lot in a Little

Poems are records of experience to be shared. Poets see or do or think or feel, and they pass along their recorded observations and actions and ideas and emotions to the reader. This is what prose writers do also, but the poet's job is a special one. Prose writers can develop their themes at length, making abundant use of details. But poets are often forced, by the poetic form they choose, to call forth emotional and intellectual response in the fewest possible words. They choose their material with special care and screen their language for useless words. Careful selection and sifting result in *compression:* Poets say a lot in a little. For example:

Thy friendship oft has made my
    heart to ache:
Do be my enemy—for friendship's
    sake.

Blake, "To Haley"

These highly compressed lines by William Blake require rereading and reflection. Try describing the meaning in prose. About how many words does it take to express the same thought?

Like anyone else, poets use words for their usual meanings or *denotations.* But because they try to pack into a single word as much meaning as possible, poets are also concerned with the *connotations* of words, the emotions and associations they stir up in us. For example, read the following two quotations taken from Tennyson's "The Brook":

I chatter, chatter as I flow
I babble on the pebbles . . .

and

I murmur under moon and
stars. . . .

What two very different pictures of, and responses to, a brook do these quotations convey?

Because poets cut away needless words and pack those they use with multiple meanings and a range of emotions, poetry should be read slowly and carefully. To understand a poem fully, you have to be aware of the denotation and connotation of each word. And to develop that awareness, you need to keep a dictionary at hand as you read, not only to check the meanings of unfamiliar words but to discover at times unfamiliar meanings for familiar words.

See how well you understand the poem at the right:

George Rodger/MAGNUM PHOTOS

William Blake. "To Haley" from *A Treasury of Great Poems* by Louis Untermeyer, ed. (New York: Simon and Schuster), MCMXLII.

Apparently with No Surprise

Emily Dickinson

Apparently with no surprise
To any happy Flower
The Frost beheads it at its play—
In accidental power—
5 The blonde Assassin passes on—
The Sun proceeds unmoved
To measure off another Day
For an approving God.

What happens in the first three lines of the poem? Which word in line 2 implies a comparison between the flower and humans? What is unusual about the flower's response to being beheaded? In what ways does this response differ from the human response to death? What meanings does the word "accidental" carry with it?

What is the literal meaning of "blonde Assassin" (line 5)? What other meanings might it have? What connotations does "blonde" carry with it? Would you be more apt to think of death as having "blonde" or "brunet" hair? Why? What is the meaning of "proceeds unmoved" (line 6)? Why might the Sun and God accept death so readily? What criticism of human thinking may be implied?

3.

A famous poet extends an invitation.

The Pasture

Robert Frost

I'm going out to clean the pasture spring;
I'll only stop to rake the leaves away
(And wait to watch the water clear, I may):
I shan't be gone long.—You come too.

5 I'm going out to fetch the little calf
That's standing by the mother. It's so young
It totters when she licks it with her tongue.
I shan't be gone long.—You come too.

Gerhard Gscheidle from Peter Arnold

Discussion

1. (a) What do you infer about the occupation and the personality of the speaker? **(b)** What seem to be the speaker's feelings toward the person being addressed? How can you tell?

2. (a) Which words in the poem give it a conversational tone? **(b)** Does punctuation add to, or does it detract from, the informality? Explain. **(c)** Find examples of repetition in the poem. What purpose or purposes do they serve?

3. Robert Frost began several collections of his work with "The Pasture." What additional invitation does this placement suggest?

Extension • Speaking

Locate in your school or local library other poems by Robert Frost. Select two you would be willing to read aloud. You may choose either to tape-record the selections or to read them "live" before the class.

Some observations on one of Nature's smaller creatures.

The Chipmunk's Day

Randall Jarrell

Discussion

1. What words suggest the speed of the chipmunk and the directions in which he moves?

2. Note that the poet uses *and* only once. **(a)** Where else might he have used it? **(b)** How does its absence affect the rhythm of the poem?

3. (a) Cite examples of *inversions* in the poem. **(b)** What purpose do you think they serve?

4. Would the last line be improved if it read "Curls to his rest"? Why or why not?

Extension • Writing

By selecting his verbs carefully, Randall Jarrell makes his reader see the quick, precise movements of the chipmunk.

Imagine that you are a reporter writing a story about an automobile race at the Indianapolis Speedway. List ten verbs that should help your reader see the movements of the cars. Now imagine you are assigned to write about a hike your class is to take through the countryside. List ten verbs that might help your reader see the movements of class members. Finally, write a short paper (using vivid verbs) that begins, "When he started chasing me, I . . ." and ending, "At last I was safe."

In and out the bushes, up the ivy,
Into the hole
By the old oak stump, the chipmunk flashes.
Up the pole

5 To the feeder full of seeds he dashes,
Stuffs his cheeks,
The chickadee and titmouse scold him.
Down he streaks.

Red as the leaves the wind blows off the maple,
10 Red as a fox,
Striped like a skunk, the chipmunk whistles
Past the love seat, past the mailbox,

Down the path,
Home to his warm hole stuffed with sweet
15 Things to eat.
Neat and slight and shining, his front feet

Curled at his breast, he sits there while the sun
Stripes the red west
With its last light: the chipmunk
20 Dives to his rest.

Woodpeckers in Summer Frolic

David Nava Monreal

Dizzy red-headed
birds,
you make me laugh
with your babbling
5 and throaty gibberish.
Darting and dashing
between trees like
fickle children
in indecision.
10 You are madmen
playing the hatter's
game,
pounding insanely at
the bark with your
15 yellow beaks as
though your
souls were enclosed
within.
Your noise is
20 shattering
and your antics
are crazy,
but your brilliant
life adds
25 plumage to the
drab
leaves.

Discussion

1. Through most of the poem, what seems to be the speaker's attitude toward the woodpeckers? How do you know?

2. At what point does the speaker's attitude toward the woodpeckers seem to change? How can you tell?

3. What is meant by ". . . your brilliant/life adds/ plumage to the/drab/leaves"?

David Nava Monreal

In 1975 David Nava Monreal won a nationwide contest sponsored by the Chicano Cultural Center of Bakersfield College. Monreal has worked as a library assistant and as a group supervisor in the Tulare County Probation Department. He lives in Santa Cruz, California.

Some unscientific advice on how to measure raindrops.

Rain

Ross Parmenter

Discussion

1. (a) How does the wind reveal itself? (b) To what sense(s) do these images of the wind appeal? (c) According to the speaker, how can the size and force and weight of raindrops be determined? (d) To what sense(s) do the images of rain appeal?

2. (a) If someone said to you, "I don't understand this poem," how would you explain it in your own words? (b) What words do you think a reader must be able to define in order to understand the poem fully?

The parts of trees,
leaves, twigs and moving boughs,
reveal the wind.

But rain can be most surely gauged
5 on the surface of still water.
The punctured holes
make clear the congregation of the drops,
and each circumference the size,
and force is manifest
10 in brief beads popping
above the spreading circles
linking the water
in a coat of living mail.[1]

1. *mail,* flexible armor made of metal rings or small loops of chain linked together for protecting the body against arrows, spears, etc.

Denley Carlson/STOCK, BOSTON

Song of the Sky Loom[1]

Tewa Indian

Oh our Mother the Earth, oh our Father the Sky,
Your children are we, and with tired backs
We bring you the gifts that you love.

Then weave for us a garment of brightness;

5 May the warp be the white light of morning,
May the weft be the red light of evening,
May the fringes be the falling rain,
May the border be the standing rainbow.

Thus weave for us a garment of brightness
10 That we may walk fittingly where birds sing,
That we may walk fittingly where grass is green,

Oh our Mother the Earth, oh our Father the Sky!

Herbert J. Spinden, translator. "Song of the Sky Loom" from *Songs of the Tewa*.
Published under the auspices of The Exposition of Indian Tribal Arts, Inc., New
York, 1933.
1. *Sky Loom.* To the Indians of the desert, a rain shower, viewed against the
backdrop of the open Southwest landscape, resembled a giant loom hung from
the sky.

Discussion

1. The Tewa Indians live in the dry Southwest region of the United States. "Song of the Sky Loom" is a Tewa prayer for well-being. **(a)** To whom or what is the song addressed? **(b)** What request do the speakers make? Why do they make this request? **(c)** What do they offer in return? **(d)** What, specifically, might these offerings be? What phrase provides a clue?

2. **(a)** Describe the four items that would make up the garment of brightness. **(b)** To what degree is the falling rain an important part of the garment? Explain. **(c)** What do you think the garment of brightness is meant to represent?

Extension • Speaking

Bring to class two other songs by Native Americans you would be willing to read aloud or to tape-record for later playing. If you need assistance in locating such songs, ask your school or local librarian to help you.

Harald Sund

after any sunset

Mary Celinia Bruce

after any sunset
there is a glint
a certain afterglow
a rainbow show
5 of starflake snow
some dim glimmer
of sweet evening
shimmer
after any sunset
10 the end of day
the end of love
the end of living
a soft celebration
of once holding
15 now that is passed

Discussion

1. (a) What time of day is described in the poem? (b) According to the speaker, this is the time of day for doing what?

2. (a) To what two other events is this time of day compared? (b) Which word best indicates the speaker's attitude toward the events being compared: *angry, sad, fearful, accepting, joyful?* Explain.

3. Is "after any sunset" a more appropriate title for the poem than "after the sunset" or "after a sunset"? Why or why not?

Unit Review Tests 7: Poetry

CONTENT REVIEW

For each of the following ten statements about the unit you have just completed, explain whether you *strongly agree* with the statement, *agree, have no opinion, disagree,* or *strongly disagree.*

Whenever possible, be prepared to support each of your opinions with evidence from the selections.

1. In an age of astronauts, "who knows if the moon's" is too old-fashioned to be included in a poetry unit.

2. "Business" would be better if it were titled "Monkey Business."

3. In "after any sunset," the lines "a rainbow show/of star-flake snow" don't make sense.

4. The poem that most made me think was "Words."

5. "Portrait" would be improved if words in it were spelled correctly.

6. Poets shouldn't write poems that don't have capital letters, commas, or periods.

7. Humorous poems like "The Hunter" or "To a Dead Goldfish" are more interesting than serious poems like "Street Window" or "The Forecast."

8. Poems about human relationships like "Portrait" or "Kidnap Poem" are more interesting than poems about nature like "Rain" or "Woodpeckers in Summer Frolic."

9. In most poems in this unit, the poet and the speaker seem to be the same person.

10. If I had edited this book, I wouldn't have put so many poems together in one place.

Unit 7, Test I

INTERPRETATION: NEW MATERIAL

Read the poem below and on your paper answer the questions. You may refer to the poem as often as necessary.

Farewell   Liz Sohappy Bahe

You sang round-dance[1] songs.
I danced not to thundering drums
but to your voice singing.

You chiseled wood sculpture.
5 I watched not the tools or chips fly
but your strong hands carving.

You lived in a northern village.
I went there not to meet your people
but to walk where you had walked.

10 You followed calling drums.
I waited, willing the drums to stop.

From *New York Quarterly,* Summer, 1967. Reprinted by permission of the author.
1. round dance, a folk dance with dancers in a circle.

Notice that the characters in the poem are not given names. This makes asking questions about them a little awkward but not impossible. There are some assumptions—but only assumptions—to be made about these characters: that one is a male and the other a female and that (because of references to dances and drums and villages) they are probably native Americans. (It can be argued that these references can be applied to other ethnic groups as well.) With these suggestions in mind, answer the following questions.

1. Who is the speaker in the poem? (a) the person referred to as *you;* (b) the person referred to as *I;* (c) a person from the northern village; (d) an outside observer.

2. Why did the speaker dance? (a) for fun; (b) because it was expected; (c) because the person called *you* was singing; (d) because the drums were playing.

3. From the information in the second stanza, you can infer that the speaker's main interest was (a) the art of sculpting; (b) the skill of the sculptor; (c) the finished product; (d) the person who was doing the sculpting.

4. Why did the speaker go to a northern village? (a) because the person called *you* suggested it; (b) for a vacation; (c) to meet *you*'s family; (d) because *you* came from there.

5. (a) Whose actions are always mentioned first? (b) Who then reacts?

6. (a) Which of the two characters seems to be a doer? (b) Which seems more a follower and observer?

7. What might the "calling drums" of line 10 be? (a) literally, drums to summon people to war; (b) figuratively, a call to adventure, travel, new experiences; (c) neither *a* nor *b;* (d) either *a* or *b.*

8. What did the speaker do when *you* followed the drums?

9. Which of the following best describes the speaker's tone? (a) full of joy and hope; (b) angry; (c) full of persistence and devotion; (d) grief-stricken.

10. Which of the following statements best explains the significance of the title "Farewell"? (a) The speaker is saying farewell to childish and romantic feelings. (b) The *you* and the speaker have met for one last farewell. (c) The speaker waited apparently in vain for *you* to return and so, with sad acceptance, is saying farewell. (d) The speaker is furious and never wants to see *you* again.

Unit 7, Test II
COMPOSITION

Choose one of the following assignments to write about.

1. Reread "Street Window" by Carl Sandburg and pick out one of the items mentioned in the poem. What story does it suggest to you? Write a story using the object you have chosen as the focal point or center of interest. In composing your story, you should keep in mind the following questions: Who owns the object? How did that person obtain it? How valuable is the object? What caused the owner to pawn it? What effect on the owner did pawning the object have?

2. Although each has its own theme, tone, and overall effect, "To a Dead Goldfish," "The Pasture," "The Chipmunk's Day," and "Woodpeckers in Summer Frolic" all are based on close observation of other living creatures. Reread the poems, taking particular notice of the authors' attention to detail. Then take some time to watch the activities of a single nonhuman creature—the family dog or cat, a robin at the bird feeder, a bear cub at the zoo. Write a description of what you see, including not only what the creature does but your reaction to it. If you like, write your description in the form of a poem.

With family members you share ties of love and trust.

With friends you share mutual interests.

With people of your community

  you share needs for food, clothing, and security,

  needs to accomplish, needs to move ahead.

With every human being in the world

  you share connections, similarities,

AFFINITIES

There is terrible excitement and frustration in the house. My small brother T.W.—Thomas Warren Grieves—is missing. It's Saturday morning, and true summer weather. (Technically, it has been summer for some time, but the blue, deep, green-carpeted, *true* summer weather is finally here.) My older sister Lennie has found a note pinned to T.W.'s bunk bed. The note says: *I have been treated like a child. Goodbye forever. Your once-friend, T.W.*

Lennie, or Leonora if you want to be fancy, comes bouncing into the living room with the note (spelling correct, written in red crayon on lined paper). Lennie is seventeen, I am one year younger, and T.W. is ten. Behind Lennie, who is wearing one of my shirts and blue jeans, trail two dogs: Doctor, a four-year-old Irish setter, and Weasel, a

dog of many ancestors, among them possibly a mop. Lennie waves the note under my mother's nose, my father's nose, and mine. It is now nine-thirty, the sunlight is beating in at every window and the whole day promises everything. We have been searching around the house for T.W. for about fifteen minutes. Up until this minute the excitement and frustration have been terrible because T.W. was supposed to go for his piano lesson at nine. My father hands me the note and says, "Let's be calm and do some figuring." But he is a trifle white-faced. "Now, could anyone have insulted T.W.?" my father asks.

I say, "Nobody insulted the sprat. Last night, when you and Mom were out—"

Lennie interrupts: "We had to discipline him a little, if that's what you mean. He

*"Maybe you can see it in someone, too, in flashes.
It's those flashes we have to hang on to."*

A Few Notes
About the Arabian Oryx[1]

Paul Darcy Boles

wouldn't go to bed, and finally Tony," she jerks a thumb at me, "made him undress and get his pajamas on."

"He was doing experiments," I say. "He had some of those chemistry books and a bunch of wires and some kind of salts and test tubes and dry cells. He was squatting in the middle of a mess in the corner of his room he calls the lab, and he kept roaring at me to go away, get lost, whenever I reminded him he had to get some sleep. Finally I stripped him and dunked him—"

"You gave him a bath?" my mother says. Worried as she is, she approves of that. "Congratulations, it's a major job."

"Even the ears," I say. "All right, maybe I was a little mad. Then I popped him in his pajamas and turned out the lights and patrolled a while to see that he really was

asleep. That's all."

"All right," my father says. He is heading for the phone. "First thing to do is call the police. I suppose they get a lot of calls about missing children."

"Yes," my mother says, white-faced now. The phrase "missing children" has gone down to her stomach like lead. It rings in the air like doom. I think very hard about T.W.; I think how wonderful he is, living in a world of his own which he refuses to let anybody touch or bother from the outside. I think how radiant he is on many occasions,

1. *oryx* (ôr′iks), a cream-colored antelope with long, sharp horns, now nearly extinct.

completely filled with the joy of being alive—just like one of the grass blades that shine green and marvelous in the daylight.

While my father is on the phone, my mother scoots upstairs saying she is going to find out, by process of deductive elimination, what clothes T.W. may be wearing. Doctor, the Irish setter, comes and sticks his nose in my hand, his eyes soulful with mysteries far beyond my reach. I mutter to Doctor, "Where is he, Doctor? Where did that kid go?" The other dog, Weasel, walks to the door and whines. I get up and open the door and Weasel scoots out, bounding along with purpose. Watching his floppy progress, I suddenly remember something, and I wheel around to Lennie. I yell, "Where's *Milford?*"

Milford is our third dog, except that maybe he should be called our first dog because he's been around longer than the others. He's about twelve years old, a very fat cocker spaniel, coal black except for a distinguished snow-white muzzle and very clean white paws.

Lennie's eyes get dramatically large and she clutches her hands over the front of my shirt and says, "T.W.'s taken Milford with him!"

And indeed it is so. None of us has seen Milford all morning, and Milford, in his declining years, likes to be around the family a lot and no longer goes on rabbit-slaughtering and cat-chasing expeditions.

Quickly now, Lennie and I run all around the house, upstairs and down, hollering and whistling for Milford, but no Milford. This is a great clue. We come back downstairs to where my father is on the phone talking to a desk sergeant, and we nudge him until we can tell him about Milford's being missing. He relays this hot information. In the back of my mind I can see the sergeant's matter-of-fact face and I want to grab the phone and say, "Listen, sir, don't be bored; don't think of this as routine; this is a wonderful kid; this is T.W. and we want him because we love him." But, of course, I don't. My mother comes down again and joins us around the phone; my father goes on talking, muscles working in his jaws, but his face seems calm except for its whiteness. He gives all the information about T.W. he can think of: color of eyes, green-brown; color of hair, mousy but a little red, etc. My mother steps close to my father and whispers, "He's wearing his stetson hat and a red shirt and blue jeans and sneakers, I think, and he took the first-aid kit he bought at the army surplus store." My father nods and gives the information to the desk sergeant. The back of my throat is dry, and I know Lennie's is the same way. I can tell by the manner in which she keeps gulping.

I keep thinking of what a big city it is, how careless of life it is, and what can be waiting for T.W. At last my father hangs up, takes a breath, and says: "They're putting out an APB on him. An All Points Bulletin. The sergeant was reassuring. He says lots of kids go away like this, on impulse, and most of the time they're found in a hurry."

Nobody remarks on that phrase "most of the time." It's a piece of doom that flickers at the edge of the conscious mind.

I say, "Look, how about Lennie and me taking the convertible while you guys take the other car, and we'll check likely places." I have just that second remembered the bridge. The bridge is in an area where some new building has been going on, not far from our house. There are deep ravines around it, with ivy growing rampant; there's a creek running under it and at certain times of the year, of which this is one, the creek gets fairly high. T.W. swims a little like a puppy;

he is not what I'd call an expert.

I am on fire to go right now, but my mother says, "Wait. Let's—quickly—see if we can't think of several possible places so we don't cover the same ground; we'll take some, and you and Lennie take the others. No, wait—I'd better stay here in case he comes back."

"Yes, you'd better do that," my father says. He is gazing off into the distance, frowning, still calm, still white, as he sits beside the phone. "But it's a sound idea to get all our ducks in a row so that we don't cover the same ground."

So we do that, making quick mental lists of areas to be covered, in which I casually insert the bridge. T.W. and his friends have haunted that place in spite of family orders not to; there is something about the gold-brown swift-moving water that draws them. Then we're all set to move.

My mother says, "I believe I've called the home of every real friend of T.W.'s I can think of, but there may be a few more. I'll try to find some more."

And she is at the phone as my father leaves, and as Lennie and I leave. On our way out, Weasel passes us. He looks a little disconsolate, as if he had thought he knew where T.W. was, but turned out to be in error.

It seems impossible, as Lennie and I coast down the driveway, that we are not on some regular, happy-enough errand around town. The Saturday traffic, buzzing up and down the road below our house, is already tremendous. Everybody and his cousin are out enjoying the great, gracious weather. I drive (my father has taken the sedan off in another direction) and Lennie rides shotgun, holding tight to the door panel. "The little dope," she mutters. I nod but don't answer because I'm using all the powers of concentration I have to drive and, at the same time, look for some little telltale thing—a stetson hat, the flash of a small red shirt—anything that spells T.W.

At Old Rushing Drive, I wheel sharply left and head in under the cool of the oaks and the pines toward the ravine area. There are children of all kinds and descriptions playing along the boulevard grass; they're jumping rope and playing planet-seeking rocket men. There's one with a space helmet covering his face and he hollers merrily as we coast by. I think of T.W.'s FSC, which is short for Flying Saucer Club. I remember how he organized it the preceding summer and how it is still going great guns as far as he's concerned, even though members have been few and hardly loyal. When it was first formed by T.W., for the purpose of getting in touch with flying saucers from outer space, he had quite a few buddies who sat around in trees all day looking through telescopes for evidence of flying saucers. They had the right spirit, anyhow, and I know if I'd been a flying-saucer pilot I'd have somehow felt their enormous seriousness and dedication and paid them a visit. But some of the kids got skeptical after a while. This enraged T.W., who cannot stand a lapse in faith of any kind. A few members stuck, but T.W. thought he ought to enlarge the membership by taking in members from out-of-state. He wrote a lot of letters, laboriously, with good spelling, to friends of his who had, during the course of his short life, moved away. There were three or four out-of-state members with whom he corresponded faithfully.

Now, on Old Rushing Drive, as we leave the populous section and approach the bridge (somehow it looks gloomy and romantic, a place Edgar Allan Poe[2] might have doted on), I slow up and come to a stop beside the gray and fawn stone of the bridge.

Lennie and I hop out and gaze down into the fast-moving, twinkling water. There's the shred of an old boat, its sail crumpled and torn and dirty, nosed into the bank. There are old breakfast food boxes and other trash. I cup my hands around the sides of my mouth and call up through the scrub oaks and the pines, "T.W.! Ohhhhhhhhhh, T.W.!"

The noise beats against the stone of the bridge and seems to be swallowed beneath it. There aren't any other people around here right now. A couple of birds seem to swim from bough to bough of the bigger oaks, downstream. I put my hands on the stone of the bridge, and it's cold. I call and call. Lennie joins me. There's the feeling that neither of us wants to stop calling because we know when we do, all we'll get back is that echo, that mocking reverberation. We shake our heads at each other and I say, "Wait a minute." I slither down the bank as fast as I can around the end of the bridge. I stick my head under it where it's so dark I can't see anything for a second or two; then I can make out bits of things—the stonework above my head flashing in a prismatic dazzle, a water shaking—and here I yell for T.W. again. Nothing comes back but my own voice, magnified and yet lost. There is nobody there. I scrounge back up the bank and get in the car. Lennie says, "Next, that way," curving her arm to the south.

I drive on and take the next road. We come out into an area where kids, hundreds, thousands of children, none of them T.W., are playing. We coast past. Sometimes Lennie spots one of them who knows T.W., and we stop and ask if the child has seen him. The answer is a cheerful negative, as if in the minds of children of this age there is

---

2. *Edgar Allen Poe* (pō), American writer of poems and stories notable for their gloomy atmosphere and mood of terror (1809–1849).

473

nothing terrible that can happen, as if this is merely an incident for adults to be worried about. The whole thing has nothing to do with the immediate moment spent enjoying the beautiful weather.

Down this road we go, and then at last we come out on the main road again, moving south. There are so many people out in the air, breathing in huge chunks of it, that one of them *must* be T.W. I think of a game T.W. and I used to play when he was about five and I was just about a year older than he is now; I told him stories in which he assumed the name of Thump Frog, and I became the Fox. Sometimes, even now, we call each other Frog and Fox, as if the distance between us is shortened for a moment or so.

Lennie grabs my arm. "Stop at this gas station. I'll call home and see if—and I'll ask if the gas station men've seen him." I stop; she heads for a phone. She asks one of the men if he's seen T.W. I ask the same thing of the other attendant. As I describe T.W.— about so big, red shirt, black stetson hat, and maybe a cocker spaniel along with him—I realize I cannot tell anybody what makes T.W. so special. I understand that anybody describing someone special cannot get that quality into the description.

Maybe some of the way I feel about this gets through to the man I'm talking to; he has the name Sam stenciled on his breast pocket. He seems very sympathetic. "I've seen him," he says. "He's been around here; I know him. I know that dog too. But not this morning. See, people've been in and out of here like popcorn all morning, and—"

Negative, negative, why couldn't it have been positive? I just stand still for a second, trying to let my instinct take over. I think of the time I was going to take T.W. to see something special—some Saturday afternoon science-fiction movie—but something

else of my own came up. I think of many such times, and how you get so used to the people you love that their specialness seems to wear off and doesn't come back in focus until there's an emergency. I think of the wonder, the terror, of just being alive, just being able to breathe as I'm doing now, and under my breath, right there in the gas station, I say, "Thump Frog, where are you? This is Fox, wanting to know."

Lennie comes running back from the gas station phone. She shakes her head. "Nothing. But, Tony, he's got the money from his bank with him. Mom discovered the empty bank."

"Good, good," I lie, thinking he could get on a bus and go a long way with about twelve dollars. I can tell, looking at Lennie's face, that she, too, has been thinking of all the shutouts she's given T.W. over the years. We thank the gas station men quickly and get back in the car.

"Where?" I say, and she shakes her head harder this time, sitting there with her palms shut tight together.

"All right," I say, breathing deeply. If I could only reach out among all the people whizzing past us in cars, strolling up and down, and get T.W. "All right, where would I go? If I were T.W., and mad at the family and maybe the world, where would I go?" No big answer comes back.

Without saying anything else I back up and we meander back the way we've come, watching every chunk of shrubbery, every open lawn, every dog and cat, every child, every house, every glimmer at a window.

We shoot along in traffic, with Lennie holding onto the door panel, sighting for anything that looks even a little like T.W. The sun swarms down on us, remote and not any part of the world where we now live. At last we drive into Willow Square. Years ago, it was just acres of willow trees, but now it's an enormous shopping center. There's no special place to look, although I think of several likely possibilities: the Hobby Shop, one of the big five-and-dime stores. We park and go in different directions—I to the Hobby Shop and Lennie to one of the department stores. Everybody today seems to swing with great joy. There are children everywhere, a sea of children's faces. Now and then I spot one belonging to somebody who knows T.W. and I stop and ask the rote question: "Have you seen him this morning?" and every time the answer is a casual no. If the mothers and fathers happen to be with their offspring, they show concern, instant sympathy; this touches something in them which is alert to danger, and they urge the child to *think,* to *try to remember.* But they might as well be urging the summer wind or the grasses to remember yesterday's rain.

Somebody in the Hobby Shop is running a motor scooter, testing it out on the stand. Above that giant bee-buzz it's hard to talk, but I yell my questions to the clerks. They know T.W.; he buys a lot of his scientific supplies here, and a lot of his saucer books as well. But no one has seen him today. The hardware and balsa smells mix in our nostrils; the gaiety of the world beckons in splashing signs and small, colored plastic rockets, but there is no T.W. staring or formulating questions.

Out of the shop I go, and a dog scampers up and looks sharply up into my face for a second—a terrier, not a fat, patient, white-muzzled cocker spaniel. It whines for attention and I scratch its ears briefly, feeling the plates of bone under the friendly fur. I remember the smell of T.W.'s hair (just fresh and clean, no special odor, yet somehow very special) after he has been plopped

into the tub by somebody like me, as he was the night before.

Savagely I try to justify myself. I didn't treat him badly; he asked for it, he was in a poisonous mood. But I can't do it, and all that self-justifying stuff floats into the air.

I run back to where I parked the convertible. For a second I can't remember just where it is and I think I have the wrong lane. Then I see, but Lennie isn't there yet. I climb in on the sun-hot seat, sit there for another second, then stand up and look all around me in a 360-degree circle, like a short lighthouse watching for a special boat. Once, I see a kid about T.W.'s height in a red shirt, and I'm out of the car like a guided missile, but when I get close, it's another kid. I go slowly back to the car. It seems hours before Lennie shows up, and I can see by her face, even before she shakes her head, that it's no soap there either.

So we leave Willow Square. I say, looking at my wristwatch, "It's only ten-thirty." Even with the sick feeling in me, I'm able to say, "Maybe we're making too much over all this, Len. You know, maybe he's enjoying himself, and he'll come back okay, in his own time. . . . " I take another breath. "He can take care of himself." That's a lie, and she slides her eyes toward me and shakes her head. She is white and pinched (she's rather beautiful, even now) and she flips her head away and looks out over the grass strips alongside the road. I brake for the stoplight before we can turn up our street. "We'll go on home; maybe there's news," I say, my hands sliding along the steering wheel.

Everything smells so fine; the grass being mowed along our street has a scent that rises to surround us in a lazy wave. Some child yells at us from a car and I wheel to look. But it's not T.W.; it's a friend of his, waving from a station wagon window. Then the light changes and we're moving down the street, every little rise and decline seeming familiar, the houses so known—and yet so unknown.

Then, quick and soft as a leaf settling on grass in deep autumn, Lennie touches my shoulder and says, simply, "There he is."

There he is. I slow up. He's ahead of us on the right, hugging the curb but walking on the grass. Milford is waddling along, panting heavily, at his side, and an enormous leash of chain links drags along the ground between Milford's red collar and T.W.'s fist. In his arms T.W. carries a Japanese lantern, a tall, wide, paper affair like a good-sized accordion on end, purple and lilac and splashy gold. As I slow up and then brake just a little ahead of him, I can see how red his face is from the walk in the sun; there's a bloom of wetness over his freckles and his eyes look suddenly glad to see us. He looks like a lost lamb: mildly stubborn and apprehensive. Everything that made my throat dry goes away; I can feel something grateful and hot in my chest, and I call very casually, "Well. Like a ride?"

He nods, his eyes weighing and judging and scared under the shadow of the silly stetson's brim. He gets in the back; Milford also gets in with a great, lumpy sigh. Something in me is so thankful it goes out and up and up, spinning like a fireworks display. We mosey on along the street, cars passing us, and Lennie says, "Okay, you mad at us?"

In the rearview mirror I can see T.W.'s face. He shakes his head very swiftly. "No, I'm not. I was. I was very mad. I was angry as anything. Boy, I'm tired. I got up at six o'clock, and Milford and I went to Willow Square; we waited till it opened. I got a lock made for my science stuff at the locksmith's." He holds it up. It's large enough to keep a tiger out. I remember passing the

locksmith's at the square just a few minutes ago, and not asking him if he'd seen T.W. It didn't seem likely. T.W. sighs even more hugely than Milford. "Then I went to the pet shop and got a leash for Milford. We can use the leash, can't we?"

The leash is so outsize it will never be used; anyhow, Milford is a very tractable dog and since his last fight four years ago he has stuck close to home. Lennie says, "Yes, we can use it," and I nod in the rearview mirror. T.W. goes on: "Then I had breakfast at the Pancake Shop. I had to leave Milford outside, tied to a fireplug. I had blackberry pancakes and maple syrup; it was very good. I brought some out to Milford. Then—" He squirms back into the seat, relaxing further, beginning to enjoy the sheer goodness of being transported, the outlaw home from the wars. "—then we went to the dime store. The escalators, oh, boy, Milford didn't want to go on them, I had to drag him to get him on. I got this." He holds up the Japanese lantern. "For Mother." It is a terrible lantern, but it is great. "Isn't it beautiful?" says T.W.

Now it's night and everything has been settled. It becomes an anecdote to be told for years in family annals. T.W. has been punished, as he expected to be; he's grounded for two weeks, and in summer that's quite a punishment. But he took what he had coming to him. Things are back to normal, almost, with everybody saying what he really thinks (but not as deep as his thoughts while T.W. was gone). It's a splendid night with the moon beginning to rise over the oaks out in the side yard. The young dogs, Doctor and Weasel, are padding around the yard, barking now and then just for the fun of it. Lennie is out on a date, she'll be home around midnight. I have a date too; I'm to pick mine up in half an hour.

T.W.'s up in his room. I just went up there, opening the door quietly so I wouldn't disturb him in case he happened to be in the middle of an interesting and, who knows, valuable scientific experiment. He was writing something, scowling at the typewriter, hunt-and-pecking as he does with enormous concentration, as though the words had to come just right or he would spend his life bullying them into shape. He was in his pajamas. The door leading onto the porch roof from his room was propped open with a chair. Beyond the chair I could see the outlines of my old telescope, which I had worked and saved for the summer I was fourteen.

I'm standing there, and I want to say to T.W., "Look, don't ever do this again. You are so much a part of us that what you did was evil and unforgivable. More than you know, or will know for a couple of years. Unforgivable, even though you're forgiven. Please, along with everything bright and sure and powerful and noble that's in you, get a little sense. Just do that and everything will be okay all the way."

But I don't say it. I can't say it. I say, instead, "You writing to somebody?"

"Yes," he says, suffering me patiently, trying to find just the right words. Then, in the light of what happened today, he loosens up more and says, "I won't leave home again. Not till I'm even a good deal older than you, Tony."

"Good," I say.

"I'm writing to Melinda Stark. You know, she used to live over on Grantwood."

"Oh, sure, I remember her," I tell him.

"She's an out-of-state member of the FSC."

"Say, that's fine," I say.

"Did you know," he says thoughtfully, "she has leukemia?"

I shake my head no, and he says, "Well, she has. It's incurable, you know, Tony. They give her about a year to live. I was just out signaling—" He nods toward the porch roof. "I thought I got an answer, but it could've been just a star-flicker; I'm not sure. It didn't *feel* like an answer yet. I think I'll get one finally, though, from a saucer—or maybe even from a mother ship, if I can reach that far. I watched through the 'scope, and then signaled with the flashlight. They come low, you know, when they come." He squints out over the dark treetops into the moonlight. Everything is alive and pulsing out there, but nothing, so far, has signaled back.

He says firmly, looking at me again, "I'm dedicated to making contact with flying saucers and getting a message to them and getting one back, *soon*. They know so much. Obviously, they do. They must have a cure. Wouldn't it be great if I could get the cure?"

After a second or two I say: "It'd be great. Real boss." Then I start stepping back and shutting the door again. T.W. says with cheer, "Love you." I nod and go out in the hall and down the stairs.

Now I'm sitting in the living room, waiting until it's time to pick up my date. I think about T.W., our family, this world. And I think, as well, of a little item I read somewhere not long ago about the fact that specialists are trying to learn about the life and habits of the Arabian oryx. Nobody knows much about its life cycle. Its elusive ways have made it an impossible subject for study in the wild.

For me, there's a real connection between the Arabian oryx and T.W. Maybe you can see it in someone, too, in flashes. It's those flashes we have to hang onto. They're bright. Oh, buddy, are they bright. □□

Discussion

1. (a) What was the reason T.W. ran away? **(b)** Do you think he had reason enough? Why?

2. When the family discovers T.W. has run away, what are their individual reactions? Consider Mother, Father, Lennie, and Tony.

3. T.W. is an unusual ten-year-old boy. Give specific examples of the following characteristics that make him special: **(a)** his organizing skills; **(b)** his persistence; **(c)** his writing; **(d)** his generosity; **(e)** his compassion or sympathy for others less fortunate; **(f)** his curiosity.

4. Anyone running away usually takes personal items along. What did T.W. take? For what reasons?

5. While T.W. was away, he bought certain items that showed he planned to come home again. What were these items?

6. Why were T.W.'s purchases amusing to Tony?

7. (a) How was T.W. punished for running away? **(b)** Do you agree that this was right? **(c)** Did T.W. seem to mind?

8. Tony is an emotional person. Describe how his feelings cause him to react **(a)** when he discovers T. W. is missing; **(b)** while searching for T.W.; **(c)** when he first sees T.W. walking along the street.

9. What are some of the things Tony wants to say but doesn't? Why doesn't he say them?

10. What was the one time Tony remembers failing T.W.?

11. During the search, what lies does Tony tell himself and Lennie to make them feel better?

12. (a) Do you think the household will soon be back to normal? Will T.W.'s specialness once again be overlooked and will others once again treat him as a child? Explain. **(b)** What does Tony mean by saying at the end that one sees specialness in someone in flashes, bright flashes?

Vocabulary • Context

Determine from context clues the meaning of the italicized word in each sentence below. Then choose from the words that follow the one closest in meaning to the italicized word.

1. After the death of her father and the accident that left her crippled, Edith became *disconsolate;* even daily visits from the Reverend Brown could not raise her spirits.

Disconsolate means (a) full of fear; (b) without hope; (c) calm; (d) unable to speak.

2. Muffin had always been so *tractable* that Jerry knew something was wrong when the dog suddenly refused to take another step, no matter how firmly Jerry spoke or how hard he yanked on the leash.

Tractable means (a) stubborn and mean; (b) overly friendly; (c) easily managed; (d) not very bright.

3. During their brief wait for the bus, Aunt Shelley entertained Dorrie and her friends with an amusing *anecdote.*

Anecdote means (a) a dinner party; (b) a short account of an interesting event; (c) a long, detailed account of a person's life; (d) a shopping expedition.

4. Mr. Hart's words were kind ones, but the children could tell by his *scowl* that he was really furious with them.

Scowl means (a) a smile; (b) a stare; (c) a frown; (d) a limp.

5. Unlike Marla, who was certain the plan would work, Dolores was *skeptical.*

Skeptical means (a) not believing easily; (b) uncaring; (c) carefully studying; (d) furious.

Extension • Writing

Think about someone who is special to you. Write a short paper telling about this person's specialness. Give specific examples to support your description. Perhaps you can relate an incident which demonstrates why you feel this person is special, or a time when you saw this person's specialness in "bright flashes," as Tony says about T.W.

Best of all is the promise . . .

Mama Is a Sunrise

Evelyn Tooley Hunt

When she comes slip-footing through the door,
    she kindles us
    like lump coal lighted,
    and we wake up glowing.
5 She puts a spark even in Papa's eyes
and turns out all our darkness.

When she comes sweet-talking in the room,
    she warms us
    like grits and gravy,
10   and we rise up shining.
Even at night-time Mama is a sunrise
that promises tomorrow and tomorrow.

From *The Lyric* (1972). Reprinted by permission of the author.

Discussion

1. (a) List some of the phrases which describe Mama's effect on her family. (b) What kind of impression of her do you get from these phrases?

2. A hyphenated word is found in the first line of each stanza and seems to "set the stage" for the rest of that stanza. What are these two hyphenated words, and what do they tell you about Mama?

3. What does the speaker mean by the statement, "She . . . turns out all our darkness"?

4. What do you usually associate with a sunrise that you could apply to Mama as well?

5. Who do you infer the speaker of the poem is?

Extension • Writing

In the first stanza the speaker suggests that Mama's mere presence in a room can light up the others. In the second stanza the speaker suggests that Mama's words can warm others. If there were a third stanza, what else might the poet have included? List some other possible qualities that Mama might have. Or, write a third stanza of your own. Keep the tone and the imagery consistent with what has gone before.

Evelyn Tooley Hunt

"It's fun!" says Evelyn Tooley Hunt about writing poetry. She has been composing verse since she was a little girl. Though she writes some free verse, she prefers the challenge of fitting her ideas to the pattern of a definite rhyme and rhythm.

There is a sleep that feels neither cold nor heat . . . .

While I Slept

Robert Francis

While I slept, while I slept and the night grew colder
She would come to my bedroom stepping softly
And draw a blanket about my shoulder
While I slept.

5 While I slept, while I slept in the dark still heat
She would come to my bedside stepping coolly
And smooth the twisted troubled sheet
While I slept.

Now she sleeps, sleeps under quiet rain
10 While nights grow warm or nights grow colder
And I wake and sleep and wake again
While she sleeps.

Reprinted by permission of Robert Francis and the University of Massachusetts Press from *Come Out into the Sun: Poems New and Selected*, Copyright © 1936, 1964 by Robert Francis.

Discussion

1. (a) Who is the "she" of this poem? (b) What relationship does the speaker probably have to her? Why do you think so?

2. (a) In the first two stanzas what actions does "she" perform? (b) What kind of person do these actions show her to be?

3. (a) What change in focus takes place in the third stanza? What has actually taken place? (b) How has this event made the speaker feel? (c) What words or phrases in the poem are clues to this?

4. Describe in your own words the tone of this poem. What words help set the tone?

Robert Francis 1901 •

Robert Francis has taught the art of writing poetry for many years. When not teaching, he prefers to live in his small house in Amherst, Massachusetts, where he spends most of his time reading, writing, and gardening.

My Father and the Hippopotamus

*"They stared at one another
for what seemed ages,
my father and that female hippopotamus,
deep into one another's eyes;
then my father let go and giggled. . . ."*

Leon Hugo

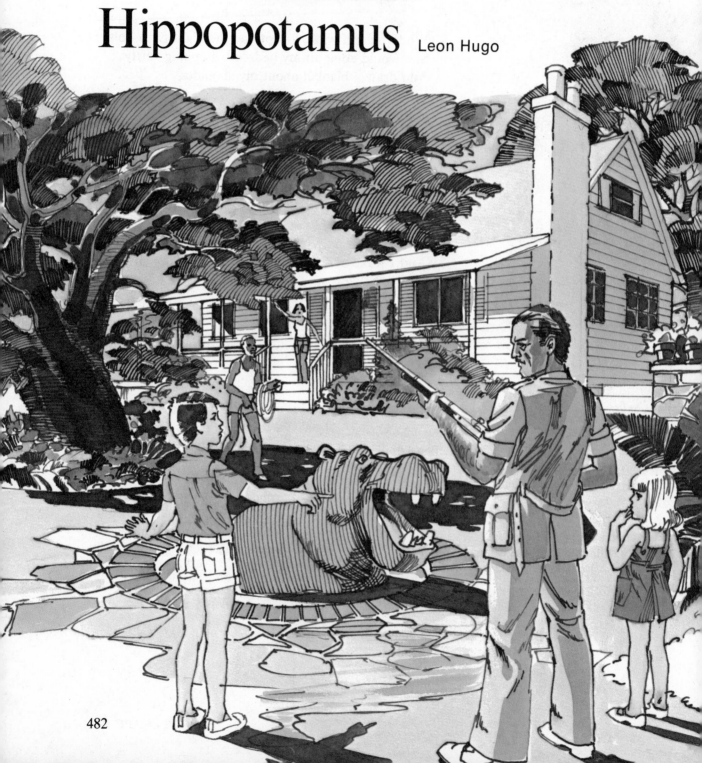

My father's farm was in the bushveld of the eastern Transvaal,[1] about thirty miles from the Kruger National Park. Wild animals therefore were common in our daily lives. They were nearly all, in their peculiar ways, destructive. Jackals stole my mother's chickens, koodoo[2] broke the fencing round the farm, giraffes entangled their necks in the telephone wires and lions occasionally carried off a cow. Sometimes they were dangerous. A lion once ate a herdboy instead of a heifer, and I still remember with a shudder the time I picked up a green stick which hissed, twisted, and bit my thumb.

Against most wild beasts my father had to wage unceasing war. On the whole he won—except against the hippos. The Letaba River ran through one end of our farm, and during the winter, when in its lower reaches the water level dropped, hippos would move upstream from the game reserve and settle on our farm. They always had. They sneaked in during the night, sank softly into one of the deep pools in the river, and having done so announced their arrival with an amiable deep bellow. That would start my father's annual dance of rage on the veranda. It used to frighten me nearly out of my wits, but never the hippos, which was not surprising as they were a mile away. I still remember thinking (when I was eight): "If you could see my dad now, you hippos, you'd clear out before tomorrow. Gee, he's mad!"

My father may well have seemed so to me (my sister was too young to notice and my mother used merely to sigh), but as I grew older I began to realize that his roarings and stampings and vows to blow all hippopotamuses to kingdom come were simply excessive face-saving devices. He knew, I grew to know, and the hippos must have guessed, that he could do nothing.

For one thing there were strict laws about the shooting of hippos; and for another, when on the mornings following their arrival my father stamped down to the river, there was never a sign of one. The reeds were crushed, of course, and the riverbank looked as though it had been put through a mincing-machine, but none of us ever saw a single shining rump or head above the silent green surface. My father always swore that the animals were near. He could feel, he said, the calculating gaze of sleepy hippos lurking among the reeds on the opposite bank. Occasionally he would hear a sniff or a coarse gurgle, and that made him angrier than ever. He would walk up and down the bank cursing, and daring any hippo to show its face, until my mother sent a message to say that breakfast was ready.

After these formalities there was nothing my father could do except see that fires round the lands were kept going during the night. These usually protected the crops from the hippos' darkling gambols, but during their two-month stay my father was an anxious and overworked man.

"Give me a herd of stampeding buffalo, rather," he once remarked bitterly. "At least you can see them. But these hippos! I wish," he added wistfully, "I could catch one—just one—with its pants down. I'd teach it who's boss. By golly, I would!"

His chance came, I remember, on a Sunday.

The hippos had been making a dreadful noise the night before: an army of swine

From *Blackwood's Magazine* (February 1960). Reprinted by permission of William Blackwood & Sons Limited.

1. **bushveld . . . Transvaal** (trans väl´). A bushveld is an area of grassy plains and scrubby bushes; the Transvaal is a northeastern province of the Union of South Africa.
2. **koodoo,** a large African antelope, usually spelled *kudu*.

would have been nightingales in comparison. The crashing splashes, the snorts, grunts and squeals coming up to us through the dark in blasts of shattering sound, pointed to a hippopotamus frolic of unprecedented scope. To add to the pandemonium our two dogs, which were kept chained in the back yard, started howling. My father, with visions before him of a concerted hippo attack on his crops, if not on our very house, made four journeys on foot round his lands to see that the farm hands were keeping the fires going; and although he took a powerful flashlight with him—and a servant carrying a rifle—caught only one gray fleeting form in the beam of the torch.

When he came in for the fourth time he looked as though he had had enough. "They can eat everything," he muttered. "Everything—I don't care any more. There's enough for them anyway. About a ton of tomatoes per belly. I hope. . . . "

"Oh, John, I'm sure it will be all right," said my mother.

"I hope they burst, I do. I really do." My father spoke very calmly. "Laurie," he said to me, "shut the dogs up."

My sister, as I walked out, said, "Daddy, has a hippo got a curly tail like a piggy's?" When I came in again she was crying and my father had gone to bed.

A tremendous yell woke me the next morning. I shot up in bed to hear flat native feet pounding through the garden toward the house, the yell repeated, and then a burst of insane giggling. I was out in the passage in a moment and saw Matiba, my mother's kitchen boy, still giggling as he banged on my parents' bedroom door.

"What's the matter, Matiba?" I cried.

He only rolled his eyes and continued his giggle until my father opened the door.

"What is it?" my father growled.

Matiba managed to point to the garden. We hurried to the veranda. It was still early, but the sun had risen enough to make the garden fairly easy to see: particularly the cause of old Matiba's fright; for Nature, as though to heighten the effect, had directed through the trees a shaft of golden light onto the fishpond. Cosily basking in this, half-submerged in the water, was a hippopotamus, fast asleep.

My mother called, "What is it, John?"

"A hippo," said my father, extraordinarily calm.

"A what?"

"I said a hippo," said my father.

"Good heavens!" said my mother. After a pause she called out, "Where?"

"In your fishpond."

There was another pause from my mother, a long one. Then, "The poor goldfish!" we heard her gasp.

My father laughed shortly. "Laurie," he said, "fetch my rifle."

My mother was on the veranda when I got back. She looked pale. I handed my father the rifle. "You aren't going to shoot it, are you, John?" she said.

My father opened the breech. "I jolly well am," he answered grimly.

Sunlight had swept in a flood into the garden by then, and we could see our visitor down to the last wrinkle on its hide. It was a calf, a small one, weighing about eight hundred pounds, and it fitted snugly into the pond, like a round balloon wedged in a tin can. As my father raised the rifle to his shoulder the hippo moved. Water splashed out of the pond as it snuggled in more deeply; and then it yawned, opening its jaws to cavernous proportions and displaying a set of young but immense canines.

I waited, holding my breath for the report of the rifle.

"How will you get it out?" my mother asked.

A spasm ran through my father's body, and for a moment it looked as though he would still pull the trigger. But he did not. Slowly he lowered the rifle. "What did you say?" he said softly.

"How are you going to get it out?"

"Quite simple, dear," said my father patiently. "We'll pull it out."

"You couldn't."

"Couldn't?"

"You couldn't possibly drag a huge beast that weighs thousands of pounds out without ruining the fishpond."

I could see by the look on my father's face that my mother had presented a poser. "We'll hack it up first," he suggested.

"You will not," said my mother firmly. "I'm not having any hippos cut up in my front garden, and anyway I think it's horrid. and cruel. He's only a calf."

My father said, "If you want the goldfish to have a playmate, dear, just say so and we'll leave little Jumbo[3] to have his wallow."

"That's not a Jumbo," remarked my sister, who had joined us.

"You're quite right, darling," my mother told her. "Daddy's just being altogether ridiculous."

In the fishpond the hippo belched, not softly.

"No," my mother went on. "What you've got to do is get rid of it without ruining the pond or flowers. I've slaved for years in this garden and I'm not going to stand by and let you destroy it just because you can't get rid of a baby hippo."

"You make me sound so ineffectual," my father grumbled, but he was, I think, secretly glad that he could not conscientiously go on with the killing. "Matiba," he said, "call the boys."

The natives came running from their huts, all of them agog. Stealthily we crept up to one side of the sleeping hippo. As we drew closer we could hear it breathing, slow and deep, with the faintest rumbling snore.

"Now!" yelled my father, and the din started. In addition to ten or so full-blooded yells, empty paraffin tins clashed under smiting sticks and my father's rifle cracked five times as he fired into the air. Altogether it was a most discordant and satisfying noise, and it seemed to electrify our hippo.

It stood up in the pond. Drops shook from it in a silver shower and a goldfish slid from its rump into the water. And it bellowed. Awed by the majesty of that blast we fell silent. We looked at the hippo, it at us. There was something regal about a hippo, even a baby one. We squirmed under its angry gaze. Then, as we silently watched, it sniffed, blinked, and settled slowly back into the pond.

We started our noise again, of course, but shamefacedly and with much less gusto; in any case the more we shouted and banged, the deeper into the pond did the hippo try to get. Only a circlet of rump, its ears, eyes and snout remained above the water eventually. We gave up after half an hour when jabs (with a very long pole) had produced no effect beyond indignant snorts and showers of spray.

"No good," my father whispered, as he and I returned to the house, and the natives, strangely quiet, to their huts for their day off. "We'll have to think of something else."

Breakfast was a silent meal. Even my sister, after mentioning sadly that hippos' tails were straight, said nothing. Shortly afterwards my mother left for church, but

---

3. *Jumbo,* an elephant. The name comes from a famous elephant named Jumbo, exhibited in P. T. Barnum's circus during the late nineteenth century.

before driving off she asked my father to promise not to kill the hippo. Which he did, rather irritably.

My father spent the greater part of the morning staring pensively at the hippo in the pond. Finally he said, "We'll have to drag it out, all the same," and went to fetch the truck. He brought it round, reversed it between the trees surrounding the garden to as near the pond as he could go.

"This is what we do, Laurie," he said. "Tie this rope to the bumper and loop the other end round the blighter's neck. If I can't manage a dead one, a live hippo's going to find itself doing a quick sprint out of that pond."

I was only ten then, but I saw a difficulty at once. "Who's going to put the rope round its neck?" I asked.

"Matiba, of course; who else?" said my father, surprised. "Call him."

I did. Matiba came running from the kitchen. We told him what we wanted him to do and he started running again.

"Oh, well," said my father, when the wails of the objecting domestic had faded in the bush. "I'll do it myself."

First we tied the rope to the rear bumper; then my father made a wide noose of the other end and advanced slowly toward the pond. The hippo watched him suspiciously, snorting softly. It was wide-awake and clearly still annoyed.

I heard my father talking to it. "Steady now, boy. Don't worry, we don't want to hurt you. Just pull your head off at the worst. . . . " Carefully he inched forward to within about three yards of the pond. "Steady. . . !" He threw the rope. It was a good shot and the noose dropped over the hippo's ears. For a second my father looked quite pleased. Then the hippo bellowed straight into his face and wrenched its head

upwards. My father catapulted back into a bed of flowers where he lay cursing; but in jerking its head the hippo had helped the noose to fall farther over its ears and round its neck.

It was some moments before I could bring my father to realize this happy accident. When he did, though, he cheered up considerably, and after a few furtive flicks on the slack of the rope, the noose was reasonably tight round the hippo's neck.

"Well," my father remarked as we climbed into the truck, "that's nearly that. But one thing's got me slightly bothered."

"What?" I asked.

"Once we've got him out he'll still be attached to us—to the truck. Can't let the fellow go with twenty yards of good rope still round his neck."

The vision of a baby hippo permanently tied to the back of our truck made me long for its realization; but I saw with regret that it could hardly be practical.

"Anyway," my father continued happily, switching on, "we'll deal with that when it comes up." He revved the engine and slowly let in the clutch. The truck moved forward.

I could not see, sitting beside my father, but could feel when the rope tautened. We could hear too. Behind us, from the fish-pond, came tremendous splashings and snorts of rage. The engine hummed, raced, roared; the wheels screamed in the earth. Then we shot away, bounded away rather, like an impala, and thundered along the car track toward the river.

"Golly!" my father yelled jubilantly. "He can run! Thirty—and not the slightest strain. . . . " A few seconds passed and then a worried look came into his face. He slowly braked.

We climbed out to look. There was no baby hippo behind us and no rope. There

was no rear bumper.

Up to that moment my father had been exceptionally calm. But the strain began to tell on him then and I grew a little afraid. He got very red in the face and started muttering through clenched teeth. As we drove back to the farmhouse I felt glad I was not that poor hippopotamus.

"You going to shoot him now, Dad?" I ventured.

"No!" my father roared. "I'll get him out alive if it takes me a week!"

The hippo was in the pond, the rope was still round its neck—the torn-off rear bumper skulked in a flower bed—and my sister was sitting on her haunches beside the pond gazing earnestly into the hippo's eyes. They seemed to be getting on well together; so well, in fact, that she strongly objected when

my father, swooping on her like a bird of prey, carried her into the house and locked her up.

"Untie that rope!" he yelled at me as he disappeared through the doorway. Shaking, I ran to obey, but his rage had so unnerved me that by the time he came back I had not managed a single knot. Up to then I had been enjoying myself immensely; now I began rather to dislike my father for spoiling the fun.

"You're an idiot," he informed me stridently. He pushed me aside, tried to untie the rope himself, tore his thumbnail, cursed, and cut the rope. I felt a little better.

He passed me the severed end. "Hold this," he said. "I'm getting under the truck to tie it to the axle." He glared at the hippo. "Just let him try to pull the axle off!" he snarled. "Hand me the rope when I'm ready."

He slid under the rear end of the truck. I was standing facing the pond. A sudden inexplicable gust of warm air struck the back of my neck and I swung round.

I question whether there is anything more conducive to a lightning upsurge of adrenalin than the sudden sight, from twelve inches, of an adult hippopotamus. The ancient wicked eyes, the primeval face, the enormous expanse of a two-and-a-half-ton amphibian, all make for extremely rapid action. A tree was close at hand. I was up it in about a millionth of a second, staring down, goggle-eyed and dumb, at the hippopotamus cow that had appeared from nowhere at my shoulder. She gave me a perfunctory glance before turning. The part of my father that protruded from the back of the truck caught her eye. She bent her head to examine it.

It was horrible. There I was up the tree, quite speechless with fright, expecting her to open her mouth and bite my father's backside off. But she merely gave a long, interested sniff and my father said, "What the devil are you doing, Laurie?" and wriggled pettishly. Then he said, "All right, give me the rope," and his hand strayed out. The hippopotamus sniffed at that.

My father, sensing that something was near and thinking it was the rope, said, "Give it to me," and grabbed. His fingers closed unerringly on the hippo's snout.

I found my voice at last. "Daddy," I squeaked, "get underneath! Get underneath!"

He did not. His hand seemed riveted to that snout; and some strange power, instead of sending him slithering for safety under the truck, brought him ineluctably out into the open. They stared at one another for what seemed ages, my father and that female hippopotamus, deep into one another's eyes; then my father let go and giggled, while the hippo breathed long, slow exploratory breaths and twitched her ears. My father rose slowly to his feet, murmuring noncommittally, "Good chap, good old girl," only just restraining himself from patting her on the head. Then the hippo opened her mouth.

What happened next was too quick for me to see. It was a blur of action and there was my father just beneath me in the tree gasping, "Get higher you fool, higher!" and I crying, "I can't, I'm stuck!" and my father appearing magically in the fork above my head and the hippo looking disappointedly up at him, as though she regretted not having tried a piece of human while the going was good. But if that was her thought it was only a passing one, for she turned almost immediately to the fishpond and grunted.

The calf squeaked in reply and squirmed. The mother—the new arrival must have been that—grunted again, more peremptorily, the young hippo slowly emerged, leaving a trail of destruction through my mother's dahlias. As it reached her she bit it, not viciously but with enough vigor to make the calf squeal sharply, spring aside, and start off at a smart gallop for the river. Without a glance up at us, she followed.

As they reached the trees the calf tossed its head and the noose flew free of its neck. In another moment the two animals had disappeared.

We climbed down and without a word to one another slunk into the house. . . .

The first rain of the season fell that night and the hippos left the river pool. They never came back. But five years had to pass before my father (avoiding my eye) dared boast that he had taught them a lesson. ▢▢

Discussion

1. What annual problem do the hippos create?

2. (a) What are the various plans for driving the young hippo away? **(b)** Why does each fail?

3. (a) What does Laurie mean by saying that his father's "roarings and stampings" were only "face-saving devices"? **(b)** Why does his father eventually claim to have taught the hippos "a lesson"? **(c)** Is this a natural reaction? Explain.

4. How might the tone of the story have differed if the father had been the narrator?

5. (a) Which events in the story are funniest to you? **(b)** What do the reactions of Laurie's mother and sister add to the humor?

6. According to Leon Hugo's comments in the author biography, how "true" is his story?

Vocabulary · Structure

Study the structure of the italicized word in each sentence below, then on your paper answer the questions that follow.

1. Professor Thomas told Cassie that her paper on the pitcher plant was *extraordinarily* good.

a. What is the root of the italicized word?

b. Was Cassie's paper fairly good or very good? What part of the word tells you this?

2. Henry's *unceasing* singing annoyed his coworkers.

a. What is the prefix of the italicized word? What is the root?

b. How often did Henry sing?

3. The cleaning agent Lee had seen in the commercial proved *ineffectual* in removing the spots from the rug.

a. What is the prefix of the italicized word? What is the root?

b. What happened to the spots?

4. Fearing cancer, her doctor recommended that Ms. Hynes come into the hospital for *exploratory* surgery.

a. What is the root of the italicized word?

b. Is there a possibility the doctor will remove nothing surgically? Explain.

Extension · Speaking

As you read "My Father and the Hippopotamus," which side did you find yourself on? Did you hope the father would succeed—or that the hippo would be able to hold out? Explain your position in a short talk, giving examples from the story—or from your personal experiences—which will help your audience understand your choice.

Leon Hugo

Regarding "My Father and the Hippopotamus," Leon Hugo writes, "I grew up in the eastern Transvaal (a Province or 'State' of South Africa), not far from the 'bushveld' and the famous wildlife sanctuary, the Kruger National Park.

"For the benefit of pupils whose knowledge of Africa begins and ends with the epithet 'darkest,' lions do *not* prowl through the streets of our towns and hippos do *not* settle into fishponds—except in fiction, which this story is, of course. But the story is 'true' in the sense that hippos are remarkably nomadic creatures. They sometimes leave their normal home in rivers for long stretches of time and appear in the most unexpected places. One hippo, popularly called Huberta, became a legend in her lifetime. She covered many hundreds of miles in the course of her wanderings, showed herself in several country towns, and was (I should imagine) well on her way to becoming a National Institution when a trigger-happy ignoramus shot her. Less spectacular is an incident of my boyhood: a baby hippo suddenly appeared in a nearby dam. No one knew where it had come from or how it had got there. Perhaps this was the source of my story, although I wrote the piece in London—come to think of it, I was riding on top of a London Transport bus when the idea first occurred to me!"

We all want to keep someone we love . . .

The River
Took My Sister

Shirley Crawford

Up on the green bank of the
river I stand waiting for
the sister I once called mine.

She left me years ago. The
5 day was bright, warm. We raced
to the clear blue water.

We raced back to shore. I
found myself alone. The blue
water kept my sister.

10 He loved her too.

Discussion

1. (a) What actually happened to the speaker's sister? (b) How long ago?

2. How does the speaker seem to feel about what happened? What clues to this are there in the poem?

3. What might cause the speaker to return to the river bank?

4. Do you think, judging only from what is presented in the poem, that the speaker is old enough to understand what has happened? Explain.

Shirley Crawford

Shirley Crawford is a member of the Kalispel Indian tribal group, also known as the *Pend d'Oreilles* (pà dô re′yə), or earring people, because when first encountered by early French explorers they were wearing large shell earrings.

Dan Morrill

Everywhere there are questions,
but there are answers, as well.

Who Am I?

Felice Holman

The trees ask me,
And the sky,
And the sea asks me
Who am I?

5 The grass asks me,
And the sand,
And the rocks ask me
Who I am.

The wind tells me
10 At night fall,
And the rain tells me
Someone small.

Someone small
Someone small
15 *But a piece*
of
it
all.

Discussion

1. What characteristics of nature—sea, rocks, trees, or sky—might suggest the type of question asked in the poem?

2. (a) Can this type of question best be answered by giving facts, opinions, or what? (b) Is it an easy question to answer? Why or why not?

3. (a) What is the answer the speaker in the poem hears? (b) What is most emphasized in the answer? (c) Is this an answer you would accept? Why or why not?

Extension • Speaking

Have you ever experienced a natural occurrence (a storm, for instance) or come upon a scene in nature (a mountain landscape, perhaps) that has made you feel both "small" but "a part of it all"? Explain to the class how you felt during and after the experience.

*The old man had agreed to sell his land,
but there was one thing he could not sell . . .*

Gentleman of Río en Medio

Juan A. A. Sedillo

It took months of negotiation to come to an understanding with the old man. He was in no hurry. What he had the most of was time. He lived up in Río en Medio,[1] where his people had been for hundreds of years. He tilled the same land they had tilled. His house was small and wretched, but quaint. The little creek ran through his land. His orchard was gnarled and beautiful.

The day of the sale he came into the office. His coat was old, green and faded. I thought of Senator Catron, who had been such a power with these people up there in the mountains. Perhaps it was one of his old Prince Alberts.[2] He also wore gloves. They were old and torn and his fingertips showed through them. He carried a cane, but it was only the skeleton of a worn-out umbrella. Behind him walked one of his innumerable kin—a dark young man with eyes like a gazelle.

The old man bowed to all of us in the room. Then he removed his hat and gloves, slowly and carefully. Chaplin[3] once did that in a picture, in a bank—he was the janitor. Then he handed his things to the boy, who stood obediently behind the old man's chair.

There was a great deal of conversation, about rain and about his family. He was very proud of his large family. Finally we got down to business. Yes, he would sell, as he had agreed, for twelve hundred dollars, in cash. We would buy, and the money was

"Gentleman of Río en Medio" by Juan A. A. Sedillo from *The New Mexico Quarterly*, August 1939. Reprinted by permission of the author.

Juan (hwän) **Sedillo** (se dē′yô).

1. **Río en Medio** (rē′ô en me′dyô), the name of the town means "River in the Middle."
2. **Prince Alberts,** long, double-breasted coats, named after Prince Albert (1819–1861), husband of Queen Victoria of England.
3. **Chaplin,** Charles Chaplin (1889–1977), English motion picture actor, especially noted for his comedy pantomime in early silent movies.

ready. "Don Anselmo,"[4] I said to him in Spanish, "we have made a discovery. You remember that we sent that surveyor, that engineer, up there to survey your land so as to make the deed. Well, he finds that you own more than eight acres. He tells us that your land extends across the river and that you own almost twice as much as you thought." He didn't know that. "And now, Don Anselmo," I added, "these Americans are *buena gente,*[5] they are good people, and they are willing to pay you for the additional land as well, at the same rate per acre, so that instead of twelve hundred dollars you will get almost twice as much, and the money is here for you."

The old man hung his head for a moment in thought. Then he stood up and stared at me. "Friend," he said, "I do not like to have you speak to me in that manner." I kept still and let him have his say. "I know these Americans are good people, and that is why I have agreed to sell to them. But I do not care to be insulted. I have agreed to sell my house and land for twelve hundred dollars and that is the price."

I argued with him but it was useless. Finally he signed the deed and took the money but refused to take more than the amount agreed upon. Then he shook hands all around, put on his ragged gloves, took his stick and walked out with the boy behind him.

A month later my friends had moved into Río en Medio. They had replastered the old adobe house, pruned the trees, patched the fence, and moved in for the summer. One day they came back to the office to complain. The children of the village were overrunning their property. They came every day and played under the trees, built little play fences around them, and took blossoms. When they were spoken to they only

laughed and talked back good-naturedly in Spanish.

I sent a messenger up to the mountains for Don Anselmo. It took a week to arrange another meeting. When he arrived he repeated his previous preliminary performance. He wore the same faded cutaway, carried the same stick and was accompanied by the boy again. He shook hands all around, sat down with the boy behind his chair, and talked about the weather. Finally I broached the subject. "Don Anselmo, about the ranch you sold to these people. They are good people and want to be your friends and neighbors always. When you sold to them you signed a document, a deed, and in that deed you agreed to several things. One thing was that they were to have the complete possession of the property. Now, Don Anselmo, it seems that every day the children of the village overrun the orchard and spend most of their time there. We would like to know if you, as the most respected man in the village, could not stop them from doing so in order that these people may enjoy their new home more in peace."

Don Anselmo stood up. "We have all learned to love these Americans," he said, "because they are good people and good neighbors. I sold them my property because I knew they were good people, but I did not sell them the trees in the orchard."

This was bad. "Don Anselmo," I pleaded, "when one signs a deed and sells real property one sells also everything that grows on the land, and those trees, every one of them, are on the land and inside the boundaries of what you sold."

"Yes, I admit that," he said. "You know," he added, "I am the oldest man in

---

4. *Don Anselmo* (dôn än sel′mô).
5. *buena gente* (bwā′nä hen′te), good people.

the village. Almost everyone there is my relative and all the children of Río en Medio are my *sobrinos* and *nietos*,[6] my descendants. Every time a child has been born in Río en Medio since I took possession of that house from my mother I have planted a tree for that child. The trees in that orchard are not mine, *Señor,* they belong to the children of the village. Every person in Río en Medio born since the railroad came to Santa Fe owns a tree in that orchard. I did not sell the trees because I could not. They are not mine."

There was nothing we could do. Legally we owned the trees but the old man had been so generous, refusing what amounted to a fortune for him. It took most of the following winter to buy the trees, individually, from the descendants of Don Anselmo in the valley of Río en Medio. ☐☐

6. *sobrinos* (sô brē′nôs) *and nietos* (nē e′tôs), nephews and nieces, and grandchildren.

Discussion

1. What kind of man was Don Anselmo? Consider (a) his physical appearance; (b) his house; (c) his occupation; (d) his standing or reputation in the village; (e) his favorite topics of conversation; (f) his personal traits (such as generosity, pride, and courtesy) and how he showed them.

2. What was the relationship of the people living in Río en Medio to Don Anselmo?

3. Explain how Don Anselmo is a "gentleman."

4. The narrator, the lawyer, does not say directly what he thinks of Don Anselmo, but the reader can understand from his "tone" the way he feels about him. What is his feeling?

5. (a) Why did it always take so long to set up an appointment with Don Anselmo if he wasn't very busy? (b) How did the lawyer contact him?

6. Why did Don Anselmo feel it was an insult for the Americans to offer more money?

7. If Don Anselmo had no money and was not interested in a great deal of money, in what did he take great pride?

8. (a) How were the children bothering the new American tenants? (b) Were the children disrespectful?

9. Why didn't the Americans press charges against Don Anselmo and legally take the trees?

10. (a) If the Americans had to buy the trees individually from the people in Río en Medio, who benefited from this? (b) Do you think Don Anselmo knew this would happen?

Vocabulary
Pronunciation, Dictionary

Use the Glossary or a dictionary to answer the questions about the words in the list below. You will not use one of the words in the list.

gnarled	innumerable
preliminary	gazelle
quaint	cutaway

1. What do the pronunciations of the words *gnarled* and *pneumonia* have in common?

2. If you told a woman that she ran like a *gazelle,* would she be more likely to be pleased or insulted?

3. Does the prefix *in-* in *innumerable* mean the same thing as the *in-* in *indoors*?

4. Which is more likely to be described as *quaint*, a hand-painted china teacup or a photo encased in a clear plastic cube?

5. Which of the words has its origin in the Latin word meaning *threshold?*

Extension • Speaking

"What you are and what you or your family owns is not important—the important thing is how you respect yourself and others, and whether your life is built on these principles of respect." Explain to the class how each part of this quotation might describe Don Anselmo.

How important is it to have friends?

I Am Through

Nguyen Trai

I am through living with others and their tricks.
I stay in the country, care only to be left alone.
Bamboo and plum trees do not betray you,
Monkeys and cranes are tolerant of independent souls.
5 I pick chrysanthemums, tend orchids:
Their fragrance stays in my coat.
I step on the moon in search of my plum trees,
The snow wets my kerchief.
My ears are attuned to the harp music of the brook.
10 As for friends, a green mountain is enough for me.

Discussion

1. What words or phrases help explain why the speaker has chosen to live by himself?

2. (a) What does the speaker find most attractive about living in the country? (b) What kind of life does the speaker seem to lead?

3. In line 7 the speaker says "I step on the moon in search of my plum trees." How could this possibly happen?

4. What might the speaker mean by "a green mountain is enough for me" (line 10)?

5. The poet Nguyen Trai once said he would trade fame and honor for a fishing pole. Is this belief reflected in the poem? In what lines?

Nguyen Trai 1380 • 1442

Nguyen Trai was a Vietnamese of many accomplishments. He was a military genius who helped drive Chinese invaders out of his country. He helped rebuild his devastated country as its prime minister; he wrote the first major geography of Vietnam; and he devoted his last years to writing poetry.

Nguyen wrote his poetry in a Vietnamese character script called *chu nom*. His creativity marked a turning point in the development of the Vietnamese language because he demonstrated that Vietnamese was a language capable of poetry.

A Time To Talk

Robert Frost

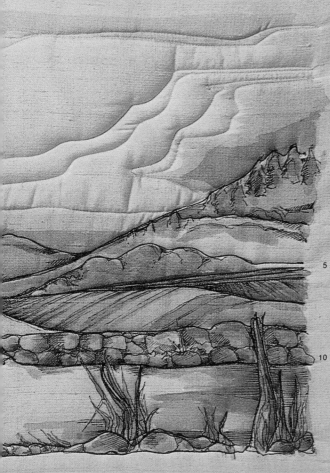

When a friend calls to me from the road
And slows his horse to a meaning walk,
I don't stand still and look around
On all the hills I haven't hoed,
5 And shout from where I am, "What is it?"
No, not as there is a time to talk.
I thrust my hoe in the mellow ground,
Blade-end up and five feet tall,
And plod: I go up to the stone wall
10 For a friendly visit.

Discussion

1. When called by a friend, what actions does the speaker take? What does the speaker refuse to do?

2. What does the farmer want more—to avoid work or to visit with the friend? How do you know?

3. Do you think the two friends see each other often? Why do you think so?

4. What reasons might the farmer have for standing the hoe upright in the ground?

5. What tone does this poem have: (a) bitter and hurried; (b) sad and complaining; (c) kind and leisurely? Explain.

6. Robert Frost once said, "Every time a poem is written, it is written not by cunning, but by belief." In this poem what is Frost's belief?

Extension • Writing

Do you regard friends and friendship more as the speaker does in "I Am Through" or as the speaker does in "A Time to Talk"? Perhaps you feel like one on some days but like the other on other days.

Choose a line or a sentence from either poem as the opening for your composition. Explain why you agree or disagree with the speaker's position. If you wish, you may include the specific circumstances (describe your "good" or "bad" days) in which you feel like (or different from) the speaker.

Robert Frost 1874 • 1963

Robert Frost was a New England farmer who loved the earth and the things close to it. Rocky farms, lush woodlands, old houses, stone fences, and the rugged people who work the soil are the stuff his poems are made of.

During his life, Frost worked at many jobs, but his main vocations were farming and teaching. His poetry expresses a gentle philosophy and love of life that made him one of America's most popular poets.

*"Freddie's thirteen. As for I.Q., he functions somewhere
on the seven-year level. But no trouble. . . . As for learning—he's a challenge.
A real challenge to any teacher—"*

Teacher, Teacher

Ellison Carroll

CAST OF CHARACTERS

HAMILTON CADE
CHARLES CARTER
F. NILES PUTNAM
FREDDIE PUTNAM
JOEY (CARTER'S NEPHEW)
WOMAN

Hallmark Hall of Fame, National Broadcasting Company Television Network, February 5, 1969. Copyright © 1969, Hallmark Cards, Inc. Reprinted by permission.

PROLOGUE

(Fade in on gate—day. We are looking through an iron gate from the inside of a driveway of a two-plus acre estate in suburbia. A convertible is just pulling up. It is a somewhat seedy car. Similarly seedy, with the air and the garb of a faded Ivy Leaguer,[1] is the man behind the wheel: HAMILTON CADE. *He blows the horn. Nothing happens. He blows again. Nothing. He climbs out of the car.*

CADE *checks the gate; it is locked. Shaking it has no effect. He is puzzled. He goes to the gatepost on which is a metal grille, the outlet of an intercom. Above the grille is a plaque:* F. NILES PUTNAM, A.S.A.[2] *Below the nameplate there is a pushbutton with the legend,* TALK. CADE, *with the air of "How dare they do this to me," shrugs, pushes the button. From the grille, a voice:)*

PUTNAM'S VOICE. Putnam here. . . .

CADE *(talking into the intercom).* Hamilton Cade. . . .

PUTNAM'S VOICE. Come on up to the house.

(A buzzer sounds; CADE *pushes the gate: it opens. Then as* CADE *returns to his car:)*

PUTNAM'S VOICE. Close the gate after you.

CADE. Of course. . . .

*(*CADE *drives through, stops, pushes the gate, which swings but does not quite "catch.")*

PUTNAM'S VOICE. All the way, please.

(Irritated, CADE *climbs out of the car, closes the gate properly, returns to the car, drives off.*

As CADE'S *car proceeds along the driveway we see a modern but quite modest house. We catch a glimpse of a trampoline. On the trampoline is* FREDDIE, *13, small for his age. He is jumping up and down. No tricks—just going up and down.* CADE *watches the boy as his car passes the area, but* FREDDIE *does not acknowledge his presence.*

The camera goes in on FREDDIE, *who continues to go up and down. He goes into slow motion . . . a plane is heard overhead.* FREDDIE *jumps off, looks around and up for the plane. As he looks up we notice that the buttons of his shirt are done wrong; that is, he has one buttonhole too many and one button too few. He looks up with a vacant expression. But as the plane sound fades away, he lifts his arms to the sky, his fingers outstretched and grasping hopefully the empty air. But his expression is changeless.)*

ACT ONE

(Fade in on PUTNAM'S *study, a combination living room and architect's studio: drawing board, desk, lamp, blueprints, a cork wall on which are architectural projections. As* CADE *comes in,* PUTNAM *is on the phone. His voice is heard off-camera as* CADE *looks around the room.)*

PUTNAM'S VOICE. Listen, do you have to call me from London to tell me about this? . . . Well, I knew—I knew all that last week . . . . How can you change it when you haven't even called me to talk about it? . . . Look, the specifications call for pre-stressed concrete—impossible. It's absolutely basic to the total conception.

---

1. *Ivy Leaguer,* one who attended a college in the Ivy League, a group of eight old and important universities in the eastern U.S. having a reputation for conservatism and high standards.
2. *A.S.A.,* American Standards Association.

It's not a group of individual structures—it's a completely interrelated complex! . . . Unquestionably. Test borings before the hard weather sets in. Look, we've gone over the logistics a dozen times—now do they want design—or do they want glass boxes? . . . Fine. Fine. Next week— . . . Again? It's the third time you've changed the schedule on me! . . . No, no, I can make it. It's just that—all right. I'll confirm by cable. And I'll expect to hear from you in London. . . . No, no, I'll pick them up at the airport. Goodbye. *(He hangs up. He is tense, edgy. He turns to* CADE.*)* Well, they've changed the schedule on me again. Now I have to fly the day after tomorrow.

CADE. How long will you be gone?

PUTNAM. A minimum of three weeks . . . more likely a month. I have a commission in the North of England . . . it's an entire community—from the ground up. Designed around a college.

CADE *(indicating a drawing).* Yes, I see you did the science building at Hollenbeck.

PUTNAM *(glancing at* CADE'S *letters in a folder).* I don't really need these . . . what with your letter . . . and some asking around. These recommendations aren't very recent. . . .

CADE. They—ah—do go back a bit, yes. You see, I—I taught Hillsgrove Academy five years . . . then Colebrook. . . .

PUTNAM *(cutting* CADE *off).* Hillsgrove five years, Colebrook three years, Westford Academy six months . . . the schools get less impressive and your stay gets shorter. You're like an actor carrying around old reviews. What happened?

CADE. I'm an excellent teacher, Mr. Putnam.

PUTNAM. Ivy Leaguer, Phi Bete,[3] started at the top—worked your way down. West-ford Academy six months. Why did they fire you, Mr. Cade?

CADE. I resigned.

PUTNAM. You were *allowed* to resign. Why?

CADE. I had a nervous breakdown.

PUTNAM. You were teaching less and drinking more.

CADE. That's all over now.

PUTNAM. I know, or you wouldn't be here. What I'm really interested in, Mr. Cade, is why you started to reverse your career.

CADE. Oh—I don't know. I—ah—I was depressed by kids from rich homes.

PUTNAM. You were giving them A's and B's to keep your job and they were wiping out on the college boards.

CADE. You've done a very thorough investigation.

PUTNAM. I've designed buildings for two of these schools. I know a few of the Directors.

CADE *(putting the letters back into his case).* Well, yes, you have me at a disadvantage.

PUTNAM. Why did you answer my ad?

CADE. It seemed like an ideal situation for a man with my—history. I need a one-to-one relationship. Away from the pressure of large classes. Prep school[4] boys can be quite cruel, you know.

PUTNAM. I know. I used to be one.

CADE. Yes. I could tell by your approach. *(*PUTNAM *laughs rather cruelly.)* To answer your question as to why I applied, your ad did say "an exceptional child" . . . and I need the job, Mr. Putnam. But I am also an exceptionally good teacher. I would have liked the challenge of an exceptional child—it would have allowed me

---

3. *Phi Bete,* nickname for Phi Beta Kappa (fī′ bā′tə kap′ə), an honorary society of college students and graduates who have ranked high in scholarship.
4. *Prep school,* preparatory school, a private school, usually from grades 9 through 12, that prepares students for college.

to regain a little confidence.

(PUTNAM motions CADE to wait while he pushes a button on the console on his desk. A bell rings outside the house.)

(Cut to the trampoline. We see FREDDIE jumping. He is not immediately conscious of the bell. It continues to ring. FREDDIE stops jumping and heads for the house.)

(Cut back to the study.)

CADE. Where's he been to school?

PUTNAM. Right here. There hasn't been a school invented that's right for him.

(By now FREDDIE has arrived at the house and entered the study. Seeing CADE, he comes to PUTNAM and leans against him shyly.)

PUTNAM. This is Mr. Cade, Freddie. Shake hands with Mr. Cade, Freddie.

(FREDDIE goes to CADE, puts out his hand. FREDDIE does not shake—it is CADE doing all the shaking. CADE all but knows. FREDDIE pulls his hand from CADE'S and turns to fiddle with a lamp, making it bend up and down on its elbow joint. PUTNAM watches CADE, who watches FREDDIE.)

PUTNAM. All right, Freddie. *(FREDDIE continues playing with the lamp.)* All *right*, Freddie! *(Physically he removes FREDDIE'S hand from the lamp and gives him a turn so he is facing him.)* Hey, go wash your hands and face. Use soap.

(FREDDIE dutifully goes off, but stops in the entranceway.)

FREDDIE. I saw the airplane. Up up up. Down down down. And it went away. *(He exits.)*

CADE. Your ad said "exceptional child."

PUTNAM. The word "retarded" does not attract many applicants.

CADE. How old is he?

PUTNAM. Freddie's thirteen. As for IQ, he functions somewhere on the seven-year

level. But no trouble. No trouble at all. . . . Eats anything you put in front of him. Toilet trained. Dresses himself. Answers the bell. Does what you tell him to do—if he can do it. As for learning—he's a challenge. A real challenge to any teacher—

CADE. Well, how many teachers answered your ad?

PUTNAM. You're the ninth.

CADE. And they all turned you down?

PUTNAM. I turned them down. My son is very precious to me, Mr. Cade.

CADE. I need a job, Mr. Putnam, but I'm not qualified. I've never been trained to work with retarded children.

PUTNAM. Okay, I'm sorry to put you through all this.

CADE. You've only put me through five minutes.

(FREDDIE *enters. He shows his hands to* PUTNAM.)

PUTNAM. Hey, good boy.

(FREDDIE *shows his hands to* CADE.)

CADE. Hmmm. Good and clean.

(CADE *turns to* PUTNAM, *who is now back behind his desk.* FREDDIE *hovers around* CADE. *He examines and fingers the patches on* CADE'S *jacket-sleeve.*)

FREDDIE. What's that?

CADE. That—ah—that's leather. . . . (PUTNAM *watches* CADE *narrowly as* FREDDIE *touches one of two pens in* CADE'S *jacket-pocket.* CADE *takes the pen out and hands it to* FREDDIE. FREDDIE *examines it.* CADE *reaches out—it is a push-button ballpoint—and shows* FREDDIE *how it works.*) Here, let me show you—you do it like this. You see, you push it.

(FREDDIE *fiddles with the pen and succeeds in making it work. His face lights up.*)

FREDDIE. I did it.

(*He sets about pushing the end of the pen,* *making the point go in and out, in and out.* CADE *shoves a piece of paper toward* FREDDIE.)

CADE. It's for writing. Can you write? (FREDDIE *nods.*) Show me.

(FREDDIE *makes a meaningless scrawl.*)

FREDDIE. See?

PUTNAM. Testing, Professor?

CADE. Teaching.

PUTNAM. He can't write. Or read. And nobody can teach him.

(FREDDIE *scribbles all over the paper. As he does so,* CADE *shakes his head ever so slightly "no," and begins to put his papers into his briefcase.*)

PUTNAM (*after a pause*). Say goodbye to Mr. Cade, Freddie. (FREDDIE *turns and dutifully puts out his hand to shake. But he holds the hand with the pen in it behind his back.*) And give Mr. Cade his pen.

(FREDDIE *keeps his hand hidden.*)

CADE. That's all right. You can keep it, Freddie.

PUTNAM. Freddie, say thank you to Mr. Cade.

(*But* FREDDIE, *without the automatic prompting, jumps the gun on* PUTNAM.)

FREDDIE. Thank you.

(CADE *is about to rise when* FREDDIE, *without warning, throws his arm around* CADE'S *neck and hugs. Thrown off guard,* CADE *responds almost automatically with a hug; then all pretense and aside gone from his face, he kisses* FREDDIE'S *forehead.*)

PUTNAM. I think you ought to take the job.

CADE. Based on what?

PUTNAM. What I just saw.

CADE. I'm not in the habit of kissing children.

PUTNAM. Have you had any? (CADE *shakes his head "no."*) Will you take the job? Cade, I'm not kidding anybody. I need you. I've built this world for Freddie and it takes everything I can earn to keep it going. I've had five housekeepers in the last seven years. I've just hired a handyman. Who knows if he will stay. *(pause)* I don't care if all you can teach him is C-A-T!

CADE. I won't settle for that.

PUTNAM. I think you will. What do you say?

CADE *(after a pause)*. I say *yes*.

(CADE, briefcase in hand, moves toward the door of the study. PUTNAM is with him, stops him.)

PUTNAM. You come through for me—and I'll pull every string I can to get you back in Hillsgrove. No Shakespeare, no algebra—just the bottom line.[5] You teach him two plus two or how to write his name and you're back in business.

CADE. I don't believe in bottom lines, Mr. Putnam. I'll take him as far as he can go.

PUTNAM. Take him as far as you like—but no farther than that front gate.

CADE. Why not?

PUTNAM. For one thing, he hasn't set foot outside of it since his mother died. For another, this is all the world that Freddie needs.

CADE. Six acres?

PUTNAM. He makes it here or nowhere. Here, nobody laughs at Freddie—and nobody pities him . . . or me.

(Cut to the exterior of the house. CADE and PUTNAM have come out and are watching FREDDIE on the trampoline.)

CADE. Does he spend all of his time on that trampoline?

PUTNAM. Yes, and your job will be to get him off it. (CADE *walks toward his car.)* I'll open the gate for you.

(PUTNAM returns to the study. CADE has been watching FREDDIE on the trampoline. As the
boy goes up and down, CADE gets an idea. He pushes the button on the dashboard of his car that operates the convertible top. It goes up and down, up and then down. FREDDIE gets off the trampoline and crosses to the car, fascinated.)

FREDDIE. It goes up and down.

CADE. Yes—so you like things that go up and down, do you? Hey, come on, why don't you come for a ride with me down to the gate. (FREDDIE *gets into the car beside* CADE.) How old are you?

FREDDIE. Thirteen.

(CADE drives down the driveway with FREDDIE. As CADE stops the car at the gate, the buzzer sounds. FREDDIE hops out and opens the gate. CADE drives through and stops the car on the other side. He gets out and walks back to FREDDIE on the other side of the gate, which isn't fully closed yet.)

CADE. Freddie, Freddie. How would you like to go see the place where the airplanes go up and down? (FREDDIE *takes a step closer.)* . . . And maybe even a fire engine with a ladder that goes way way up. . . . All you have to do is step outside the gate. I know a merry-go-round—a merry-go-round with horses you can ride. Horses that go up and down and up. . . . *(He beckons to* FREDDIE.) Come on, Freddie. It's easy. Just one step and you're right outside in the world. Come on, and show your Daddy you can do it . . . do it for me—do it for your teacher. . . . Come on. (FREDDIE *is tempted. . . . His face reflects the strain and the fear. . . . He almost makes it. Then he freezes, afraid. He slams the gate shut.)* It's all right, Freddie. We'll do it some other time. . . . Maybe.

(CADE climbs into his car and drives off.

---

5. **the bottom line,** that is, only the basic and necessary subjects.

FREDDIE *stands behind the gate and watches him go.)*

(Fade to the hallway of the house. It is two days later. PUTNAM *and* CADE *are in the hallway.* PUTNAM *is dressed for travel.* CADE *wears a different tweedy jacket. They are carrying* CADE'S *bags. They enter a room from the hallway.)*

PUTNAM. Now this will be yours. *(He sets the bag down.)* It's right across from Freddie's room. I've left a list of how-to's on my desk, also some phone numbers you might need.

CADE. You said there'd be a handyman.

PUTNAM. Yes—Well, the agency said he'd be here this morning, probably after I leave. He'll stay over the garage. They say he can cook, do the gardening, repairs, just about everything.

CADE. I didn't know they came that way anymore.

PUTNAM. You'll be in charge. If he doesn't work out, call the agency—get somebody else.

(They go out into the hall. PUTNAM *opens a door.)*

PUTNAM. This is my room . . . there's another phone in there. . . . *(indicating another door)* That was my wife's room. *(as they go on)* Freddie doesn't even remember her. Seven years of housekeepers, practical nurses, homemakers, college kids. . . . If I'd put in a turnstile, I'd make money. . . . This is Freddie's room.

(He opens the door to FREDDIE'S *room. We look in from the hall. It has none of the clutter of the "normal" 13-year-old. The things are on a kindergarten level—stuffed animals, etc. Pasted on the ceiling are gold and silver stars of all sizes, over a child's bed on which* FREDDIE *is fast asleep, sucking his thumb.* CADE *looks up at the stars as they enter the room.* PUTNAM *raises a shade.)*

PUTNAM. When he was very little, we had a game. We cut these out together. And I used to hold him up to touch the stars. As he got older, he lost interest—he hasn't asked for that in a long time. *(He goes over to* FREDDIE *and gently stirs him.)* Freddie. . . . *(*FREDDIE *awakens.)* Good morning. Do you remember Mr. Cade, Freddie? *(He helps* FREDDIE *sit up.)* He's going to stay and be your teacher while Daddy's away. *(*FREDDIE *remains in bed.* PUTNAM *is sitting on the edge of the bed.)* . . . And it's just about time for me to go.

FREDDIE. In an airplane?

PUTNAM. That's right. . . . You be a good boy, now, and I'll—bring you presents from London . . . and I'll write you postcards.

FREDDIE. You come back. *(It is a simple order.)*

PUTNAM. I promise.

FREDDIE. When?

PUTNAM. Soon. The minute I know, I'll let *you* know. *(He crosses the room to where* CADE *is standing by the door.)* Sometimes . . . I don't think he knows me from the milkman. That's what makes it so—

FREDDIE. Daddy? *(*PUTNAM *goes to him. He tries to betray emotion[6] to protect himself and not upset* FREDDIE.*)* Goodbye. *(*PUTNAM *breaks and sweeps the boy into his arms.* FREDDIE *is merely surprised at the gesture. For all we know,* PUTNAM, *his back to the camera, is weeping. Not* FREDDIE. *Fade out.)*

(Fade in on the driveway, with CHARLES CARTER, *a solid middle-aged black man in clean work clothes. We see a sign on his station wagon:* CARTER HOME SERVICE. ESTATE WORK—PAINTING—*etc.* CARTER'S *tire has blown out. He stands with his hands on his hips, ruefully studying a flat rear tire.*

CARTER *opens the back of his wagon, revealing valises, lawn mowers, rakes, a tool chest, etc., and hauls things about to get at his jack.)*

CARTER. Just what I need. Everything's at the bottom. *(As he comes up with a small, old-fashioned jack,* FREDDIE *turns up, watching.* CARTER *inserts the jack-handle into the jack and operates it. He sees* FREDDIE.*)* Well, hi! *(*FREDDIE *makes his shy little hello-wave as* CARTER, *operating the jack-handle to make the jack-handle lower, goes toward the flat.)* You live here? *(*FREDDIE *nods.)* Cat got your tongue? *(*FREDDIE *frowns, then points his tongue out and looks down to see if it is still there. Then he shakes his head "no."* CARTER *laughs.)* Has your father got a heavy-duty jack in his garage? Something bigger than this?

FREDDIE *(after a pause).* What's a jack?

CARTER. What's a jack? *(He operates the up-and-down mechanism.)* This is a jack.

FREDDIE *(coming closer).* Make it go up and down.

CARTER. I'm trying—how about you helping me?

FREDDIE. Can't.

CARTER. No such word as can't. *(He kneels down to* FREDDIE'S *level.)* C'mon . . . you just do what I do. *(*CARTER *puts the jack-handle lug-end on one of the wheel lugs, loosens it—then puts* FREDDIE'S *hand on the handle. He guides* FREDDIE'S *hands as the boy loosens the lug, which comes off.)* That's got it.

FREDDIE. Make it go up and down.

CARTER. One thing at a time. *(But* FREDDIE *reaches for the jack-handle.* CARTER *gently pulls his hands away—then takes the boy's face in his hands.)* What's your name, son?

---

6. **betray emotion,** that is, Putnam tries to deny his own emotions by hiding them.

FREDDIE. Freddie. Make it go up.

CARTER. How old are you, Freddie?

FREDDIE. Thirteen years old.

(Cut to CARTER'S *reaction. He knows now.)*

FREDDIE. *Please.*

CARTER. All right—we'll do it together. You and me.

*(*CARTER *starts to put the lug-wrench on another lug, but now* FREDDIE *cups* CARTER'S *face in his hands. He studies* CARTER'S *face.)*

FREDDIE. What's your name?

CARTER *(after a moment).* Charley.

FREDDIE. How old are you?

CARTER. Oh . . . old enough to know better. . . .

FREDDIE. Will you stay here?

CARTER. Uh-huh.

FREDDIE. And play with me?

CARTER. Uh-huh. *(He can only shake his head up and down. Then, together, they set to work,* CARTER *guiding* FREDDIE'S *hands.)*

(Fade to the front hall. FREDDIE *leads* CARTER *into the hallway.* CARTER *lugs a heavy B-4 bag[7] and a tool chest.)*

FREDDIE. Teacher! Teacher! Teacher! *(*CADE *comes out of the study.)* Teacher! Teacher!

CADE. Oh! Mr. Carter? My name is Hamilton Cade.

CARTER. Nice to meet you. . . .

(They shake hands.)

CADE. I see you've already met Freddie.

CARTER. Oh. Yeh . . . he helped me change a tire.

FREDDIE. I made it go up and down.

CADE. I wondered what kept you. . . . Well, it'll be the three of us. I hope you're a better cook than I am.

CARTER. Steaks and chops are about it.

CADE. Yes. Well, I'm sure we'll manage.

(He sees FREDDIE *playing with a knife.)* Freddie, put that down. *(*FREDDIE *puts the knife down and examines* CARTER'S *tool chest.)* Stop playing with that.

*(*FREDDIE *ignores him.)*

CARTER. Oh . . . that's all right. There's nothing in that box he can hurt. He's a good kid—

CADE. Yes. Well, he's a little slow. I supposed you noticed.

CARTER. I don't know about that—I showed him how to handle a jack. He could be taught.

CADE. Yes—well, that's what I'm here for.

*(*FREDDIE *has removed a big Yankee screwdriver[8] while they are speaking. He holds it up.)*

FREDDIE. What's that?

CARTER. A Yankee screwdriver. It goes up and down.

FREDDIE. Show me.

*(*CARTER *kneels down to make himself* FREDDIE'S *height and shows him how it works.)*

CARTER. All right, this way. Put your hand right here—this hand up here—down it goes—down.

(Cut to CADE, *whose face reflects the beginnings of insecurity, even jealousy. As* CARTER *holds the tool out to* FREDDIE, CADE *takes it, replaces it in the chest.)*

CADE. Well, I don't want him to hurt himself. Freddie, you take this to Mr. Carter's room.

FREDDIE. I want to play with Charley.

CADE. Freddie.

CARTER. Go ahead, Freddie, move out. We'll play later.

*(*FREDDIE *starts out with the tool chest.)*

CADE. Hurry up. *(He starts to lift* CARTER'S

---

7. B-4 bag, piece of canvas luggage of a type widely used by flyers.
8. Yankee screwdriver, a type of screwdriver which is operated not by twisting, but by pushing and pulling the handle; an arrangement of gears causes the screwdriver to revolve.

B-4 bag off the table. On the bag, in faded black letters, we read: CARTER, CHARLES, CAPT. USAF.[9] *The two men exchange a look. Then* CADE *hands the bag to* CARTER.) I'll show you to your room, Captain.

(Fade to the kitchen at night. The kitchen is roomy and modern. At the table, FREDDIE *and* CADE *are eating.* CARTER, *wearing an apron, serves each of them a sizzling lambchop.)*

CARTER. Freddie, chops à la Charley.[10] *(He serves one to his empty plate and sits down with the others.)* How do they look? Hmmm—good?

FREDDIE. Cut my food.

CARTER. Cut my food, please.

FREDDIE. Cut my food, *please.*

CADE *(starting to cut* FREDDIE'S *food).* That's better.

CARTER. I bet you could do that yourself. *(CADE shoots him a look.)* Maybe get Mr. Cade to teach you how.

(CADE finishes. They eat. CARTER *pours a glass of milk for* FREDDIE. *He offers some to* CADE. CADE *shakes his head.)*

CADE. How's the room?

CARTER. Just fine.

CADE. You know we're going to have to do something about laundry.

CARTER. I'll take it down to the village to my sister.

CADE. How long have you lived here?

CARTER. A few weeks. My wife died. I came to live with my sister and her son. I didn't have a profession so I decided to start a business of my own—very useful.

CADE. You were in the Air Force, though.

CARTER. Nine years.

CADE. What sort of work did you do?

CARTER. Bomber pilot.

CADE. What made you leave?

CARTER. I found out they used real bombs.

CADE. I would have thought a fully-qualified pilot. . . .

CARTER. There is very little demand for black commercial pilots, Mr. Cade. Right now this suits me just fine. . . . Nothing like a man—ah—being in business for himself. *(For a moment they are busy eating.)* How did you come to get into child psychology?

CADE. I'm not a psychologist.

CARTER. Oh.

(He is willing to let it go at that, but CADE *goes on compulsively—)*

CADE. I'm a teacher. I took my major in the humanities . . . the humanities and education. And a minor in psychology.

(CARTER makes a generalized gesture indicating the surroundings, then a significant inclination of his head toward FREDDIE.)

CARTER. All that educational clout—and this—? *(CADE recognizes the needle,[11] but he is holding back.)* I mean, there's such a shortage of teachers. . . . I would think a man like you could just write his own ticket.

CADE *(he has regained his self-control).* Yes—well, in a sense, I have. As you said—to be in business for one's self. I did teach for a while . . . Colebrook and Hillsgrove. . . .

CARTER. Good schools.

CADE *(more assured).* Yes, but I, ah . . . got fed up with the educational establishment, the institutional complex. . . . *(CARTER nods, not buying a word.)* I find this much more rewarding. The one-to-one relationship . . . the flexibility, the—ah—freedom to move at one's own pace, the pupil, teacher. . . .

CARTER. Uh-hm.

---

9. *U.S.A.F.,* United States Air Force.
10. *à la* (ä′lə) *Charley,* in the manner or style of Charley; that is, according to Charley's recipe [French].
11. *needle,* tease; dig; mild insult.

CADE (to FREDDIE). Before you leave the table, you say excuse me. (FREDDIE *looks to* CARTER.)

CARTER. That's right, Freddie.

FREDDIE. Excuse me, excuse me.

CADE. All right—off you go and play. . . . (FREDDIE *leaves.*) As I was saying—no rigid classroom structure . . . no—time-clock tyranny . . . and above all—the challenge. (*He looks at* CARTER.) Yes . . . the challenge. (*He says it directly to* CARTER—*but straight and sincere, not realizing that he has clued* CARTER *in completely.*) The greater the challenge—the more the personal satisfaction. Not for the school—but for the teacher.

CARTER. Hmmm.

(CARTER *lifts a platter, gestures as if to ask "Would you like more?", but* CADE *declines.* CARTER *helps himself to another chop and begins to eat it with evident relish.*)

(*Fade to* CADE'S *room at night.* CADE *is unpacking books and putting them on shelves. Along with Shakespeare, collections of poets, drama, etc., he takes out some brand-new elementary teaching materials—first-grade readers, kindergarten workbooks, etc.*)

FREDDIE'S VOICE. Teacher, teacher! Teacher, teacher! Teacher, teacher, teacher, teacher! Teacher!

(CADE *hurries to* FREDDIE'S *room.* FREDDIE *is standing in the center of the room as* CADE *comes in.* FREDDIE *lifts his arms.*)

FREDDIE. Stars? Stars? Stars, stars, stars.

(CADE *looks up to the stars on the ceiling.* FREDDIE *is doing the same thing with his hands and fingers, reaching and clutching, as he had done with the airplane.*)

CADE. Freddie? Freddie, listen! . . . No. You're a big boy now. Freddie—you're a big boy . . . .

FREDDIE. Stars — stars — stars — stars — stars.

(CADE *finally lifts* FREDDIE *up so he can touch the stars with his fingertips.*)

CADE. All right—touch the stars.

FREDDIE (*whispers*). Stars, stars, stars, stars—

Discussion

1. Putnam has advertised that his child is "exceptional." (a) What kind of child does Cade discover Freddie is? (b) In what ways does Freddie fit the description "exceptional"?

2. Why were the previous nine applicants for the job turned down?

3. (a) During the interview, Cade says that he is an exceptionally good teacher. Does Cade seem to believe this? Explain. (b) What reasons does Cade give for preferring a single pupil?

4. (a) What causes Putnam suddenly to offer Cade the job? (b) What does Putnam promise Cade if Cade can teach Freddie? (c) What is Cade's response when Putnam says Freddie need only learn to write his name and add two and two?

5. (a) How does Putnam act just before he leaves? (b) What do Putnam's actions reveal about his feelings for Freddie? Explain.

6. Putnam tells Cade he doesn't think Freddie knows his father from the milkman. Do you agree? Which of Freddie's actions in the play so far prove or disprove this statement?

7. (a) How does Carter come to know Freddie is retarded? (b) Compare his behavior toward Freddie before and after he knows this.

8. (a) Why does Cade try to talk Freddie out of wanting to touch the stars? (b) Why does he finally give in and lift Freddie up?

ACT TWO

(Fade in on FREDDIE's *room, daytime.* FRED-DIE *is playing with plastic boxes, trains, tunnel.* CADE *enters with teaching cards.)*

CADE. Good morning, Freddie.

FREDDIE. Good morning, Teacher.

*(*CADE *moves some of* FREDDIE's *stuffed animals aside and sits across from* FREDDIE *at his child-sized table.)*

CADE. Ah—what do we have here—ah hah—a tunnel. *(*CADE *sweeps the clutter of trains and tunnel into a box.)* Well, that's enough playing for now. C'mon, help me put them in here. . . . Time for our lesson—now then, now then, let's see what we can remember. Now here we're going to have some pictures again this morning. *(*CADE *holds up a card: on it is a picture of a boat, and underneath the picture the word "boat.")* Here we are, now what's this?

FREDDIE. I don't know. I like pictures.

CADE. This is a boat. Now then—this is the picture of a boat and this is the word for "boat. . . ." This is the picture of a boat and this is the word for "boat." *(*CADE *covers the picture, leaving the printed word visible.)* What's this? *(*FREDDIE *just looks.* CADE *holds up a card of a boy.)* What's this picture?

FREDDIE. Boy!

CADE. This is the word for "boy." *(He points to the word underneath the picture.)* What is this word? *(*FREDDIE *just looks.)* Now, Freddie, we know what words are, don't we? Do you know what a *word* is, Freddie? A *word* is something that we make work for us. We *use* words to write with. Well, there's a word for everything—*(*CADE *shows him a card with "Daddy" on it.)* This is the word for "Daddy." There's a word even for where

your Daddy's gone. Now—where's your Daddy gone?

FREDDIE. My Daddy's far away.

CADE. That's right. He's gone to London. This is the word for "London. . . . This is the word for "Daddy." *(*CADE *draws it out.)* This is "London" . . . this is "Daddy."

FREDDIE *(grabbing the card).* That's not my Daddy! My Daddy's far away! *(He throws the card.)*

CADE. Pick it up. . . . Sit down—now then, we'll start again—This is the word for "London"—this is the word for "Daddy"—this is "London" and this is "Daddy"—

*(*FREDDIE *snatches the card and throws it across the room again.)*

FREDDIE. That's not my Daddy—My Daddy's far away.

CADE. Pick it up—hurry up—c'mon!

*(*FREDDIE *runs out of the room.)*

(Fade to the garage workshop. CARTER *is building a carry-all box for tools. He is about to screw one of the sideboards into place. He sets the board in place and picks up a Yankee screwdriver. He adjusts the ratchet.* FREDDIE *enters.)*

CARTER. Hi!

FREDDIE *(grabbing at the screwdriver).* It goes up and down!

CARTER. Sure. But that's not all it does. Give me a hand. *(He guides* FREDDIE's *hand and shows him how to drive a screw.)* See? It does the work for you.

FREDDIE. I want to do it again!

CARTER. No—let's not do it again. Let's do something different. We're making a tool box. *(*CARTER *turns to the bench and picks up a board for the other side of the* box. *He takes a folding ruler from his pocket.)* See? This goes up and down too. *(CARTER unfolds the ruler. FREDDIE grabs it and starts to open it. CARTER stops him.)* It tells you how long a thing is. You know what *long* means? *(He measures FREDDIE with the ruler.)* Awright? See, you're that *long*, right? *(He lays the ruler along the board.)* Now I want to find twenty-four on here because I want to make it twenty-four inches.

FREDDIE. What's *inches?*

CARTER. Every one of these little marks here is an inch. It's that much. . . . *(He indicates with two fingers.)* And every one of these big marks are feet. *(FREDDIE looks down at his feet. CARTER smiles.)* No—that's a different kind of feet. But don't let it bother you. We're going to mark off twenty-four inches on this. You take the pencil. . . . Come on this side— *(CARTER makes a line, using a T-square.[1])* . . . That's it. Now we're gonna saw that line—right—turn the board this way. *(He gets a saw and guides FREDDIE's hand. They saw the board together.)* That's got it! *(The board is sawn through. CARTER holds up the board and then fits it to make the other side of the tool box.)*

FREDDIE. We're doing it!

CARTER. We sure are. *(CARTER feels a third presence in the workshop—he looks over his shoulder and sees CADE watching them.)* Oh! Hello, Mr. Cade. *(to FREDDIE)* Say hello to your teacher.

FREDDIE. Hello, Teacher.

(CARTER proceeds working on the tool box.)

FREDDIE. My Daddy makes houses.

CARTER. So he does.

FREDDIE. I'm gonna make a house.

CARTER *(after a bit).* Oh no.

FREDDIE. Oh yes!

CARTER. First you are going to learn to use

tools. Then—*we're* gonna *build* a house. *(CARTER turns to CADE behind him.)* The three of us—

(CADE says nothing.)

(Fade to FREDDIE's room, daytime. The camera pans slowly across crudely drawn pictures of houses. Closeup on one of FREDDIE's pictures. We see FREDDIE's hand. He is trying to write the word "house" on it. He fails and scribbles all over it. As the camera pans around the room we hear:)

FREDDIE'S VOICE. House.

CADE'S VOICE. Good.

FREDDIE'S VOICE. Crane.

CADE'S VOICE. Crane.

FREDDIE'S VOICE. Crane.

CADE. Right. Now we go back to the beginning—okay, we'll do it again. Everything we did before, we'll do again. Now then—

(Fade to PUTNAM's study. CADE has taped signs to most things in the room in an effort to teach FREDDIE to identify objects and learn the spelling of the words. CADE moves from one object to the next as FREDDIE identifies them.)

CADE. What does this say? *(He points to a word card on the chair.)*

FREDDIE. Chair.

CADE. It's a chair—right. Now—*(pointing to the card)*—what's this?

FREDDIE. Chair.

CADE. Chair, right—now you're reading it, aren't you. It's a chair. . . . Now this—

FREDDIE. Window.

CADE. Window, right—the window. *(CADE stands next to the fireplace.)* Now what's this?

FREDDIE. Bricks.

---

1. *T-square,* a T-shaped ruler used for marking parallel or right-angle lines.

CADE. Right. Read this (*indicating another card*)—

FREDDIE. Fire.

CADE. Fire—right. And this—

FREDDIE. Lamp.

CADE. Right. . . . Here?

FREDDIE. Steps.

CADE (*now at the opposite end of the room*). Louder.

FREDDIE (*louder*). Steps.

CADE. Good—very good. Now what about this?

FREDDIE. Table.

CADE. This is a table. . . . Now you're reading . . . Let's make sure you're reading. (*CADE crosses to the table where FREDDIE has been sitting. There are word cards on the table as well as teaching "props"—flowers, a lemon, a knife, etc. CADE holds up the flowers.*) Now what are these?

FREDDIE. Flowers.

CADE. Right. Now show me the card for "flower." Read it. (*FREDDIE holds up the wrong word card.*) All right—put it down. I want you to read the card, Freddie. . . . Now, what's this?

FREDDIE. Lemon.

CADE. Right. Lemon. Now read the card. (*FREDDIE cannot read the card and again chooses one he thinks may be right. CADE is becoming more frantic with each wrong card.*) I want the card for "lemon." What's this? (*CADE holds up the knife.*) . . . Look at it.

FREDDIE. Knife.

CADE. A *knife* with which we cut the lemon. Now show me the card for "knife." (*FREDDIE again chooses the wrong word card.*) Now listen, I want you to *read* the cards. *Knife*, Freddie, *knife!* (*CADE grabs the word card.*) *This* is the *card* for "knife." (*FREDDIE takes the card from him.*) All right. Put it down. (*CADE starts over again.*) Do it once more. . . . Now here are the flowers. Show me the card for "flow. . . ." (*FREDDIE's attention span is exhausted.*) Freddie, I want you to learn these things.

(*FREDDIE starts to stand up and CADE takes his arm. He is a little desperate now.*)

FREDDIE. Why?

CADE. Because I want you to be able to write; I want you to make the words work for you—

FREDDIE. I make nice pictures.

CADE. Yes, you do.

FREDDIE. I make nice pictures.

CADE. Yes—I know you do . . . but making nice pictures isn't using words. Words can help you. When you go out into the world—the words can help to keep you safe. (*FREDDIE just looks at CADE.*) And if you can read books, you need never be alone. Books are wonderful friends. Freddie—your Daddy will be home soon and. . . . (*no response*). . . . It would make your Daddy very happy if you could make the words work for you. . . . (*He gives up and lets FREDDIE go.*) All right, Freddie. That's enough for today. Go out and play. (*FREDDIE starts to leave.*) Here, put your shoes on. (*But FREDDIE starts to put the shoes on the wrong feet. CADE stops him. CADE is losing control out of frustration. He jams the right shoe on FREDDIE's right foot, then holds FREDDIE's right hand up in front of his face, saying:*)

CADE. Right, right, right. Put your *right* shoe on your *right* foot. (*FREDDIE fumbles.*) Well, try . . . go on.

(*FREDDIE stares at him a moment—and takes off. CADE is left alone, discouraged and shaken.*)

(*CARTER's workshop. CARTER and FREDDIE are discussing the "house" they are building.*)

CARTER. Freddie, Freddie—now what are we gonna do today—?

FREDDIE. Build a house.

CARTER. Build a house. What kinda house?

FREDDIE. A wooden house.

CARTER. What's the roof on the house?

FREDDIE. A wall. . . .

CARTER. Hold this—here, hold this. *(He hands* FREDDIE *a board.)* Where are we gonna put this?

FREDDIE. On the side.

CARTER. Which side—

FREDDIE. A wall.

CARTER. Which wall—the right wall or the left wall?

FREDDIE *(guessing).* Right wall—

CARTER. Right wall—exactly—right—go to the house—show me the right wall. . . .

(They walk down the hill outside the workshop to where their almost completed "house"—a hut—stands.)

CARTER. All right—inside. *(*FREDDIE *enters the "house,"* CARTER *follows him.)* All right—show me the right wall. *(*FREDDIE *goes to the left.)* Not left, Freddie—that board goes on the right—don't you know what the right is? Huh? Come here. *(*FREDDIE *comes over to* CARTER.*)* I'm gonna fix it so you'll always know what the right is. *(*FREDDIE *looks at him.* CARTER *takes a roll of friction tape out of his pocket. He tears off an inch and sticks it on* FREDDIE'S *right shoe.)* Pull up your foot—there you are. Now you can always tell. That one is right.

FREDDIE. I like you, Charley.

CARTER *(taking* FREDDIE'S *face in his hands).* I like you, too, Freddie.

FREDDIE. I don't like Mr. Cade.

CARTER. Uh-uh—I don't like to hear you talking like that. Mr. Cade's a good man. Maybe he's just lonely—like you're lonely for your Dad.

FREDDIE. Oh. *(He looks sad.)*

CARTER. Come on—we've got a house to finish building! Right?

FREDDIE. That's right! *(He looks at his shoe with the tape.)* Right, right, right!

CARTER *(indicating the board).* All right— put it here. Here's the nail—now—right, right, right—

(Fade to FREDDIE'S *room.* CADE *and* FREDDIE *are standing over a globe.* CADE *is moving a toy airplane across the globe.)*

CADE. . . . And your Daddy went in an airplane to London. Show me London. . . . No. Here, put your finger up there. That's London.

FREDDIE. London. . . .

*(*FREDDIE'S *"house."* FREDDIE *is sitting in the completed hut. He smiles up at the sign he has made. It says:* MY HOUSE.*)*

(Fade to closeup on a calendar. We see the date . . . the third day of the month.)

(The front of the house, daytime. FREDDIE *runs down the driveway to the front door. In one hand he carries a batch of letters, in the other hand he has a big over-sized postcard with a picture of London Bridge on it. He runs in the front door, into the downstairs hall.)*

FREDDIE *(calling).* Teacher . . . teacher. . . .

(He drops the mail on the stairs and runs upstairs with the postcard in his hand. CADE *is at the desk in* FREDDIE'S *room laying out the day's lessons. He hears:)*

FREDDIE'S VOICE. Teacher . . . teacher!

*(*FREDDIE *runs down the upstairs hall.)*

FREDDIE. Teacher . . . teacher! *(He goes into his room and runs over to* CADE—*he holds up the postcard for him to see. He is very excited.)*

CADE. Oh. It's from your Daddy.

FREDDIE *(pointing to the picture on the card).* I saw this one.

CADE. That's right.

FREDDIE *(pointing to the picture).* Read it.

CADE *(takes the postcard).* It's the same picture. But different words.

FREDDIE. Read it.

CADE. No, no, no. This time you're going to read this one all by yourself. *(CADE gives FREDDIE the postcard.)*

FREDDIE. Too many words—

CADE. Well, there isn't a word there you don't know. *(FREDDIE hands back the postcard. CADE points to the words on the postcard.)* Look. What's that?

FREDDIE. London.

CADE. Right. See, what's that?

FREDDIE. London.

CADE. Right. Now come on—you can read it.

FREDDIE. Read it.

CADE. Now come on, Freddie.

FREDDIE. *Read* it.

CADE. You read it.

FREDDIE. *You* read it.

CADE *(gives up).* All right. *(reading)* "Dear Freddie. I am back in London. I will try to come home on the 15th. Love—Daddy."

FREDDIE *(snatching the postcard and sniffing).* Why? Why is it far? Why?

(FREDDIE is sitting in the greenhouse, studying his father's postcard, trying to read it. CARTER is raking leaves—he passes the greenhouse and sees FREDDIE. He sits next to FREDDIE.)

CARTER. What's your Daddy say this time?

FREDDIE *(handing over the card).* Too many words.

CARTER. What's that mean?

FREDDIE. They all go together.

CARTER *(studying him).* What you need is a little helper. Like the one I made my nephew Joey. *(He has been fishing in his pocket for something, and comes up with a card. With a knife, he carefully cuts out a rectangular opening in its center.)* . . .

Now those words won't just run together. (Freddie *comes in close as* CARTER *finishes the cut-out.* CARTER *takes the postcard and lays the cut-out card over the writing so that only a word or two can be seen at a time through the "window."*) Now read it.

FREDDIE. "Dear—Freddie. I am back—in London—I will try—to come home—on the 15th—Love Daddy."
(*Suddenly* FREDDIE *holds the card up to his face and peers through the opening. We go in to an extreme close-shot to reveal what* CARTER *has cut up—his business card:* CHARLES CARTER, *Home Service, 223 Wicker Street, 345–7602.*)

(*Fade to the kitchen at night.* CADE, CARTER, *and* FREDDIE *have finished dinner.* CADE *drinks his coffee.* CARTER *reads half of the evening paper.* FREDDIE *is occupied with the rest of the paper. As* CADE *watches,* FREDDIE *takes his "helper" out of his breast pocket and begins to read words aloud.*)

FREDDIE. "I am in the—school play—I am a—turkey. But—this—those—are real duck—wings. I am—a turkey. Turkey, turkey, turkey."

CADE. What's that?

FREDDIE. Charley made it. To help me read.

CADE. Hmmm—show me. (FREDDIE *won't give it up. He puts it back in his pocket.*) Freddie—

FREDDIE. No! I want to go to the bathroom.

CADE. All right! Go to the bathroom. (FREDDIE *exits.* CADE *looks at* CARTER. CARTER *puts the paper down flat.*) I'd like to teach him to read *my* way.

CARTER. I think you're doing a fantastic job. (CADE *doesn't respond.*) Is something bugging you, *Mr.* Cade?

CADE. Nothing at all.

CARTER. Ever since I set foot on this place I got funny vibrations from you. . . . If there's something on your mind, I'd like to hear about it. If I bother you, I can just pack up and move out.

CADE. I wouldn't want you to do that.

CARTER. Then why don't you level with me? Is it the boy?

CADE. Yes, I suppose it is. I was hired to be his teacher. I'm a good teacher—

CARTER. I can see that.

CADE. Frankly, I have a difficult time relating to Freddie.

CARTER. All you have to do is be yourself.

CADE. Well, that's easy for you—it's not for me.

CARTER. I still don't see what that's got to do—

CADE. He's attached to you. You're a playmate for him. He'd rather be having fun with you than doing his lessons. All I ask is that you leave the teaching to me—

CARTER. I think I get the message—

CADE. Well, don't misunderstand.

CARTER. Your place is the teacher, my place is the handyman—that's it, *isn't* it?

CADE. Well—yes—if you have to put it that way.

CARTER. I have to put it like it is, Mr. Cade—otherwise things get all mixed up. *(He rises.)*

CADE. Carter— *(CARTER turns back to face him.)* This has nothing to do with skin.

CARTER. Man, I got past that one a long time ago. . . .

(FREDDIE and CADE *are standing in front of* FREDDIE'S *blackboard on which teaching cards are tacked up.* FREDDIE *is pointing to each card and giving the meaning.)*

FREDDIE. Bow-wow! . . . Green! . . . Yellow! . . . Red! *(He points to a picture of a stop sign.)* Stop! *(He playfully pushes* CADE *on the bed.)* Stop! *(He claps and laughs—quite amused with his action.)*

(Now CADE *and* FREDDIE *are seated on the rug. There are educational toys all around*

them. FREDDIE *is attempting to fit different shaped blocks into the properly shaped boxes. He attempts to jam a square block into a round opening.)*

FREDDIE. Doesn't fit. *(CADE helps him.)*

(FREDDIE and CADE *are seated at the kitchen table.* CADE *is holding up objects for* FREDDIE *to identify.)*

CADE. . . . And this one is a cup. . . .

FREDDIE. Cup.

CADE. And just under the cup is a saucer.

FREDDIE *(can't quite make it).* Sau—sau. . . .

CADE *(pronouncing it slowly).* Sau—cer.

FREDDIE. Sau. . . .

CADE. *Sau—cer.*

FREDDIE. Sau. . . .

CADE. It's a saucer.

FREDDIE. Sau. . . .

(CADE and FREDDIE *are working over a large white pad. He is teaching* FREDDIE *to write the alphabet.* FREDDIE *traces* CADE'S *letter "A" with his finger.)*

CADE. Okay—you do one . . . careful.

(FREDDIE draws a rather crude "A.")

(Another scene with FREDDIE *and* CADE— *this time they are practicing the alphabet on a lined pad.* FREDDIE *draws a neat "A" in the lined space. He turns to* CADE *for approval.)*

(FREDDIE and CADE *are sitting together in another lesson.)*

CADE. . . . And what does a cook do?

FREDDIE. Cooks.

CADE. Cooks, right! And what does he cook?

FREDDIE. Food.

CADE. Food! So—you eat what the cook cooks. Now what does the cook cook?

FREDDIE. Food.

CADE (slowly). Food—say, *food.*

FREDDIE (carefully). Food.

CADE. Now where does the food go?

FREDDIE. In the stove.

CADE. No—where does the food go when you eat it? (CADE *points to his mouth.*) It goes in there, doesn't it?

FREDDIE. Mouth.

CADE. Show me where it goes. (FREDDIE *opens his mouth.*) It goes in your mouth. *Mouth.*

FREDDIE. Mouth.

CADE (*drawing the word out*). Mouth.

FREDDIE. Mouth.

CADE. You look very silly doing that. (FREDDIE *giggles.*) Now—c'mon, be serious. Now then, if you have a cook, what do you have to have for him to cook?

FREDDIE. Food.

CADE. Give me the name of a food.

FREDDIE (*a pause as he thinks*). Beans!

CADE. Beans—where do you get beans?

FREDDIE. From an animal.

CADE. From an animal? They don't grow on animals—a bean animal? (FREDDIE *laughs.*) No. What's the name of an animal with beans—? He's a bean? (FREDDIE *laughs at this nonsense.*)

(*Fade to closeup on a calendar. We see the date . . . the fifteenth of the month.*)

(*Fade to the driveway, morning.* FREDDIE *is fully dressed and in the driveway waiting for his father.* CADE *comes out in robe and pajamas.*)

CADE (*calling*). Freddie. . . . (*He goes to* FREDDIE.) Freddie, there's plenty of time. Your Daddy hasn't left London yet—probably hasn't even got on the plane. You see, there's a different time there—

FREDDIE. Why?

CADE. Why—well, you see as the earth goes around the sun— (CADE *uses his hands to demonstrate.*)

FREDDIE. No! (*then pointing*) When I get up, the sun is there. . . . When I go to sleep, the sun is . . . *there.* (*He makes a big arc with his hand.*) Nothing goes around *anything.* It just goes *up*—and down.

CADE. Well, wait a minute—you see—

FREDDIE (*interrupting*). I *see* it!

CADE. C'mon—let me explain something to you. . . . (*They start toward the house.*)

(FREDDIE'S *room, night.* FREDDIE *is crouched on the floor near his bed.* CADE *and* CARTER *are standing over him.*)

FREDDIE. I hate you!

CARTER. Freddie—c'mon, Freddie. Freddie, your Daddy's just been delayed.

FREDDIE. Go away!

CARTER. Your Daddy's just been delayed. (*He can't get through to* FREDDIE.)

FREDDIE. Go away—go away!

CADE. Your Daddy's just been delayed. He's coming home, Freddie.

FREDDIE. I hate you!

CARTER. He's coming home.

FREDDIE. Go away!

CADE. Your Daddy *is* coming home.

CARTER (*picks* FREDDIE *up and puts him in bed*). Come on, now, simmer down.

FREDDIE. Go 'way!

CADE (*putting* PUTNAM'S *cable in* FREDDIE'S *hand*). Let me read it to you.

(FREDDIE *grabs the telegram and tears it to shreds with his teeth.*)

CARTER. Come on, Freddie—

CADE. He's been delayed but he *is* coming home.

FREDDIE. No. You tell lies! You tell lies!

CADE. No. No. It's not a lie. He is coming home late Friday. (FREDDIE *pulls the covers over him.* CADE *turns to* CARTER.) You have any ideas?

CARTER. Will you leave me alone with him a minute?

(CADE nods and exits. CARTER goes to FREDDIE who is under the blankets. He puts his hand on FREDDIE's shoulder.)

CARTER. I think I know what you need, son.

(Fade to the workshop, daytime. CARTER is planing a piece of wood. We hear the soft sounds of two children playing in the background. CADE enters the garage workshop from the rear door.)

CADE. I'm looking for Freddie—it's time for his lesson.

CARTER. Right out there. *(He points with his thumb.)*

(CARTER and CADE walk to the wide front door of the workshop. Outside, FREDDIE and JOEY, CARTER's nephew, are playing kickball.)

FREDDIE. Joey, Joey, catch.

JOEY. Okay—here.

CARTER. How about that?

CADE. Who's the child?

CARTER. My sister's kid.

CADE. I wish you'd consulted me.

CARTER. I didn't think you'd mind. I bet that's the first time Freddie has had anybody to play with.

CADE. That's not the point. I'm responsible for that boy. I promised myself I'd teach him something useful, at least how to write his own name.

CARTER. Is that so important?

CADE. You're right it's important. Niles Putnam isn't going to live forever, you know. Someday that boy will have to leave this prison and face the world. Why, just to cross the street, he'll have to read a "Don't Walk" sign, and know the difference between the Ladies' Room and the Men's. Why, I can't teach him anything if you have him out there playing games all the time.

CARTER. I was trying to help.

CADE. I'm a trained teacher, Mr. Carter. If I need your help, I'll ask for it.

CARTER. I was thinking more about what the *boy* needs. . . .

(He resumes planing the piece of wood. CADE watches the boys for a moment. The two boys are kicking a soccer ball. FREDDIE kicks it over the fence.)

FREDDIE. Get the ball, please.

JOEY. You get it. You kicked it outside.

FREDDIE. You get it! *(He looks at the fence.)* I can't go out.

JOEY. You get it. You kicked it over.

FREDDIE. No. You. *(He tries to push JOEY toward the fence.)* You get it, please. Please. Please.

JOEY. Stop pushin'!

FREDDIE. Please! *(JOEY pushes FREDDIE back. FREDDIE gives him a bear hug.)*

JOEY. Quit huggin'! *(FREDDIE continues to hug, pushing JOEY toward the fence. JOEY becomes frightened.)* Let go! Uncle Charley, Uncle Charley! *(He shoves FREDDIE away from him just as CADE runs to them. CADE thrusts JOEY away from FREDDIE.)* Freddie, I'm sorry, I'm sorry. *(CARTER runs over to them. JOEY rushes to him.)* Uncle Charley, he pushed me.

CADE *(to FREDDIE)*. Freddie, are you all right?

FREDDIE. He hurt me.

CADE. Where?

FREDDIE. My hand. *(He shows CADE a scraped hand with some blood on it.)*

CARTER *(stepping toward them)*. Let's see that.

CADE *(to CARTER)*. I'll handle it. *(He gives FREDDIE a handkerchief.)* All right, Freddie, you go on up to the house and wash your hands. Go on. *(FREDDIE hides along-*

side the workshop. CADE *turns to* CARTER.)
You better take your nephew home.

CARTER. They were just playing. Don't make a big deal out of this.

(CADE *stares at him angrily and turns and walks back to the workshop.)*

JOEY. I'm sorry.

CARTER. That's all right, Joey. You'd bet-ter go down to the station wagon and wait there.

JOEY. But—

CARTER *(his eyes on* CADE). Do as I say. I just want to go and get some tools. Go on.

(JOEY *goes.* CARTER *turns his back on* CADE *and walks into the workshop.)*

Discussion

1. Freddie shows fascination with and a desire to handle certain objects. (a) What types are they? (b) Why do you suppose he prefers these to Cade's learning devices?

2. (a) What is the difference between Cade's approach to teaching Freddie and Carter's approach? Give instances that demonstrate this difference. (b) Who seems to have more success with Freddie at first? (c) Who seems more impatient with Freddie? How does Freddie react to this impatience? (d) Whom does Freddie seem to like better?

3. Describe the device that helps Freddie read the postcard from his father. How does it help him?

4. (a) How does Cade react to Carter's helping Freddie? (b) Why do you think he reacts this way? (c) What is your opinion of Cade's remarks to Carter during the scene on pages 515 b, line 10–516 a, line 30? (d) What is your opinion of Carter's response?

5. (a) In what way does the relationship between Freddie and Cade seem to change? (b) Point out instances of their changed relationship. (c) What reasons can you give for this change?

6. (a) What is Freddie's reaction when he learns his father is delayed? (b) Why do you think he pays no attention to the men's explanations? (c) What does Carter have in mind when he says, "I think I know what you need, son"?

7. (a) What two fears does Freddie show when he plays with Joey? (b) In your opinion, are Freddie's fears reasonable? Why do you suppose he has them? (c) Why does Cade become so upset about Joey's presence?

ACT THREE

(Fade in on the workshop. CADE *is looking out the workshop window.* CARTER *is gathering his tools together and placing them in his tool chest. It is obvious that he intends to quit.)*

CADE. Carter, I didn't mean—

CARTER *(turns on him, blazing).* What did you mean? Don't you think my nephew has feelings?

CADE. I didn't mean to hurt his feelings, but Freddie is a handicapped child.

CARTER. They're both handicapped—

CADE. I have to decide what's best for him!

CARTER. For him? Or for you? Mr. Cade, I'm gonna get out of here but before I go, I got a word for you. Every time you look at Freddie, it's to get him to do something for you. Every time you come near the pressure is on. *(sarcastically)* You're like those folks who give their kids piano lessons. Because they love music? No. *(imitating)* It's "play a piece for the people." "Say a big word for Uncle John." Do your trick. "Say something in algebra for Aunt." Come on, Freddie, come on, look at the picture—say the word—for Mr. Cade. *(then grimly)* You're always trying to get Freddie to do something to make you feel better! *(with pure scorn)* Why can't you just let him be what he is—

(He throws the last of the tools into the tool chest, and with a loud bang slams the cover down and exits from the workshop. CADE *stands where he is.)*

(Cut to the driveway. CARTER'S *station wagon whips around and down the drive. We see the trampoline . . .* FREDDIE *has retreated to it.)*

(Fade to PUTNAM'S *study. The phone is ringing.* CADE *comes down the stairs, enters the study, and answers it.)*

CADE. Putnam residence. Hamilton Cade speaking.

PUTNAM'S VOICE. Cade? This is Mr. Putnam.

CADE. Hello.

PUTNAM'S VOICE. I'm at the airport. Just got in. Finished the job sooner than we thought. How's Freddie?

CADE. Fine, just fine.

PUTNAM'S VOICE. Good. Any problems?

CADE. No, no—nothing special. I—ah—I had to fire the handyman.

PUTNAM'S VOICE. Oh? Well, that's no tragedy. As long as the boy's all right.

CADE. Would you like to speak with him?

PUTNAM'S VOICE. No, he'll just get anxious. I'll get a taxi right away and surprise him.

CADE. Right.

PUTNAM'S VOICE. You okay? You sound a little strange.

CADE. No—I'm fine, fine . . . just fine.

(pause) Ah—Mr. Putnam?

PUTNAM'S VOICE. Yes?

CADE. I got your son off the trampoline. *(He hangs up.)*

(CADE is walking down the driveway toward the trampoline. FREDDIE *is bouncing up and down on it, monotonously.)*

CADE. Freddie? *(FREDDIE ignores him.)* Freddie! *(FREDDIE ignores him.)* Stop jumping, Freddie. Freddie, come off that trampoline! *(FREDDIE continues bouncing.)* Listen, Freddie—I'm sorry I made your friend go away, but you and I have a lot of work to do together. Freddie, stop that! When your Daddy gets here, we're going to show him all the things we've learned. We're going to read to him and we're going to copy out all the words from the cards. We'll really show him all the things we can do. *(FREDDIE continues to jump.)* Come off the trampoline—! Stop doing that! *(He grabs at* FREDDIE *and* FREDDIE *falls.)*

FREDDIE. You hurt my arm.

CADE. I didn't mean to. Look at me. Do you hear me? Look at me. Look at me. I'm your teacher, aren't I? And I've taught you a great deal, haven't I. *Look* at me, *look* at me. I taught you how to read and write from your cards. Didn't I? *Didn't* I? *(FREDDIE makes no response.)* I did, didn't I? I've taught you a lot of things. *(CADE realizes his own total defeat.)* I did, didn't I?

FREDDIE. I make nice pictures. I make nice pictures.

(CADE turns and walks back to the house. FREDDIE *stares after him.)*

(PUTNAM'S study. CADE *is taking down the signs he has placed around the room for* FREDDIE. *He is waiting for* PUTNAM *to arrive home.)*

(On the trampoline, in slow motion, FREDDIE *bounces up and down, up and down, up and down. We hear the voices that* FREDDIE *hears in his head:)*

CARTER'S VOICE. How old are you?

PUTNAM'S VOICE. You be a good boy now.

CADE'S VOICE. Fire engines . . . merry-go-round.

(Fade to CADE, *waiting in* PUTNAM'S *study. There is the sound of the door as* PUTNAM *enters the front hall.)*

PUTNAM. Freddie! Freddie, it's Daddy! I'm home! *(He comes into the study and sees* CADE.*)*

PUTNAM. Hey! Hello, Mr. Cade. Where is he?

CADE. He's back on his trampoline.

PUTNAM. No. He's not there. *(*CADE *stands, alarmed.)* Where is he? *(*CADE *runs out the front door;* PUTNAM *runs up the stairs.)* Freddie? *(*PUTNAM *is running through the house shouting.)* Freddie! Freddie! *(He runs into* FREDDIE'S *room, where he finds* FREDDIE'S *note on the bed.* PUTNAM *comes halfway down the staircase as* CADE *enters the house. He shows* CADE *the note.)* Look at this!

CADE *(reads it).* Where was it?

PUTNAM. It was on his bed.

CADE *(reading the note aloud).* "I—gone—see—my—fren." *(*CADE *shakes his head in disbelief.)*

PUTNAM. He couldn't have written that. Where is he, Cade?

CADE. He wrote this. . . .

PUTNAM. Cade, where is my son?

CADE. He wrote it. He *wrote* it.

PUTNAM. If my son wrote that note, I'll build you a prep school of your own. But if anything has happened to him, I swear I'll kill you!

*(*FREDDIE *is walking along a suburban street. He stops in front of a lawn to study a set of lawn-ornaments: A mama duck and four ducklings following her. The last duckling is lying on its side.* FREDDIE *goes right up to the ornaments, and fixes the fallen duckling so that it, too, is upright. A sturdy* BOY *of* FREDDIE'S *age comes wildly down a hill on a skateboard, shouting—)*

BOY. Look out, look out! Get out of the way!

(The camera follows him and reveals FREDDIE *at the foot of the hill just standing there, watching in amazement. The* BOY *manages to swerve and miss* FREDDIE, *but falls. Picking himself up, he rushes toward* FREDDIE *full of fight.)*

BOY. What's the matter with you, anyway?

(But FREDDIE *goes and picks up the skateboard, and hands it to the* BOY.*)*

FREDDIE. I have to find my friend.

*(*FREDDIE *walks away; leaving the* BOY *puzzled, and somewhat comprehending, turning the wheels of the skateboard with his hand.)*

*(*FREDDIE *is walking down another street. He stares at a stop sign. For a moment he frowns. Then his lips move, forming the letters* S-T-O-P. *Then aloud:)*

FREDDIE. Stop.

*(*FREDDIE *is at an intersection. The sudden sound of a blow-out is heard, and then the chunketa-chunketa-chunketa of a car rolling on the rim.* FREDDIE *looks in the direction of the sound—fascinated. The car drives onto the shoulder of the road with a flat. As* FREDDIE *runs over to it, a* WOMAN *gets out of the car. She opens the trunk of the car.)*

FREDDIE. That's a jack.

WOMAN. Yes, it is and I don't know how to use it. *(*FREDDIE *comes right up to her and puts his hands on his hips—like* CARTER.

The WOMAN *turns to him.)* Is there a garage around here?

FREDDIE. My Daddy's got one. But I can fix it.

WOMAN. Are you sure? *(FREDDIE nods his little nod.)* Well, if your father's got a garage. . . . *(She looks at* FREDDIE *with some concern as he lifts out the jack.)* You can't handle that heavy tire—

FREDDIE. No such word as can't.

(Just the same, the WOMAN *helps* FREDDIE *lift the spare tire out of the trunk. Fade out.)*

(Fade in on the roadside, late day. FREDDIE *has finished changing the tire, and he steps back, hands on hips, to look over the work.)*

FREDDIE. *That's got it. (He smiles up at the* WOMAN.*)* There's no such word as can't. *(And he starts away. But the* WOMAN *catches his arm.)*

WOMAN *(gently).* What's your name?

FREDDIE. Freddie.

WOMAN. How old are you?

FREDDIE. Thirteen years old.

WOMAN *(very softly).* Thirteen. *(The* WOMAN *opens her purse and takes out a dollar. She hands it to* FREDDIE.*)*

FREDDIE. What's that for?

WOMAN. It's for you.

FREDDIE *(studies the bill curiously).* Thank you.

WOMAN. You're welcome. Freddie—where do you live?

FREDDIE *(pointing).* With my teacher. I can read! *(He reaches into his pocket and takes out the cut-out "reading helper"* CARTER *made for him. As the* WOMAN *studies it:)* You look through the little window to see the words. *(He takes it and holds it up to his eyes.)* See?

WOMAN *(so gently).* I see. *(She takes the card and reads aloud:)* "Charles Carter . . . Home Service . . . 223 Wicker Street."

. . . *(Then she takes* FREDDIE *by the hand and leads him to the car door, opens it—and* FREDDIE *climbs in.)*

(While the car is in motion, FREDDIE *is holding his precious card up to his eyes and peering through it. We see what* FREDDIE *sees, framed in the card: a street with a row of self-respecting frame houses with little front yards. Now into the frame of the card comes* CARTER'S *station wagon with the ladders on top, parked in the driveway. The car stops and* FREDDIE *jumps out. The* WOMAN *waits until he enters the house.)*

(The interior of CARTER'S *house.* FREDDIE *runs through the house looking for* JOEY. CARTER *follows him.)*

FREDDIE *(all excited).* Where's Joey? Where's Joey?

CARTER. Freddie, now you simmer down. Joey went to the grocery store with his mother. And the first thing you're going to do, young man—you're going to call Mr. Cade on that phone.

FREDDIE. No!

CARTER. No? Since when do you sass me back? You're asking for a spanking!

FREDDIE. What's a spanking?

CARTER. You might just find out! *(CARTER sits down at a telephone table.)* You come here while I make this phone call. . . . You stand right here. *(After he dials, he reaches out and pulls* FREDDIE *toward him and onto his lap.)* Come over here. . . . *(into phone)* Cade? Oh, Mr. Putnam. This is Charles Carter—the Carter Home Service. The handyman? . . .

(In PUTNAM'S *study,* PUTNAM *is on the phone.* CADE *is standing near him.)*

CARTER'S VOICE. Yes. Yes, sir, I understand, Mr. Putnam. . . . Your son's right here.

(Then, at CARTER's *house:)*

CARTER *(to* FREDDIE*).* Freddie—say hello to your Daddy.

FREDDIE *(putting his mouth right close to the phone).* Hello. . . . *(pause)* Hello? Hello? Hello? *(to* CARTER*)* Why doesn't he answer?

CARTER *(into the phone).* It's all right, Mr. Putnam. Yes. he's just fine and I'll bring him right over. . . .

*(*PUTNAM's *driveway, evening.* CARTER's *station wagon pulls up the drive.)*

*(*PUTNAM's *study.* FREDDIE *bursts into the room, followed by* CARTER *and* JOEY. FREDDIE *runs to his father.)*

FREDDIE. Daddy! Daddy, you came back!

PUTNAM. Where have you been?

FREDDIE. I found my friend! *(He hugs* JOEY.*)*

JOEY. Quit huggin'!

CARTER *(to* PUTNAM*).* I'm Charles Carter, Mr. Putnam. I don't know how he found my house, but he did.

*(*FREDDIE *takes the dollar out of his pocket.)*

PUTNAM. Well—where did you get that?

FREDDIE. I fixed a tire.

CARTER. He earned it.

PUTNAM. You earned it?

FREDDIE. Hmm-mm.

*(*PUTNAM *examines the dollar in disbelief. Then he hands it back to* FREDDIE.*)*

JOEY. Can he come home with us?

FREDDIE. Can I?

PUTNAM. Well—we'll have to ask your teacher.

*(*CADE's *room, evening.* CADE *is packing his suitcase. He puts the note that* FREDDIE *wrote in the suitcase atop his clothes, but leaves the suitcase open.* PUTNAM *knocks and enters.)*

PUTNAM. What's going on?

CADE. Just packing.

PUTNAM. What for?

CADE. I fired myself.

PUTNAM. Why?

CADE. For using Freddie.

PUTNAM (takes FREDDIE's *note from the open suitcase*). You're a fool.

CADE. Yes. I know that.

PUTNAM. You're also a good teacher.

CADE. Yes. I know that, too.

PUTNAM. Why don't you stick around a couple of weeks till I can get some recommendations off to my buddies at Hillsgrove? (CADE *shoots him a quick look*.) Just a suggestion. (*He holds up the note*.) You mind if I keep this?

CADE (*his look softens*). No.

(*In the hallway,* CARTER *comes down the stairs carrying* FREDDIE's *small overnight bag. He passes* CADE, *who is in the living room reading the paper*.)

CARTER. Where are the kids?

CADE (*nodding toward the study*). In there. . . . Carter, I'm sorry about this morning.

CARTER. Forget it, man . . . you're a fine teacher.

CADE. You're not so bad yourself.

CARTER (*goes toward the door of the study—then, jokingly*). Of course—I wouldn't want you flying a plane.

(*On the floor of the study,* PUTNAM *is playing with* FREDDIE *and* JOEY. PUTNAM *is demonstrating a toy that has steel balls attached to strings*.)

PUTNAM (*extending one ball*). Now—watch this. . . . What happens when I let two balls go?

JOEY. I don't know.

PUTNAM (*demonstrates*). Now how about what happens when I let three balls go?

(*For a moment, he holds the three balls out on the ends of their strings—then lets go. The gadget behaves according to Newton's first*

law of dynamics[1] *and the children are delighted*. CARTER *enters, followed by* CADE.)

CARTER. Mr. Putnam, can I have them now?

PUTNAM. Sure.

CARTER. Okay! Freddie, Joey! Let's go! (*They tear themselves away from the toy*.) Say goodbye to your Daddy. . . . I'll wait for you fellas in the car.

(FREDDIE *hugs his father. He is about to leave without saying goodbye to* CADE *when he notices* CADE *standing slightly off, watching*. FREDDIE *runs to* CADE, *who bends to embrace him*.)

FREDDIE. Goodbye, Teacher.

CADE. Goodbye, Freddie.

PUTNAM. You better hurry up, it'll be dark soon.

FREDDIE. I know why it gets dark.

PUTNAM. Why?

FREDDIE. Because the sun goes to sleep.

JOEY. No. That's wrong! Because the earth revolves around the sun.

FREDDIE. What's *revolves?*

CADE. Well—revolves—revolves is to turn— (*He takes* FREDDIE *by the shoulders and slowly turns him*.) You see the world turns—you see, if you're the world, you turn—like that—see— (*He is turning* FREDDIE.) You're going around. And—and—I— (CADE *stops. He looks at—then gestures to—* PUTNAM.) Your Daddy—look at your Daddy—your Daddy's the sun. Now you're the world and your Daddy's the sun. . . . Now you can see the sun. . . . (*He turns* FREDDIE *to face his father*.) It's day. (*He turns* FREDDIE *to face away from his father*.) Night.

---

1. *gadget . . . Newton's first law of dynamics.* Sir Isaac Newton (1642–1727) discovered this principle of motion and the action of forces (dynamics). This toy is designed to demonstrate the principle: when an end ball is swung against the others, a ball from the opposite end moves, though those in between remain at rest.

(He continues to turn FREDDIE. *When* FRED-DIE'S *face is turned away from his father, he keeps his eyes shut.)*

FREDDIE *(eyes shut).* Night! *(He turns to face his father and opens his eyes.)* Day! *(He stops, facing his father.)* Daddy? I'm the world! . . . (He looks at his father expectantly.)*

PUTNAM *(softly).* And I'm the sun.

CADE *(sets* FREDDIE *turning again).* Faster—Day—Night—Day—

FREDDIE. I'm dizzy.

*(*PUTNAM *crosses over to* FREDDIE *and sweeps him into his arms, proudly, joyfully. The camera lingers on* FREDDIE'S *face.)*
□□

Discussion

1. (a) Why does Carter leave? **(b)** What does he accuse Cade of before he leaves? **(c)** In your opinion, how accurate is Carter's accusation? **(d)** How does Cade explain Carter's leaving to Putnam? Why does he do so?

2. (a) Why do you suppose Freddie ignores Cade's attempts to persuade him off the trampoline? **(b)** Why is Cade so upset by Freddie's behavior?

3. Why does the note from Freddie amaze both Putnam and Cade?

4. (a) How does Freddie know how to change the woman's tire? **(b)** What mannerisms does he exhibit which show he has been influenced by Carter? **(c)** On his walk, how does Freddie demonstrate what he has learned from Cade? **(d)** What encounter demonstrates that Freddie has led a very sheltered life?

5. (a) Why does Carter threaten Freddie with a spanking? **(b)** In your opinion, does Carter behave differently toward Freddie in this scene than he has before? Explain.

6. When Joey asks if Freddie can come home with them, why does Putnam say they will have to ask Cade?

7. Why does Cade "fire himself"?

8. When Putnam calls Cade both a fool and a good teacher, Cade replies, "I know." **(a)** How can he be both of these things? **(b)** Do you agree or disagree with Putnam's description? Explain. **(c)** How does Cade show that he has learned something himself?

9. What kind of future would you predict for each of these three characters: **(a)** Freddie; **(b)** Carter; **(c)** Cade? Support your predictions with evidence from the play.

10. What does *Teacher, Teacher* say to you about teaching and learning? about dealing with other people? State briefly what you think is the main theme of the play.

Extension • Writing

Below are various comments about learning. Choose one to lead off your composition, and use it in one of the following ways:

(a) Agree with the quotation or disagree with it. Develop your theme by showing how the quotation does or does not apply to one of the characters in *Teacher, Teacher.* Use specific instances from the play to prove your point.

(b) Write about your own experiences. Use specific instances from your background to show how the quotation does or does not apply to you or someone you know well.

"Personally I'm always ready to learn, although I do not always like being taught." —Winston Churchill, *The Eloquence of Winston Churchill* (New American Library).

"Learning is acquired by reading books; but the much more necessary learning, the knowledge of the world, is only to be acquired by reading people."—Lord Chesterfield, *Letter to his son, March 16, 1752.*

"Men learn while they teach."—Seneca, *Epistulae morales ad Lucilium.*

Able Though Disabled

Some disabilities are acquired at birth; some result from accidents or diseases. Most physical disabilities, however, can be overcome or compensated for.

Helen Keller, left blind and deaf from fever in her infancy, nevertheless learned to read, to write—and eventually to speak. She was during her lifetime a scholar, philosopher, author, movie actress, and lecturer. Her story is told in an inspiring play and movie, *The Miracle Worker*.

José Feliciano moved with his family from Puerto Rico to New York when he was very young. José, born blind, learned to play the guitar by ear. At seventeen he began playing professionally, recording five albums in English and Spanish before he found his personal style. Feliciano became a success with his hit recording of "Light My Fire." He now plays the banjo, bass, piano, organ, harmonica, and other instruments, and has turned to composing music.

Franklin D. Roosevelt was a State Senator (N.Y.), Assistant Secretary of the Navy, and a Vice-Presidential candidate before being stricken with polio. Rarely did someone of his age recover, but Roosevelt was determined. Months of exercises, massages, and swimming therapy enabled him finally to move on crutches. When he was elected governor of New York, he was able to stand and walk about in heavy steel braces from his hips to his feet. Later he was elected to four terms as President of the U.S., during the depression of the 1930's and World War II.

Jill Kinmont grew up a normal, active girl. In high school she took up skiing and became hopeful of making the Olympics. Then, a fall during a race severed her spinal cord. She still is almost totally paralyzed, yet with various mechanical aids she can maneuver an electric wheelchair, feed herself, type, paint—and teach. Soon after her accident, she earned her teacher's certificate, and later she developed special reading courses for Paiute Indian children. Two movies have been made about her life: *The Other Side of the Mountain, I* and *II*.

Christy Brown was born in a Dublin, Ireland, slum, with extensive brain damage. Because Christy was unable to sit up by himself, and unable to speak, doctors advised that he was a hopeless case. Then, at age five, Christy picked up a piece of chalk—using his left foot. His mother showed him how to write letters on a blackboard, and slowly he learned to write. His first book was an autobiography, *My Left Foot*. His second was a novel that brought him international fame. He now writes with an electric typewriter, and he also paints—using his feet.

The lives of these and many more people demonstrate that most physical disabilities can be overcome, given a chance. But what chance has a *mentally* disabled person like Freddie in *Teacher, Teacher?*

Many people with mental disabilities can lead nearly normal lives. The large majority of retarded persons are capable of self-supporting, productive work. Like Freddie, they can learn to read and write to a degree, work with tools, and acquire some basic work skills. They can make friends and deal successfully with other people. Halfway houses or "sheltered workshops" operate with private industry to provide unskilled work, so that retarded persons may lead independent —or less dependent—lives.

Success in overcoming a disability depends upon an individual's determination and the medical and technical help that person gets. But almost all experts agree that it's the human contact—love and patient caring—that counts the most.

8: Affinities

1. Look up the meaning of *affinity* in the Glossary. Then, explain in what ways a character (or characters) in each of the following selections demonstrates an affinity for someone or something: **(a)** "A Few Notes About the Arabian Oryx"; **(b)** "Mama Is a Sunrise"; **(c)** "While I Slept"; **(d)** "Gentleman of Río en Medio"; **(e)** *Teacher, Teacher.*

2. Explain in what ways the speakers in "The River Took My Sister," "Who Am I?" and "I Am Through" express similar attitudes toward nature.

3. Pride or self-esteem plays an important part in several selections in this unit. Explain in what way a sense of pride—in themselves or for others—influences each of the following characters: **(a)** the father in "My Father and the Hippopotamus"; **(b)** Don Anselmo in "Gentleman of Río en Medio"; **(c)** Tony in "A Few Notes About the Arabian Oryx"; **(d)** Hamilton Cade in *Teacher, Teacher.*

4. For what character in this unit—or in the book—do you feel the closest affinity? Explain your choice.

Unit 8, Test I
INTERPRETATION: NEW MATERIAL

Read the story and answer the questions that follow. You may look back at the story.

The Hummingbird That Lived Through Winter

William Saroyan

Sometimes even instinct is overpowered by individuality—in creatures other than men, I mean. In men instinct is supposed to be controlled, but whether or not it ever actually is I leave to others. At any rate, the fundamental instinct of most—or all—creatures is to live. Each form of life has an instinctive technique of defense against other forms of life, as well as against the elements. What happens to hummingbirds is something I have never found out—from actual observation or from reading. They die, that's true. And they're born somehow or other, although I have never seen a hummingbird's egg, or a young hummingbird.

The mature hummingbird itself is so small that the egg must be magnificent, probably one of the most smiling little things in the world. Now, if hummingbirds come into the world through some other means than eggs, I ask the reader to forgive me. The only thing I know about Agass Agasig Agassig Agazig (well, the great American naturalist) is that he once studied turtle eggs, and in order to get the information he was seeking, had to find fresh ones. This caused an exciting adventure in Boston to a young fellow who wrote about it six or seven years before I read it, when I was fourteen. I was fourteen in 1922, which goes to show you how unimportant the years are when you're dealing with eggs of any kind. I envy the people who study birds, and some day I hope to find out everything that's known about hummingbirds.

I've gathered from rumor that the hummingbird travels incredible distances on incredibly little energy—what carries him, then? Spirit? But the best things I know about hummingbirds are the things I've noticed about them myself: that they are on hand when the sun is out in earnest, when the blossoms are with us, and the smell of them everywhere. You can hardly go through the best kind of day without seeing a hummingbird suspended like a little miracle in a shaft of light or over a big flower or a cluster of little ones. Or turning like gay insanity and shooting straight as an arrow toward practically nothing, for no reason, or for the reason that it's alive. Now, how can creatures such as that—so delicately magnificent and mad—possibly find time for the routine business of begetting young? Or for the exercise of instinct in self-defense? Well, however it may be, let a good day come by the grace of God, and with it will come the hummingbirds.

As I started to say, however, it appears that sometimes even instinct fails to operate in a specie. Or species. Or whatever it is. Anyhow, when all of a kind of living thing turn and go somewhere, in order to stay alive, in order to escape cold or whatever it might be, sometimes, it appears, one of them does not go. Why he does not go I cannot say. He may be eccentric, or there may be exalted reasons—specific instead of abstract passion for another of its kind—perhaps dead—or for a place. Or it may be stupidity, or stubbornness. Who can ever know?

There was a hummingbird once which in the wintertime did not leave our neighborhood in Fresno, California.

I'll tell you about it.

Across the street lived old Dikran, who was almost blind. He was past eighty and his wife was only a few years younger. They had a little house that was as neat inside as it was ordinary outside—except for old Dikran's garden, which was the best thing of its kind in the world. Plants, bushes, trees—all strong, in sweet black moist earth whose guardian was old Dikran. All things from the sky loved this spot in our poor neighborhood, and old Dikran loved *them*.

One freezing Sunday, in the dead of winter, as I came home from Sunday School I saw old Dikran standing in the middle of the street trying to distinguish what was in his hand. Instead of going into our house to the fire, as I had wanted to do, I stood on the steps of the front porch and watched the old man. He would turn around and look upward at his trees and then back to the palm of his hand. He stood in the street at least two minutes and then at last he came to me. He held his hand out, and in Armenian he said, "What is this in my hand?"

I looked.

"It is a hummingbird," I said half in English and half in Armenian. Hummingbird I said in English because I didn't know its name in Armenian.

"What is that?" old Dikran asked.

"The little bird," I said. "You know. The one that comes in the summer and stands in the air and then shoots away. The one with the wings that beat so fast you can't see them. It's in your hand. It's dying."

"Come with me," the old man said. "I can't see, and the old lady's at church. I can feel its heart beating. Is it in a bad way? Look again, once."

I looked again. It was a sad thing to behold. This wonderful little creature of summertime in the big rough hand of the old peasant. Here it was in the cold of winter, absolutely helpless and pathetic, not suspended in a shaft of summer light, not the most alive thing in the world, but the most helpless and heartbreaking.

"It's dying," I said.

The old man lifted his hand to his mouth and blew warm breath on the little thing in his hand which he could not even see. "Stay now," he said in Armenian. "It is not long till summer. Stay, swift and lovely."

We went into the kitchen of his little house, and while he blew warm breath on the bird he told me what to do.

"Put a tablespoonful of honey over the gas fire and pour it into my hand, but be sure it is not too hot."

This was done.

After a moment the hummingbird began to show signs of fresh life. The warmth of the room, the vapor of the warm honey—and, well, the will and love of the old man. Soon the old man could feel the change in his hand, and after a moment or two the hummingbird began to take little dabs of the honey.

"It will live," the old man announced. "Stay and watch."

The transformation was incredible. The old man kept his hand generously open, and I expected the helpless bird to shoot upward out of his hand, suspend itself in space, and scare the life out of me—which is exactly what happened. The new life of the little bird was magnificent. It spun about in the little kitchen, going to the window, coming back to the heat, suspending, circling as if it were summertime and it had never felt better in its whole life.

The old man sat on the plain chair, blind but attentive. He listened carefully and tried to see, but of course he couldn't. He kept asking about the bird, how it seemed to be, whether it showed signs of weakening again, what its spirit was, and whether or not it appeared to be restless; and I kept describing the bird to him.

When the bird was restless and wanted to go, the old man said, "Open the window and let it go."

"Will it live?" I asked.

"It is alive now and wants to go," he said. "Open the window."

I opened the window, the hummingbird stirred about here and there, feeling the cold from the outside, suspended itself in the area of the open window, stirring this way and that, and then it was gone.

"Close the window," the old man said.

We talked a minute or two and then I went home.

The old man claimed the hummingbird lived through that winter, but I never knew for sure. I saw hummingbirds again when summer came, but I couldn't tell one from the other.

One day in the summer I asked the old man.

"Did it live?"

"The little bird?" he said.

"Yes," I said. "That we gave the honey to. You remember. The little bird that was dying in the winter. Did it live?"

"Look about you," the old man said. "Do you see the bird?"

"I see humming*birds*," I said.

"Each of them is our bird," the old man said. "Each of them, each of them," he said swiftly and gently. ☐☐

1. Which of the following best describes the narrator's tone? **(a)** full of anger and bitterness; **(b)** self-satisfied; **(c)** full of kindness and wonder; **(d)** uninvolved.

2. Which method of characterization is *not* used in telling the reader about Dikran? **(a)** giving physical description; **(b)** having Dikran speak; **(c)** telling Dikran's innermost thoughts; **(d)** showing Dikran in action.

3. The conflict (see *plot* in the *Handbook of Literary Terms*, page 547) is between **(a)** Dikran and the narrator; **(b)** the narrator and the bird; **(c)** the bird and Dikran; **(d)** the bird and the winter weather.

4. The conflict in the story is **(a)** internal; **(b)** external; **(c)** both; **(d)** neither.

5. Which of the following sentences states the climax of the story? **(a)** Dikran finds the half-dead bird. **(b)** The bird recovers and is released. **(c)** The narrator decides to stay and help Dikran nurse the bird.

(d) All the hummingbirds return to the garden.

6. When Dikran says "Each of them is our bird," he means that **(a)** because he is blind, he can't distinguish one bird from another; **(b)** it is impossible for anyone to tell one hummingbird from another; **(c)** because of their kindness to one bird, all the hummingbirds have returned; **(d)** regardless of whether the bird lived, its qualities have survived in other hummingbirds.

Unit 8, Test II
COMPOSITION

Choose *one* of the following to write about.

1. Of all the characters you have met in this unit, which would you like most to have as "kin"? Write a short paper explaining to your classmates why you have chosen this person.

2. In many of the selections in this unit, one member of a family tells about another. The ways in which the reader is given this information range

from humorous accounts ("My Father and the Hippopotamus"), through poems of praise ("Mama Is a Sunrise") to poems of mourning ("The River Took My Sister"). Describe a member of your family to your classmates. Your description may be an essay, a poem, a story, or any other written form.

3. Have you ever felt you would like to get away from people as the speaker in "I Am

Through" has done? If so, where would you go? How would you survive? With what kinds of activities would you fill your days? Imagine that you have been living your solitary life for a month. Write a letter about your experiences to one of your classmates. In the letter you should mention specific details of your isolation and tell whether you are happy with your new life.

Handbook of Literary Terms

satire   foreshadowing
hyperbole

characterization 532

connotation/denotation 534

figurative language 535

flashback 536

imagery 538

inference 539

inversion 541

irony 542

metaphor 544

mood 545

plot 546

point of view 549

rhyme 550

rhythm 552

setting 553

simile 555

stereotype 556

symbol 557

theme 559

tone 560

characterization

An author can use several methods to create a fictitious character, and the better an author is at using these techniques, the more a character comes alive. Read the lines below. These lines and the examples that follow are from *National Velvet* by Enid Bagnold.

Velvet was fourteen. Velvet had short pale hair, large, protruding teeth, a sweet smile, and a mouthful of metal.

What do you know about Velvet from this passage? If you were an artist, what would you include in a drawing of her? What else might you want to know?

Obviously this is only a physical description of Velvet, and it is one method by which authors tell you what a character is like.

Another method by which authors create characters is that of having the characters speak. In the passage below, Velvet is walking beside an elderly neighbor.

. . . They walked on again, he in his black hat and black waistcoat and shirt-sleeves.

"Going to the stables," said he. "Why, are you fond of horses?"

There was something about him that made Velvet feel he was going to say good-bye to her. She fancied he was going to be carried up to heaven like Elisha.[1]

"Horses," he said. "Did you say you had horses?"

"Only an old pony, sir."

"All my life I've had horses. Stables full of them. You like 'em?"

"I've seen your chestnut," said Velvet. "Sir Pericles. I seen him jump."

"I wish he was yours, then," said the old gentleman, suddenly and heartily. "You said you rode?"

"We've on'y got Miss Ada. The pony. She's old."

"Huh!"

"Not so much *old*," said Velvet hurriedly. "She's obstinate."

He stopped again.

"Would you tell me what you want most in the world? . . . would you tell me that?"

He was looking at her.

"Horses," she said, "sir."

"To ride on? To own for yourself?"

He was still looking at her, as though he expected more.

"I tell myself stories about horses," she went on, desperately fishing at her shy desires. "Then I can dream about them. Now I dream about them every night. I want to be a famous rider; I should like to carry dispatches. I should like to get a first at Olympia; I should like to ride in a great race; I should like to have so many horses that I could walk down between the two rows of loose boxes and ride what I chose. I would have them all under fifteen hands. I like chestnuts best, but bays are lovely too, but I don't like blacks."

She ran out the words and caught her breath and stopped.

What does this excerpt reveal about Velvet? Is she tactful? polite? ambitious? imaginative? Refer to lines or words in the example to support your answers. In what manner do you suppose Velvet speaks her last long speech about horses? Do you think she is looking at the old gentleman when she speaks these lines? Is there any physical description of Velvet here? of the old man?

Read the next passage, which shows another technique an author uses to create a character.

. . . They all went up to the field to try the horses.

Velvet mounted Sir Pericles. She had ridden Miss Ada for eight years, hopped her over bits of brushwood and gorse-bushes, and trotted her round at the local gymkhana.[2] Once she had ridden a black pony belonging to the farmer at Pendean. She had a natural seat, and her bony hands gathered up the reins in a tender way. But she had never yet felt reins that had a trained mouth at the end of them, and, as she cantered up the slope of the sunny field with the brow of the hill and the height of the sky in front of her, Sir Pericles taught her in three minutes what she had not

From *National Velvet* by Enid Bagnold. Copyright 1935 by Enid Bagnold Jones. Copyright renewed 1963 by Enid Bagnold Jones. Reprinted by permission of Brandt & Brandt and William Heinemann Ltd.

1. **Elisha** (i li′shə), probably a reference to Elijah (i li′jə), Hebrew prophet of the 800s B.C. who was carried up in a whirlwind to heaven (2 Kings 2:11).

2. **gymkhana** (jim kä′nə), sports contest or meeting.

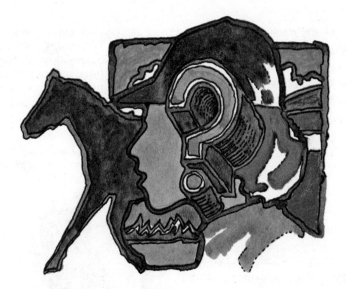

known existed. Her scraggy, childish fingers obtained results at a pressure. The living canter bent to right or left at her touch. He handed her the glory of command.

When she slid to the ground by the side of the head groom she was speechless, and leant her forehead for a second on the horse's flank.

What does this excerpt describe? What information does it give about Velvet? How does this riding experience differ from a ride on Miss Ada? What is Velvet's reaction to this ride? How do you know?

Here the author has, for the most part, described Velvet's actions, both in the past and at the present, and we are able to come to several more conclusions about Velvet.

Sometimes an author reveals directly what a character is thinking.

. . . Velvet was conscious of her father's case. It was a good one. There was no benefit to him in the horses. The lovely creatures ate, and were sterile. They laboured not, and ate and ate, and lost their shoes. Velvet had no answers and no comfort to offer.

What is Velvet concerned about?

Finally, an author may tell about one character by showing you what another character thinks.

"If she were a boy . . ." he said longingly to himself. With that light body and grand heart he would get her into a racing stable. He knew of many up North. He had friends here and there. She'd be a great jockey some day. Fancy wasting those hands and that spirit and that light weight on a girl. "No more'n a skeleton," he said. "An' never will be, likely. She'd ride like a piece of lightning. No more weight'n a piece of lightning."

What further things do we learn about Velvet? Is Velvet a likeable character? If you were drawing a picture of Velvet now, what things would you include?

characterization

The methods an author uses to create a fictional person. An author may develop a character through describing the character's physical appearance, speech, actions, and inner thoughts or through revealing attitudes and reactions of other characters.

Copy the words below on your paper and as you copy each one, write beside it the first word that you associate with it. Don't stop to think about it—simply write the first word that occurs to you in each case. (There are no wrong answers.)

homesick	star
swing	picnic
breeze	island
parade	old

If you compare what you wrote with what others in your class wrote, you may find some similarities, but chances are you all associated different things with the printed words. Because each of us is unique, we have reactions and thoughts about our experiences that are often unlike those of anyone else.

Think about the word *homesick*, for instance. Can you remember the first time you were homesick? Where were you? How old were you? Did you feel homesick for a few minutes or a long time? The personal interpretation you bring to a word like *homesick* is the *connotation* of the word. The dictionary meaning or *denotation* is "overcome by sadness because of being far away from home." The *connotation* of *homesick* is what additional feelings or experiences an individual associates with the word.

Read the dictionary entry for *cat* below and then notice how the writer of the poem expresses the connotations that a particular cat has for him.

cat (kat), *n.* a small, furry, four-footed, carnivorous mammal, often kept as a pet or for catching mice and rats.

What Could It Be?

I really do not like that cat;
I don't know why, perhaps it's that
She's vicious, cruel, rude, ungrateful,
Smelly, treacherous, and hateful,

5 Supercilious, stupid, eerie,
Thoroughly boring, dull, and dreary,
Scheming, cold, and unproductive,
Inconvenient and destructive—
But most, I've just a *feeling* that
10 I *really* do not like that cat!

William Cole

From *A Book of Animal Poems* by William Cole. Copyright © 1973 by William Cole. Reprinted by permission of The Viking Press.

What connotations does *cat* have for the speaker in this poem? Is any part of the dictionary definition of *cat* included in the poem?

connotation/denotation

Connotation is the associations surrounding a word that are not part of its literal dictionary meaning. Denotation is the exact dictionary meaning of a word. The denotation of *home* is "place where one lives," but the word *home* has various connotations.

figurative language

The hair on her head was dark brown streaked with gray. The hairpiece was completely gray. It clung to the back of her neck—a squirrel with its tiny paws clutching and its furry back bent almost double in an effort to hold on. Her blue raincoat hung nearly to the ground in front and was several inches shorter in the back. She carried a shopping bag in each hand. In that city neighborhood, she was a sign of spring. Like a battered crocus or a soot-sprinkled daffodil planted too near the sidewalk, she shrugged off the dirt and burst forth each year. She was a dark flower though. And none ventured too near, for she droned as she plowed her way from trash basket to trash basket and anybody—child or adult—who got too close was liable to be pelted with words like tiny sharp stones, words they didn't want to hear.

In your own words, describe the person in the paragraph above. Is your retelling more interesting or less interesting than the paragraph?

The author of the paragraph has combined ideas, images, and facts in such a way as to make it clear and forceful. The descriptions are not to be taken literally. The hairpiece is not really a squirrel, the woman is not a dark flower, and she did not literally plow the streets. The writer has used *figurative language* rather than literal language. Literal language uses words according to their usual meaning, without imaginative coloring. Figurative language departs from ordinary language to make meaning more vivid and more interesting. In figurative language, thoughts, images, and concepts are presented as comparisons. Whenever we use words in nonliteral ways we are using *figures of speech.* Two things that seem unlike each other are compared in a figure of speech, and the reader suddenly sees similarities between them:

> Her hair drooped round her pallid cheeks
> Like seaweed on a clam.

What things are compared here? Do these lines call to mind a pretty or a grotesque picture?

In some figures of speech, forces of nature are given human qualities:

> I saw you toss the kites on high
> And blow the birds about the sky;
> And all around I heard you pass,
> Like ladies' skirts across the grass—
> 5   O wind, a-blowing all day long,
>   O wind, that sings so loud a song!
>
> Stevenson, "The Wind"

What human characteristics does the poet give the wind? How do you know whether the wind is gentle or violent?

Appropriate figurative language has a quality of freshness about it. (For example, "sweet as sugar" is overused and lacks the quality of freshness. It does not surprise us.)

Poets, especially, use figurative language to suggest an idea in a few words. Below are some excerpts. Read each one and then answer the questions that follow.

> The moon, like to a silver bow
> new-bent in heaven.
>
> Shakespeare,
> *A Midsummer Night's Dream*

1. What two things are being compared?
2. Is the moon full?

> Anger rides sparkling in her eyes.

3. Describe the girl's eyes in literal terms.
4. What kind of person might the girl be?

> Like a lobster boiled, the morn
> From black to red began to burn.
>
> Butler, *Hudibras*

5. What kind of day is suggested?
6. Explain the meaning of the second line.

Day after day, day after day,
We stuck, nor breath nor motion;
As idle as a painted ship
Upon a painted ocean.

Coleridge,
Rime of the Ancient Mariner

7. Explain the meaning of the last two lines.

. . . the Lady stretch'd a vulture throat
And shot from crooked lips a haggard smile.

8. In the first line the Lady's throat is compared to a vulture's (bird's). What does the word *shot* suggest about the way the Lady smiled?

Life's but a walking shadow, a poor player
That struts and frets his hour upon the stage.

Shakespeare, *Hamlet*

9. To what does the speaker compare life?

figurative language

Language expanded beyond its ordinary literal meaning. It uses comparisons to achieve new effects, to provide fresh insights, or to express a fitting relationship between things essentially unlike. An effective figure of speech is original, appropriate in tone, and usually brief. See also SIMILE and METAPHOR.

Below is part of a short story. As you read, pay particular attention to the order of events.

from The Apprentice

The day had been one of those unbearable ones, when every sound had set her teeth on edge like chalk creaking on a blackboard, when every word her father or mother said to her or did not say to her seemed an intentional injustice. And of course it would happen, at the end to such a day, that just as the sun went down back of the mountain and the long twilight began, she noticed that Rollie was not around.

Tense with exasperation—she would simply explode if Mother got going—she began to call him in a carefully casual tone: "Here, Rollie! He-ere, boy! Want to go for a walk, Rollie?" Whistling to him cheerfully, her heart full of wrath at the way the world treated her, she made the rounds of his haunts; the corner of the woodshed, where he liked to curl up on the wool of Father's discarded old windbreaker; the hay barn, the cow barn, the sunny spot on the side porch—no Rollie.

Perhaps he had sneaked upstairs to lie on her bed where he was not supposed to go—not that *she* would have minded! That rule was a part of Mother's fussiness, part too of Mother's bossiness. It was *her* bed, wasn't it? But was she allowed the say-so about it? Not on your life. They told her she could have things the way she wanted in her own room, now she was in her teens, but—her heart raged against unfairness as she took the stairs stormily, two steps at a time, her pigtails flopping up and down on her back. If Rollie was on her bed, she was just going to let him stay right there, and Mother could shake her head and frown all she wanted to.

But he was not there. . . .

Before she would let her father and mother know she had lost sight of him, forgotten about him, she would be cut into little pieces. They would not scold her, she knew. They would do worse. They would look at her. And in their silence she would hear droning on reproachfully what they had repeated and repeated when the sweet, woolly collie-puppy had first been in her arms and she had been begging to keep him for her own.

How warm he had felt! Astonishing how warm and alive a puppy was compared to a doll! She had never liked her dolls much, after she had held Rollie, feeling him warm against her breast, warm and wriggling, bursting with life, reaching up to lick her face—he had loved her from that first instant. As he felt her arms around him, his beautiful eyes had melted in trusting sweetness. . . .

Even then, at the very minute when as a darling baby dog he was beginning to love her, her father and mother were saying, so cold, so reasonable—gosh! how she *hated* reasonableness!—"Now, Peg, remember that, living where we do, with sheep on the farms around us, it is a serious responsibility to have a collie dog. If you keep him, you've got to be the one to take care of him. You'll have to be the one to train him to stay at home. We're too busy with you children to start bringing up a puppy, too." Rollie, nestling in her arms, let one hind leg drop awkwardly. It must be uncomfortable. She looked down at him tenderly, tucked his dangling leg up under him and gave him a hug. He laughed up in her face—he really did laugh, his mouth stretched wide in a cheerful grin.

All the time her parents kept hammering away: "If you want him, you can have him. But you must be responsible for him. If he gets to running sheep, he'll just have to be shot, you know that."

And now, this afternoon, when he was six months old, tall, rangy, powerful, standing up far above her knee, nearly to her waist, she didn't know where he was. But of course he must be somewhere around. He always was. She composed her face to look natural and went downstairs to search the house.

Dorothy Canfield Fisher

Following is a list of events in the order they are mentioned in the excerpt above. Rearrange these items in the order in which they actually occurred.

1. Peg discovers that Rollie is missing.

2. Peg searches outside.

3. Peg looks in her bedroom for Rollie.

4. Peg thinks about how her parents will react to Rollie's absence.

5. Peg falls in love with the puppy and wants to keep it.

6. Peg's parents warn her of the responsibility of keeping a collie.

7. Peg continues to look for Rollie.

You have rearranged the events in *chronological order*, the order in which events occur in time. In the story, which events are *not* mentioned in chronological order?

A *flashback* is an interruption in the narrative to show a scene or scenes that occurred earlier. A flashback allows the author to include an incident from the past that helps a reader or viewer better understand events or personalities in the present.

1. Find the words or phrases in this excerpt that alert you to the beginning of the flashback.

2. What would happen if the flashback were simply removed?

3. If the author had not used a flashback, how might she have presented the same information to the reader?

Often an author wants a work to cover a limited span of time. A flashback may then be employed to fill in background or to make the characters or the situation more understandable. In this selection, Peg's concern about Rollie's absence would not mean nearly so much if the reader were unaware of her parents' earlier warnings.

Instead of showing how Peg and her parents reacted to the puppy, the author might merely have said the following: "Six months earlier, Peg's parents had allowed her to keep Rollie, who was then a puppy. At that time, they warned her of the responsibility involved in keeping a collie in sheep country."

Although this statement provides the same information, it is not a flashback.

flashback

An interruption in the action of a story, play, or work of nonfiction to show an episode that happened at an earlier time. A flashback is used to provide background information necessary to understanding the characters or the plot.

imagery

When you consider what words suggest, you form pictures and sense impressions in your imagination. Such pictures or sense impressions are called *images*. Read the poem below.

March Morning

Two girls in slippery green jackets
against low rainy clouds,
sisters, by the look of them,
both blonde, one taller,
5 stop to shift papers, books, lunches,
so the shorter one can tug at her
drooping white knee socks.

1. What are the chief visual images here?
2. How many colors are mentioned? Are any other colors suggested? If so, what?

When writers present what can be seen, heard, touched, tasted, smelled, as well as what can be felt inside (joy, pain, fear), they are using images or *imagery*. Images help to create or re-create an experience so that readers can respond as participants in the event.

The sun is up today. Water drips from the eaves of the house. Icicles melt into water and drip-drip from nine in the mornin' till three in the evenin'. White clouds scud the sky. Winter has started breakin' up. Warm thaw winds blow through the bare Kentucky trees. One can feel them, warm soft winds, winds that remind one of rain.

Stuart, "Dark Winter"

Jesse Stuart. "Dark Winter" from *A Jesse Stuart Harvest*. New York: Dell Publishing Co., Inc., 1936.

1. What sounds are presented?
2. What visual images appear in the passage?
3. What image appeals to the sense of touch?

Good writers choose images with care and try to make those images as specific as possible. The writers of these next lines might have said "There was a blizzard," but instead wrote the following:

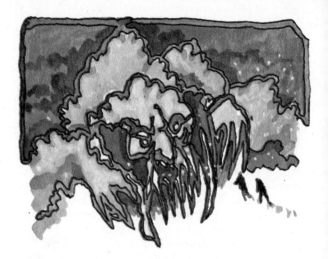

About five o'clock the next morning the storm slammed into us with all its blizzardous fury. It clamped its icy jaws around us and sucked us into its frigid mouth.

Vera and Bill Cleaver,
Where the Lilies Bloom

Vera & Bill Cleaver. *Where the Lilies Bloom*. Philadelphia: J. B. Lippincott Company, 1969.

Why is this more effective than "There was a blizzard"?

Writers are able to convey certain attitudes and feelings about a subject through sharp images. Notice how the writer of the following poem presents changes in a student.

Foreign Student

In September she appeared
row three, seat seven,
heavy pleated skirt,
plastic purse, tidy notepad,
5 there she sat,
silent,
straight from Taipei,[1]

---

1. *Taipei* (tī′pā′), capital of Taiwan, the seat of the Chinese nationalist government.

and she bowed
when I entered the room.
10 A model student
I noticed,
    though she walked
    alone through the halls,
every assignment neat,
15 on time, complete,
and she'd listen
when I talked.

But now it's May
and Si Lan
20 is called Lani.
She strides in
with Noriyo, and Lynne
and Natavidad.
She wears slacks.
25 Her gear is crammed
into a macramé
shoulder sack.
And she chatters with Pete
during class
30 and
I'm glad.

Barbara B. Robinson

Drawing by W. Miller; © 1976, The New Yorker Magazine, Inc.

"Foreign Student" by Barbara Robinson from *English Journal,*
May 1976. Copyright © 1976 by the National Council of Teachers
of English. Reprinted by permission of the publisher and the
author.

What has happened to Si Lan between September and May? What are some images that reveal change?

imagery

Concrete words or details that appeal to the senses of sight, sound, touch, smell, taste, or to internal feelings. Language that causes a scene to flash before the reader's eye, or that summons up a sudden sound or smell or feeling, or gives reality to a written work.

W hat do you think the man has in the carrying case? What are the clues on which you based your answer? When you draw a reasonable conclusion based on the evidence at hand, you are making an *inference.*

Writers, as well as cartoonists, very often expect you to make inferences about setting, characters, and action. To understand fully what you read, you must be alert to what words imply; you have to be able to read between the lines and draw logical inferences from clues an author provides.

Laura and Mary were up next morning earlier than the sun. They ate their breakfast of cornmeal mush with prairie-hen gravy, and hurried to help Ma wash the dishes. Pa was loading everything else into the wagon and hitching up Pet and Patty.

When the sun rose, they were driving on across the prairie. There was no road now. Pet and Patty waded through the grasses, and the wagon left behind it only the tracks of its wheels.

Before noon, Pa said, "Whoa!" The wagon stopped.

"Here we are, Caroline!" he said. "Right here we'll build our house."

Laura and Mary scrambled over the feedbox and dropped to the ground in a hurry. All around them there was nothing but grassy prairie spreading to the edge of the sky.

Wilder, *Little House on the Prairie*

Laura Ingalls Wilder. *Little House on the Prairie.* New York: Harper & Row, Publishers, 1953.

1. Do you think this story takes place before 1920? Why?

2. What kind of wagon do you think these people have?

3. Who are Pet and Patty?

4. Who is Caroline? Who are Laura and Mary?

From the limited information given, you can make several general inferences. You can infer, for instance, that Pet and Patty are pulling the wagon, but you cannot tell whether they are horses or oxen. You can infer that Laura and Mary are children since there is a woman called "Ma" whom they help with the dishes. Their scrambling from the wagon suggests the high spirits of children. You cannot tell from this passage, however, how old they are. You can tell that the weather is fair, but you can't tell whether it's spring, summer, or fall.

Read the paragraphs below and decide whether the inferences that follow are correct or incorrect. Be ready to support your answers.

from Roll of Thunder, Hear My Cry

"Little Man, would you come on? You keep it up and you're gonna make us late."

My youngest brother paid no attention to me. Grasping more firmly his newspaper-wrapped notebook and his tin-can lunch of cornbread and oil sausages, he continued to concentrate on the dusty road. He lagged several feet behind my other brothers, Stacey and Christopher-John, and me, attempting to keep the rusty Mississippi dust from swelling with each step and drifting back upon his shiny black shoes and the cuffs of his corduroy pants by lifting each foot high before setting it gently down again. Always meticulously neat, six-year-old Little Man never allowed dirt or tears or stains to mar anything he owned. Today was no exception.

"You keep it up and make us late for school, Mama's gonna wear you out," I threatened, pulling with exasperation at the high collar of the Sunday dress Mama had made me wear for the first day of school—as if that event were something special. It seemed to me that showing up at school at all on a bright August-like October morning made for running the cool forest trails and wading barefoot in the forest pond was concession enough; Sunday clothing was asking too much. Christopher-John and Stacey were not too pleased about the clothing or school either. Only Little Man, just beginning his school career, found the prospects of both intriguing.

"Y'all go ahead and get dirty if y'all wanna," he replied without even looking up from his studied steps. "Me, I'm gonna stay clean."

"I betcha Mama's gonna 'clean' you, you keep it up," I grumbled.

"Ah, Cassie, leave him be," Stacey admonished, frowning and kicking testily at the road.

"I ain't said nothing but—"

Stacey cut me a wicked look and I grew silent. His disposition had been irritatingly sour lately. If I hadn't known the cause of it, I could have forgotten very easily that he was, at twelve, bigger than I, and that I had promised Mama to arrive at school looking clean and ladylike. "Shoot," I mumbled finally, unable to restrain myself from further comment, "it ain't my fault you gotta be in Mama's class this year."

Stacey's frown deepened and he jammed his fists into his pockets, but said nothing.

Christopher-John, walking between Stacey and me, glanced uneasily at both of us but did not interfere. A short, round boy of seven, he took little interest in troublesome things, preferring to remain on good terms with everyone. Yet he was always sensitive to others and now, shifting the handle of his lunch can from his right hand to his right wrist and his smudged notebook from his left hand to his left armpit, he stuffed his free hands into his pockets and attempted to make his face as moody as Stacey's and as cranky as mine. But after a few moments he seemed to forget that he was supposed to be grouchy and began whistling cheerfully. There was little that could make Christopher-John unhappy for very long, not even the thought of school.

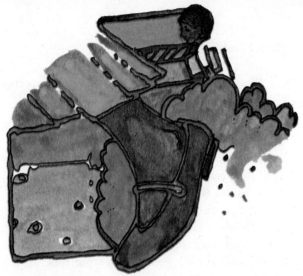

I tugged again at my collar and dragged my feet in the dust, allowing it to sift back onto my socks and shoes like gritty red snow. I hated the dress. And the shoes. There was little I could do in a dress, and as for shoes, they imprisoned freedom-loving feet accustomed to the feel of the warm earth.

"Cassie, stop that," Stacey snapped as the dust billowed in swirling clouds around my feet. I looked up sharply, ready to protest.

Mildred Taylor

1. The narrator is a girl.
2. The children's mother is a teacher.
3. Little Man's corduroy pants are new.
4. The story takes place in Georgia.
5. The children attend a country school.
6. Cassie understands the reason for Stacey's mood.
7. The weather is crisp and cool.
8. Cassie is bossy and in a bad mood.

inference

A reasonable conclusion drawn by the reader or viewer from hints, or implications, provided by the author.

SUBJECT   VERB   COMPLEMENT

The river is dark brown.

The line above illustrates the normal pattern of an English sentence: subject, followed by verb, followed by complement. Now read the four lines below.

> Dark brown is the river,
> Golden is the sand.
> It flows along forever,
> With trees on either hand.
>
> Stevenson,
> "Where Go the Boats?"

The parts of the sentence in lines 1 and 2 are not in normal order. The complement comes before the verb in both the first and second lines. Are the parts of the sentence in lines 3 and 4 in normal order? Would this verse rhyme if the first two lines had been written in normal order?

Now look at the line below:

> Announced by all the trumpets of the sky,
> Arrives the snow. . . .
>
> Emerson,
> "Announced by All the Trumpets of the Sky"

Again, the parts of this line are not in normal order. They are *inverted*. When the sentence is rewritten in normal order, it reads:

The snow arrives, announced by all the trumpets of the sky.

What seems to be the main idea of the rewritten sentence? What does the original sentence seem to emphasize most?

Writers often use *inversion* for emphasis or to achieve a certain poetic effect. Sometimes a writer may simply reverse the normal order of noun and modifier.

inverted: noun + modifier→This is the forest primeval.

Longfellow, "The Song of Hiawatha"

normal: modifier + noun → This is the primeval forest.

Or the normal order of noun, verb, and modifiers may be reversed:

> Merrily, merrily shall I live now,
> Under the blossom that hangs on the bough.

Shakespeare, *The Tempest*

Although an inverted line may seem difficult at first, inversion should cause no problem for the alert reader. Read the poem below and answer the questions.

Washed in Silver

> Gleaming in silver are the hills!
> Blazing in silver is the sea!
> And a silvery radiance spills
> Where the moon drives royally!
> 5 Clad in silver tissue, I
> March magnificently by!

James Stephens

From *Collected Poems* by James Stephens. Copyright 1915 by Macmillan Publishing Co., Inc., renewed 1943 by James Stephens. Reprinted by permission of Mrs. Iris Wise, Macmillan London and Basingstoke, The Macmillan Company of Canada Limited and Macmillan Publishing Co., Inc.

1. How are the hills, the sea, and the "I" in the poem alike?

2. What has caused this similarity?

3. Try reading the first two lines in normal order, beginning with the subjects, "the hills" and "the sea." Does this change the meaning of the lines? Does it change the emphasis? Explain.

inversion

The reversal of the usual order of words in a sentence to create a special effect or to provide emphasis.

Verbal Irony

"What a nice guy you are," Tom said as his brother ate the last slice of Tom's birthday cake.

Tom's comment is an example of *verbal irony*. In verbal irony speakers say the opposite of what they really mean or what they think is true. All of us speak ironically at times: if you say "What a great day!" when the temperature is 106 degrees in the shade, you are using verbal irony. You indicate what you really mean by the expression on your face and by your tone of voice.

In literature, verbal irony may extend beyond a single statement to include the author's attitude toward a subject. In such cases the writer's real attitude contrasts with the attitude he or she pretends to have. What is *ironic* about the following lines?

Tribute

> I do not mind my neighbor's dog,
> In fact I love the cur;
> I like the way he curls his lip,
> I like his mottled fur.

5 I like his bark at 3 a.m.,
    I like his throaty growls,
    I treasure every playful nip
    And both his quivering jowls.

    His body scarred and overfed,
10 His baleful eye, his groans and sighs,
    All strike in me a keen delight
    As on my chest he lies.

Understanding irony requires experience in reading. An inexperienced reader might be misled into thinking that the writer is truly fond of the neighbor's dog. What words tell you that this is not the case?

Irony of Situation

Irony of situation is the term given to a happening that is the opposite of what one would expect. It is an ironic situation if you take a winter vacation to a tropical island to enjoy the sun, and it rains all the time you are there. In literature very often an ironic twist does not come until the end of a poem, a story, or a play. What is ironic in the following poem?

The Rich Man

    The rich man has his motor-car
      His country and his town estate.
    He smokes a fifty-cent cigar
      And jeers at Fate.

5 He frivols through the livelong day,
      He knows not Poverty, her pinch.
    His lot seems light, his heart seems gay;
      He has a cinch.

    Yet though my lamp burns low and dim,
10   Though I must slave for livelihood—
    Think you that I would change with him?
      You bet I would!

                        Franklin P. Adams

"The Rich Man" from *Tobogganing on Parnassus* by Franklin P. Adams. Copyright 1911 by Doubleday & Company, Inc. Reprinted by permission.

Dramatic Irony

Sometimes the words or actions of a character in a play or story carry meaning significant to the audience or reader but not to the character. This is called *dramatic irony*. For instance, a character may discuss her plans for the future while the audience or reader knows that several things will prevent her from carrying out those plans. The purpose of dramatic irony may be to elicit sympathy for a character, to build suspense, or create a comic effect.

In the cartoon below, what is the reader aware of that the woman is not?

"Come on, everybody—dinner's on the table."

Reprinted with permission from *The Saturday Evening Post* © 1960 The Curtis Publishing Company.

irony

A contrast between what appears to be and what really is. *Verbal irony* occurs when what one says or writes is the opposite of the intended meaning. *Irony of situation* exists when an event is contrary to what is expected or appropriate. *Dramatic irony* occurs when the reader or spectator knows more about the true state of affairs than a character does. The word *ironic* is often used to describe any statement or situation contrary to what is expected or the opposite of what is intended.

metaphor

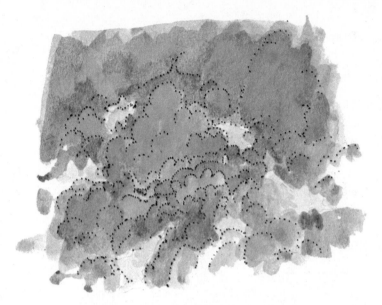

Broken Sky

The sky of gray is eaten in six places,
   Rag holes stand out.
It is an army blanket and the sleeper
   Slept too near the fire.

                  Carl Sandburg

From *Good Morning, America*, copyright 1928, 1956 by Carl Sandburg. Reprinted by permission of Harcourt Brace Jovanovich, Inc.

The poet says the sky is an army blanket. What are the similarities between this sky and an army blanket? What do the "rag holes" represent?

A weather forecaster might have made a literal statement: "The sky is partly cloudy." Sandburg chose to describe the sky figuratively by comparing it to a ragged blanket.

Writers often compare two things that are basically unlike but with some similarities. When the figurative comparison uses the words *like* or *as,* it is called a *simile.* When the comparison does not use *like* or *as,* and is therefore implied, it is called a *metaphor.* (See also the entry for SIMILE.) A metaphor is a type of FIGURATIVE LANGUAGE.

Metaphors are used not to make writing more difficult to read but to communicate a fresh way of looking at a common object, person, scene, event, or emotion. When a comparison pleases or surprises or stimulates a new way of looking at something, then the metaphor is effective.

What things are being compared in the following metaphor? Do you think the comparison is effective?

Metaphor

Morning is
a new sheet of paper
for you to write on.

Whatever you want to say,
5 all day,
until night
folds it up
and files it away.

The bright words and the dark words
10 are gone
until dawn
and a new day
to write on.

                Eve Merriam

From *It Doesn't Always Have To Rhyme.* Copyright © 1964 by Eve Merriam. Used by permission of Atheneum Publishers.

1. How is morning like a new sheet of paper?

2. Is the metaphor continued throughout the poem?

metaphor

A figure of speech that involves an implied comparison between two basically unlike things.

mood

Joseph Freamon, courtesy of Joanna and Hy Dales.

Does the photograph evoke in you a feeling of peacefulness? hopelessness? loneliness? terror? happiness? What is it about the photo that stimulates this response?

In this picture the photographer created a special atmosphere, or *mood*, by emphasizing certain details (the windowless and partially destroyed house, the littered ground, the bare trees). Writers create mood through their choice of details. Read the following passage.

The kitchen had a cold stone floor. The walls, also of stone, were slightly damp to the touch. Above the stove—itself a hulking black creature—an unpainted shelf held misshapen clay pots and jars ranging in color from dirty gray to blood red. A bench, hard and uninviting, ran along one wall.

1. Is the kitchen a cheery room? a comfortable room? Find words in the passage to support your answer.

2. Are the pots and jars pleasant to look at? Why?

3. Which of the two passages below makes the best closing for the paragraph? Why?

A. In a corner near the stove on a piece of warm plaid flannel a brown setter lay peacefully asleep with a litter of puppies nestled around her. A cat, fat in its puffy winter coat, curled up near the fire.

B. In the corner near the stove lurked a huge, liver-colored dog surrounded by a horde of squealing puppies. A cat, scrawny and ill-tempered, paced the littered floor.

4. Which of the words below does *not* describe the mood of the passage? **(a)** sinister; **(b)** bleak; **(c)** peaceful; **(d)** gloomy?

mood

The atmosphere or feeling within a work of art. Mood should not be confused with TONE, which is the author's attitude toward a subject.

Read the following short story.

Take Over, Bos'n

1 Hour after hour I kept the gun pointed at the other nine men. From the lifeboat's stern, where I'd sat most of the twenty days of our drifting, I could keep them all covered. If I had to shoot at such close quarters, I wouldn't miss. They realized that. Nobody jumped at me. But in the way they all glared I could see how they'd come to hate my guts.

2 Especially Barrett, who'd been bos'n's mate; Barrett said in his harsh, cracked voice, "You're a dope, Snyder. Y-you can't hold out forever! You're half asleep now!"

3 I didn't answer. He was right. How long can a man stay awake? I hadn't dared shut my eyes in maybe seventy-two hours. Very soon now I'd doze off, and the instant that happened they'd pounce on the little water that was left.

4 The last canteen lay under my legs. There wasn't much in it after twenty days. Maybe a pint. Enough to give each of them a few drops. Yet I could see in their bloodshot eyes that they'd gladly kill me for those few drops. As a man I didn't count any more. I was no longer third officer of the wrecked *Montala*. I was just a gun that kept them away from the water they craved. And with their tongues swollen and their cheeks sunken, they were half crazy. . . .

5 The way I judged it, we must be some two hundred miles east of Ascension. Now that the storms were over, the Atlantic swells were long and easy, and the morning sun was hot—so hot it scorched your skin. My own tongue was thick enough to clog my throat. I'd have given the rest of my life for a single gulp of water.

6 But I was the man with the gun—the only authority in the boat—and I knew this: once the water was gone we'd have nothing to look forward to but death. As long as we could look forward to getting a drink later, there was something to live for. We had to make it last as long as possible. If I'd given in to the curses and growls, if I hadn't brandished the gun, we'd have emptied the last canteen days ago. By now we'd all be dead.

7 The men weren't pulling on the oars. They'd stopped that long ago, too weak to go on. The nine of them facing me were a pack of bearded, ragged, half-naked animals, and I probably looked as bad as the rest. Some sprawled over the gunwales, dozing. The rest watched me as Barrett did, ready to spring the instant I relaxed.

8 When they weren't looking at my face they looked at the canteen under my legs.

9 Jeff Barrett was the nearest one. A constant threat. The bos'n's mate was a heavy man, bald, with a scarred and brutal face. He'd been in a hundred fights, and they'd left their marks on him. Barrett had been able to sleep—in fact, he'd slept through most of the night—and I envied him that. His eyes wouldn't close. They kept watching me, narrow and dangerous.

10 Every now and then he taunted me in that hoarse, broken voice:

11 "Why don't you quit? You can't hold out!"

12 "Tonight," I said. "We'll ration the rest of the water tonight."

13 "By tonight some of us'll be dead! We want it now!"

14 "Tonight," I said.

15 Couldn't he understand that if we waited until night the few drops wouldn't be sweated out of us so fast? But Barrett was beyond all reasoning. His mind had already cracked with thirst. I saw him begin to rise, a calculating look in his eyes. I aimed the gun at his chest—and he sat down again.

16 I'd grabbed my Luger on instinct, twenty days ago, just before running for the lifeboat. Nothing else would have kept Barrett and the rest away from the water.

17 These fools—couldn't they see I wanted a drink as badly as any of them? But I was in command here—that was the difference. I was the man with the gun, the man who had to think. Each of the others could afford to think only of himself; I had to think of them all.

18 Barrett's eyes kept watching me, waiting. I hated him. I hated him all the more because he'd slept. He had the advantage now. He wouldn't keel over.

19 And long before noon I knew I couldn't fight any more. My eyelids were too heavy to lift. As the boat rose and fell on the long swells, I could feel sleep creeping over me like paralysis. It bent my head. It filled my brain like a cloud. I was going, going . . .

20 Barrett stood over me, and I couldn't even lift the gun. In a vague way I could guess what would happen. He'd grab the water first and take his gulp. By that time the others would be screaming and tearing at him, and he'd have to yield the canteen. Well, there was nothing more I could do about it.

21 I whispered, "Take over, bos'n."

22 Then I fell face down in the bottom of the boat. I was asleep before I stopped moving . . .

23 When a hand shook my shoulder I could hardly raise my head. Jeff Barrett's hoarse voice said, "Here! Take your share o' the water!"

24 Somehow I propped myself up on my arms, dizzy and weak. I looked at the men, and I thought my eyes were going. Their figures were dim, shadowy; but then I realized it wasn't because of my eyes. It was night. The sea was black; there were stars overhead. I'd slept the day away.

25 So we were in our twenty-first night adrift—the night in which the tramp *Groton* finally picked us up —but now as I turned my head to Barrett there was no sign of any ship. He knelt, beside me, holding out the canteen, his other hand with the gun steady on the men.

26 I stared at the canteen as if it were a mirage. Hadn't they finished that pint of water this morning? When I looked up at Barrett's ugly face, it was grim. He must have guessed my thoughts.

27 "You said, 'Take over, bos'n,' didn't you?" he growled. "I been holdin' off these apes all day." He hefted the Luger in his hand. "When you're bossman," he added with a sheepish grin, "in command and responsible for the rest—you—you sure get to see things different, don't you?"

Oscar Schisgall

Originally appeared in *This Week Magazine*, 1950. Reprinted by permission of the author.

The following discussion covers *conflict, details, pattern of events, climax,* and *conclusion,* all of which are elements of *plot.*

Conflict

1. What is the source of the disagreement between Snyder, the third officer, and Barrett, the bos'n's mate?

2. What reasons does Snyder give for waiting until evening to share the water? What feelings of his own has Snyder had to combat in arriving at this decision?

3. Against what force or forces are Snyder and the other men in the boat struggling?

Most stories, novels, and plays are built around a *conflict* or struggle. The conflict may be fairly simple: the hero, who stands for the forces of good, fights the villain, who represents the forces of evil. Usually, however, a work of fiction will be built around a more complicated struggle, and more than one struggle may take place at the same time. For example, in "Take Over, Bos'n," Snyder must fight Barrett and the men to keep them from drinking the water. He must also struggle with himself: although he believes in his responsibility as leader, he, too, is thirsty. Finally, both Snyder and the men must combat nature in the form of the weather and the sea.

A conflict in which the main character (or group) struggles with other characters, society, or nature is called an *external conflict.* A conflict in which the main character struggles with his or her own beliefs or feelings is called an *internal conflict.*

1. With what does the boy struggle in "The Circuit" (page 12)? Is the conflict internal or external?

2. When her grandmother gives up the lavaliere, which kind of conflict confronts Molly in "I'll Give You Law" (page 24)?

Details

1. At the beginning of "Take Over, Bos'n," how long has the lifeboat been adrift? How long has it been since Snyder has slept?

2. What is the weather like?

3. Reread paragraph 9. What kind of man is Barrett?

In answering the questions above, you selected *details* provided in the story. Is each of these details important? Explain.

From all the things that might be said about a subject, a capable author chooses only those details that help to develop the conflict. Schisgall provides a description of the weather because the heat serves to intensify the men's desire for water and Barrett's determination to take the canteen. The author does not give a detailed account of the shipwreck or tell whether any other lifeboats survived because such information is not important to developing the conflict in the story.

Pattern of Events

1. Arrange the following incidents in the order in which they occurred in the story.

a. Snyder tells Barrett to take over and then falls asleep.

b. Snyder points the gun at Barrett's chest.

c. Barrett takes the gun and guards the water until nightfall.

d. Barrett sits down and waits for Snyder to fall asleep.

e. Barrett moves toward Snyder and the canteen.

f. Snyder guards the canteen with the last of the water in it.

2. If any of these events were removed, would the story make sense? Why or why not?

When you arranged the events above in the order in which they occurred, you organized them according to a cause-effect relationship.

Each incident is caused by and logically follows the preceding one. (For example, Snyder would have no reason to aim the gun at Barrett's chest if Barrett had not moved to take the canteen.) No incident could be removed without weakening the story. In telling a story, an author chooses events to form a pattern in which each event grows out of the one that happened before, and all events lead to a conclusion.

Climax and Conclusion

1. At what point in the story do we know that a major change is about to occur in the situation aboard the lifeboat?

2. What happens to Barrett once he has the gun? Why?

In a work of literature the *climax* is the turning point in the conflict. A character may do something to cause a change, or events may dictate that some change must take place. Once Snyder falls asleep, we know that conditions on board the boat cannot remain as they had been.

The *conclusion,* or ending, is the solution of the conflict. When Barrett takes over the care of the water supply, the conflict between him and Snyder no longer exists. A conclusion may contain some comment on the conflict. Barrett's analysis of his own behavior (paragraph 27) states the theme of the story. Often such a comment is implied rather than directly stated as it is here.

---

plot

A pattern of related events selected by the author to present and resolve some internal or external conflict. In a carefully constructed plot, each event is important: the incidents are selected and arranged in a cause-effect relationship, with each incident becoming a necessary link leading to the climax and conclusion of the work.

point of view

Read the following passages.

A. I had never seen my family look so stern. Oh, maybe I'd seen one or two of them look that way at the same time, but never the whole crew. And with mom and dad and—including me—six girls, we do make up a crew.

I played with my food, trying not to look at anybody, especially Karen Beth, who wasn't even pretending to eat. There really wasn't anything to say or do—to her or anybody else. I'd been the one to sneak Furface into the room I share with Karen Beth. And I'd been the one to leave the closet door open even though I knew Furface was looking for a place to have her kittens. So when the cat pulled Karen's red velvet party dress off the hanger and made it a nest for herself and six newborn kittens, who could be blamed but me?

B. The parents and their six daughters sat around the dinner table in silence. Beverly pushed the food around on her plate but didn't appear to be eating any of it. Karen Beth, her mouth drawn into a thin line, didn't even pretend to eat. Mr. Anderson cleared his throat. "We all know where Furface had her kittens. And we all know how she got into the closet to make Karen Beth's Christmas dress a bed for seven cats."

C. Nobody seemed to be eating much; all eight members of the family sat looking serious. Beverly, the most serious of all, wondered for the hundredth time how she could have been foolish enough to let a cat due to have kittens at any moment into the bedroom she shared with Karen Beth, her sister. She should have known, she continued to scold herself silently, that Furface would make a nest in the closet—and what would make a better nest than Karen's red velvet dress?

Karen Beth couldn't have cared less about the velvet dress. It could be a permanent nest as far as she was concerned. She and Bulldog Hershbine had broken up that morning after English class; she'd have no need for a party dress this Christmas.

Mr. Anderson struggled to keep his face from betraying his true feelings. Although the family myth was that she belonged to the girls, Furface was really his cat, and everybody knew it. Privately he thought there was no prettier picture than the long-haired white cat and six varicolored kittens lying against the red velvet.

1. Each of the accounts above describes the same basic situation. Using as few words as possible, summarize that situation.

2. What is the main difference between passage **A** and passages **B** and **C**?

3. What do you learn in **A** that you do not learn in **B**?

4. What is the main difference between **B** and the other two accounts?

5. In which account are you given the most information?

All writing is told, or narrated, by someone. That someone is called the *narrator.* (In poetry that someone is more frequently called the *speaker.*) The angle from which an account is told is called its *point of view.*

First Person, or Personal, Point of View

The narrator may be a character in the narrative, as in passage **A.** In this first person, or personal, account the narrator, using the pronoun *I,* can tell the reader what she sees and hears and also what she is thinking. However, she cannot see into the minds of others to tell us what they are thinking or feeling; she can only report what they say and do. An author may use the first person point of view to create an element of surprise or discovery that helps the reader experience the same things as the narrator. For example, what did you learn about Karen Beth in passage **C** that you did not learn in passage **A?** If the first person account were continued using the events in passage **C,** how would the author reveal the true feelings of Karen Beth and her father to both Beverly and the reader?

Third Person Objective Point of View

The narrator of passage **B** is an outsider, not a character in the story. Because the narrator refers to the characters as *he, she, they,* etc., this account is said to be written in the third person. The narrator cannot see into the minds of any of the characters, but can only report facts as they occur. The narrator gives no opinion and makes no judgments on what is reported. Most newspaper accounts are written from the third person objective point of view, as are many mystery and suspense stories. This is sometimes called the third person dramatic point of view because it is the one playwrights often use.

Third Person Omniscient (om nish′ənt) Point of View

The narrator of passage **C** is also an outsider. But this narrator is able to see into the minds of characters. Like a superhuman being, this narrator is omniscient, or all-knowing. The reader of an account written from this point of view finds a certain satisfaction in being "in on" what all the characters are thinking and feeling.

Through the selection of point of view, an author can control the development of a story.

point of view

The author's choice of narrator. This choice determines the amount of information a reader will be given. The three major points of view are these:

1. First Person or Personal
The narrator ("I") is a character in the story who can reveal only his or her own thoughts and feelings and what he or she is told by others.

2. Third Person Objective
The narrator is an outsider who can report only what he or she sees and hears.

3. Third Person Omniscient
The narrator is an all-knowing outsider who can enter the minds of the characters.

Read the following poem.

Minnie Morse

Of all the problems no one's solved
The worst is Minnie Morse's;
I mean why Minnie's so involved
With horses.

5 Since Minnie bought a horse this spring
(An animal named Mable)
She doesn't care to do a thing
But hang around the stable.

In school, she'll never ever pass.
10 She fills her notebook spaces
And messes up her books in class
By drawing horses' faces.
Last week our teacher, Miss McGrew,
Made Minnie stand—and said
15 She didn't mind a sketch or two
But now please write instead.
And Minnie sat again, and drew
Another horse's head.

"I said to *write*," cried Miss McGrew,
20 "Does someone have to force you?"
At which point, Minnie stomped her shoe
As if she wore a horseshoe,
And tossing back her mane of hair
While all the class just waited,
25 She said that horses didn't *care*
If girls got educated.

Well, if a horse is what you've got,
It's fine to want to please one;
But what I brood about a lot
30 Is Minnie acts like *she's* one.

In fact, the way she is today,
You can't get far with Minnie
Unless you live on oats and hay—
And whinny.

Kaye Starbird

In the first stanza of "Minnie Morse," what words rhyme at the ends of lines? In the second stanza what words rhyme?

Ending two or more lines of poetry with words that sound alike is called *end rhyming;* end words that share a particular sound are called *end rhymes.*

When they are used in a poem, end rhymes set up a pattern of sounds called a *rhyme scheme.* You can chart a rhyme scheme with letters of the alphabet by using the same letter for end words that rhyme. Read the following poem.

Beetle Bemused

With careful tread, through dim green-pillared halls,
Inch by long inch the purblind[1] beetle crawls.
I watch, my forehead tickled by the grasses;
    Time passes.

5 Beetle, bemused,[2] where every way's the same,
Turns and sets back along the road he came.
I roll upon my side and break my glasses;
    Time passes.

R. P. Lister

1. *purblind* (pėr'blīnd'). 1 nearly blind. 2 slow to discern or understand; dull; obtuse.
2. *bemused* (bi myüzd'). 1 confused; bewildered; stupefied. 2 absorbed in reverie or thought.

1. If the last word of the first line were labeled *a,* what other words at the ends of lines would also be labeled *a?*

2. If the last word of line 3 were labeled *b,* what other words at the ends of lines would also be labeled *b?*

3. With what letter would you label line 5? Why?

The rhyme scheme for the poem is *aabb ccbb.* The *a's* represent the rhymes in lines 1 and 2, the *b's* represent the rhymes in lines 3

and 4, the *c's* represent the rhymes in lines 5 and 6, and the *b's* represent the rhymes in lines 7 and 8 because they are like those in lines 3 and 4. If the poem had two more lines that rhymed with sounds unlike any of those before, what letter would represent those sounds?

1. On a sheet of paper, chart the rhyme scheme for "Minnie Morse."

2. Can you chart a rhyme scheme for "Old Age Sticks" (page 29)?

A poem does not have to contain a rhyme scheme, but end rhyme does serve a purpose in poetry. The sound of rhyming words can be pleasant to hear. And end rhyme may help to divide a poem into stanzas, as it does in "Beetle Bemused," where each of the two stanzas ends in *bb.* In "Minnie Morse" end rhyme also contributes to the amusing effect of the poem. (Note especially the two-syllable rhymes in lines 20 and 22 and again in lines 28 and 30.)

rhyme

The repetition of syllable sounds. End words that share a particular sound are called *end rhymes.* The pattern of end rhymes in a poem is called a *rhyme scheme.*

rhythm

Read the lines below aloud.

from The Wreck of the Hesperus

It was the schooner Hesperus,
    That sailed the wintry sea;
And the skipper had taken his little daughter,
    To bear him company. . . .

5 The skipper he stood beside the helm,
    His pipe was in his mouth,
And he watched how the veering flaw[1] did blow
    The smoke now West, now South.

Then up and spake an old Sailor,
10   Had sailed to the Spanish Main,
"I pray thee, put into yonder port,
    For I fear a hurricane.

"Last night the moon had a golden ring,
    And tonight no moon we see!"
15 The skipper, he blew a whiff from his pipe,
    And a scornful laugh laughed he.

                Henry Wadsworth Longfellow

---

1. flaw, a gust of wind.

Did you notice that as you read you automatically stressed some words and syllables more than others? This pattern of stressed and unstressed words or syllables is called *rhythm.*

We respond to rhythm because it is enjoyable, but poets have other reasons for using rhythm, beyond the important one of creating a poem with a pleasing beat. Rhythm allows a poet to fit the movement of the poem to the MOOD. Read the poem below.

The White Seal's Lullaby

Oh! hush thee, my baby, the night is behind us,
    And black are the waters that sparkled so green.
The moon, o'er the combers,[1] looks downward to
    find us
    At rest in the hollows that rustle between.
5 Where billow meets billow, then soft be thy pillow;
    Ah, weary wee flipperling, curl at thy ease!
The storm shall not wake thee, nor shark overtake
    thee,
    Asleep in the arms of the slow-swinging seas.

                Rudyard Kipling

From *The Jungle Book* by Rudyard Kipling. Reprinted by permission of The National Trust and the Macmillan Co. of London & Basingstoke.

1. comber, breaker.

The rhythm in this poem is regular; that is, every line has the same kind of rhythm. What is the mood of this poem? Is the rhythm in keeping with the mood?

Some poets try to avoid regular rhythm because it may lead, as is probably intended in the poem above, to drowsiness in the reader, or it may actually take the inexperienced reader *away* from the meaning. Read the lines below. The syllables that are emphasized, or stressed, are in capital letters.

Had I but PLENty of MONey, MONey eNOUGH and to
  SPARE,
The HOUSE for ME, no DOUBT, were a HOUSE in the
  CITY SQUARE;
Ah, SUCH a LIFE, SUCH a LIFE, as one LEADS at the
  WINDOW THERE!

        Browning, "Up at a Villa—Down in the City"

1. How many stressed syllables are there in the first line? in the second? in the third?

2. Where is the first pause? the second pause? Where is the longest pause before the end of the last line?

3. Where does the "I" in the poem want to live? Why? What prevents his or her living there?

Rhythm can also be used to emphasize important words in a poem.

When the green woods laugh with the voice of joy,
And the dimpling stream runs laughing by;
When the air does laugh with our merry wit,
And the green hill laughs with the noise of it.

Blake, "Laughing Song"

Notice how many times the words *laugh* or *laughing* are stressed here. What other stressed words contribute to an atmosphere of merriment?

Many poems do not have a regular pattern of sound throughout. All poems have rhythm, however, since there are always some words that are stressed more than others. Read the lines below, being careful not to pause unless the punctuation indicates that there should be a pause. Which words do you think the poet wants stressed?

Trees and Evening Sky

I saw the black trees leaning
In different ways, their limbs
Tangled on the mottled clouds,
The clouds rolling on themselves:
5 A wide belt of four colors,
Yellow, orange, red, and black;
And stars in the tangled limbs.

N. Scott Momaday

"Trees and Evening Sky" by Scott Momaday from *Carriers of the Dream Wheel* published by Harper & Row, 1975. Reprinted by permission of the author.

rhythm

The arrangement of stressed and unstressed sounds in writing and speech. The rhythm in a poem may have a regular beat, or it may be varied within the poem to fit different moods or to emphasize certain words.

The year my brother Joseph went to Vietnam as a fighter pilot, I was sent to live with my Aunt Harriet. I spent the first weeks there being dreadfully homesick and trying to act as if I weren't. Even after school started, I found myself lonely and almost totally friendless. I spent my evenings shooting baskets in Aunt Harriet's driveway, or lying moodily in the hammock under the orange tree in the back yard, or baking cookies to send to Joseph.

Three days before Christmas vacation, I was shooting my usual solitary baskets when a girl I'd seen in the halls at school came by on her bicycle.

She stopped and asked to take a turn, and before long we had a game going. We didn't talk much that first evening, but she came back the next and the next. And so I met Leah, who was to become my friend as well as my teammate on the all-state basketball squad.

1. The paragraphs above are the beginning of a short story. The story takes place in the **(a)** 1860s; **(b)** 1920s; **(c)** 1940s; **(d)** 1960s. How do you know?

2. Aunt Harriet lives in **(a)** a high-rise apartment in the city; **(b)** a mountain cabin; **(c)** a house in town. What details helped you decide?

3. The story probably takes place in **(a)** New York; **(b)** Florida; **(c)** Illinois; **(d)** Oregon. On what did you base your answer?

4. The conditions under which the narrator lives might best be described as **(a)** poverty-stricken; **(b)** comfortable; **(c)** humiliating; **(d)** unhealthy.

Setting is the word used to indicate the time, the location, and the general environment. The time setting might be a particular day, a season of the year, or a period in history. The place might be one room, a city, or the countryside. The environment, or general conditions surrounding the characters, may be one of affluence and joy, poverty and despair, or anything in between.

An author may directly state the setting:

In 1968 I went to stay with my Aunt Harriet, who lived in a town in Texas.

Usually, though, the author informs readers about the background of the story through scattered details that hint at time and location.

Sometimes setting also aids understanding of people in a story by revealing something about their personalities:

Thad Lemonovich left work at the usual time and returned to the rented room he had occupied ever since he'd finished college.

Like most furnished rooms, this one contained the bare necessities: a narrow bed with a headboard of painted wood, a dresser and chest that matched neither the bed nor each other, an armchair, and a small metal bookcase.

But Thad had added his own touches, and the room was like no other in Mrs. Glott's rooming house. Arranged on the wall above the bed were three felt pennants—a little faded, perhaps, but still bright enough to stand out against the pale green wall. All three were from the college Thad had attended twenty years before. Another wall held an assortment of framed photographs and yellowed newspaper clippings, also in frames. "Lemonovich Clicks as Soph at State" one headline read. Another announced that "Star Quarterback Lemonovich Leads State to Victory." Some of the photos were of the whole team. Others were of Thad alone: throwing a pass, running with the ball into the end zone, unhelmeted and grinning at a mob of fans clustered around him.

The bookcase was empty except for four college yearbooks, but the tops of both the dresser and the chest were covered with trophies and more photos—these of groups of young men all wearing sweaters with the school initials on them. A silver mug engraved with the same letters stood nearby.

1. What was Thad's main interest when he was in college? How do you know?

2. Describe the room as it would look without Thad's belongings in it.

3. What kind of person do you think Thad is now? How can you tell?

At times setting may be vital to the development of the plot.

The elevator held six people. The two young men who had just visited the Statue of Liberty for the first time talked of their adventure; the middle-aged couple stood silently, each of them balancing a sack stuffed full of groceries on the rail at the back of the car; the jogger stood panting and dripping from his run through the park under a relentless sun; and Luis carefully held the box containing his sister's birthday cake that he'd carried all the way from Harlem.

They were between floors when the blackout began. The elevator stopped with a soft bump. At the same time the lights went out and the piped-in music died.

The little group was silent for the several seconds it took for the unwelcome truth to dawn on them.

One of the young men was the first to speak. "Ah, is this a . . . well, is this . . ." he tried to stop his voice from shaking, ". . . is this one of your famous New York blackouts? H-How do we get out of here?"

1. In what city does the action occur?

2. What time of year is it?

3. Where are the people?

4. How do you think the setting will influence the behavior of the characters?

An author may also use details of setting to create a particular atmosphere or MOOD.

setting

The time, place, and general environment in which the events of a narrative occur. Details of setting may be either stated or suggested. Although setting in modern fiction serves primarily as background for the action, it can also be used to reveal character and to help develop plot.

simile

The southern sky was as white and burning as a desert; there was one cloud, and it drifted like a traveling oasis.

> Capote, "A Ride Through Spain"

Truman Capote. "A Ride Through Spain" from *Selected Writings*. New York: Random House, Inc., 1950.

1. By comparing the sky to a desert, what does the writer tell you about the sky?

2. To what is the cloud compared?

3. In describing the scene the writer might have said, "The sky was white-hot, and one cloud drifted across it." Which of the two descriptions is more effective? Why?

In the sentence above Truman Capote has twice used a *simile.* A simile directly states a comparison between two basically dissimilar objects by using the word *like* or *as.* A figurative comparison that does not use *like* or *as* is called a METAPHOR. If Capote had said, "The sky was a white and burning desert," he would have been using a metaphor.

Similes are common in everyday speech, and some similes are used so often that they become stale and lifeless:

The cake was as light as a feather.

His eyes were as blue as the sky.

George shook like a leaf in a storm.

Writers attempt to create fresh images by using comparisons that help you look at things in a new way.

Read the following poem.

Simile: Willow and Ginkgo

The willow is like an etching,
Fine-lined against the sky.
The ginkgo[1] is like a crude sketch,
Hardly worthy to be signed.

5 The willow's music is like a soprano,
Delicate and thin.
The ginkgo's tune is like a chorus
With everyone joining in.

The willow is sleek as a velvet-nosed calf;
10 The ginkgo is leathery as an old bull.
The willow's branches are like silken thread;
The ginkgo's like stubby rough wool.

The willow is like a nymph with streaming hair;
Wherever it grows, there is green and gold and fair.
15 The willow dips to the water,
Protected and precious, like the king's favorite
    daughter.

The ginkgo forces its way through gray concrete;
Like a city child, it grows up in the street.
Thrust against the metal sky,
20 Somehow it survives and even thrives.

My eyes feast upon the willow,
But my heart goes to the ginkgo.

> Eve Merriam

From *It Doesn't Always Have To Rhyme.* Copyright © 1964 by Eve Merriam. Used by permission of Atheneum Publishers.

1. *ginkgo* (ging′kō, jing′kō), a large tree with fan-shaped leaves and edible nuts.

1. To what things is the willow compared?

2. To what things is the ginkgo compared?

3. In the last two lines the poet sums up her reaction to the two trees. Do you agree with her? Why or why not?

simile (sim′ə lē)

A comparison in which the word *like* or *as* is used to point out a similarity between two basically unlike things. A simile is a type of FIGURATIVE LANGUAGE.

stereotype

Marvin Gregg laughed wildly and clutched his hair, pulling it until it stood straight out on either side of his head. Then, mumbling and chuckling to himself, he again leaned over the test tube.

Smoke poured from one corner of the lab; somebody knocked on the door; the telephone rang. Gregg never took his attention from the thick green liquid in the tube.

His chuckles became groans as before his eyes the liquid slowly turned brown. With an anguished cry, he smashed the test tube against the far wall and ran from the laboratory.

In the passage above, Marvin Gregg is presented as intense, highly emotional, and slightly mad. If the story were continued and Marvin bumped into a fellow scientist on his way out, would he be more likely to stop and apologize or turn away, still muttering to himself?

In fiction a stereotype is a character that embodies only those traits that are most commonly expected from members of the group to which the character belongs. The stereotype of the mad scientist is founded on the assumption that anyone so wrapped up and emotionally involved in work that most of us cannot understand must be out of his or her mind. When a character is presented as a stereotype, the qualities that make that character an individual are ignored. Stereotypes may embody either favorable or unfavorable qualities. The kindly, overworked country doctor, the hot-tempered red-head, and the shrewd, tough private detective are all familiar stereotypes. Can you name other stereotypes? (Consider not only those from your reading but characters from television and movies as well.)

Stereotypes are used in fiction because they are easily recognized by the reader, who already has a knowledge of what they are like and how they will behave. They permit an author to sketch certain characters quickly; such stereotypes serve as a type of fictionalized shorthand. But because they lack individualizing qualities, stereotyped characters do not present people as they really are in any fullness of personality. In addition to using stereotypes, capable authors also create characters who, like real people, are complicated and many-sided.

Read the following passages.

A. Professor Townley put on his glasses, grabbed his tweed coat from the back of a chair, and rushed downstairs.

"I completely forgot about my eight o'clock class," he told Joanie, his wife.

"You've been meeting that class for a whole term now." Joanie smiled and went back to her toast and tea.

"Where are my books?"

"Right where you left them, on the table by the door," Joanie replied.

"Have you seen the car keys?"

"You left them in the car when you came home

yesterday." Joanie reached for the newspaper. "I put them on the hook in the kitchen."

Professor Townley dashed about gathering books and keys. Joanie sighed as she heard him run back upstairs and begin to search the bedroom. She abandoned her breakfast and paper and slowly climbed the stairs.

"Now what is it?"

"Joanie," he rushed up to her, "have you seen my glasses?"

"Yes. In fact, dear, I'm looking right at them."

B. Kimmie's hair was dark and curly, too curly as far as Kimmie was concerned. Heat and dampness made it curl even more, and the day was nothing if not hot and damp.

Kimmie wriggled her shoulders to shift the weight of the pack strapped to her back and wondered why she'd ever agreed to a hike on such a day. She dreaded the climb ahead of her, and she was sorry that in her enthusiasm yesterday she had volunteered to cook dinner for the group. Cooking stew over a campfire no longer seemed such a good way to end the day.

1. Which of the passages does not contain a stereotype?

2. Can you name the stereotype found in the other passage?

In a *stereotyped plot* the action follows a familiar and predictable pattern. A talented understudy who suddenly becomes a star, the lady in distress who is rescued by a handsome man with whom she falls in love, the poor boy from a bad neighborhood who makes good—all are examples of stereotyped plots.

stereotype (ster′ē ə tīp′)

A character in fiction that fits a standardized mental picture of what members of a certain group are like, or a plot in which the action follows a predictable pattern. When used as characters, stereotypes are portrayed as having only one trait and thus lack the depth that people in real life have.

W hat does each of the following suggest to you?

>a red paper heart
>a handshake
>a red cross
>a bright yellow sports car
>the American flag

Each of the above has some special meaning to most people. The meaning may be the same for everyone: a red paper heart, for example, almost always suggests love. Or the meaning may vary from person to person, as is the case with the sports car. The sports car might represent either glamor and wealth or the competitive and dangerous life of a racer.

The paper heart, the sports car, and the rest of the items listed above are *symbols.* A symbol may be an object, a person, an action, a situation—anything that has a meaning of its own but suggests other emotional meanings as well.

In addition to the symbols we share with others, most of us have private symbols to which we attach values and meanings that others do not see in them. Read the following account.

With increasing uneasiness, Karina searched the top of the dresser. She was sure she had left the coin—a shiny half dollar—in the little china dish. Still, she lifted the hand mirror and a vase of flowers to be sure the coin wasn't hidden under one of them.

She thought of the day nearly two years ago when she won the half dollar in the race at the Sons of Italy picnic. At thirteen, Karina had been the youngest in the race. That was the first time in her life that she had won anything—and the first time she had seen any advantage in having such long legs.

Since then, she had run every evening after supper. Her posture was better now that she didn't mind being tall. She won other and better prizes, but she intended to keep the half dollar forever.

Until yesterday Karina hadn't told anyone else about the coin; she'd kept it in a little velvet box in the bottom drawer. But yesterday she had shown it to her new friend Jennifer and then left it in the china dish on the dresser. With increased concern, she began to search the floor. . . .

"It's not like I've stolen anything," Karina's little brother Jeff assured himself as he went into the store. "She won't care that I didn't ask, and I can return it all tomorrow when I get my allowance. In fact, I can give part of it back this afternoon." Having convinced himself, he marched up to the counter, slapped down the half dollar, and ordered one scoop of bubble gum fudge ice cream in a sugar cone.

1. What does the coin symbolize to Karina?
2. How does Jeff view the coin?

Characters in fiction can have their own private symbols. You can usually recognize literary symbols by paying careful attention to the objects, persons, or situations for which a character has special feelings. By analyzing the character's attitude toward these objects, persons, or situations, you can infer what they mean to that character. This knowledge may help you to understand the character more fully.

Printed below are two excerpts from short stories. Try to find the symbol in each.

She hadn't seen her for two years, but Kelly knew that when Aunt Kathy came back next week, everything at the farm was going to be different. Kelly remembered each detail of the last visit—how her aunt had come breezing in carrying two heavy suitcases as if they didn't weigh an ounce and how lovely her suit had been and how she had started to laugh and talk to all of them almost before she'd gotten through the door.

Kelly had been ten then, but Aunt Kathy (against Kelly's parents' polite objections) had included her in the adult conversation. The two of them had had lunch at a restaurant in town, where her aunt had told Kelly all about the city and her apartment and her job. That whole week Kelly sailed through her chores, hurrying back to the house where her mother and aunt visited. Her bedtimes were ignored as the whole family sat up talking and laughing.

1. (a) From the description above, what can you tell about Kelly's day-to-day life? (b) How was life different during Aunt Kathy's visit?

2. Kelly obviously is fond of her aunt, but—in addition to that—what might Aunt Kathy symbolize to Kelly?

"How old are you?" the woman asked.
"Eleven, ma'am."
"Aren't you getting too big for this sort of thing? I've got two kids younger'en you who woudn't be caught dead out trick or treatin'. Some of you kids never grow up."

The boy said nothing, merely held out his empty sack.

Thinking she had failed in her attempt to shame the boy, the woman sullenly tossed a popcorn ball into the sack and slammed the door.

But the boy's pride had been hurt. She's not going to make me grow up any faster than I feel like doing, he thought. If I want to act like a kid, I will. He reached into the bag for the popcorn ball, unwrapped it and put it up to his mouth. It had a delicious, sugary smell, but—for some reason—he couldn't bear to take a bite out of it. Holding it away from himself, he stared at it defiantly. It seemed to be echoing the woman's words, to be laughing at him. He tossed it into a nearby mud puddle and watched it grow soggy as it absorbed the dirty brown water. Feeling he had won some sort of victory, he went on to the next house.

1. What is the woman's attitude toward the eleven-year-old trick or treater?
2. How does she make the boy feel?
3. Why can't he eat the popcorn ball?
4. What does the ball symbolize to him?
5. Why does he feel better after he throws the ball away?

symbol

A person, place, event, or object that has a meaning in itself but suggests other meanings as well. A particular symbol may mean different things to different people.

For an Old Man

I wish I had listened then. When you began
Those long old stories, I was bored and ran
Outdoors to play; or, older, tactfully drew
The talk away to light immediate things . . .
5 And all the while your generation lay
Behind your baffled eyes and wistful speech
Groping toward mine: and I can never reach
It now. The things you did not say
Are buried with you, and the bright thin line
10 Of contact broken. For I closed a door
And let you go away, your stories all untold:
I wish I had listened more.

                                    Floris Clark McLaren

From *The Dalhousie Review*. Reprinted by permission.

1. How did the speaker react to the old man's stories as a child? when he or she grew older?

2. What did the old man hope to accomplish by telling his stories? What lines in the poem tell you this?

3. Now that the old man is dead, how does the speaker feel about his or her behavior toward him?

4. Do you think that the speaker is the only person who has had an experience like this? Why or why not?

5. Which of the following best expresses the main idea of the poem? **(a)** A young person who has never been willing to take the time to establish communication with an old man regrets that behavior after the old man dies. **(b)** Be nice and pay attention to old people or you will feel guilty when they die. **(c)** Youth may not appreciate the value of communication between generations until it is no longer possible.

The *theme* of a work of literature is the main idea of the selection. Statement *c* above expresses the theme of "For an Old Man."

While the subject of a work is the topic on which an author has chosen to write, the theme makes some statement about or expresses some opinion on that topic. The topic of "For an Old Man" is youth and age. The theme is that youth may not place enough value on contact and communication with old people until the opportunity for such sharing is gone.

Statement *b* gives a moral rather than a theme. A moral is a lesson or a rule to live by: its purpose is to change human behavior. Although the speaker in this poem expresses regret for his or her behavior, he or she does not tell readers what they should do in a similar situation.

Statement *a* tells what happens in "For an Old Man." It gives the PLOT, or pattern of events that make up the poem. The theme of the poem states the significance, or underlying meaning, of the plot. Sometimes the theme of a work may be stated directly, but more often it is implied. The reader must often examine the pattern of events in a work in order to determine its theme.

A work of literature does not have to contain a theme. Works written purely for entertainment or escape—mystery stories, for example—may not have themes.

---

theme

The main idea or underlying meaning of a literary work. A theme may be directly stated, but more often it is implied.

---

tone

Don't you dare move an inch before I tell you to!

Please stay right there until I come back.

1. How are the two statements above similar? How are they different?

2. Read each statement aloud as you think it might be spoken.

Read through the following, paying careful attention to the way the authors use words.

Dear Son,

Now that you have left home for school, our house seems empty and lonely. Mom and I cheer ourselves up every evening remembering the good times we had when you were little. Do you remember the time we played Easter Bunny when you were five, and I had to hop around the house wiggling my ears, and you wouldn't let me eat anything but carrots and lettuce for three days? Remember how we used to spread the funnies out on the living room rug and read them together every Sunday morning? And how you used to sneak up and sock me in the tummy just for the fun of it? And how funny you were when Mr. Nash would come to visit and you used to climb all over him? I suppose he loved every minute of it, although he was too shy ever to say so.

Well, we miss you, sonny boy. You're on your own now in the big, wide world, and we know you'll do well. Write right away and tell us how things are starting off at your new school.

Love, Dad

Let's straighten this out, my little man,
And reach an agreement if we can.
I entered your house an honored guest.
My shoes are shined and my trousers are pressed,
5   And I won't stretch out and read you the funnies.
And I won't pretend that we're Easter bunnies . . .
You may take a sock at your daddy's tummy
Or climb all over your doting mummy,
But keep your attention to me in check
10 Or, sonny boy, I will wring your neck . . .

Nash, "To a Small Boy Standing on My Shoes
While I Am Wearing Them"

From "To a Small Boy Standing on My Shoes While I Am Wearing Them" from *Family Reunion* by Ogden Nash. Copyright 1931 by Ogden Nash. Reprinted by permission of Little, Brown and Co., The Estate of the Late Ogden Nash and J. M. Dent & Sons Ltd.

1. To whom is the speaker in each selection talking?

2. What two very different attitudes are expressed in these selections?

3. Point out words and phrases that helped you determine the speaker's attitude in each.

Everything ever said is expressed in some tone of voice. The tone in which you speak helps listeners understand your feelings on the subject you are talking about.

An author also expresses a *tone* in writing. Sometimes an author will write in anger, and the choice of short, tense-sounding words, such as *fret, rush,* or *hit* will indicate tone. Or, in order to ridicule a situation, a writer may say the opposite of what is meant. In short, a tone may be despairing, triumphant, admiring, affectionate, defiant, resentful, happy, or amused—it may reflect a wide variety of emotions.

Tone in literature has much the same purpose as tone of voice: it helps readers understand an author's attitude toward the subject. To interpret a work of literature accurately, a reader must sense its tone.

To determine the tone of a selection, analyze the words and details used by the author to describe setting, to portray characters, and to present events. For example, a paragraph containing words such as *grim, gray, bleak, dejected,* and *beaten* might have an unhappy or despairing tone. A description like "unique as a snowflake" or "graceful as a gazelle" might convey the author's admiration for the subject.

---

tone

An author's expressed attitude toward the subject in a literary work. Tone is conveyed through the author's particular choice of words and details in describing setting, portraying characters, and presenting events.

Glossary

The pronunciation of each word is shown just after the word, in this way: **ab bre vi ate** (ə brē′vē āt). The letters and signs used are pronounced as in the words below. The mark ′ is placed after a syllable with primary or heavy accent, as in the example above. The mark ′ after a syllable shows a secondary or lighter accent, as in **ab bre vi a tion** (ə brē′vē ā′shən).

Some words, taken from foreign languages, are spoken with sounds that do not otherwise occur in English. Symbols for these sounds are given in the key as "foreign sounds."

Full pronunciation key

a	hat, cap	j	jam, enjoy	u	cup, butter	**foreign sounds**
ā	age, face	k	kind, seek	u̇	full, put	
ä	father, far	l	land, coal	ü	rule, move	Y as in French *du*.
		m	me, am			Pronounce (ē) with the lips rounded as for (ü).
b	bad, rob	n	no, in	v	very, save	
ch	child, much	ng	long, bring	w	will, woman	à as in French *ami*.
d	did, red			y	young, yet	Pronounce (ä) with the lips spread and held tense.
		o	hot, rock	z	zero, breeze	
e	let, best	ō	open, go	zh	measure, seizure	œ as in French *peu*.
ē	equal, be	ô	order, all			Pronounce (ā) with the lips rounded as for (ō).
ėr	term, learn	oi	oil, voice	ə	represents:	
		ou	house, out		a in about	N as in French *bon*.
f	fat, if				e in taken	The N is not pronounced, but shows that the vowel before it is nasal.
g	go, bag	p	paper, cup		i in pencil	
h	he, how	r	run, try		o in lemon	H as in German *ach*.
		s	say, yes		u in circus	Pronounce (k) without closing the breath passage.
i	it, pin	sh	she, rush			
ī	ice, five	t	tell, it			
		th	thin, both			
		ᴛʜ	then, smooth			

Grammatical key

adj.	adjective	*prep.*	preposition
adv.	adverb	*pron.*	pronoun
conj.	conjunction	*v.*	verb
interj.	interjection	*v.i.*	intransitive verb
n.	noun	*v.t.*	transitive verb
sing.	singular	*pl.*	plural

From *Thorndike-Barnhart Advanced Dictionary*, Second Edition. Copyright © 1974 by Scott, Foresman and Company.

ab a lo ne (ab′ə lō′nē), *n.* an edible salt-water mollusk with a large, rather flat shell lined with mother-of-pearl, found along the Pacific coast of North America. [< Mexican Spanish]

ab er ra tion (ab′ə rā′shən), *n.* 1 a deviating from the right path or usual course of action. 2 an abnormal structure or development. 3 a temporary mental disorder. [< Latin *aberrationem* < *ab-* away + *errare* wander]

a bet (ə bet′), *v.t.,* **a bet ted, a bet ting.** 1 encourage by aid or approval in doing something wrong. 2 urge on or assist in any way. [< Old French *abeter* arouse < *a-* to + *beter* to bait] —**a bet′ment,** *n.* —**a bet′tor, a bet′ter,** *n.*

-able, *suffix forming adjectives from verbs and nouns.* 1 that can be ____ed: *Enjoyable = that can be enjoyed.* 2 giving ____; suitable for ____: *Comfortable = giving comfort.* 3 inclined to ____: *Peaceable = inclined to peace.* 4 deserving to be ____ed: *Lovable = deserving to be loved.* 5 liable to be ____: *Breakable = liable to be broken.* [< Old French < Latin *-abilem*]

ab nor mal (ab nôr′məl), *adj.* away from the normal; deviating from the ordinary conditions, the standard, or a type; markedly irregular; exceptional. —**ab nor′mal ly,** *adv.*

a breast (ə brest′), *adv., adj.* 1 side by side. 2 up with; alongside of: *Keep abreast of what is going on. Keep abreast with the flow of events.*

ab scond (ab skond′), *v.i.* go away hurriedly and secretly, especially to avoid punishment; go off and hide. [< Latin *abscondere* < *abs-* away + *condere* store up] —**ab-scond′er,** *n.*

ab sorbed (ab sôrbd′, ab zôrbd′), *adj.* very much interested; engrossed. —**ab-sorb′ed ly,** *adv.* —**ab sorb′ed ness,** *n.*

a byss (ə bis′), *n.* 1 a bottomless or very great depth; chasm. 2 anything too deep or great to be measured; lowest depth. 3 the chaos before the Creation. [< Greek *abyssos* < *a-* without + *byssos* bottom]

ac cede (ak sēd′), *v.i.,* **-ced ed, -ced ing.** 1 give in; agree; consent *(to): Please accede to my request.* 2 become a party *(to): Our government acceded to the treaty.* 3 come, attain, or succeed *(to an office or dignity): When the king died, his eldest son acceded to the throne.* [< Latin *accedere* < *ad-* to + *cedere* move, go]

ac cus tomed (ə kus′təmd), *adj.* 1 usual; customary. 2 **accustomed to,** used to; in the habit of: *The editor was accustomed to hard work. She is accustomed to jogging daily.*

ac ti vate (ak′tə vāt), *v.t.,* **-vat ed, -vat ing.** 1 make active; cause to act. 2 make radioactive. 3 make capable of reacting or of speeding up a chemical reaction. 4 purify (sewage) by treating it with air and bacteria. 5 make (charcoal, carbon, etc.) capable of absorbing impurities, especially in the form of gases. —**ac′ti va′tion,** *n.* —**ac′ti va′tor,** *n.*

a cute (ə kyüt′), *adj.* 1 acting keenly on the senses; sharp; intense: *acute pain.* 2 coming quickly to a crisis; brief and severe: *an acute disease.* 3 crucial; critical: *an acute shortage of water.* 4 quick in perceiving and responding to impressions; keen: *Dogs have an acute sense of smell.* 5 quick in discernment; sharp-witted; clever: *an acute thinker,* 6 high in pitch; shrill: *A fife makes an acute sound.* 7 having or ending in a sharp point. 8 (of a vowel) having an acute accent over it. 9 having one or more acute angles. —*n.* an acute accent. [< Latin *acutum* sharpened < *acuere* sharpen] —**a cute′ly,** *adv.* —**a cute′ness,** *n.*

ad he sion (ad hē′zhən), *n.* 1 act or condition of adhering; sticking fast. 2 faithfulness; adherence. 3 the molecular attraction exerted between the surfaces of unlike bodies in contact, as a solid and a liquid. 4 a growing together of body tissues that are normally separate, especially after surgery. [< Latin *adhaesionem* < *adhaerere*]

ad just ment (ə just′mənt), *n.* 1 act or process of adjusting. 2 process by which a person adapts himself to the natural or social conditions around him. 3 means of adjusting one thing to another. 4 settlement of a dispute, claim, etc.

ad mi ra tion (ad′mə rā′shən), *n.* 1 a feeling of wonder mingled with approval. 2 a regarding with delight (something fine, great, or beautiful). 3 person or thing that is admired: *My new canoe was the admiration of all my friends.*

ad mon ish (ad mon′ish), *v.t.* 1 advise against something; warn: *admonish a person of danger.* 2 scold gently; reprove: *admonish a student for careless work.* 3 urge strongly; advise earnestly; exhort: *admonish one to be more careful.* 4 recall to a duty overlooked or forgotten; remind. [< *admonition*] —**ad-mon′ish er,** *n.* —**ad mon′ish ment,** *n.*

a droit (ə droit′), *adj.* 1 resourceful in reaching one's objective; ingenious; clever. 2 skillful in the use of the hands or body; dexterous. [< French < *à droit* rightly] —**a droit′ly,** *adv.* —**a droit′ness,** *n.*

aer o dy nam ics (er′ō dī nam′iks, ar′ō-dī nam′iks), *n.* branch of physics that deals with forces such as pressure or resistance exerted by air or other gases in motion on both flying and wind-blown bodies.

aer o nau tics (er′ə nô′tiks, ar′ə nô′tiks), *n.* science or art having to do with the design, manufacture, and operation of aircraft.

af fa ble (af′ə bəl), *adj.* 1 courteous and pleasant in receiving and responding to the conversation or approaches of others. 2 gracious: *an affable smile.* [< Latin *affabilis* easy to speak to < *affari* speak to < *ad-* to + *fari* speak] —**af′fa ble ness,** *n.* —**af′fa bly,** *adv.*

af fin i ty (ə fin′ə tē), *n., pl.* **-ties.** 1 a natural attraction to a person or liking for a thing: *If you have an affinity for mathematics, you will probably enjoy physics.* 2 relation; connection. 3 relationship by marriage. 4 resemblance between species, genera, etc., that makes a common ancestry probable. 5 force that attracts certain chemical elements to others and keeps them combined. [< Latin *affinitatem* relation < *affinis* related, bordering on < *ad-* on + *finis* border]

a gen cy (ā′jən sē), *n., pl.* **-cies.** a special department of the government concerned with the administration of affairs within a specific field: *the Central Intelligence Agency.*

a ghast (ə gast′), *adj.* struck with surprise or horror; filled with shocked amazement. [past participle of obsolete *agast* terrify < Old English *on-* on + *gæstan* frighten. Related to GHOST.]

a gue (ā′gyü), *n.* 1 a malarial fever with chills and sweating that alternate at regular intervals. 2 any fit of shaking or shivering; chill. [< Middle French *aguë* < Latin *(febris) acuta* severe (fever)]

air borne (er′bôrn′, er′bōrn′; ar′bôrn′, ar′bōrn′), *adj.* 1 supported by the air; off the ground: *The kite was finally airborne.* 2 carried in aircraft: *airborne troops.* 3 carried by air: *airborne dust.*

-al¹, *suffix forming adjectives from nouns.* of; like; having the nature of: *Ornamental = having the nature of ornament.* Also, **-ial.** [< Latin *-alem*]

-al², *suffix forming nouns from verbs.* act of ____ing: *Refusal = act of refusing.* [< Latin *-alia,* neuter plural of *-alem*]

al fal fa (al fal′fə), *n.* a plant of the pea family with deep roots, cloverlike leaves, and bluish-purple flowers; lucerne. Alfalfa is grown as food for livestock and can be cut several times a season and then dried as hay. [< Spanish < Arabic *al-fasfas* the best kind of fodder]

a lign (ə līn′), *v.t.* 1 bring (anything) into line; adjust to a line: *align the sights of a gun.* 2 join with others for or against a cause: *Germany was aligned with Japan in World War II.* —*v.i.* form a line: *The troops aligned.* Also, **aline.** [< French *aligner* < *a-* to + *ligne* line]

al lure (ə lür′), *v.,* **-lured, -lur ing,** *n.* —*v.t.* tempt or attract very strongly; fascinate; charm: *City life allured her with its action and excitement.* —*n.* great charm; fascination. [< Middle French *alurer* < *a-* to + *leurre* lure] —**al lur′er,** *n.*

Al pine (al′pīn), *adj.* 1 of or like the Alps. 2 **alpine, a** of or like high mountains: *alpine terrain.* **b** very high. **c** growing at high places, especially on mountains above the timber line: *alpine plants.* —*n.* **alpine,** an alpine plant.

a mi a ble (ā′mē ə bəl), *adj.* having a good-natured and friendly disposition; pleasant and agreeable. [< Old French < Late Latin *amicabilis* < Latin *amicus* friend. Doublet of AMICABLE.] —**a′mi a ble ness,** *n.* —**a′mi a bly,** *adv.*

a mid (ə mid′), *prep.* in the middle of; surrounded by; among.

a mid ship (ə mid′ship), *adv.* amidships.

a mid ships (ə mid′ships), *adv.* in or toward the middle of a ship; halfway between the bow and stern.

am phib i an (am fib′ē ən), *n.* 1 any of a class of cold-blooded vertebrates with moist, scaleless skin that, typically, lay eggs in water where the young hatch and go through a larval or tadpole stage, breathing by means of gills; the larval forms lose their gills and develop lungs for breathing and limbs. Frogs, toads, newts, and salamanders belong to this class. 2 animal living both on land and in water but unable to breathe under water. Crocodiles, seals, and beavers are amphibians. 3 plant that grows on land or in water. 4 aircraft that can take off from and land on either land or water. 5 a tank, truck, or other vehicle able to travel across land or water. —*adj.* 1 able to live both on land and in water. 2 able to start from and land on either land or water.

an-¹, *prefix.* 1 not: *anastigmatic = not astigmatic.* 2 without: *Anhydrous = without water.* Also, **a-,** before consonants except *h.* [< Greek]

an-², *prefix.* form of **ad-** before *n,* as in *annex.*

-an, *suffix forming adjectives and nouns, especially from proper nouns.* 1 of or having to do with ____: *Mohammedan = of or* having to do with Mohammed. 2 of or having to do with ____ or its people: *Asian = of or having to do with Asia or its people.* 3 native or inhabitant of ____: *American = native or inhabitant of America.* 4 person who knows much about or is skilled in ____: *Magician = person skilled in magic. Historian = person who knows much about history.* Also, **-ian, -ean.** [< Latin *-anus*]

a nach ro nism (ə nak′rə niz′əm), *n.* 1 error in fixing a date or dates; erroneous reference of an event, circumstance, or custom to a wrong, especially an earlier date. 2 anything out of keeping with a specified time, especially something proper to a former age but not to the present. [< Greek *anachronismos* < *ana-* back + *chronos* time]

a nal y sis (ə nal′ə sis), *n., pl.* **-ses** (-sēz′). 1 a breaking up of anything complex into its various simple elements. 2 this process as a method of studying the nature of a thing or of determining its essential features. An analysis can be made of a book, a person's character, a situation, etc. 3 **in the last analysis** or **in the final analysis,** fundamentally; ultimately. 4 a brief presentation of essential features; outline or summary. 5 in chemistry: **a** the determination of the nature or amount of one or more components of a substance. **b** the intentional separation of a compound into its parts or elements. 6 in mathematics: **a** algebraic reasoning, especially as applied to geometry. **b** treatment by the calculus. 7 psychoanalysis. [< Greek *analyein* loosen up < *ana-* up + *lyein* loosen]

-ance, *suffix forming nouns chiefly from verbs.* 1 act or fact of ____ing: *Avoidance = act or fact of avoiding.* 2 quality or state of being ____ed: *Annoyance = quality or state of being annoyed.* 3 thing that ____s: *Conveyance = thing that conveys.* 4 what is ____ed: *Contrivance = what is contrived.* 5 quality or state of being ____ant: *Importance = quality or state of being important.* [< Old French < Latin *-antia, -entia*]

and i ron (and′ī′ərn), *n.* one of a pair of metal supports for wood in a fireplace; firedog. [< Old French *andier; -iron* by association with *iron*]

an ec dote (an′ik dōt), *n.* a short account of some interesting incident or single event, especially one in the life of a person. [< Greek *anekdota* (things) unpublished < *an-* not + *ek-* out + *didonai* give]

an es the tist (ə nes′thə tist), *n.* person specially trained to give anesthetics. Also, **anaesthetist.**

an es the tize (ə nes′thə tīz), *v.t.,* **-tized, -tiz ing.** 1 make (a person, animal, area of the body, etc.) unable to feel pain, touch, cold, etc.; make insensible. 2 lessen or deaden (the emotional or critical response of a person). Also, **anaesthetize.** —**an es′the ti za′tion,** *n.* —**an es′the tiz′er,** *n.*

an guish (ang′gwish), *n.* 1 severe physical pain; great suffering: *the anguish of unrelieved toothache.* 2 extreme mental pain or suffering: *the anguish of despair.* [< Old French *anguisse* < Latin *angustia* tightness < *angustus* narrow]

a noint (ə noint′), *v.t.* 1 apply an ointment, oil, or similar substance to; cover or smear with oil, etc.: *Anoint sunburned arms with cold cream.* 2 consecrate by applying oil. 3 rub or smear with any other substance or liquid. [< Old French *enoint* smeared on < Latin *inunctum* < *in-* on + *unguere* to smear] —**a noint′er,** *n.* —**a noint′ment,** *n.*

ant-, *prefix.* form of **anti-** before vowels and

h, as in *antacid.*

-ant, *suffix forming adjectives and nouns from verbs.* 1 that ____s; ____ing: *Compliant = that complies* or *complying.* 2 one that ____s: *Assistant = one that assists.* [< Old French < Latin *-antem*]

ante-, *prefix.* 1 before: *Antedate = to date before.* 2 in front of: *Anteroom = a room in front of (another).* [< Latin]

anti-, *prefix.* 1 against ____; opposed to ____: *Antiaircraft = against aircraft.* 2 not ____; the opposite of ____: *Antisocial = the opposite of social.* 3 rival ____: *Antipope = rival pope.* 4 reducing or counteracting ____: *Antifriction = reducing or counteracting friction.* 5 preventing, curing, or alleviating ____: *Antiscorbutic = preventing or curing scurvy.* Also, **ant-** before vowels and *h.* [< Greek]

an tic (an′tik), *n.* 1 Usually, **antics,** *pl.* a funny gesture or action; silly trick; caper: *the antics of a clown.* 2 ARCHAIC. clown. —*adj.* grotesque; odd. [< Italian *antico* old < Latin *antiquus.* Doublet of ANTIQUE.]

an ti sep tic (an′tə sep′tik), *n.* substance that prevents the growth of germs that cause infection. Iodine, peroxide, Mercurochrome, alcohol, and boric acid are antiseptics. —*adj.* 1 preventing infection by stopping the growth of disease germs. 2 of, having to do with, or using antiseptics. —**an′ti sep′ti cal ly,** *adv.*

ap o gee (ap′ə jē), *n.* 1 the point farthest from the earth in the orbit of the moon or any other earth satellite. 2 furthermost point; highest point; peak; apex. [< Greek *apogaion* < *apo-* + *gē* or *gaia* earth]

ap pall or **ap pal** (ə pôl′), *v.t.,* **-palled, -pall ing.** fill with consternation and horror; dismay; terrify: *The thought of another war appalled us.* [< Old French *apallir* make pale < *a-* to + *pale* pale]

ap pa ra tus (ap′ə rā′təs, ap′ə rat′əs), *n., pl.* **-tus,** or **-tus es.** 1 the tools, machines, or other equipment necessary to carry out a purpose or for a particular use: *apparatus for an experiment in chemistry, gardening apparatus.* 2 a mechanism or piece of machinery: *An automobile is a complicated apparatus.* 3 the group of organs of the body by which a specific natural process is carried on: *the digestive apparatus.* [< Latin < *ad-* + *parare* make ready]

ap pease (ə pēz′), *v.t.,* **-peased, -peas ing.** 1 put an end to by satisfying (an appetite or desire): *A good dinner will appease your hunger.* 2 make calm or quiet; pacify. 3 give in to the demands of (especially those of a potential enemy): *The English appeased the Vikings with payments of gold.* —**ap peas′er,** *n.* —**ap peas′ing ly,** *adv.*

ap pen dec to my (ap′ən dek′tə mē), *n., pl.* **-mies.** removal of the vermiform appendix by a surgical operation.

ap pen di ci tis (ə pen′də sī′tis), *n.* inflammation of the vermiform appendix.

ap pre ci ate (ə prē′shē āt), *v.,* **-at ed, -at ing.** —*v.t.* 1 think highly of; recognize the worth or quality of; value: *Her merits are appreciated.* 2 be thankful for: *We appreciate your help.* 3 have an opinion of the value, worth, or quality of; estimate: *A scholar appreciates knowledge.* 4 be aware of; be sensitive to; discern: *I appreciate the risk I am taking.* 5 raise in value: *New buildings appreciate the price of land.* —*v.i.* rise in value. [< Latin *appretiatum* appraised < *ad-* + *pretium* price] —**ap pre′ci a′tor,** *n.*

ap pre ci a tive (ə prē′shē ā′tiv, ə prē′-

hat, āge, fär; let, ēqual, tėrm;
it, īce; hot, ōpen, ôrder;
oil, out; cup, put, rüle;
ch, child; ng, long; sh, she;
th, thin; ᴛʜ, then; zh, measure;

ə represents *a* in about, *e* in taken,
i in pencil, *o* in lemon, *u* in circus.

< = from, derived from, taken from.

shə tiv), *adj.* feeling or showing appreciation: *appreciative of the smallest kindness.* —**ap pre′ci a′tive ly,** *adv.* —**ap pre′ci a′tive ness,** *n.*

ap pre hen sion (ap′ri hen′shən), *n.* 1 expectation of misfortune; dread of impending danger; fear. 2 arrest. 3 understanding.

ap pre hen sive (ap′ri hen′siv), *adj.* afraid that some misfortune is about to occur; anxious about the future; fearful. —**ap′pre hen′sive ly,** *adv.* —**ap′pre hen′sive ness,** *n.*

ar chi tect (är′kə tekt), *n.* 1 person whose profession it is to design, lay out plans for, and thereafter to supervise generally the construction of buildings. 2 designer; maker; creator. [< Greek *architektōn* < *archi-* chief + *tektōn* builder]

ar mor y (är′mər ē), *n., pl.* **-mor ies.** 1 place where weapons are kept; arsenal. 2 place where weapons are manufactured. 3 a building with a drill hall, offices, etc., for militia. 4 ARCHAIC. armor; arms.

ar ro gance (ar′ə gəns), *n.* excessive pride with contempt of others; haughtiness.

ar ro gant (ar′ə gənt), *adj.* excessively proud and contemptuous of others. [< Latin *arrogantem* < *ad-* to + *rogare* ask] —**ar′ro gant ly,** *adv.*

-ary, *suffix forming nouns and adjectives.* 1 place for ____: *Infirmary = place for the infirm.* 2 collection of ____: *Statuary = collection of statues.* 3 person or thing that ____s: *Boundary = thing that bounds.* 4 of or having to do with ____: *Legendary = of legend.* 5 being; having the nature of ____: *Secondary = being second.* 6 characterized by ____: *Customary = characterized by custom.* [< Latin *-arium*]

ash cake (ash′kāk), *n.* a corn meal cake baked in hot ashes.

as phalt (as′fôlt), *n.* 1 a dark, waterproof substance much like tar, found in natural beds in various parts of the world or obtained by refining petroleum. 2 mixture of this substance with crushed rock or sand, used to pave streets, etc. —*v.t.* cover, permeate, or lay with asphalt. [< Greek *asphaltos*]

a sphyx i ate (a sfik′sē āt), *v.t., v.i.,* **-at ed, -at ing.** produce asphyxia in; suffocate. —**a sphyx′i a′tion,** *n.* —**a sphyx′i a′tor,** *n.*

as sail (ə sāl′), *v.t.* 1 attack repeatedly with violent blows. 2 attack with hostile words, arguments, or abuse. 3 (of a feeling) come over (a person) strongly; beset; trouble: *No doubts ever assail them.* [< Old French *asalir* < Latin *ad-* at + *salire* to leap] —**as sail′a ble,** *adj.* —**as sail′er,** *n.*

as sent (ə sent′), *v.i.* express agreement; agree; consent: *Everyone assented to the plans for the building.* —*n.* acceptance of a proposal, statement, etc.; agreement. [< Latin *assentire* < *ad-* along with + *sentire* feel, think]

as sert (ə sėrt′), *v.t.* 1 state positively; declare firmly; affirm: *She asserts that she will go whether we do or not.* 2 maintain (a right, a claim, etc.); insist upon: *Assert your independence.* 3 **assert oneself**, put oneself forward; make demands: *A leader must assert himself sometimes in order to be followed.* [< Latin *assertum* asserted < *ad-* to + *serere* join] —**as sert′er, as ser′tor,** *n.*

as sim i late (ə sim′ə lāt), *v.,* **-lat ed, -lat ing.** —*v.t.* 1 take in and make part of oneself; absorb; digest: *assimilate what one reads. The human body will not assimilate sawdust.* 2 cause to be like the people of a nation in customs, viewpoint, character, etc.: *We have assimilated immigrants from many lands.* 3 make (a speech sound, usually a consonant) more like the sound which follows or precedes. —*v.i.* 1 become absorbed; be digested. 2 become like the people of a nation in customs, viewpoint, character, etc. 3 become like. [< Latin *assimilatum* made similar < *ad-* to + *similis* like] —**as sim′i la tor,** *n.*

as sume (ə süm′), *v.t.* **-sumed, -sum ing.** 1 take for granted without actual proof; presume; suppose: *She assumed that the train would be on time.* 2 take upon oneself formally; undertake (an office or responsibility): *assume leadership.* 3 take on; put on: *The problem had assumed a new form.* 4 pretend; feign; simulate: *You are more likely to make a good impression if you assume an air of confidence.* 5 take for oneself; appropriate; usurp. [< Latin *assumere* < *ad-* to + *sumere* take]

-ate¹, *suffix forming adjectives, verbs, and nouns.* 1 of or having to do with ____: *Collegiate = having to do with college.* 2 having or containing ____: *Compassionate = having compassion.* 3 having the form of ____; like ____: *Stellate = having the form of a star.* 4 become ____: *Maturate = become mature.* 5 cause to be ____: *Alienate = cause to be alien.* 6 produce ____: *Ulcerate = produce ulcers.* 7 supply or treat with ____: *Aerate = treat with air.* 8 combine with ____: *Oxygenate = combine with oxygen.* [< Latin *-atus, -atum,* past participle endings]

-ate², *suffix forming nouns.* office, rule, or condition of ____: *Caliphate = rule of a caliph.* [< Latin *-atus*]

-ation, *suffix forming nouns chiefly from verbs.* 1 act or process of ____ing: *Admiration = act or process of admiring.* 2 condition or state of being ____ed: *Cancellation = condition or state of being canceled.* 3 result of ____ing: *Civilization = result of civilizing.* [< Latin *-ationem*]

at tune (ə tün′, ə tyün′), *v.t.,* **-tuned, -tun ing.** put in tune or accord; tune. —**at tune′ment,** *n.*

au di ble (ô′də bəl), *adj.* that can be heard; loud enough to be heard. [< Latin *audire* hear] —**au′di bly,** *adv.*

au thor i ta tive (ə thôr′ə tā′tiv, ə thor′ə tā′tiv), *adj.* 1 proceeding from a recognized authority; official: *The president issued an authoritative declaration of policy.* 2 of or characterized by authority; commanding: *In authoritative tones the policeman shouted, "Keep back."* 3 entitled to obedience and respect; having the authority of expert knowledge. —**au thor′i ta′tive ly,** *adv.* —**au thor′i ta′tive ness,** *n.*

awe (ô), *n., v.,* **awed, aw ing.** —*n.* 1 a feeling of wonder and reverence inspired by anything of great beauty, sublimity, majesty, or power: *The sight of the great iceberg filled us with awe. The young girl stood in awe before the queen.* 2 dread mingled with reverence. —*v.t.* 1 cause to feel awe; fill with awe: *The majesty of the mountains awed us.* 2 influence or restrain by awe. [< Scandinavian (Old Icelandic) *agi*]

awe some (ô′səm), *adj.* 1 causing awe. 2 showing awe; awed. —**awe′some ly,** *adv.* —**awe′some ness,** *n.*

ax le (ak′səl), *n.* 1 bar or shaft on which or with which a wheel turns. 2 axletree. [shortened from Middle English *axeltre* axletree < Scandinavian (Old Icelandic) *öxul-tré* < *öxul* axle + *tré* tree]

az ure (azh′ər), *n.* the clear blue color of the unclouded sky; sky blue. —*adj.* sky-blue. [< Old French *l'azur* the azure < Arabic *lāzuward* < Persian *lajward* lapis lazuli]

back wa ter (bak′wô′tər, bak′wot′ər), *n.* 1 stretch of water held, thrown, or pushed back. 2 a backward place. 3 a sluggish, stagnant condition or situation.

bale (bāl), *n., v.,* **baled, bal ing.** —*n.* a large bundle of merchandise or material closely pressed, tightly corded or hooped, and (sometimes) wrapped or bound for shipping or storage: *a bale of cotton, a bale of hay.* —*v.t.* make into bales; tie in large bundles. [< Flemish < Old French *balle* round package] —**bal′er,** *n.*

bale ful (bāl′fəl), *adj.* 1 full of hurtful or deadly influence; destructive. 2 full of misfortune; disastrous. —**bale′ful ly,** *adv.* —**bale′ful ness,** *n.*

bal sa (bôl′sə), *n.* 1 a tropical American tree with very lightweight, strong wood. 2 its wood, used in making rafts, airplane models, etc. [< Spanish]

ban dan na or **ban dan a** (ban dan′ə), *n.* a large, gaily colored kerchief or handkerchief, often worn on the head or neck. [< Hindustani *bāndhnū* way of tying cloth so as to produce designs when dyed]

ban dy-leg ged (ban′dē leg′id, ban′dē legd′), *adj.* having legs that curve outward like a bow; bowlegged.

ban gle (bang′gəl), *n.* 1 a small ornament suspended from a bracelet. 2 a bracelet or anklet without a clasp. [< Hindustani *bangrī* glass bracelet]

ban ish (ban′ish), *v.t.* 1 compel (a person) to leave a country by order of political or judicial authority; exile. 2 force to go away; drive away; dismiss; expel: *banish all cares.* [< Old French *baniss-,* a form of *banir* < Germanic. Related to BAN.] —**ban′ish er,** *n.* —**ban′ish ment,** *n.*

ban ter (ban′tər), *n.* playful teasing; joking. —*v.t.* tease playfully; make fun of. —*v.i.* talk in a joking way. [origin uncertain] —**ban′ter er,** *n.* —**ban′ter ing ly,** *adv.*

bard (bärd), *n.* 1 a Celtic minstrel and poet who from earliest times to the Middle Ages sang his own poems, usually to harp accompaniment, celebrating martial exploits, etc. 2 any poet. [< Irish and Scottish Gaelic]

ba roque (bə rōk′, bə rok′), *adj.* 1 having to do with a style of art and architecture that prevailed in Europe from about 1550 to the late 1700's, characterized by the use of curved forms and lavish ornamentation. 2 having to do with a style of music characterized by complex rhythms and melodic ornamentation. 3 tastelessly odd; fantastic; grotesque. 4 irregular in shape: *baroque pearls.* —*n.* a baroque style. [< French < Portuguese *barroco* irregular]

bar ren (bar′ən), *adj.* 1 not producing anything; unproductive: *A sandy desert is barren.* 2 not able to produce offspring or yield fruit; not fertile; sterile. 3 without interest; unattractive; dull. 4 of no advantage; fruitless; unprofitable. —*n.* 1 stretch of barren land. 2 Usually, **barrens,** *pl.* area of level land, mostly unproductive, poorly forested, and generally having sandy soil. [< Old French *baraine*] —**bar′ren ly,** *adv.* —**bar′ren ness,** *n.*

bar row (bar′ō), *n.* mound of earth or stones over an ancient grave. [Old English *beorg*]

ba ton (ba ton′), *n.* 1 a light stick or wand used by the leader of an orchestra, chorus, or band to indicate the beat and direct the performance. 2 staff or stick carried as a symbol of office or authority. 3 stick passed from runner to runner in a relay race. 4 a light, hollow, metal rod twirled by a drum major or majorette as a showy display. [< Middle French, ultimately from Late Latin *bastum* stick]

bay (bā), *n.* 1 a deep, prolonged barking of a dog when pursuing or attacking. 2 position of a hunted animal that turns to face its pursuers when further flight is impossible: *The stag stood at bay on the edge of the cliff.* 3 a stand by a person forced to face a foe, difficulty, persecution, etc. 4 position of an enemy or pursuers thus faced or kept off: *The bear held the hounds at bay.* 5 **bring to bay,** put in a position from which escape is impossible. —*v.i.* bark with long, deep sounds. —*v.t.* 1 bark at; assail with barking. 2 utter or express by baying. 3 bring to bay. [< Old French *abai* a barking]

be guile (bi gīl′), *v.t.,* **-guiled, -guil ing.** 1 trick or mislead (a person); deceive; delude: *Your flattery beguiled me into thinking that you were my friend.* 2 take away from deceitfully or cunningly. 3 win the attention of; entertain; amuse. 4 while away (time) pleasantly. —**be guile′ment,** *n.* —**be guil′er,** *n.*

be lie (bi lī′), *v.t.,* **-lied, -ly ing.** 1 give a false idea of; misrepresent: *Her frown belied her usual good nature.* 2 show to be false; prove to be mistaken. 3 fail to come up to; disappoint: *He stole again, and so belied our hopes.* [Old English *belēogan*] —**be li′er,** *n.*

be nev o lence (bə nev′ə ləns), *n.* 1 desire to promote the happiness of others; good will; kindly feeling. 2 act of kindness; something good that is done; generous gift. [< Latin *benevolentia* < *bene* well + *velle* to wish]

be nign (bi nīn′), *adj.* 1 kindly in feeling; benevolent; gracious: *a benign old woman.* 2 showing a kindly feeling; gentle: *a benign countenance.* 3 favorable; propitious. 4 mild: *a benign climate.* 5 not dangerous to health; not malignant: *a benign tumor.* [< Latin *benignus* < *bene* well + *-gnus* born] —**be nign′ly,** *adv.*

be siege (bi sēj′), *v.t.,* **-sieged, -sieg ing.** 1 surround by armed forces in order to compel surrender; lay siege to: *For ten years the Greeks besieged the city of Troy.* 2 crowd around: *Hundreds of admirers besieged the famous astronaut.* 3 overwhelm with requests, questions, etc. —**be sieg′er,** *n.*

bil low (bil′ō), *n.* 1 a great, swelling wave or surge of the sea. 2 a great rolling or swelling mass of smoke, flame, air, etc. —v.i. 1 rise or roll in big waves; surge. 2 swell out; bulge: *The washing on the line billowed in the wind.* [< Scandinavian (Old Icelandic) *bylgia*]

bi plane (bī′plān′), *n.* airplane having two wings on each side of the fuselage, one above the other.

bi zarre (bə zär′), *adj.* strikingly odd in appearance or style; fantastic; grotesque. [< French < Spanish *bizarro* brave < Italian *bizzarro* angry < *bizza* anger] —**bi zarre′ly,** *adv.* —**bi zarre′ness,** *n.*

bland (bland), *adj.* 1 gentle or soothing; balmy: *a bland summer breeze.* 2 smoothly agreeable and polite: *a bland smile.* 3 soothing to the palate or digestive tract; not irritating: *a bland diet of baby food.* [< Latin *blandus* soft] —**bland′ly,** *adv.* —**bland′ness,** *n.*

bloke (blōk), *n.* BRITISH SLANG. man; fellow. [origin unknown]

bloom ers (blü′mərz), *n.pl.* 1 loose trousers, gathered at the knee, formerly worn by women and girls for physical training, sports, etc. 2 underwear made like these. [< Amelia J. *Bloomer*, 1818-1894, who first referred to them in a magazine she published]

blow hole (blō′hōl′), *n.* nostril or hole for breathing, in the top of the head of whales, porpoises, and dolphins.

board (bôrd, bōrd), provide with regular meals, or room and meals, for pay.

bog (bog, bôg), *n., v.,* **bogged, bog ging.** —*n.* piece of wet, spongy ground, consisting chiefly of decayed or decaying moss and other vegetable matter, too soft to bear the weight of any heavy body on its surface; marsh; swamp. —*v.t., v.i.* 1 sink or get stuck in a bog. 2 **bog down,** sink in or get stuck so that one cannot get out without help: *She is bogged down with problems.* [< Irish or Scottish Gaelic, soft]

bois ter ous (boi′stər əs), *adj.* 1 noisily cheerful; exuberant: *a boisterous game.* 2 rough and stormy; turbulent: *a boisterous wind.* 3 rough and noisy; clamorous: *a boisterous child.* [Middle English *boistrous*] —**bois′ter ous ly,** *adv.* —**bois′ter ous ness,** *n.*

bond (bond), *n.* 1 anything that binds or fastens, as a rope, cord, or other band. 2 any force or influence that serves to unite people.

bon ny or **bon nie** (bon′ē), *adj.,* **-ni er, -ni est.** 1 fair to see; rosy and pretty: *a bonny baby.* 2 gay or cheerful. [Middle English *bonne,* apparently < Old French *bone* good < Latin *bonus*] —**bon′ni ly,** *adv.* —**bon′ni ness,** *n.*

boor ish (bur′ish), *adj.* like a boor; rude or rustic. —**boor′ish ly,** *adv.* —**boor′ish ness,** *n.*

bore dom (bôr′dəm, bōr′dəm), *n.* a bored condition; weariness caused by dull, tiresome people or things.

bow (bou), *n.* the forward part of a ship, boat, or aircraft. [probably < Middle Dutch *boegh* or Danish *bov.* Related to BOUGH.]

breast plate (brest′plāt′), *n.* armor for the chest.

breech (brēch), *n.* the part of a gun behind the barrel.

breech load ing (brēch′lō′ding), *adj.,* (of a gun) loaded at the rear end of the barrel instead of at the muzzle end.

bridge (brij), *n.* platform above the deck of a ship from which the officer in command directs the course of the ship. [Old English *brycg*] —**bridge′a ble,** *adj.* —**bridge′like′,** *adj.*

bris tle (bris′əl), *n., v.,* **-tled, -tling.** —*n.* 1 one of the short, stiff hairs of a hog or wild boar, used to make brushes. 2 any short, stiff hair of an animal or plant. 3 a synthetic substitute for a hog's bristles. —*v.t.* 1 provide with bristles. 2 cause (hair) to stand up straight. —*v.i.* 1 stand up straight: *The angry dog's hair bristled.* 2 have one's hair stand up straight: *The frightened kitten bristled when it saw the dog.* 3 show that one is aroused and ready to fight: *The whole country bristled with indignation.* [Middle English *brustel,* Old English *byrst* bristle] —**bris′tle like′,** *adj.*

broach (brōch), *v.t.* begin conversation or discussion about; introduce: *broach a subject.* [< Old French *broche* < Latin *broccus* projecting] —**broach′er,** *n.*

bro ker (brō′kər), *n.* person who buys and sells stocks, bonds, grain, cotton, etc., for other people. [< Anglo-French *brocour* retailer of wine. Related to BROACH.]

bronze (bronz), *n., adj.,* **bronzed.** —*n.* 1 a brown metal, an alloy of copper and tin. 2 a similar alloy of copper with zinc or other metals. 3 statue, medal, disk, etc., made of bronze. 4 a yellowish brown or reddish brown. —*adj.* 1 made of bronze. 2 yellowish-brown or reddish-brown. [< Middle French < Italian *bronzo* bell metal]

bruit (brüt), *v.t.* spread a report or rumor of: *News of their engagement was bruited about.* —*n.* ARCHAIC. report; rumor. [< Old French, a roar < *bruire* to roar]

brusque (brusk), *adj.* abrupt in manner or speech; blunt. [< French < Italian *brusco* coarse] —**brusque′ly,** *adv.* —**brusque′ness,** *n.*

bru tal i ty (brü tal′ə tē), *n., pl.* **-ties.** 1 brutal conduct; cruelty; savageness. 2 a cruel or savage act. 3 coarse behavior; sensuality.

buck board (buk′bôrd′, buk′bōrd′), *n.* an open, four-wheeled carriage having a seat fastened to a platform of long, springy boards instead of a body and springs.

Bud dha (bü′də, bùd′ə), *n.* 563?-483? B.C., a religious teacher of northern India and the founder of Buddhism.

Bud dhist (bü′dist, bùd′ist), *n.* believer in Buddhism. —*adj.* having to do with Buddha or Buddhism.

bull ock (bùl′ək), *n.* 1 a castrated bull; ox; steer. 2 (originally) a young bull. [Old English *bulluc* bull calf]

bun ga low (bung′gə lō), *n.* a small house, usually of one story or a story and a half, with low, sweeping lines. [< Hindustani *banglā* of Bengal]

buoy ant (boi′ənt, bü′yənt), *adj.* 1 able to float: *Wood and cork are buoyant in water; iron and lead are not.* 2 able to keep things afloat: *Air is buoyant; helium-filled balloons float in it.* 3 tending to rise. 4 cheerful and hopeful; light-hearted: *Children are usually more buoyant than adults.* —**buoy′ant ly,** *adv.*

bur row (bèr′ō), *n.* 1 hole dug in the ground by woodchucks, rabbits, and various other animals for refuge or shelter. 2 a similar dwelling, shelter, or refuge. —*v.i.* 1 dig a hole in the ground: *The mole quickly burrowed out of sight.* 2 live in burrows. 3 work a way into or under something: *She burrowed under the blankets.* 4 hide oneself. 5 search carefully or diligently: *She burrowed in the library for a book about Indian life.* —*v.t.* 1 make burrows in; dig: *Rabbits have burrowed the ground for miles around.* 2 hide in

hat, āge, fär; let, ēqual, tėrm;
it, īce; hot, ōpen, ôrder;
oil, out; cup, pùt, rüle;
ch, child; ng, long; sh, she;
th, thin; ᴛʜ, then; zh, measure;

ə represents *a* in about, *e* in taken,
i in pencil, *o* in lemon, *u* in circus.

< = from, derived from, taken from.

---

a burrow or something like a burrow: *The runaway burrowed himself in the haystack.* 3 make by burrowing: *Their dens are burrowed in the mountainside.* [Middle English variant of *borough*] —**bur′row er,** *n.*

butt (but), *v.i.* strike or push by knocking hard with the head: *A goat butts.*

by-play (bī′plā′), *n.* action that is not part of the main action, especially on the stage.

byre (bī′ər), *n.* a stable for cows or pigs.

---

cache (kash), *n., v.,* **cached, cach ing.** —*n.* 1 a hiding place, especially of goods, treasure, food, etc. 2 the store of food or supplies hidden. —*v.t.* put or store in a cache; hide. [< French < *cacher* to hide]

ca dence (kād′ns), *n.* 1 the measure or beat of music, dancing, marching, or any movement regularly repeating itself; rhythm: *the cadence of a drum.* 2 fall of the voice. 3 a rising and falling sound; modulation.

ca jole (kə jōl′), *v.t.,* **-joled, -jol ing.** persuade by pleasant words, flattery, or false promises; coax. [< French *cajoler*] —**ca jol′er,** *n.*

cal dron (kôl′drən), *n.* a large kettle or boiler. Also, **cauldron.** [< Old French *caudron* < Late Latin *caldaria* < Latin *calidus* hot]

can o py (kan′ə pē), *n., pl.* **-pies.** 1 a rooflike covering; shelter or shade. 2 the sliding transparent cover of the cockpit of a small aircraft.

can ti lev er (kan′tl ev′ər, kan′tl ē′vər), *n.* a large, projecting bracket or beam that is supported at one end only, especially one designed to bear a weight or structure over a space where supports cannot be placed or are not desired. —*v.t.* build (something) with cantilevers or a cantilever. —*v.i.* extend outward, as a cantilever. [origin uncertain]

cap i tal ist (kap′ə tə list), *n.* 1 person whose money and property are used in carrying on business. 2 a wealthy person. 3 person who favors or supports capitalism.

ca reen (kə rēn′), *v.i.* lean to one side or sway sharply; tilt; tip: *The ship careened in the strong wind.* —*v.t.* cause to lean to one side or sway sharply: *The gale careened the sailboat.* [< Middle French *carène* keel < Latin *carina*]

car ri on (kar′ē ən), *n.* 1 dead and decaying flesh. 2 rottenness; filth. —*adj.* 1 dead and decaying. 2 feeding on dead and decaying flesh. 3 rotten; filthy. [< Old French *caroine* carcass < Popular Latin *caronia* < Latin *carnem* flesh. Doublet of CRONE.]

car rou sel (kar′ə sel′, kar′ə zel′), *n.* merry-go-round. Also, **carousel.** [< French]

cash mere (kash′mir, kazh′mir), *n.* 1 a fine, soft wool from a breed of long-haired goats of Tibet and Kashmir. 2 a costly kind of shawl made of this wool. 3 a fine, soft wool from sheep. **4** a fine, soft woolen cloth. [< variant of *Kashmir*]

cat a pult (kat′ə pult), *n.* **1** an ancient weapon for shooting stones, arrows, etc. **2** slingshot. **3** device for launching an airplane from the deck of a ship. —*v.t.* throw; hurl. —*v.i.* shoot up suddenly; spring. [< Latin *catapulta* < Greek *katapeltēs*, probably < *kata-* down + *pallein* to hurl]

cease less (sēs′lis), *adj.* going on all the time; never stopping; continual. —**cease′- less ly,** *adv.* —**cease′less ness,** *n.*

Cel lu loid (sel′yə loid), *n.* trademark for a hard, transparent, combustible substance made from cellulose and treated with camphor. Combs, toilet articles, camera films, etc., are often made of celluloid.

cer e mo ni al (ser′ə mō′nē əl), *adj.* **1** of or having to do with ceremony. **2** very formal: *The President received his guests in a ceremonial way.* —*n.* the formal actions proper to an occasion. Bowing the head and kneeling are ceremonials of religion. —**cer′e mo′- ni al ly,** *adv.* —**cer′e mo′ni al ness,** *n.*

chi can er y (shi kā′nər ē), *n., pl.* -er ies. low trickery; unfair practice. [< Middle French *chicanerie* < *chicaner* to quibble]

churl (chèrl), *n.* **1** a rude, surly person; boor. **2** person of low birth; peasant. **3** person stingy in money matters; miser. **4** (in Anglo-Saxon and medieval England) a freeman of the lowest rank; ceorl. [Old English *ceorl*]

cir cuit (sèr′kit), *n.* **1** route over which a person or group makes repeated journeys at certain times. Some judges make a circuit, stopping at certain towns along the way to hold court. **2** the part of the country through which such journeys are made.

cir cum fer ence (sər kum′fər əns), *n.* **1** the boundary line of a circle or of certain other surfaces. Every point in the circumference of a circle is at the same distance from the center. **2** the distance around: *The circumference of the earth at the equator is almost 25,000 miles.* [< Latin *circumferentia* < *circum* around + *ferre* bear]

claim ant (klā′mənt), *n.* person who makes a claim.

clam ber (klam′bər), *v.i., v.t.* climb, using both hands and feet; climb awkwardly or with difficulty; scramble. —*n.* an awkward or difficult climb. [Middle English *clambren*. Related to CLIMB.] —**clam′ber er,** *n.*

clam or (klam′ər), *n.* **1** a loud noise or continual uproar; shouting. **2** a shout; outcry. **3** a noisy demand or complaint. —*v.i.* **1** make a loud noise or continual uproar; shout. **2** demand or complain noisily. —*v.t.* utter or assert by making loud noise. Also, **clamour.** [< Latin < *clamare* cry out] —**clam′or er,** *n.*

clan (klan), *n.* **1** group of related families that claim to be descended from a common ancestor. **2** group of people closely joined together by some common interest. [< Scottish Gaelic *clann* offspring, family < Latin *plantam* sprout, plant] —**clan′like′,** *adj.*

clar i ty (klar′ə tē), *n.* clearness.

claus tro pho bi a (klô′strə fō′bē ə), *n.* an abnormal fear of enclosed spaces. [< Latin *claustrum* closed place + English *phobia*]

claus tro pho bic (klô′strə fō′bik), *adj.* of or having to do with claustrophobia.

cleat (klēt), *n.* strip of wood or iron fastened across anything for support or for sure footing.

cleave (klēv), *v.,* **cleft** or **cleaved** or **clove, cleft** or **cleaved** or **clo ven, cleav ing.** —*v.t.* **1** cut, divide, or split open. **2** pass through; pierce; penetrate: *The airplane cleft the clouds.* **3** make by cutting: *They cleft a path through the wilderness.* —*v.i.* **1** split, especially into layers. **2** pass; penetrate. [Old English *clēofan*] —**cleav′a ble,** *adj.*

clench (klench), *v.t.* **1** close tightly together: *clench one's fists.* **2** grasp firmly; grip tightly: *The farmer clenched the ax and took a mighty swing.* **3** clinch (a nail, staple, etc.). —*n.* **1** a firm grasp; tight grip. **2** clinch of a nail, staple, etc. [Old English *(be)clencan* hold fast] —**clench′er,** *n.*

co-, *prefix.* **1** with; together: *Coexist = exist together or with.* **2** joint: *Coauthor = joint author.* **3** equally: *Coextensive = equally extensive.* [< Latin, variant of *com-*]

cod dle (kod′l), *v.t.,* **-dled, -dling.** treat tenderly; pamper: *coddle sick children.*

com-, *prefix.* with; together; altogether: *Commingle = mingle with one another. Compress = press together.*

com mend (kə mend′), *v.t.* **1** speak well of; praise. **2** recommend. [< Latin *commendare* < *com-* + *mandare* commit, command]

com mo tion (kə mō′shən), *n.* **1** violent movement; agitation; turbulence: *the commotion of the storm.* **2** bustle or stir; confusion: *the commotion of the marketplace.*

com pe tent (kom′pə tənt), *adj.* **1** properly qualified; able; fit: *a competent bookkeeper, competent to decide.* **2** legally qualified: *Two competent witnesses testified.* —**com′pe tent ly,** *adv.*

com ple ment (*n.* kom′plə mənt; *v.* kom′plə ment), *n.* **1** something that completes or makes perfect. **2** number required to fill: *The ship now has its full complement of men, and no more can be taken on.* **3** word or group of words completing a predicate. In "The man is good," *good* is a complement. —*v.t.* supply a lack of any kind; complete. [< Latin *complementum* < *complere* to complete]

com ply (kəm plī′), *v.i.,* **-plied, -ply ing.** act in agreement with a request or command: *I will comply with the doctor's request.* [< Italian *complire* < Spanish *cumplir* < Latin *complere* fulfill, complete] —**com pli′er,** *n.*

com pul sor y (kəm pul′sər ē), *adj.* **1** compelled; required: *Attendance at school is compulsory for children.* **2** compelling; using force. —**com pul′sor i ly,** *adv.*

con-, *prefix.* form of **com-** before *n,* as in *connote,* and before consonants except *b, h, l, m, p, r, w,* as in *concern.*

con cert ed (kən sèr′tid), *adj.* **1** arranged by agreement; planned or made together; combined: *a concerted effort.* **2** (in music) arranged in parts for several voices or instruments. —**con cert′ed ly,** *adv.*

con de scend (kon′di send′), *v.i.* **1** come down willingly or graciously to the level of one's inferiors in rank: *The king condescended to eat with the peasants.* **2** grant a favor with a haughty or patronizing attitude. **3** stoop or lower oneself: *condescend to bribery.* [< Late Latin *condescendere* < Latin *com-* together + *descendere* descend]

con du cive (kən dü′siv, kən dyü′siv), *adj.* favorable; helpful: *Exercise is conducive to health.* —**con du′cive ness,** *n.*

con duct (kon′dukt), *n.* way of acting; behavior: *win a medal for good conduct.*

Con es to ga wagon (kon′ə stō′gə), a covered wagon with broad wheels, used especially by the American pioneers for traveling on soft ground or on the prairie. [< *Conestoga* Valley, Pennsylvania, where they were first built]

con fec tion er y (kən fek′shə ner′ē), *n., pl.* -er ies. **1** candies or sweets; confections. **2** business of making or selling confections. **3** place where confections, ice cream, cakes, etc., are made or sold.

con found (kon found′, kən found′), *v.t.* **1** confuse; mix up: *The shock confounded me.* **2** surprise and puzzle. [< Old French *confondre* < Latin *confundere* pour together, mix up, confuse] —**con found′er,** *n.*

con jure (kon′jər, kun′jər for *v.t.* 1-3, *v.i.;* kən jür′ for *v.t.* 4), *v.,* **-jured, -jur ing.** —*v.t.* **1** compel (a spirit, devil, etc.) to appear or disappear by a set form of words. **2** cause to appear or happen as if by magic: *conjure up a whole meal in a jiffy.* **3** cause to appear in the mind: *conjure a vision.* **4** make a solemn appeal to; request earnestly; entreat. —*v.i.* **1** summon a devil, spirit, etc. **2** practice magic. **3** perform tricks by skill and quickness in moving the hands. [< Old French *conjurer* < Latin *conjurare* make a compact < *com-* together + *jurare* swear]

con jur er or **con jur or** (kon′jər ər, kun′jər ər), *n.* **1** person who performs tricks with quick, deceiving movements of the hands; juggler. **2** magician.

con ning tower (kon′ing), tower on the deck of a submarine, used as an entrance and as a place for observation. [*conning,* present participle of obsolete *con* direct the steering of a ship < Old French *conduire* to conduct]

con so la tion (kon′sə lā′shən), *n.* **1** a consoling. **2** a being consoled. **3** a comforting person, thing, or event.

con sole (kən sōl′), *v.t.,* **-soled, -sol ing.** ease the grief or sorrow of; comfort: *I tried to console the lost child.* [< Middle French *consoler* < Latin *consolari* < *com-* + *solari* soothe] —**con sol′a ble,** *adj.*—**con sol′er,** *n.*

con sort (kon′sôrt), *n.* husband or wife. The husband of a queen is sometimes called the prince consort. [< Middle French < Latin *consortem* sharer < *com-* with + *sortem* lot]

con strict (kən strikt′), *v.t.* draw together; contract; compress: *A tourniquet stops the flow of blood by constricting the blood vessels.* [< Latin *constrictum* constricted < *com-* together + *stringere* pull tightly]

con tem pla tive (kon′təm plā′tiv, kən tem′plə tiv), *adj.* **1** deeply thoughtful; meditative. **2** devoted to religious meditation and prayer. —**con′tem pla′tive ly,** *adv.* —**con′tem pla′tive ness,** *n.*

con temp tu ous (kən temp′chü əs), *adj.* showing contempt; scornful: *a contemptuous look.* —**con temp′tu ous ly,** *adv.* —**con temp′tu ous ness,** *n.*

con tort (kən tôrt′), *v.t.* twist or bend out of shape; distort: *The clown contorted his face.* [< Latin *contortum* contorted < *com-* + *torquere* to twist]

con trail (kon′trāl), *n.* trail of water vapor left by an aircraft flying at a high altitude; vapor trail. [< *con(densation) trail*]

con verge (kən vèrj′), *v.,* **-verged, -verg ing.** —*v.i.* **1** tend to meet in a point: *The sides of a road seem to converge in the distance.* **2** turn toward each other: *If you look at the end of your nose, your eyes converge.* **3** come together; center: *The interest of all the students converged upon the celebration.* —*v.t.* cause to converge. [< Late Latin *convergere* < Latin *com-* together + *vergere* to incline]

con vic tion (kən vik′shən), *n.* 1 act of proving or declaring guilty. 2 condition of being proved or declared guilty. 3 act of convincing (a person). 4 a being convinced. 5 firm belief; certainty.

con vul sive (kən vul′siv), *adj.* 1 violently disturbing. 2 having convulsions. 3 producing convulsions. **—con vul′sive ly,** *adv.* **—con vul′sive ness,** *n.*

corps man (kôr′mən, kōr′mən), *n., pl.* **-men.** an enlisted man in the United States Navy or Army who performs medical duties or helps with the wounded.

cor re la tion (kôr′ə lā′shən, kor′ə-lā′shən), *n.* 1 the mutual relation of two or more things: *There is a close correlation between climate and crops.* 2 act or process of correlating. 3 condition of being correlated.

cor re spond ing (kôr′ə spon′ding, kor′ə-spon′ding), *adj.* 1 similar; matching. 2 in harmony; agreeing. **—cor′re spond′ing ly,** *adv.*

cot (kot), *n.* 1 a narrow, light bed. A cot is sometimes made of canvas stretched on a frame that folds together. 2 BRITISH. a child's crib. [< Hindustani *khāt*]

coup (kü), *n., pl.* **coups** (küz). 1 a sudden, brilliant action; unexpected, clever move; master stroke. 2 coup d'état. [< French, literally, a blow, stroke < Late Latin *colpus* < Greek *kolaphos*]

cow er (kou′ər), *v.i.* 1 crouch in fear or shame. 2 draw back tremblingly from another's threats, blows, etc. [apparently < Scandinavian (Old Icelandic) *kūra* doze, lie quiet]

crave (krāv), *v.t.,* **craved, crav ing.** 1 long for greatly; yearn for; desire strongly: *The thirsty man craved water.* 2 ask earnestly for; beg: *crave a favor, a problem craving solution.* [Old English *crafian* demand]

cre mate (krē′māt, kri māt′), *v.t.,* **-mat ed, -mat ing.** 1 burn (a dead body) to ashes instead of burying it. 2 burn. [< Latin *crematum* burned] **—cre′ma tor,** *n.*

Crete (krēt), *n.* Greek island in the Mediterranean, southeast of Greece. *Capital:* Canea. 483,000 pop.; 3200 sq. mi. **—Cret′an,** *adj., n.*

crim son (krim′zən), *n.* a deep red. **—***adj.* deep-red. **—***v.t., v.i.* make or become deep-red. [< Italian *cremesino* < *cremisi, chermisi* the color crimson < Arabic *qirmizī* < *qirmiz* kermes]

crys tal lize (kris′tl īz), *v.,* **-lized, -liz ing.** **—***v.i., v.t.* 1 form into crystals; solidify into crystals: *Water crystallizes to form snow.* 2 form into definite shape: *Our vague ideas crystallized into a clear plan.* 3 coat with sugar. **—crys′tal liz′a ble,** *adj.* **—crys′-tal li za′tion,** *n.*

cu bi cle (kyü′bə kəl), *n.* a very small room or compartment. [< Latin *cubiculum* bedroom < *cubare* to lie]

cudg el (kuj′əl), *n., v.,* **-eled, -el ing** or **-elled, -el ling.** **—***n.* 1 a short, thick stick used as a weapon; club. 2 **take up the cudgels for,** defend strongly. **—***v.t.* beat with a cudgel. [Old English *cycgel*]

cue (kyü), *n., v.,* **cued, cue ing** or **cu ing.** **—***n.* 1 action, speech, or word which gives the signal for an actor, singer, musician, etc., to enter or to begin. 2 hint or suggestion as to what to do or when to act: *Take your cue from me at the party about when it is time to leave.* 3 part one is to play; course of action. 4 frame of mind; mood. **—***v.t.* provide (a person) with a cue or hint. [perhaps a spelling for *q.,* abbreviation of Latin *quando* when (a word used in directions to actors)]

cu po la (kyü′pə lə), *n.* 1 a rounded roof; dome. 2 a small dome or tower on a roof. [< Italian < Late Latin *cupula,* diminutive of Latin *cupa* tub]

curb (kėrb), *v.t.* 1 hold in check; restrain: *My hunger was curbed by the snack.* 2 provide with a curb. [< Middle French *courbe* < Latin *curvus* bent, curved]

cur dle (kėr′dl), *v.t., v.i.,* **-dled, -dling.** 1 form into curds: *Milk curdles when kept too long.* 2 thicken.

curt (kėrt), *adj.* rudely brief; short; abrupt: *a curt way of talking.* [< Latin *curtus* cut short] **—curt′ly,** *adv.* **—curt′ness,** *n.*

curt sy (kėrt′sē), *n., pl.* **-sies,** *v.,* **-sied, -sy ing.** **—***n.* bow of respect or greeting by women and girls, made by bending the knees and lowering the body slightly. **—***v.i.* make a curtsy. [variant of *courtesy*]

cut a way (kut′ə wā′), *n.* man's coat for formal daytime wear with the lower part cut back in a curve or slope from the waist in front to the tails in back.

dark ling (därk′ling), *adv.* in the dark. **—***adj.* dark; dim; obscure.

da ta (dā′tə, dat′ə), *n.pl.* of **datum.** facts from which conclusions can be drawn; things known or admitted; information. [< Latin, plural of *datum* (thing) given.]

dec a dence (dek′ə dəns, di kād′ns), *n.* a falling off; growing worse; decline; decay: *The decadence of morals was one of the causes of the fall of Rome.* [< Middle French *décadence* < Medieval Latin *decadentia* < Latin *de-* + *cadere* to fall]

de cap i tate (di kap′ə tāt), *v.t.,* **-tat ed, -tat ing.** cut off the head of; behead. [< Late Latin *decapitatum* beheaded < Latin *de-* + *capitem* head] **—de cap′-i ta′tion,** *n.*

de ceit ful (di sēt′fəl), *adj.* 1 ready or willing to deceive. 2 meant to deceive; deceiving; misleading. **—de ceit′ful ly,** *adv.* **—de ceit′ful ness,** *n.*

de ceive (di sēv′), *v.,* **-ceived, -ceiv ing.** **—***v.t.* make (a person) believe as true something that is false; mislead. **—***v.i.* use deceit; lie. [< Old French *deceiv-* < Latin *decipere* ensnare, catch < *de-* + *capere* take] **—de ceiv′a ble,** *adj.* **—de ceiv′er,** *n.* **—de ceiv′ing ly,** *adv.*

de co rum (di kôr′əm, di kōr′əm), *n.* 1 proper behavior; good taste in conduct, speech, dress, etc.: *act with decorum, observe decorum at church.* 2 observance or requirement of polite society: *a meeting completely lacking in decorum.* [< Latin, (that which is) seemly < *decor* seemliness]

de cree (di krē′), *n., v.,* **-creed, -cree ing.** **—***n.* 1 something ordered or settled by authority; official decision. 2 a decision or order of a court or judge. 3 law of a church council, especially one settling a disputed point of doctrine. **—***v.t.* 1 order or settle by authority: *Fate decreed that Ulysses should travel long and far.* 2 decide; determine. **—***v.i.* decide; determine. [< Old French *decre* < Latin *decretum* < *de-* + *cernere* distinguish, separate]

de duc tive (di duk′tiv), *adj.* of or using deduction; reasoning by deduction. **—de-duc′tive ly,** *adv.*

de fi ant (di fī′ənt), *adj.* showing defiance; openly resisting. **—de fi′ant ly,** *adv.* **—de-fi′ant ness,** *n.*

deign (dān), *v.i.* think fit; condescend. **—***v.t.*

hat, āge, fär; let, ēqual, tėrm;
it, īce; hot, ōpen, ôrder;
oil, out; cup, pùt, rüle;
ch, child; ng, long; sh, she;
th, thin; ᴛʜ, then; zh, measure;

ə represents *a* in about, *e* in taken,
i in pencil, *o* in lemon, *u* in circus.

< = from, derived from, taken from.

condescend to give (an answer, a reply, etc.). [< Old French *deignier* < Latin *dignari* < *dignus* worthy]

dem i god (dem′i god′), *n.* a god who is partly human. Hercules was a demigod.

de par ture (di pär′chər), *n.* act of going away; leaving.

de plor a ble (di plôr′ə bəl, di plōr′ə bəl), *adj.* 1 that is to be deplored; regrettable; lamentable. 2 wretched; miserable. **—de-plor′a ble ness,** *n.* **—de plor′a bly,** *adv.*

de pose (di pōz′), *v.t.,* **-posed, -pos ing.** put out of office or a position of authority, especially a high one like that of king.

de prav i ty (di prav′ə tē), *n., pl.* **-ties.** 1 a being depraved; corruption. 2 a corrupt act; bad practice.

dep re cate (dep′rə kāt), *v.t.,* **-cat ed, -cat ing.** express strong disapproval of: *Lovers of peace deprecate war.* [< Latin *deprecatum* pleaded in excuse, averted by prayer < *de-* + *precari* pray] **—dep′re cat′ing ly,** *adv.*

de pre ci ate (di prē′shē āt), *v.t.,* **-at ed, -at ing.** speak slightingly of; belittle: *Some people depreciate the value of exercise.* [< Latin *depretiatum* lessened in price < *de-* + *pretium* price]

de ride (di rīd′), *v.t.,* **-rid ed, -rid ing.** make fun of; laugh at in scorn. [< Latin *deridere* < *de-* + *ridere* to laugh] **—de rid′er,** *n.* **—de rid′ing ly,** *adv.*

de sert (di zėrt′), *n.* Usually, **deserts,** *pl.* what one deserves; suitable reward or punishment: *The reckless driver got his just deserts when his driver's license was revoked.* [< Old French *deserte,* past participle of *deservir.*]

de spair (di sper′, di spar′), *n.* loss of hope; a being without hope; a feeling that nothing good can happen to one; helplessness.

de tached (di tacht′), *adj.* 1 separate from others; isolated; unattached: *a row of detached houses.* 2 impartial. 3 reserved; aloof. **—de tach′ed ly,** *adv.* **—de tach′-ed ness,** *n.*

de vour (di vour′), *v.t.* 1 eat (usually said of animals): *The lion devoured the zebra.* 2 eat like an animal; eat very hungrily: *The hungry boy devoured his dinner.* 3 consume, waste, or destroy: *The raging fire devoured the forest.* 4 swallow up; engulf. 5 take in with eyes or ears in a hungry, greedy way: *devour a new book.* 6 absorb wholly: *devoured by anxiety, devoured by curiosity.* [< Old French *devorer* < Latin *devorare* < *de-* down + *vorare* to gulp]

di ag no sis (dī′əg nō′sis), *n., pl.* **-ses** (-sēz′). 1 act or process of identifying a disease by careful investigation of its symptoms: *X rays and blood samples were used in the diagnosis.* 2 a careful study of the facts about something to find out its essential features, faults, etc. 3 decision reached after a careful study of symptoms or facts. [< Greek < *dia-* apart + *gignoskein* know]

dic ta tor (dik′tā tər, dik tā′tər), n. 1 person exercising absolute authority, especially a person who, without having any claim through inheritance or free popular election, seizes control of a government. 2 (in Roman history) an official given absolute authority over the state in times of emergency. 3 person who dictates.

dif fe ren ti ate (dif′ə ren/shē āt), **-at ed, -at ing.** —v.t. tell the difference in or between; find or show to be different: *The botanist differentiated varieties of plants.* —v.i. tell the difference.

dig it (dij′it), n. finger or toe. [< Latin *digitus* finger]

di late (dī lāt′, də lāt′), v., **-lat ed, -lat ing.** —v.t. make larger or wider: *When you take a deep breath, you dilate your nostrils.* —v.i. become larger or wider: *The pupil of the eye dilates when the light gets dim.* [< Latin *dilatare* < *dis-* apart + *latus* wide] —**di lat′a ble,** adj.

dil et tante (dil′ə tänt′, dil/ə tan/tē), n., pl. **-tantes, -tan ti** (-tän/tē, -tan/tē), adj. —n. 1 person who follows some art or science as a pastime or without serious aim or study; dabbler. 2 lover of the fine arts. —adj. of or like a dilettante. [< Italian < *dilettare* to delight < Latin *delectare* to charm.]

dil et tant ism (dil′ə tän/tiz/əm, dil/ə tan/tiz/əm), n. quality or practice of a dilettante.

dire (dīr), adj., **dir er, dir est.** causing great fear or suffering; dreadful. [< Latin *dirus*] —**dire′ly,** adv. —**dire′ness,** n.

dis-, *prefix.* 1 opposite of; lack of; not: *Dishonest = not honest; opposite of honest. Discomfort = lack of comfort.* 2 do the opposite of: *Disentangle = do the opposite of entangle.* 3 apart; away, as in *dispel.*

dis arm (dis ärm′), v.t. 1 take weapons away from: *A police-woman surprised the robbers and disarmed them.* 2 remove anger or suspicion from; make friendly: *The speaker's honesty disarmed the angry crowd.* —**dis arm′ing ly,** adv.

dis cern (də zėrn′, də sėrn′), v.t. see clearly; distinguish or recognize: *We discerned the island through the mist. I cannot discern the meaning of that paragraph.*

dis ci pli nar i an (dis′ə plə ner/ē ən), n. person who enforces discipline or who believes in strict discipline. —adj. disciplinary.

dis close (dis klōz′), v.t., **-closed, -clos ing.** 1 open to view; uncover. 2 make known; reveal: *This letter discloses a secret.* —**dis clos′er,** n.

dis con cert (dis′kən sėrt′), v.t. 1 disturb the self-possession of; embarrass greatly; confuse: *I was disconcerted by this unexpected opposition.* 2 upset or frustrate (plans, etc.). —**dis′con cert′ing ly,** adv.

dis con so late (dis kon′sə lit), adj. without hope; forlorn; unhappy: *disconsolate over the death of a friend.*

dis course (dis′kôrs, dis′kōrs), n. 1 a formal or extensive speech or writing: *Lectures and sermons are discourses.* 2 talk; conversation.

dis cre tion (dis kresh′ən), n. 1 quality of being discreet; great carefulness in speech or action; good judgment; wise caution: *Use your own discretion.* 2 freedom to decide or choose: *It is only within the captain's discretion to punish a sailor.*

dis cus (dis′kəs), n. a heavy, circular plate,

often of wood with a metal rim, thrown for distance in an athletic contest or as an exercise. [< Latin < Greek *diskos.* Doublet of DAIS, DESK, DISH, and DISK.]

dis dain (dis dān′), v.t. think unworthy of oneself or one's notice; regard or treat with contempt; scorn. —n. a disdaining; feeling of scorn.

di shev eled or **di shev elled** (də shev/əld), adj. 1 not neat; rumpled; mussed; untidy. 2 hanging loosely or in disorder: *disheveled hair.*

dis mount (dis mount′), v.i. 1 get off a horse, bicycle, etc. —v.t. 1 throw or bring down from a horse; unhorse. 2 take (a thing) from its setting or support: *The cannons were dismounted for shipping.* 3 take apart; take to pieces: *dismount a typewriter to fix the keys.*

dis pel (dis pel′), v.t., **-pelled, -pel ling.** drive away and scatter; disperse.

dis perse (dis pėrs′), v.i., **-persed, -pers ing.** spread in different directions; scatter: *The crowd dispersed when it began raining.* [< Latin *dispersum* dispersed < *dis-* apart + *spargere* to scatter]

dis pir it (dis pir′it), v.t. lower the spirits of; discourage; depress; dishearten. —**dis pir′it ed ly,** adv. —**dis pir′it ed ness,** n.

dis port (dis pôrt′, dis pōrt′), v.t., v.i. amuse or entertain (oneself); play; sport: *bears disporting themselves in the water.* [< Old French *desporter* < *des-* dis- + *porter* carry]

dis po si tion (dis′pə zish′ən), n. 1 one's habitual ways of acting toward others or of thinking about things; nature: *a cheerful disposition.* 2 tendency; inclination: *a disposition to argue.*

dis sect ed (di sek′tid, dī sek′tid), adj. cut into many lobes, as a leaf.

dis sen tient (di sen′shənt), adj. dissenting from the opinion of the majority. —n. person who dissents.

di van (dī′van, də van′), n. a long, low, soft couch or sofa. [< Turkish *divān* < Persian *dēvān*]

di ver sion (də vėr′zhən, dī vėr′zhən), n. 1 a turning aside; diverting: *a diversion of trade from one country to another.* 2 distraction from work, care, etc.; amusement; entertainment; pastime. 3 attack or feint intended to distract an opponent's attention from the point of main attack.

dog ged (dô′gid, dog′id), adj. not giving up; stubborn; persistent: *dogged determination.* [< *dog*] —**dog′ged ly,** adv. —**dog′ged ness,** n.

dog-grate (dôg′grāt), n. a metal frame or basket supported on andirons that is used for burning coal or wood in a fireplace.

dolt (dōlt), n. a dull, stupid person; blockhead. [apparently related to Old English *dol* dull]

-dom, *suffix forming nouns.* 1 (added to nouns) position, rank, or realm of a ____: *Kingdom = realm of a king.* 2 (added to adjectives) condition of being ____: *Freedom = condition of being free.* 3 (added to nouns) all those who are ____: *Heathendom = all those who are heathen.* [Old English *-dōm* state, rank < *dōm* law, judgment]

dote (dōt), v.i., **dot ed, dot ing. dote on** or **dote upon,** be foolishly fond of; be too fond of. [Middle English *doten*] —**dot′er,** n.

down y (dou′nē), adj., **down i er, down i est.** 1 made or consisting of soft feathers or hair. 2 covered with soft feathers or hair. 3 like down; soft and fluffy. —**down′i ness,** n.

draw (drä), n. gully; the dry bed of a stream.

drone (drōn), v., **droned, dron ing.** —v.i. 1 make a deep, continuous humming sound: *Bees droned among the flowers.* 2 talk in a dull, monotonous voice. —v.t. say in a dull, monotonous voice: *drone a prayer.* [Old English *drān*]

droop (drüp), v.i. 1 hang down; bend down. 2 become weak; lose strength and energy. 3 become discouraged or depressed; be sad and gloomy. —v.t. let hang down. —n. a drooping position. [< Scandinavian (Old Icelandic) *drūpa*] —**droop′ing ly,** adv.

drow sy (drou′zē), adj., **-si er, -si est.** 1 half asleep; sleepy. 2 making one sleepy. 3 caused by sleepiness. —**drow′si ly,** adv. —**drow′si ness,** n.

dum found (dum′found′), v.t. amaze and make unable to speak; bewilder; confuse. Also, **dumbfound.** [< *dumb* + *(con)found*]

dun geon (dun′jən), n. 1 a dark underground room or cell to keep prisoners in. 2 donjon. [< Old French *donjon*]

du plic i ty (dü plis′ə tē, dyü plis′ə tē), n., pl. **-ties.** a secretly acting in one way and openly acting in another in order to deceive; deceitfulness.

-eer, *suffix added to nouns to form nouns and verbs.* 1 person who directs or operates ____: *Auctioneer = person who directs an auction.* 2 person who produces ____: *Pamphleteer = person who produces pamphlets.* 3 be concerned or deal with, as in *electioneer.* [< French *-ier*]

eer ie or **eer y** (ir′ē), adj., **eer i er, eer i est.** causing fear because of strangeness or weirdness. —**eer′i ly,** adv. —**eer′i ness,** n.

ef fi cien cy (ə fish′ən sē), n., pl. **-cies.** 1 ability to produce the effect wanted without waste of time, energy, etc. 2 efficient operation: *Friction reduces the efficiency of a machine.*

el e gant (el′ə gənt), adj. having or showing good taste; gracefully and richly refined; beautifully luxurious: *The palace had elegant furnishings.* [< Old French < Latin *elegantem*] —**el′e gant ly,** adv.

el o quence (el′ə kwəns), n. 1 flow of speech that has grace and force. 2 power to win by speaking; the art of using language so as to stir the feelings.

el o quent (el′ə kwənt), adj. 1 having eloquence. 2 very expressive: *eloquent eyes.* [< Latin *eloquentem* speaking out < *ex-* out + *loqui* speak] —**el′o quent ly,** adv.

em-1, *prefix.* form of **en-1** before *b, p,* and sometimes *m,* as in *embark, employ.*

em-2, *prefix.* form of **en-2** before *b, m, p, ph,* as in *emblem, emphasis.*

em bank ment (em bangk′mənt), n. a raised bank of earth, stones, etc., used to hold back water, support a road, etc.

em bra sure (em brā′zhər), n. 1 an opening in a wall for a gun, with sides that spread outward to permit the gun to fire through a greater arc. 2 a slanting off of the wall at an oblique angle on the inner sides of a window or door. [< French]

e merge (i mėrj′), v.i., **e merged, e merg ing.** 1 come into view; come out; come up: *The sun emerged from behind a cloud.* 2 become known: *New facts emerged as a result of a second investigation.* [< Latin *emergere* < *ex-* out + *mergere* dip]

em phat ic (em fat′ik), adj. 1 said or done

with force or stress; strongly expressed: *Her answer was an emphatic "No!"* 2 speaking with force or stress; expressing oneself strongly: *The emphatic speaker often pounded the table and shouted.* 3 attracting attention; very noticeable; striking: *The club made an emphatic success of its party.* [< Greek *emphatikos* < *emphainein*.] —**em phat′i cal ly,** *adv.*

en-¹, *prefix.* 1 cause to be ____; make ____: *Enfeeble = make feeble.* 2 put in ____; put on ____: *Enthrone = put on a throne.* 3 other meanings, as in *enact, encourage, entwine.* The addition of *en-* rarely changes the meaning of a verb except to make it more emphatic. See also **em-¹.** [< Old French < Latin *in-*]

en-², *prefix.* in; on, as in *energy.* See also **em-².** [< Greek]

-ence, *suffix forming nouns chiefly from verbs.* 1 act or fact of ____ing: *Abhorrence = act or fact of abhorring.* 2 quality or condition of being ____ent: *Prudence = quality of being prudent. Absence = condition of being absent.* Also, **-ency.** [< Old French < Latin *-entia -ency*]

en dure (en dùr′, en dyùr′), *v.,* **-dured, -dur ing.** —*v.i.* continue in existence; keep on; last: *Metal and stone endure for a long time.* —*v.t.* 1 put up with; bear; stand. 2 submit to; tolerate. [< Old French *endurer* < Latin *indurare* make hard < *in-* + *durus* hard]

en fold (en fōld′), *v.t.* 1 fold in; wrap up: *enfold oneself in a blanket.* 2 embrace; clasp: *enfold a puppy in one's arms.* Also, **infold.** —**en fold′er,** *n.* —**en fold′ment,** *n.*

en sign (en′sən), *n.* a navy officer ranking next below a lieutenant, junior grade, and next above a warrant officer. An ensign is the lowest commissioned officer in the United States Navy.

en sue (en sü′), *v.i.,* **-sued, -su ing.** come after; follow. The ensuing year means the year following this. [< Old French *ensu-,* a form of *ensivre,* ultimately < Latin *in-* + *sequi* follow]

-ent, *suffix added to verbs.* 1 *(to form adjectives)* that ____s; ____ing: *Absorbent = that absorbs or absorbing.* 2 *(to form nouns)* one that ____s: *Correspondent = one that corresponds.* 3 *(to form adjectives)* other meanings, as in *competent, confident.* See also **-ant.** [< Latin *-entem*]

en thrall or **en thral** (en thrôl′), *v.t.,* **-thralled, -thrall ing.** hold captive by beauty or interest; fascinate; charm. —**en thrall′ment,** *n.*

en tice (en tīs′), *v.t.,* **-ticed, -tic ing.** attract by arousing hopes or desires; tempt. [< Old French *enticier* stir up, incite < *en-*in + Latin *titio* firebrand] —**en tice′ment,** *n.* —**en tic′ing ly,** *adv.*

en ti ty (en′tə tē), *n., pl.* **-ties.** something that has a real and separate existence either actually or in the mind. [< Medieval Latin *entitatem* < Latin *enti-,* a form of *ens* thing, being]

en trails (en′trālz, en′trəlz), *n.pl.* 1 the inner parts of the body of a man or animal. 2 the intestines; bowels. [< Old French *entrailles* < Medieval Latin *intralia,* alteration of Latin *interanea* things inside < *inter* within]

en vi a ble (en′vē ə bəl), *adj.* to be envied; worth having; desirable: *an enviable school record.* —**en′vi a ble ness,** *n.* —**en′vi a bly,** *adv.*

e phem er al (i fem′ər əl), *adj.* lasting for

only a very short time; very short-lived; transitory. [< Greek *ephēmeros* < *epi-* upon + *hēmera* day] —**e phem′er al ly,** *adv.*

-er¹, *suffix forming nouns.* 1 *(added to verbs)* person or thing that ____s: *Admirer = a person who admires. Burner = thing that burns.* 2 *(added to nouns)* person living in ____: *New Yorker = a person living in New York. Villager = a person living in a village.* 3 *(added to nouns)* person who makes or works with ____: *Hatter = a person who makes hats.* 4 person or thing that is or has ____: *Six-footer = a person who is six feet tall.* [Old English *-ere,* ultimately < Latin *-arium* -ary]

-er², *suffix forming nouns from other nouns.* person or thing connected with ____: *Officer = person connected with an office.* [< Old French < Latin *-arium*]

-er³, *suffix forming the comparative degree of adjectives and adverbs.* more: *Softer = more soft. Slower = more slow.* [Old English, *-or, -ra, -re*]

es cort (*n.* es′kôrt; *v.* e skôrt′), *n.* 1 one or a group going with another to give protection, show honor, etc.: *an escort of ten airplanes.* 2 man who goes on a date with a woman: *Her escort to the party was a tall young man.* 3 act of going with another as an escort. —*v.t.* go with as an escort: *Warships escorted the troopship.* [< Middle French *escorte* < Italian *scorta* < *scorgere* to guide < Latin *ex-* out + *corrigere* set right]

-ess, *suffix forming nouns from other nouns.* female ____: *Lioness = female lion.* [< Old French *-esse* < Latin *-issa* < Greek]

es sence (es′ns), *n.* that which makes a thing what it is; necessary part or parts; important feature or features: *Being thoughtful of others is the essence of politeness.*

es tab lish (e stab′lish), *v.t.* 1 set up on a firm or permanent basis: *establish a government, establish a business.* 2 settle in a position; set up in a business: *A new doctor has established himself on our street.* 3 cause to be accepted and used for a long time: *establish a custom.* 4 show beyond dispute; prove: *establish a fact, establish a claim.* [< Old French *establiss-,* a form of *establir* establish < Latin *stabilire* make stable < *stabilis* stable] —**es tab′lish er,** *n.*

es ti ma tion (es′tə mā′shən), *n.* 1 judgment or opinion: *In my estimation, your plan will not work.* 2 esteem; respect. 3 act or process of estimating.

e vade (i vād′), *v.t.,* **e vad ed, e vad ing.** 1 get away from by trickery; avoid by cleverness; elude: *The thief evaded his pursuers and escaped.* 2 elude or baffle (efforts, etc.). [< Latin *evadere* < *ex-* away + *vadere* go] —**e vad′a ble,** *adj.* —**e vad′er,** *n.*

e va sive (i vā′siv, i vā′ziv), *adj.* tending or trying to evade: *"Perhaps" is an evasive answer.* —**e va′sive ly,** *adv.* —**e va′sive ness,** *n.*

e voke (i vōk′), *v.t.,* **e voked, e vok ing.** call forth; bring out; elicit: *A good joke evokes a laugh.* [< Latin *evocare* < *ex-*out + *vocare* to call]

ex-¹, *prefix.* 1 former; formerly: *Ex-president = former president.* 2 out of; from; out: *Express = press out.* 3 thoroughly; utterly: *Exterminate = terminate (finish or destroy) thoroughly.* [< Latin < *ex* out of, without]

ex-², *prefix.* from; out of, as in *exodus.* Also, **ec-** before consonants. [< Greek]

ex cru ci at ing (ek skrü′shē ā′ting), *adj.* causing great suffering; very painful; torturing. —**ex cru′ci at′ing ly,** *adv.*

hat, āge, fär; let, ēqual, tèrm;
it, īce; hot, ōpen, ôrder;
oil, out; cup, pùt, rüle;
ch, child; ng, long; sh, she;
th, thin; ᴛʜ, then; zh, measure;

ə represents *a* in about, *e* in taken,
i in pencil, *o* in lemon, *u* in circus.

< = from, derived from, taken from.

ex hil a rate (eg zil′ə rāt′), *v.t.,* **-rat ed, -rat ing.** make merry or lively; put into high spirits; cheer: *The joy of the holiday season exhilarates us all.* [< Latin *exhilaratum* made merry < *ex-* thoroughly + *hilaris* merry]

ex ile (eg′zīl, ek′sīl), *v.,* **-iled, -il ing,** *n.* —*v.t.* 1 force (a person) to leave his country or home, often by law as a punishment; banish. 2 remove (oneself) from one's country or home for a long time. —*n.* 1 person who is exiled. 2 condition of being exiled; banishment. 3 any prolonged absence from one's own country. [< Old French *exilier* < Latin *exiliare* < *exilium* period or place of exile]

ex ot ic (eg zot′ik), *adj.* 1 from a foreign country; not native: *We saw many exotic plants at the flower show.* 2 fascinating or interesting because strange or different: *an exotic tropical island.* —*n.* an exotic person or thing. [< Greek *exōtikos* < *exō* outside < *ex* out of] —**ex ot′i cal ly,** *adv.*

ex plic it (ek splis′it), *adj.* clearly expressed; distinctly stated; definite: *He gave such explicit directions that everyone understood them.* [< Latin *explicitum* unfolded, explained < *ex-* out + *plicare* to fold] —**ex plic′it ly,** *adv.* —**ex plic′it ness,** *n.*

ex plo ra tion (ek′splə rā′shən), *n.* 1 a traveling in little-known lands or seas for the purpose of discovery. 2 a going over carefully; looking into closely; examining.

ex plor a to ry (ek splôr′ə tôr′ē, ek-splōr′ə tōr′ē), *adj.* of or having to do with exploration.

ex po nent (ek spō′nənt), *n.* 1 person or thing that explains, interprets, etc. 2 person or thing that stands as an example, type, or symbol of something. [< Latin *exponentem* putting forth, expounding < *ex-* forth + *ponere* put]

extra-, *prefix.* outside ____; beyond ____: *Extraordinary = outside the ordinary.* [< Latin < *extra* outside]

ex tract (ek strakt′), *v.t.* pull out or draw out, usually with some effort: *extract a tooth, extract iron from the earth.*

ex traor di nar y (ek strôr′də ner′ē; *esp.* for 2 ek′strə ôr′də ner′ē), *adj.* 1 beyond what is ordinary; very unusual or remarkable; exceptional: *Eight feet is an extraordinary height for a person.* 2 ranking below the regular class of officials; special. An *envoy extraordinary* is one sent on a special mission. —**ex traor′di nar′i ly,** *adv.*

ex trem i ty (ek strem′ə tē), *n., pl.* **-ties.** 1 the very end; farthest possible place; last part or point. 2 an extreme degree: *Joy is the extremity of happiness.*

ex ult ant (eg zult′nt), *adj.* rejoicing greatly; exulting; triumphant: *an exultant shout.* —**ex ult′ant ly,** *adv.*

ex ul ta tion (eg′zul tā′shən, ek′sul tā′shən), *n.* an exulting; great rejoicing; triumph.

fab ri cate (fab′rə kāt), *v.t.*, **-cat ed, -cat ing.** 1 make (anything that requires skill); build or manufacture. 2 make by fitting together standardized parts: *Automobiles are fabricated from parts made in different factories.* —**fab′ri ca′tor**, *n.*

fa cade or **fa çade** (fə säd′), *n.* 1 the front part of a building. 2 any side of a building that faces a street or an open space. [< French *facade*]

fal li ble (fal′ə bəl), *adj.* 1 liable to be deceived or mistaken; liable to err. 2 liable to be erroneous, inaccurate, or false: *Strong emotion can make human judgment fallible.* [< Medieval Latin *fallibilis* < Latin *fallere* deceive] —**fal′li bly**, *adv.*

fa nat ic (fə nat′ik), *n.* person who is carried away beyond reason by his feelings or beliefs, especially in religion or politics. —*adj.* unreasonably enthusiastic or zealous, especially in religion or politics. [< Latin *fanaticus* inspired by divinity < *fanum* temple]

fa nat i cal (fə nat′ə kəl), *adj.* fanatic. —**fa nat′i cal ly**, *adv.*

fas tid i ous (fa stid′ē əs), *adj.* hard to please; dainty in taste; easily disgusted. [< Latin *fastidiosus* < *fastidium* loathing] —**fas tid′i ous ly**, *adv.* —**fas tid′i ous ness**, *n.*

fa tal (fā′tl), *adj.* 1 causing death: *fatal accidents.* 2 causing destruction or ruin: *The loss of all our money was fatal to our plans.* 3 influencing fate. The three goddesses who controlled the fate of mankind were called the **fatal sisters.** [< Latin *fatalis* < *fatum.*] —**fa′tal ly**, *adv.*

fath om (faᴛʜ′əm), *n.*, *pl.* **fath oms** or **fath om,** *v.* —*n.* unit of measure equal to 6 feet, used mostly in measuring the depth of water and the length of ships' ropes, cables, etc. —*v.t.* 1 measure the depth of (water); sound. 2 get to the bottom of; understand fully. [Old English *fæthm* width of the outstretched arms]

fat u ous (fach′ü əs), *adj.* stupid but self-satisfied; foolish; silly. [< Latin *fatuus*] —**fat′u ous ly**, *adv.* —**fat′u ous ness**, *n.*

feign (fān), *v.t.* 1 put on a false appearance of; make believe; pretend: *Some animals feign death when in danger.* 2 make up to deceive; invent falsely: *feign an excuse.* —*v.i.* make oneself appear; pretend (to be): *He isn't sick; he is only feigning.* [< Old French *feign-,* a form of *feindre* feign < Latin *fingere* to format] —**feign′er**, *n.*

fe roc i ty (fə ros′ə tē), *n.*, *pl.* **-ties.** savage cruelty; fierceness.

fer vent (fėr′vənt), *adj.* 1 showing great warmth of feeling; very earnest; ardent: *fervent devotion.* 2 hot; glowing; intense. —**fer′vent ly**, *adv.*

fes tive (fes′tiv), *adj.* of or suitable for a feast, festival, or holiday; gay; merry; joyous: *A birthday or a wedding is a festive occasion.* —**fes′tive ly**, *adv.* —**fes′tive ness**, *n.*

fick le (fik′əl), *adj.* 1 likely to change or give up a loyalty, attachments, etc., without reason; inconstant: *a fickle friend.* 2 likely to change in nature; uncertain: *fickle weather.* [Old English *ficol* deceitful] —**fick′le ness**, *n.*

fiend (fēnd), *n.* an evil spirit; devil; demon. [Old English *fēond* enemy, hater] —**fiend′like′**, *adj.*

fiend ish (fēn′dish), *adj.* very cruel or wick-

ed; devilish: *fiendish tortures, a fiendish yell.* —**fiend′ish ly**, *adv.* —**fien.d′ish ness**, *n.*

fierce (firs), *adj.*, **fierc er, fierc est.** 1 savagely cruel and wild; ferocious: *a fierce lion.* 2 vehemently raging; violent: *a fierce wind, fierce anger.* 3 very eager or active; ardent: *a fierce determination to win.* [Old French *fers, fiers* < Latin *ferus* wild] —**fierce′ly**, *adv.* —**fierce′ness**, *n.*

fie ry (fī′rē, fī′ər ē), *adj.*, **fie ri er, fie ri est.** 1 consisting of fire; containing fire; burning; flaming. 2 like fire; very hot; glowing; flashing: *a fiery red, fiery heat.* 3 full of feeling or spirit; ardent: *a fiery speech.* 4 easily aroused or excited: *a fiery temper.* [Middle English < Old English *fyr* fire] —**fie′ri ly**, *adv.* —**fie′ri ness**, *n.*

fis sure (fish′ər), *n.,* a long, narrow opening; split; crack: *a fissure in a rock.*

flail (flāl), *n.* instrument for threshing grain by hand, consisting of a wooden handle at the end of which a stouter and shorter pole or club is fastened so as to swing freely. —*v.t.* 1 strike with a flail. 2 beat; thrash. [< Old French *flaiel* < Latin *flagellum* whip]

flat (flat), *n.* apartment. [alteration of Old English *flet, flett*]

flay (flā), *v.t.* 1 strip off the skin or outer covering of; skin. 2 scold severely; criticize without pity or mercy. [Old English *flēan*] —**flay′er**, *n.*

fledg ling or **fledge ling** (flej′ling), *n.* 1 a young bird that has just grown feathers needed for flying. 2 a young, inexperienced person.

flin ders (flin′dərz), *n.pl.* small pieces; fragments; splinters. [perhaps < Scandinavian (Norwegian) *flindra*]

flint lock (flint′lok′), *n.* 1 gunlock in which a flint striking against steel makes sparks that explode the gunpowder. Flintlocks were used on guns from the 1600's to the 1800's. 2 musket, rifle, or pistol with such a gunlock.

fluc tu ate (fluk′chü āt), *v.i.,* **-at ed, -at ing.** 1 rise and fall; change continually; vary irregularly; waver; vacillate: *The temperature fluctuates from day to day. His emotions fluctuated between hopefulness and despair.* 2 move in waves. [< Latin *fluctuatum* moving as a wave < *fluctus* wave < *fluere* to flow]

fon dle (fon′dl), *v.t.,* **-dled, -dling.** handle or treat lovingly; pet; caress. —**fon′dler**, *n.*

foot hill (fut′hil′), *n.* a low hill at the base of a mountain or mountain range.

fore stay (fôr′stā′, fōr′stā′), *n.* rope or cable reaching from the top of a ship's foremast to the bowsprit. The forestay helps to support the foremast.

forge (fôrj, fōrj), *n., v.,* **forged, forg ing.** —*n.* 1 an open fireplace or hearth with a bellows attached, used for heating metal very hot to be hammered into shape. 2 a blacksmith's shop; smithy. 3 place where wrought iron is made directly from the ore. —*v.t.* 1 shape (metal) by heating in a forge and then hammering. 2 make, shape, or form.

for mu late (fôr′myə lāt), *v.t.,* **-lat ed, -lat ing.** 1 state definitely or systematically: *A church may formulate its doctrines in a creed.* 2 express in a formula; reduce to a formula. —**for′mu la′tion**, *n.* —**for′mu la′tor**, *n.*

for tress (fôr′tris), *n.* a large, permanently fortified place or building; large fort or fortification. [< Old French *forteresse* < *fort* strong < Latin *fortis*]

foun der (foun′dər), *v.i.* 1 fill with water and sink: *The ship foundered in the storm.* 2 fall down; stumble: *His horse foundered.* 3 break down; fail. —*v.t.* 1 cause to fill with

water and sink. 2 cause (a horse) to break down, fall lame, etc. [< Old French *fondrer* < *fond* bottom < Latin *fundus*]

fowl er (fou′lər), *n.* person who hunts, shoots, catches, or traps wild birds.

fray¹ (frā), *v.t.* 1 cause to separate into threads; make ragged or worn along the edge. 2 wear away; rub. —*v.i.* become frayed; ravel out or wear through. [< Middle French *frayer* < Latin *fricare* to rub]

fray² (frā), *n.* a noisy quarrel; brawl. [variant of *affray*]

fren zied (fren′zēd), *adj.* greatly excited; frantic. —**fren′zied ly**, *adv.*

fresh et (fresh′it), *n.* 1 flood caused by heavy rains or melted snow. 2 stream or rush of fresh water flowing into the sea. [< *fresh* flood, stream, or pool of fresh water + *-et*]

froth (frôth, froth), *n.* 1 foam. 2 foaming saliva coming from the mouth, caused by disease, exertion, etc. 3 something light or trifling; trivial notions, talk, etc. —*v.i.* give out froth; foam. [Middle English *frothe* < Scandinavian (Old Icelandic) *frotha*]

frow zy (frou′zē), *adj.,* **-zi er, -zi est.** 1 dirty and untidy; slovenly. 2 smelling bad; musty. [origin uncertain] —**frow′zi ness**, *n.*

frus tra tion (fru strā′shən), *n.* 1 a frustrating. 2 a being frustrated.

fry¹ (frī), *v.,* **fried, fry ing,** *n., pl.* **fries.** —*v.t., v.i.* cook in hot fat in a deep or shallow pan, often over a flame: *fry potatoes. These fish are small and will soon fry.* —*n.* 1 dish of something fried; fried food. 2 an outdoor social gathering at which food, usually fish, is fried and eaten. [< Old French *frire* < Latin *frigere*]

fry² (frī), *n., pl.* **fry.** 1 the young of fish. 2 small adult fish living together in large groups or schools. 3 young creatures; offspring; children. [< Old French *frai* spawn]

fu gi tive (fyü′jə tiv), *n.* 1 person who is fleeing or who has fled from danger, an enemy, justice, etc. 2 exile; refugee. [< Latin *fugitivus* < *fugere* flee] —**fu′gi tive ly**, *adv.* —**fu′gi tive ness**, *n.*

-ful, *suffix* added to nouns to form adjectives or other nouns. 1 full of ____: *Cheerful = full of cheer.* 2 showing ____: *Careful = showing care.* 3 having a tendency to ____: *Harmful = having a tendency to harm.* 4 enough to fill a ____: *Cupful = enough to fill a cup.* 5 that can be of ____: *Useful = that can be of use.* 6 having the qualities of ____: *Masterful = having the qualities of a master.*

ful crum (ful′krəm), *n., pl.* **-crums, -cra** (-krə). support on which a lever turns or rests in moving or lifting something. [< Latin, bedpost < *fulcire* to support]

fun da men tal (fun′də men′tl), *adj.* 1 of or forming a foundation or basis; essential; basic: *Reading is a fundamental skill.* 2 in music: **a** having to do with the lowest note of a chord. **b** designating a chord of which the root is the lowest note. —*n.* 1 something fundamental; essential part: *the fundamentals of grammar.* 2 (in music) the lowest note of a chord. —**fun′da men′tal ly**, *adv.*

fur tive (fėr′tiv), *adj.* 1 done quickly and with stealth to avoid being noticed; secret: *a furtive glance into the forbidden room.* 2 sly; stealthy: *She had a furtive manner.* [< Latin *furtivus* < *furtum* theft < *fur* thief] —**fur′tive ly**, *adv.* —**fur′tive ness**, *n.*

fur y (fyùr′ē), *n., pl.* **fur ies.** 1 wild, fierce anger; rage. 2 violence; fierceness: *the fury of a battle.* 3 a raging or violent person. 4 **Fury** (in Greek and Roman myths) any one of the three Furies. [< Latin *furia*]

fu tile (fyü′tl, fyü′tīl), *adj.* 1 not successful; useless; ineffectual: *He fell down after making futile attempts to keep his balance.* 2 not important; trifling. [< Latin *futilis* pouring easily, worthless < *fundere* pour] —**fu′tile ly,** *adv.*

futures (fyü′chers), *n.pl.* commodities and stocks bought or sold to be received or delivered at a future date.

-fy, *suffix forming verbs chiefly from adjectives.* 1 make ____; cause to be ____: *Simplify = make simple.* 2 become ____: *Solidify = become solid.* [< Old French *-fier* < Latin *-ficare* < *facere* do, make]

gait (gāt), *n.* 1 the manner of walking or running: *He has a lame gait because of an injured foot.* 2 (of horses) any one of various manners of stepping or running, as the gallop, trot, pace, etc. [< Scandinavian (Old Icelandic) *gata* way]

gale (gāl), *n.* 1 a very strong wind. 2 (in meteorology) a wind having a velocity of 32 to 63 miles per hour.

gal ley (gal′ē), *n., pl.* **-leys.** kitchen of a ship or airplane.

ga lumph (gə lumf′), *v.i.* gallop in a clumsy way: *cows galumphing home.* [coined by Lewis Carroll < perhaps blend of *gallop* and *triumphant*]

gal va nize (gal′və nīz), *v.t.,* **-nized, -nizing.** cover (iron or steel) with a thin coating of zinc to prevent rust. [< Luigi *Galvani*] —**gal′va ni za′tion,** *n.* —**gal′va niz′er,** *n.*

gam bol (gam′bəl), *n.* a running and jumping about in play; caper; frolic. —*v.i.* run and jump about in play; frolic: *Lambs gamboled in the meadow.* [earlier *gambade* < Middle French < Italian *gambata* < *gamba* leg < Late Latin *camba* < Greek *kampē* a bend]

gan grene (gang′grēn′, gang grēn′), *n.,* **-grened, -gren ing.** death and decay of tissue when the blood supply of a part of a living person or animal is cut off by injury, infection, or freezing; mortification; necrosis.

gan gre nous (gang′grə nəs), *adj.* of or having gangrene; decaying.

gape (gāp, gap), *v.,* **gaped, gap ing,** *n.* —*v.i.* 1 open wide: *A deep hole in the earth gaped before us.* 2 open the mouth wide; yawn. 3 stare with the mouth open. —*n.* 1 a wide opening. 2 act of opening the mouth wide; yawning. 3 an open-mouthed stare. —**gap′er,** *n.* —**gap′ing ly,** *adv.*

gauge (gāj), **gauged, gaug ing.** —*v.t.* measure accurately; find out the exact measurement of with a gauge. 2 determine the capacity or content of (a cask, etc.). 3 estimate; judge. [< Old North French *gauger*] —**gauge′a ble,** *adj.*

gaunt (gônt, gänt), *adj.* 1 very thin and bony; with hollow eyes and a starved look: *Hunger and suffering had made him gaunt.* 2 looking bare and gloomy; desolate. [origin uncertain] —**gaunt′ly,** *adv.* —**gaunt′ness,** *n.*

ga zelle (gə zel′), *n., pl.* **-zelles** or **-zelle.** any of a genus of small, swift, graceful antelope of Africa and Asia, having soft, lustrous eyes. [< French < Arabic *ghazāl*] —**ga zelle′like′,** *adj.*

gen ial (jē′nyəl), *adj.* 1 smiling and pleasant; cheerful and friendly; kindly: *a genial welcome.* 2 helping growth; pleasantly warming; comforting: *a genial climate.* [< Latin *genialis,* literally, belonging to the genius < *genius*] —**gen′ial ly,** *adv.* —**gen′ial ness,** *n.*

ges ture (jes′chər), *n., v.,* **-tured, -tur ing.** —*n.* 1 movement of any part of the body, to help express an idea or a feeling: *People often make gestures with their hands or arms to stress something that they are saying.* 2 the use of such movements. 3 anything said or done to impress or influence others: *Her refusal was merely a gesture; she really wanted to go.* —*v.i.* make a gesture or gestures; use gestures. —*v.t.* express by a gesture or gestures. [< Medieval Latin *gestura* < Latin *gestus* gesture < *gerere* to bear]

gib ber ish (jib′ər ish, gib′ər ish), *n.* senseless chatter; confused, meaningless talk or writing.

gin ger (jin′jər), *n.* 1 spice made from the root of a tropical plant, used for flavoring and in medicine. 2 the root, often preserved in syrup or candied. 3 the plant. 4 INFORMAL. liveliness; energy. 5 a light reddish or brownish yellow. —*adj.* light reddish- or brownish-yellow.

glimpse (glimps), *n., v.,* **glimpsed, glimpsing.** —*n.* 1 a short, quick view: *I caught a glimpse of the falls as our train went by.* 2 a short, faint appearance: *There were glimpses of truth in what he said.* —*v.t.* catch a short, quick view of. —*v.i.* look quickly; glance. [Middle English *glimsen.* Related to GLIMMER.]

glow er (glou′ər), *v.i.* stare angrily; scowl fiercely: *The rivals glowered at each other.* —*n.* an angry stare; fierce scowl. [Middle English *gloren*] —**glow′er ing ly,** *adv.*

glut (glut), *v.,* **glut ted, glut ting,** *n.* —*v.t.* fill full; feed or satisfy fully: *A year of working in a candy factory glutted my appetite for sweets.* —*n.* 1 a full supply; great quantity. 2 too great a supply. [probably < obsolete *glut,* noun, glutton < Old French]

glut ton (glut′n), *n.* 1 a greedy eater; person who eats too much. 2 person who never seems to have enough of something: *a glutton for punishment.* [< Old French *glouton* < Latin *gluttonem*]

glut ton ous (glut′n əs), *adj.* 1 greedy about food; having the habit of eating too much. 2 greedy. —**glut′ton ous ly,** *adv.* —**glut′ton ous ness,** *n.*

gnarled (närld), *adj.* containing gnarls; knotted; twisted: *The farmer's gnarled hands grasped the plow firmly.* [variant of *knurled*]

gnat (nat), *n.* any of various small, two-winged flies. Most gnats are bloodsucking and give bites that itch. [Old English *gnætt*]

gouge (gouj), *n., v.,* **gouged, goug ing.** —*n.* 1 chisel with a curved, hollow blade, used for cutting round grooves or holes in wood. 2 groove or hole made by gouging. —*v.t.* 1 cut with a gouge. 2 dig out; tear out; force out.

grif fin or **grif fon** (grif′ən), *n.* a mythical creature with the head, wings, and forelegs of an eagle, and the body, hind legs, and tail of a lion. Also, **gryphon.** [< Old French *grifon* < Popular Latin *gryphonem* < Latin *gryphus, gryps* < Greek]

grille (gril), *n.* an openwork, metal structure or screen, used as a gate, door, window, or to cover the opening in front of the radiator of an automobile; grating. [< French]

gri mace (grə mās′, grim′is), *n., v.,* **-maced, -mac ing.** —*n.* a twisting of the face; ugly or funny smile: *a grimace caused by pain.* —*v.i.* make grimaces. [< Middle French] —**gri mac′er,** *n.*

gris tle (gris′əl), *n.* cartilage, especially when found in meat. [Old English]

gris tly (gris′lē), *adj.,* **-tli er, -tli est.** of,

hat, āge, fär; let, ēqual, tėrm;
it, īce; hot, ōpen, ôrder;
oil, out; cup, pút, rüle;
ch, child; ng, long; sh, she;
th, thin; ᴛʜ, then; zh, measure;

ə represents *a* in about, *e* in taken,
i in pencil, *o* in lemon, *u* in circus.

< = from, derived from, taken from.

containing, or like gristle; cartilaginous. —**gris′tli ness,** *n.*

grits (grits), *n.pl.* 1 corn, oats, wheat, etc., husked and coarsely ground. Grits are eaten boiled. 2 U.S. coarsely ground corn or hominy cooked as a cereal.

grope (grōp), *v.,* **groped, grop ing.** —*v.i.* 1 feel about with the hands: *I groped for a flashlight when the lights went out.* 2 search blindly and uncertainly: *The detectives groped for some clue to the mysterious crime.* —*v.t.* find by feeling about with the hands; feel (one's way) slowly: *The blind man groped his way to the door.* [Old English *grāpian*] —**grop′ing ly,** *adv.*

grot to (grot′ō), *n., pl.* **-toes** or **-tos.** 1 cave or cavern. 2 an artificial cave made for coolness and pleasure. [< Italian *grotto, grotta* < Latin *crypta* < Greek *krypte* vault. Doublet of CRYPT.]

grove (grōv), *n.* group of trees standing together. An orange grove is an orchard of orange trees. [Old English *grāf*]

gru el ing or **gru el ling** (grü′ə ling), *adj.* very tiring; exhausting: *The marathon is a grueling contest.* —*n.* an exhausting or very tiring experience.

gryph on (grif′ən), *n.* griffin.

guard ed (gär′did), *adj.* 1 kept safe; carefully watched over; defended; protected. 2 careful; cautious: *"Maybe" was his guarded answer to my question.* —**guard′ed ly,** *adv.* —**guard′ed ness,** *n.*

guild (gild), *n.* 1 association or society formed by people having the same interests, work, etc., for some useful or common purpose: *the hospital guild of a church.* 2 (in the Middle Ages) an association of merchants in a town or of persons in a particular trade or craft, formed to keep standards high, promote their business interests, protect themselves, etc. [< Scandinavian (Old Icelandic) *gildi*]

gut tur al (gut′ər əl), *adj.* 1 of the throat. 2 formed in the throat; harsh: *The visitor from Bulgaria spoke in a deep, guttural voice.* 3 formed between the back of the tongue and the soft palate. The *g* in *go* is a guttural sound. [< Latin *guttur* throat] —**gut′tur al ly,** *adv.* —**gut′tur al ness,** *n.*

ha bit u al (hə bich′ü əl), *adj.* 1 done by habit; caused by habit: *a habitual smile, habitual courtesy.* 2 being or doing something by habit; regular; steady: *a habitual reader.* 3 often done, seen, used, occurring, etc.; usual; customary: *a habitual sight.* —**ha bit′u al ly,** *adv.* —**ha bit′u al ness,** *n.*

hand i cap (han′dē kap′), *n., v.,* **-capped, -cap ping.** —*n.* 1 something that puts a person at a disadvantage; hindrance: *A sore throat was a handicap to the singer.* 2 race, contest, game, etc., in which the poorer contestants are given certain advantages and the better ones are given certain disadvantages, so that all have an equal chance to win. 3 the disadvantage or advantage given in such a race, contest, game, etc.: *A runner with a 5-yard handicap in a 100-yard race has to run either 105 yards or 95 yards.* —*v.t.* 1 put at a disadvantage; hinder: *A lame arm handicapped our pitcher.* 2 give a handicap to. [< *hand in cap;* apparently with reference to an old wagering game] —**hand′i cap′per,** *n.*

har mo nize (här′mə nīz), *v.,* -**nized,** -**nizing.** —*v.t.* bring into harmony, accord, or agreement; make harmonious. —*v.i.* be in harmony or agreement. —**har′mo niza′tion,** *n.* —**har′mo niz′er,** *n.*

har ry (har′ē), *v.,* -**ried,** -**ry ing.** —*v.t.* 1 raid and rob with violence; lay waste; pillage. 2 keep troubling; worry; torment. —*v.i.* make predatory raids. [Old English *hergian* < *here* army]

hatch way (hach′wā′), *n.* hatch of a ship, building, etc.

haugh ty (hô′tē), *adj.,* -**ti er,** -**ti est.** too proud and scornful of others: *a haughty glance, haughty words.* [Middle English *haute* < Middle French *haut* < Latin *altus* high] —**haugh′ti ly,** *adv.* —**haugh′ti ness,** *n.*

haunch (hônch, hänch), *n.* 1 hip. 2 **haunches,** *pl.* the hindquarters of an animal: *The dog sat on his haunches.* [< Old French *hanche*]

ha zy (hā′zē), *adj.,* -**zi er,** -**zi est.** 1 full of haze; misty; smoky: *a hazy sky.* 2 slightly confused; vague; obscure: *a hazy idea.* —**ha′zi ly,** *adv.* —**ha′zi ness,** *n.*

head wind, *n.* wind blowing from the direction in which a ship, etc., is moving.

hear say (hir′sā′), *n.* common talk; gossip or rumor.

hearth (härth), *n.* 1 stone or brick floor of a fireplace, often extending into the room. 2 fireside; home: *The travelers began to long for their own hearths.*

heat (hēt), *n.* section of a race, consisting of a complete running of the course: *He won the first heat, but lost the final race.*

heed (hēd), *v.t.* give careful attention to; take notice of; mind: *Now heed what I say.* —*v.i.* pay careful attention; take notice. —*n.* careful attention; regard: *He paid no heed to their advice.* [Old English *hēdan*] —**heed′er,** *n.*

heft (heft), INFORMAL. *v.t.* 1 lift; heave. 2 judge the weight of by lifting. [< *heave;* patterned on *weft* < *weave*]

heir loom (er′lüm′, ar′lüm′), *n.* any piece of personal property that has been handed down from generation to generation: *This clock is a family heirloom.* [< *heir* + *loom,* originally, implement]

helm (helm), *n.* 1 handle or wheel by which a ship is steered. 2 the steering apparatus of a ship, including the wheel, rudder, and connecting parts. 3 position of control or guidance: *Upon the President's death, the Vice-President took the nation's helm.* —*v.t.* guide with a helm; steer. [Old English *helma*]

herb (erb, herb), *n.* 1 plant whose leaves or stems are used for medicine, seasoning, food, or perfume. Sage, mint, and lavender are herbs. 2 a flowering plant whose stem above ground usually does not become woody as that of a tree or shrub does. Herbs can be annual, such as corn, biennial, such as the onion, but most are perennial, such as the

rose. [< Latin *herba*] —**herb′like′,** *adj.*

hoard (hôrd, hōrd), *v.t., v.i.* save and store away (money, goods, etc.) for preservation or future use: *A squirrel hoards nuts for the winter.* —*n.* what is saved and stored away for preservation or future use; things stored. [Old English *hordian*] —**hoard′er,** *n.*

hoist (hoist), *v.t.* raise on high; lift up, often with ropes and pulleys: *hoist a flag, hoist sails.*

hos pi ta ble (hos′pi tə bəl, ho spit′ə bəl), *adj.* 1 giving or liking to give a welcome, food and shelter, and friendly treatment to guests or strangers: *a hospitable family.* 2 with the mind open or receptive: *a person hospitable to new ideas.* [< Middle French < Latin *hospitari* stay as a guest < *hospitem* guest] —**hos′pi ta bly,** *adv.*

hos tile (hos′tl; *sometimes* hos′tīl), *adj.* 1 of an enemy or enemies: *the hostile army.* 2 opposed; unfriendly; unfavorable. —*n.* a hostile person; enemy. [< Latin *hostilis* < *hostis* enemy] —**hos′tile ly,** *adv.*

hov er (huv′ər, hov′ər), *v.i.* 1 hang fluttering or suspended in air: *The two birds hovered over their nest.* 2 stay in or near one place; wait nearby: *The dogs hovered around the kitchen door at mealtime.* [Middle English *hoveren*] —**hov′er er,** *n.*

hulk ing (hul′king), *adj.* big and clumsy.

hull (hul), *n.* 1. body or frame of a ship. Masts, sails, and rigging are not part of the hull.

hu mane (hyü mān′), *adj.* 1 not cruel or brutal; kind; merciful. 2 tending to humanize and refine: *humane studies.* [variant of *human*] —**hu mane′ly,** *adv.* —**hu mane′ness,** *n.*

hu mil i ate (hyü mil′ē āt), *v.t.,* -**at ed,** -**at ing.** lower the pride, dignity, or self-respect of; make ashamed: *Do not humiliate him by referring to his failures.* [< Latin *humiliare* < *humilis* low] —**hu mil′i at′ing ly,** *adv.*

hunk er (hung′kər), *v.i.* squat on one's haunches, or with the haunches brought near the heels: *hunker down in front of the TV.* —*n.* **on one's hunkers,** in a squatting position; on one's haunches. [origin uncertain]

hypodermic syringe, *n.* syringe fitted with a hollow needle, used to inject a dose of medicine under the skin.

-ial, *suffix.* a form of **-al¹,** as in *adverbial, facial.*

-ian, *suffix.* a form of **-an,** as in *mammalian, Italian.* [< Latin *-ianus*]

-ible, *suffix* added to verbs to form adjectives. that can be ___ed: *Reducible = that can be reduced.* [< Old French < Latin *-ibilis*]

-ic, *suffix* added to nouns to form adjectives. 1 of or having to do with: *Atmospheric = of the atmosphere.* 2 having the nature of: *Heroic = having the nature of a hero.* 3 constituting or being: *Bombastic = constituting bombast.* 4 containing; made up of: *Alcoholic = containing alcohol.* 5 made by; caused by: *Volcanic = made by a volcano.* 6 like; like that of; characteristic of: *Meteoric = like a meteor.* [< French *-ique* or Latin *-icus* or Greek *-ikos*]

-ical, *suffix.* 1 *-ic,* as in *geometrical, parasitical, hysterical.* 2 *-ic* + *-al* or *-ics* + *-al,* as in *critical, musical, ethical, statistical.*

id i o syn cra sy (id′ē ō sing′krə sē), *n., pl.* -**sies.** 1 a personal peculiarity of taste, behavior, opinion, etc. 2 (in medicine) a constitutional peculiarity that causes an unusual reaction to a drug, treatment, etc. [< Greek

idiosynkrasia < *idios* one's own + *synkrasis* temperament]

il-¹, *prefix.* the form of **in-¹** before *l,* as in *illegal, illegible,* etc.

il-², *prefix.* the form of **in-²** before *l,* as in *illuminate.*

il log i cal (i loj′ə kəl), *adj.* 1 contrary to the principles of sound reasoning; not logical. 2 not reasonable; foolish: *an illogical fear.* —**il log′i cal ly,** *adv.* —**il log′i cal ness,** *n.*

im-¹, *prefix.* the form of **in-¹** before *b, m, p,* as in *imbalance, immoral, impatient.*

im-², *prefix.* the form of **in-²** before *b, m, p,* as in *imbibe, immure, impart.*

im mac u late (i mak′yə lit), *adj.* 1 without a spot or stain; absolutely clean. 2 without fault or errors. 3 without sin; pure. [< Latin *immaculatus* < *in-* not + *macula* spot] —**im mac′u late ly,** *adv.* —**im mac′u late ness,** *n.*

im mense ly (i mens′lē), *adv.* INFORMAL. very greatly; hugely.

im mor tal (i môr′tl), *adj.* 1 living forever; never dying; everlasting. 2 of or having to do with immortal beings or immortality; divine. 3 remembered or famous forever. —*n.* 1 an immortal being. 2 **immortals,** *pl.* the gods of ancient Greece and Rome. 3 person remembered or famous forever. —**im mor′tal ly,** *adv.*

im mor tal i ty (im′ôr tal′ə tē), *n.* 1 life without death; a living forever. 2 fame that lasts forever.

im per il (im per′əl), *v.t.,* -**iled,** -**il ing** or -**illed,** -**il ling.** put in danger; endanger; jeopardize.

im per i ous (im pir′ē əs), *adj.* 1 haughty or arrogant; domineering; overbearing. 2 not to be avoided; necessary; urgent. —**im per′i ous ly,** *adv.* —**im per′i ous ness,** *n.*

im per son al (im pėr′sə nəl), *adj.* 1 not referring to any one person in particular; not personal: *impersonal criticism. History is usually written from an impersonal point of view.* 2 having no existence as a person: *Electricity is an impersonal force.* —**im per′son al ly,** *adv.*

im pet u ous (im pech′ü əs), *adj.* 1 acting or done with sudden or rash energy; hasty: *Children are more impetuous than adults.* 2 rushing with force and violence: *The dam broke and an impetuous torrent of water swept away the town.* —**im pet′u ous ly,** *adv.* —**im pet′u ous ness,** *n.*

im pli ca tion (im′plə kā′shən), *n.* 1 an implying. 2 a being implied. 3 something implied; indirect suggestion; hint: *There was no implication of dishonesty in his failure in business.* 4 an implicating. 5 a being implicated.

im plic it ly (im plis′it lē), *adv.* 1 unquestioningly. 2 by implication.

im ply (im plī′), *v.t.,* -**plied,** -**ply ing.** 1 mean without saying so; express indirectly; suggest: *Her smile implied that she had forgiven us.* 2 involve as a necessary part or condition: *Speech implies a speaker.* 3 signify; mean. [< Old French *emplier* involve, put (in) < Latin *implicare* < *in-* in + *plicare* to fold. Doublet of EMPLOY, IMPLICATE.]

im preg na ble (im preg′nə bəl), *adj.* able to resist attack; not yielding to force, persuasion, etc.: *an impregnable fortress, an impregnable argument.* —**im preg′na bly,** *adv.*

im pro vise (im′prə vīz), *v.,* -**vised,** -**vising.** —*v.t.* provide offhand; make for the occasion: *The stranded motorists improvised* a tent out of two blankets and some long poles. —*v.i.* compose, utter, or do anything without preparation or on the spur of the moment. [< French *improviser*, ultimately < Latin *in-* not + *pro-* beforehand + *videre* see] —**im/pro vis/er,** *n.*

im pulse (im/puls), *n.* **1** a sudden, driving force or influence; thrust; push: *the impulse of a wave, the impulse of hunger, the impulse of curiosity.* **2** the effect of a sudden, driving force or influence. **3** a sudden inclination or tendency to act: *The angry crowd was influenced more by impulse than by reason.* [< Latin *impulsus* < *impellere*]

in-¹, *prefix.* not; the opposite of; the absence of: *Inexpensive = not expensive. Inattention = the absence of attention.* See also **i-, il-, im-,** and **ir-.** [< Latin]

in-², *prefix.* in; into; on; upon: *Incase = (put) into a case. Intrust = (give) in trust.* See also **il-, im-, ir-.** [< Latin < *in,* preposition]

in-³, *prefix.* in; within; into; toward: *Indoors = within doors. Inland = toward land.* [Old English]

in ar tic u late (in/är tik/yə lit), *adj.* **1** not uttered in distinct syllables or words: *an inarticulate mutter.* **2** unable to speak in words; dumb: *Cats and dogs are inarticulate.* **3** unable to put one's thoughts or feelings into words easily and clearly. —**in/ar tic/u late ly,** *adv.* —**in/ar tic/u late ness,** *n.*

in cense (in sens/), *v.t.,* **-censed, -cens ing.** make very angry; fill with rage. [< Latin *incensum* inflamed, enraged, set on fire < *in-* (intensive) + *candere* glow white]

in cen tive (in sen/tiv), *n.* thing that urges a person on; cause of action or effort; motive; stimulus. —*adj.* inciting; encouraging. [< Latin *incentivum* < *incinere* cause to sound < *in-* on + *canere* sing]

in cip i ent (in sip/ē ənt), *adj.* just beginning; in an early stage; commencing. [< Latin *incipientem* < *in-* on + *capere* take] —**in cip/i ent ly,** *adv.*

in ci sion (in sizh/ən), *n.* **1** cut made in something; gash: *The doctor made a tiny incision to take out the splinter in my hand.* **2** act of incising. **3** incisive quality.

in ci sive (in sī/siv), *adj.* **1** sharp or keen; penetrating; acute: *incisive criticism.* **2** incising; cutting. —**in ci/sive ly,** *adv.* —**in ci/sive ness,** *n.*

in cor po rate (*v.* in kôr/pə rāt/; *adj.* in kôr/pər it), *v.,* **-rat ed, -rat ing,** *adj.* —*v.t.* **1** make (something) a part of something else; join or combine (something) with something else: *We will incorporate your suggestion in this new plan.* **2** make into a corporation: *When the business became large, the owners incorporated it.* —*v.i.* **1** form a corporation. **2** unite or combine so as to form one body; merge. —*adj.* united; combined; incorporated. [< Latin *incorporatum* formed into a body < *in-* into + *corpus* body]

in cred u lous (in krej/ə ləs), *adj.* **1** not ready to believe; doubting; skeptical: *If they look incredulous show them the evidence.* **2** showing a lack of belief: *an incredulous smile.* —**in cred/u lous ly,** *adv.*

in cur a ble (in kyùr/ə bəl), *adj.* not capable of being cured or healed: *an incurable invalid.* —*n.* person having an incurable disease. —**in cur/a ble ness,** *n.* —**in cur/a bly,** *adv.*

in cur i ous (in kyùr/ē əs), *adj.* lacking curiosity; uninquiring; indifferent. —**in cur/i ous ly,** *adv.*

in dis tinct (in/dis tingkt), *adj.* not distinct; not clear to the eye, ear, or mind; confused: *an indistinct voice. He had an indistinct*

memory of the accident. —**in/dis tinct/ly,** *adv.* —**in/dis tinct/ness,** *n.*

in dom i ta ble (in dom/ə tə bəl), *adj.* that cannot be conquered; unyielding. [< Late Latin *indomitabilis* < Latin *indomitus* untamed < *in-* not + *domare* to tame] —**in dom/i ta bly,** *adv.*

in doors (in/dôrz/, in/dōrz/), *adv.* in or into a house or building: *Go indoors.*

in ef fec tu al (in/ə fek/chü əl), *adj.* **1** without effect; useless. **2** not able to produce the effect wanted; powerless. —**in/ef fec/tu al ly,** *adv.* —**in/ef fec/tu al ness,** *n.*

in e luc ta ble (in/i luk/tə bəl), *adj.* that cannot be escaped or avoided; inevitable. [< Latin *ineluctabilis* < *in-* not + *eluctari* to escape] —**in/e luc/ta bly,** *adv.*

in ert (in ėrt/), *adj.* **1** having no power to move or act; lifeless: *A stone is an inert mass of matter.* **2** inactive; slow; sluggish. [< Latin *inertem* idle, unskilled < *in-* without + *artem* art, skill] —**in ert/ly,** *adv.* —**in ert/ness,** *n.*

in ev i ta ble (in ev/ə tə bəl), *adj.* not to be avoided; sure to happen; certain to come: *Death is inevitable.* [< Latin *inevitabilis* < *in-* not + *evitare* avoid < *ex-* out + *vitare* shun] —**in ev/i ta ble ness,** *n.* —**in ev/i ta bly,** *adv.*

in ex pert (in/ik spėrt/, in ek/spėrt/), *adj.* not expert; unskilled. —**in/ex pert/ly,** *adv.* —**in/ex pert/ness,** *n.*

in ex pli ca ble (in/ik splik/ə bəl, in ek/splə kə bəl), *adj.* that cannot be explained, understood, or accounted for; mysterious. —**in/ex plic/a ble ness,** *n.* —**in/ex plic/a bly,** *adv.*

in flec tion (in flek/shən), *n.* **1** a change in the tone or pitch of the voice: *We usually end questions with a rising inflection.* **2** variation in the form of a word to show case, number, gender, person, tense, mood, voice, or comparison.

in fringe (in frinj/), *v.,* **-fringed, -fring ing.** —*v.t.* act contrary to or violate (a law, obligation, right, etc.); transgress: *A confusing label may infringe the food and drug law.* —*v.i.* go beyond the proper or usual limits; trespass; encroach: *infringe upon the rights of another.* [< Latin *infringere* < *in-* in + *frangere* to break] —**in fringe/ment,** *n.* —**in fring/er,** *n.*

in her ent (in hir/ənt, in her/ənt), *adj.* belonging to a person or thing as a permanent and essential quality or attribute; intrinsic: *inherent honesty, the inherent sweetness of sugar.* —**in her/ent ly,** *adv.*

in hos pi ta ble (in/hos pit/ə bəl, in hos/pi tə bəl), *adj.* **1** not hospitable; not making visitors comfortable. **2** providing no shelter; barren: *The Pilgrims landed on a rocky, inhospitable shore.* —**in hos pit/a ble ness,** *n.* —**in/hos pit/a bly,** *adv.*

in laid (in/lād/), *adj.* **1** set in the surface as a decoration or design: *The top of the desk had an inlaid design of light wood in dark.* **2** decorated with a design or material set in the surface: *The box had an inlaid cover.* —*v.* pt. and pp. of **inlay.**

in nu mer a ble (i nü/mər ə bəl, i nyü/mər ə bəl), *adj.* too many to count; very many; countless. —**in nu/mer a ble ness,** *n.* —**in nu/mer a bly,** *adv.*

in quis i tive (in kwiz/ə tiv), *adj.* **1** asking many questions; curious. **2** prying into other people's affairs; too curious. —**in quis/i tive ly,** *adv.* —**in quis/i tive ness,** *n.*

in sa tia ble (in sā/shə bəl), *adj.* that cannot be satisfied; extremely greedy: *an insatiable*

hat, āge, fär; let, ēqual, tėrm;
it, īce; hot, ōpen, ôrder;
oil, out; cup, pùt, rüle;
ch, child; ng, long; sh, she;
th, thin; ᴛʜ, then; zh, measure;

ə represents *a* in about, *e* in taken,
i in pencil, *o* in lemon, *u* in circus.

< = from, derived from, taken from.

appetite. —**in sa/tia ble ness,** *n.* —**in sa/tia bly,** *adv.*

in se cure (in/si kyùr/), *adj.* **1** exposed to danger, loss, attack, etc.; not secure; unsafe: *a region where life is insecure.* **2** lacking confidence; not sure of oneself; fearful; timid: *an insecure person.* —**in/se cure/ly,** *adv.* —**in/se cure/ness,** *n.*

in sert (*v.* in sėrt/; *n.* in/sėrt/), *v.t.* put in; set in; introduce: *insert a key into a lock.* —*n.* something inserted: *The newspaper had an insert of several pages of pictures.* [< Latin *insertum* put or joined in < *in-* in + *serere* join, entwine] —**in sert/er,** *n.*

in sig nif i cant (in/sig nif/ə kənt), *adj.* **1** of no consequence, influence, or distinction: *an insignificant position, an insignificant person.* **2** too small to be important; unimportant; trivial; petty: *an insignificant detail, an insignificant amount of money.* **3** having little or no meaning; meaningless: *an insignificant gesture.* —**in/sig nif/i cant ly,** *adv.*

in still or **in stil** (in stil/), *v.t.,* **-stilled, -still ing. 1** put in little by little; cause to enter the mind, heart, etc., gradually: *Reading good books instills a love for really fine literature.* **2** put in drop by drop. [< Latin *instillare* < *in-* + *stilla* a drop] —**in/stil la/tion,** *n.* —**in still/er,** *n.* —**in still/ment,** *n.*

in stinct (*n.* in/stingkt; *adj.* in stingkt/), *n.* **1** a chain of unlearned, coordinated acts characteristic of a particular species or group of animals; inborn tendency to act in a certain way: *Birds do not learn to build nests but build them by instinct.* **2** a natural tendency or ability; talent. —*adj.* charged or filled with something: *The picture is instinct with life and beauty.* [< Latin *instinctus* impulse < *instinguere* incite, impel]

in tel li gi ble (in tel/ə jə bəl), *adj.* capable of being understood; clear; comprehensible. [< Latin *intelligibilis* < *intelligere.* See INTELLECT.] —**in tel/li gi bly,** *adv.*

in tense (in tens/), *adj.* **1** very much; very great; very strong; extreme: *intense happiness, intense pain, intense light.* **2** full of vigorous activity, strong feelings, etc.: *An intense life is crowded with action, interests, etc.* **3** having or showing strong feeling: *an intense person, an intense face.* [< Latin *intensum* strained, stretched < *in-* toward + *tendere* to stretch] —**in tense/ly,** *adv.* —**in tense/ness,** *n.*

in tent (in tent/), *n.* **1** that which is intended; purpose; intention: *I'm sorry I hurt you; that wasn't my intent.* **2** meaning; significance: *What is the intent of that remark?* **3** to all intents and purposes, in almost every way; practically. —*adj.* **1** very attentive; having the eyes or thoughts earnestly fixed on something; earnest: *an intent look.* **2** earnestly engaged; much interested: *intent on making money.* [< Latin *intentum* strained, intense, variant of *intensum*] **—in tent′ly,** *adv.* **—in tent′ness,** *n.*

inter-, *prefix.* 1 one with the other; together: *Intercommunicate = communicate with each other.* 2 between: *Interpose = put between.* 3 between or among a group: *International = between or among nations.* [< Latin < *inter* among, between, during. Related to UNDER.]

in ter cept (in′tər sept′), *v.t.* 1 take or seize on the way from one place to another: *intercept a letter, intercept a messenger.* 2 cut off (light, water, etc.). 3 check; stop: *intercept the flight of an escaped criminal.* [< Latin *interceptum* caught between, interrupted < *inter-* between + *capere* to take, catch] **—in′ter cep′tion,** *n.*

in ter change a ble (in′tər chān′jə bəl), *adj.* 1 capable of being used or put in place of each other. 2 able to change places. **—in′ter change′a ble ness,** *n.* **—in′ter change′a bly,** *adv.*

in ter ject (in′tər jekt′), *v.t.* throw in between other things; insert abruptly: *Every now and then the speaker interjected some witty remark.* [< Latin *interjectum* thrown between < *inter-* between + *jacere* to throw]

in ter lude (in′tər lüd), *n.* 1 anything thought of as filling the time between two things; interval: *an interlude of sunshine between two showers.* 2 piece of music played between the parts of a song, church service, play, etc. 3 entertainment between the acts of a play. [< Medieval Latin *interludium* < Latin *inter-* between + *ludus* a play]

in ter mi na ble (in tér′mə nə bəl), *adj.* 1 never stopping; unceasing; endless. 2 so long as to seem endless; very long and tiring. **—in ter′mi na bly,** *adv.*

in tern (in tèrn′), *v.t.* confine within a country or place; force to stay in a certain place, especially during wartime. [< French *interner* < *interne* inner, internal < Latin *internus* < *in* in]

in tern ment (in tèrn′mənt), *n.* 1 an interning. 2 a being interned.

in ter sperse (in′tər spèrs′), *v.t.,* **-spersed, -spers ing.** 1 vary with something put here and there: *The grass was interspersed with beds of flowers.* 2 scatter or place here and there among other things: *Bushes were interspersed among the trees.* [< Latin *interspersum* scattered < *inter-* between + *spargere* to scatter]

in ter ur ban (in′tər ér′bən), *adj.* between different cities or towns.

in ter val (in′tər vəl), *n.* 1 period of time between; pause: *an interval of a week, intervals of freedom from worry.* 2 space between things; intervening space: *an interval of ten feet between trees.* 3 **at intervals, a** now and then. **b** here and there. 4 (in music) the difference in pitch between two tones. [< Latin *intervallum,* originally, space between palisades < *inter-* + *vallum* wall]

in tim i date (in tim′ə dāt), *v.t.,* **-dat ed, -dat ing.** 1 make afraid; frighten: *intimidate one's opponents with threats.* 2 influence or force by fear: *intimidate a witness.* [< Medieval Latin *intimidatum* frightened < Latin *in-* + *timidus* fearful] **—in tim′i da′tion,** *n.* **—in tim′i da′tor,** *n.*

in tol er a ble (in tol′ər ə bəl), *adj.* too much to be endured; unbearable: *intolerable pain.* **—in tol′er a ble ness,** *n.* **—in tol′er a bly,** *adv.*

in tone (in tōn′), *v.,* **-toned, -ton ing.** *—v.t.*

1 read or recite (a psalm, prayer, etc.) in a singing voice; chant. 2 utter with a particular tone. *—v.i.* recite in a singing voice, especially in monotone. [< Medieval Latin *intonare* < Latin *in-* + *tonus* tone] **—in ton′er,** *n.*

intra-, *prefix.* within; inside; on the inside, as in *intramural, intrastate.* [< Latin < *intra* inside of]

in tri cate (in′trə kit), *adj.* 1 with many twists and turns; puzzling, entangled, or complicated: *an intricate knot, an intricate plot.* 2 very hard to understand: *intricate directions.* [< Latin *intricatum* entangled < *in-* + *tricae* hindrances] **—in′tri cate ly,** *adv.* **—in′tri cate ness,** *n.*

in trigue (n. in trēg′, in′trēg′; v. in trēg′), *v.,* **-trigued, -tri guing.** *—n.* 1 secret scheming; underhand planning to accomplish some purpose; plotting. 2 a crafty plot; secret scheme. 3 a secret love affair. *—v.i.* 1 form and carry out plots; plan in a secret or underhand way. 2 have a secret love affair. *—v.t.* excite the curiosity and interest of: *The book's unusual title intrigued me.* [< French < Italian *intrigo* < *intrigare* entangle < Latin *intricare*] **—in tri′guer,** *n.*

in trude (in trüd′), *v.,* **-trud ed, -trud ing.** *—v.i.* force oneself in; come unasked and unwanted: *If you are busy, I will not intrude.* *—v.t.* give unasked and unwanted advice; force in: *intrude one's opinions upon others.* [< Latin *intrudere* < *in-* in + *trudere* to thrust] **—in trud′er,** *n.*

in vert (in vèrt′), *v.t.* 1 turn upside down: *invert a glass.* 2 turn the other way; reverse in position, direction, order, etc.: *If you invert "I can," you have "Can I?"* 3 turn inside out or outside in. [< Latin *invertere* < *in-* over, around + *vertere* to turn] **—in vert′er,** *n.*

in vin ci ble (in vin′sə bəl), *adj.* unable to be conquered; impossible to overcome; unconquerable: *invincible courage, an invincible fighter.* [< Latin *invincibilis* < *in-* not + *vincere* conquer] **—in vin′ci ble ness,** *n.* **—in vin′ci bly,** *adv.*

in vol un tar y (in vol′ən ter′ē), *adj.* 1 not voluntary; not done of one's own free will; unwilling: *involuntary consent.* 2 not done on purpose; not intended: *an involuntary injury.* 3 not controlled by the will: *Breathing is mainly involuntary.* **—in vol′un tar′i ly,** *adv.* **—in vol′un tar′i ness,** *n.*

-ion, *suffix forming nouns chiefly from verbs.* 1 act of _____ing: *Attraction = act of attracting.* 2 condition of being _____ed: *Adoption = condition of being adopted.* 3 result of _____ing: *Abbreviation = result of abbreviating.* [< Old French < Latin *-ionem,* or directly < Latin]

ir-¹, *prefix.* the form of **in-¹** before *r,* as in *irrational, irregular.*

ir-², *prefix.* the form of **in-²** before *r,* as in *irrigate.*

ir reg u lar (i reg′yə lər), *adj.* 1 not regular; not according to rule; out of the usual order or natural way. 2 not according to law or morals: *irregular behavior.* 3 not even; not smooth or straight; broken and rough; without symmetry: *New England has a very irregular coastline.* **—ir reg′u lar ly,** *adv.*

ir res o lute (i rez′ə lüt), *adj.* not resolute; unable to make up one's mind; not sure of what one wants; hesitating; vacillating. **—ir res′o lute ly,** *adv.* **—ir res′o lute ness,** *n.*

ir rev o ca ble (i rev′ə kə bəl), *adj.* 1 not able to be revoked; final: *an irrevocable decision.* 2 impossible to call or bring back: *the irrevocable past.* **—ir rev′o ca bly,** *adv.*

ir ri ta bil i ty (ir′ə tə bil′ə tē), *n., pl.* **-ties.** a being irritable; impatience.

ir ri ta ble (ir′ə tə bəl), *adj.* 1 easily made angry; impatient. 2 unnaturally sensitive or sore: *irritable skin.* **—ir′ri ta ble ness,** *n.* **—ir′ri ta bly,** *adv.*

-ish, *suffix forming adjectives from other adjectives and from nouns.* 1 somewhat _____: *Sweetish = somewhat sweet.* 2 like a _____: *Childish = like a child.* 3 like that of a _____: *Girlish = like that of a girl.* 4 of or having to do with _____: *English = of or having to do with England.* 5 inclined to be a _____: *Thievish = inclined to be a thief.* 6 near, but usually somewhat past _____: *Fortyish = near forty.* [< Old English *-isc*]

-ist, *suffix forming nouns chiefly from other nouns.* 1 person who does or makes: *Tourist = a person who tours.* 2 an expert in an art or science: *Botanist = an expert in botany.* 3 person who plays a musical instrument: *Organist = person who plays the organ.* 4 person engaged in or working with: *Journalist = a person engaged in journalism.* 5 person who believes in: *Socialist = a person who believes in socialism.* [< Greek *-istēs* < *-izein -ize*]

-ity, *suffix forming nouns from adjectives.* quality, condition, or fact of being _____: *Sincerity = quality or condition of being sincere.* Also, **-ty.** [< Old French *-ité* < Latin *-itatem*]

-ive, *suffix forming adjectives from nouns.* 1 of or having to do with, as in *interrogative, inductive.* 2 tending to; likely to, as in *active, appreciative.* [< French *-ive* (feminine of *-if* < Latin *-ivus* or directly < Latin]

-ize, *suffix forming verbs from adjectives and nouns.* 1 make _____: *Legalize = make legal.* 2 become _____: *Crystallize = become crystal.* 3 engage in or use _____: *Criticize = engage in criticism.* 4 treat or combine with _____: *Oxidize = combine with oxygen.* 5 other meanings, as in *alphabetize, colonize, memorize.* Also, **-ise.** [< French *-iser* or Latin *-izare* < Greek *-izein,* or directly < Greek]

jad ed (jā′did), *adj.* 1 worn out; tired; weary. 2 dulled from continual use; surfeited; satiated: *a jaded appetite.* **—jad′ed ly,** *adv.* **—jad′ed ness,** *n.*

jaun ty (jôn′tē, jän′tē), *adj.,* **-ti er, -ti est.** 1 easy and lively; sprightly; carefree: *The happy children walked with jaunty steps.* 2 smart; stylish: *She wore a jaunty little hat.* [earlier *janty* < Middle French *gentil* noble, gentle < Latin *gentilis.* Doublet of GENTEEL, GENTILE, GENTLE.] **—jaun′ti ly,** *adv.* **—jaun′ti ness,** *n.*

jave lin (jav′lən), *n.* 1 a light spear thrown by hand. 2 a wooden or metal spear, thrown for distance in athletic contests. [< Middle French *javeline*]

jeer (jir), *v.i.* make fun rudely or unkindly; mock; scoff. *—v.t.* speak to or treat with scornful derision. *—n.* a mocking or insulting remark; rude, sarcastic comment. [origin uncertain] **—jeer′er,** *n.* **—jeer′ing ly,** *adv.*

jerk y (jèr′kē), *n.* strips of dried meat, usually beef. [< American Spanish *charqui* jerked meat]

joc u lar (jok′yə lər), *adj.* speaking or acting in jest; said or done in jest; funny; joking. [< Latin *jocularis* < *joculus,* diminutive of *jocus* jest] **—joc′u lar ly,** *adv.*

jo vi al (jō′vē əl), *adj.* good-hearted and full of fun; good-humored and merry. [< Latin

Jovialis of the planet Jupiter (those born under the planet's sign being supposedly cheerful) < *Jovis* Jove] —**jo′vi al ly,** *adv.* —**jo′vi al ness,** *n.*

ju bi lant (jü′bə lənt), *adj.* expressing or showing joy; rejoicing. [< Latin *jubilantem* < *jubilum* wild shout] —**ju′bi lant ly,** *adv.*

kay ak (kī′ak), *n.* 1 an Eskimo canoe made of skins stretched over a light frame of wood or bone with an opening in the middle for a person. 2 a similar small craft made of canvas or other material. Also, **kaiak.** [< Eskimo]

keel (kēl), *n.* 1 the main timber or steel piece that extends the whole length of the bottom of a ship or boat. The whole ship is built up on the keel. 2 ARCHAIC. ship. 3 something that resembles a ship's keel in any way, such as the bottom of an airship or airplane. 4 **on an even keel, a** horizontal. **b** calm; steady. —*v.t.* turn upside down; upset. —*v.i.* 1 turn over. 2 **keel over, a** turn over or upside down; upset. **b** fall over suddenly. **c** IN-FORMAL. faint. [< Scandinavian (Old Icelandic) *kjölr*]

kib itz (kib′its), *v.i.* INFORMAL. look on as an outsider and offer unwanted advice. [< *kibitzer*]

kid nap (kid′nap), *v.t.,* **-naped, -nap ing** or **-napped, -nap ping.** steal or carry off (a person, especially a child) by force; seize and hold (a person) against his will by force or by fraud; abduct. [< *kid* child + *nap* snatch away, variant of *nab*] —**kid′nap er, kid′-nap per,** *n.*

kil o me ter (kə lom′ə tər, kil′ə mē′tər), *n.* unit of length equal to 1000 meters.

kin dling (kind′ling), *n.* small pieces of wood, etc., that ignite easily for setting fire to larger pieces and other fuel.

kine (kīn), *n.pl.* ARCHAIC OR DIALECT. cows or cattle. [earlier *kyen* (formed after pattern of *oxen*) < Old English *cȳ,* plural of *cū* cow]

knave (nāv), *n.* 1 a tricky, dishonest man; rogue; rascal. 2 ARCHAIC. a male servant or any man of humble birth or position. [Old English *cnafa* boy]

knead (nēd), *v.t.* 1 work over or work up (moist flour or clay) usually by pressing with the hands into dough or paste: *A baker kneads dough.* 2 make or shape by kneading. 3 press and squeeze with the hands; massage: *Kneading the muscles in a stiff shoulder will take away the stiffness.* [Old English *cnedan*] —**knead′er,** *n.*

knot (not), *n.* 1 unit of speed used on ships, equal to one nautical mile per hour: *The ship averaged about 12 knots.* 2 nautical mile: 6076.11549 feet.

la bo ri ous (lə bôr′ē əs, lə bōr′ē əs), *adj.* 1 requiring much work; requiring hard work: *Climbing a mountain is laborious.* 2 showing signs of effort; not easy; labored: *laborious excuses for being late.* 3 hard-working; in-dustrious: *Bees and ants are laborious in-sects.* —**la bo′ri ous ly,** *adv.*

la dy fin ger (lā′dē fing′gər), *n.* a small sponge cake shaped somewhat like a finger.

land fall (land′fôl′), *n.* 1 a sighting of land. 2 the land sighted or reached. 3 approach to land; landing.

lank y (lang′kē), *adj.,* **lank i er, lank i-est.** awkwardly long and thin; tall and un-graceful: *a lanky boy.* —**lank′i ly,** *adv.* —**lank′i ness,** *n.*

lap is laz u li (lap′is laz′yə lī; lap′is laz′yə lē), 1 a deep blue, opaque semipre-cious stone used for an ornament. 2 deep blue. [< Medieval Latin < Latin *lapis* stone + Medieval Latin *lazulum* lapis lazuli < Arabic *lāzuward.* See AZURE.]

lar der (lär′dər), *n.* 1 place where meat and other foods are kept; pantry. 2 stock of food.

la tent (lāt′nt), *adj.* present but not active; hidden; concealed: *latent germs of disease, latent ability.* [< Latin *latentem* lying hidden] —**la′tent ly,** *adv.*

launch (lônch, länch), *v.t.* 1 cause to slide into the water; set afloat: *A new ship is launched from the supports on which it was built.* —*n.* 1 act of launching a rocket, missile, aircraft, ship, etc. 2 movement of a boat or ship from the land into the water. [< Old French *lanchier, lancer* throw a lance < *lance* lance < Latin *lancea*] —**launch′-a ble,** *adj.* —**launch′er,** *n.*

lau rel (lôr′əl, lor′əl), *n.* 1 a small evergreen tree of southern Europe, with smooth, shiny leaves; bay; sweet bay. 2 its leaves. The ancient Greeks and Romans crowned victors with wreaths of laurel. 3 any tree or shrub of the same family as the laurel. 4 mountain laurel. [< Old French *lorier, laurier* < *lor* laurel < Latin *laurus*]

lea (lē), *n.* a grassy field; meadow; pasture. [Old English *lēah*]

leg (leg), *n.* 1 one of the limbs on which people and animals support themselves and walk, especially the part of the limb between the knee and the ankle. 2 the part of a gar-ment that covers a leg: *The legs of your trou-sers are wrinkled.* 3 anything shaped or used like a leg; any support that is much longer than it is wide: *a table leg. One leg of a com-pass holds the pencil.* 4 one of the distinct portions or stages of any course: *the last leg of a trip, the first leg of a relay race.* [< Scandinavian (Old Icelandic) *leggr*]

le git i mate (*adj.* lə jit′ə mit; *v.* lə jit′ə māt), *adj., v.,* **-mat ed, -mat ing.** —*adj.* 1 allowed or admitted by law; rightful; lawful: *a legiti-mate claim.* 2 valid; logical; acceptable: *Sickness is a legitimate reason for absence from work.* 3 conforming to accepted stan-dards; normal; regular. —*v.t.* make or de-clare lawful or legal. [< Medieval Latin *legi-timatum* made lawful < Latin *legitimus* law-ful < *lex, legis* law] —**le git′i mate ly,** *adv.* —**le git′i ma′tion,** *n.*

len ient (lē′nyənt, lē′nē ənt), *adj.* mild or gentle; not harsh or stern; merciful: *a lenient judge, a lenient punishment.* [< Latin *lenien-tem* < *lenis* mild] —**len′ient ly,** *adv.*

-less, *suffix forming adjectives from verbs and nouns.* 1 without a ____; that has no ____: *Homeless = without a home.* 2 that does not ____: *Ceaseless = that does not cease.* 3 that cannot be ____ed: *Countless = that cannot be counted.* [Old English *-lēas* < *lēas* without]

leu ke mi a (lü kē′mē ə, lü kē′myə), *n.* a cancerous, usually fatal, disease character-ized by an excessive production of white blood cells in the blood. [< New Latin < Greek *leukos* white + *haima* blood]

li a bil i ty (lī′ə bil′ə tē), *n., pl.* **-ties.** 1 state of being susceptible: *liability to disease.* 2 state of being under obligation: *liability for a debt.* 3 **liabilities,** *pl.* debts or other financial obligations of a business. 4 some-thing that is to one's disadvantage: *Poor handwriting is a liability for a teacher.*

hat, āge, fär; let, ēqual, tėrm;
it, īce; hot, ōpen, ôrder;
oil, out; cup, put, rüle;
ch, child; ng, long; sh, she;
th, thin; ᴛʜ, then; zh, measure;

ə represents *a* in about, *e* in taken,
i in pencil, *o* in lemon, *u* in circus.

< = from, derived from, taken from.

li ba tion (lī bā′shən), *n.* 1 a pouring out of wine, water, etc., as an offering to a god. 2 the wine, water, etc., offered in this way. 3 INFORMAL. liquid poured out to be drunk; drink. [< Latin *libationem* < *libare* pour out]

list less (list′lis), *adj.* seeming too tired to care about anything; not interested in things; not caring to be active; languid. —**list′less ly,** *adv.* —**list′less ness,** *n.*

loath some (lōᴛʜ′səm), *adj.* making one feel sick; disgusting. —**loath′some ly,** *adv.* —**loath′some ness,** *n.*

loft y (lôf′tē, lof′tē), *adj.,* **loft i er, loft i est.** 1 very high; towering: *lofty mountains.* 2 exalted or dignified; grand: *lofty aims, lofty thoughts.* 3 proud; haughty: *a lofty sneer.* —**loft′i ly,** *adv.* —**loft′i ness,** *n.*

log ic (loj′ik), *n.* 1 the principles of reason-ing and inference; science of reasoning or the science of proof. 2 a particular system or theory of logic. 3 use of argument; reason-ing. 4 sound sense; reason: *There is much logic in what you say.* 5 logical outcome or effect; inevitable result: *The logic of events proved them wrong.* [< Greek *logikē (technē)* reasoning (art) < *logos* word < *legein* speak]

lo gis tics (lō jis′tiks), *n.* the planning and carrying out of any complex or large-scale operation, especially one of military move-ment, evacuation, and supply. [< French *lo-gistique*]

loll (lol), *v.i.* 1 recline or lean in a lazy manner: *loll on a sofa.* 2 hang loosely or droop; dangle: *A dog's tongue lolls out in hot weather.* —*v.t.* allow to hang or droop. —*n.* a lolling. [Middle English *lollen*]

loom¹ (lüm), *n.* frame or machine for weav-ing yarn or thread into cloth. [Old English *(ge)lōma* implement]

loom² (lüm), *v.i.* appear dimly or vaguely as a large, threatening shape: *A large iceberg loomed through the thick, gray fog. War loomed ahead.* [origin uncertain]

loot (lüt), *n.* 1 goods taken from an enemy, a captured city, etc., in time of war. 2 anything taken illegally, especially by force or with violence: *burglar's loot.* —*v.t.* 1 plunder, rob, or sack (a city, building, store, etc.). 2 carry off as loot or booty. —*v.i.* plunder; rob. [< Hindustani *lūt*] —**loot′er,** *n.*

lop sid ed (lop′sī′did), *adj.* larger or heavi-er on one side than the other; unevenly balanced; leaning to one side. —**lop′-sid ed ly,** *adv.* —**lop′sid′ed ness,** *n.*

lore (lôr, lōr), *n.* 1 the body of knowledge on a particular subject, especially traditional facts, anecdotes, or beliefs: *bird lore, Irish lore.* 2 learning; knowledge. 3 ARCHAIC. teaching or something taught. [Old English *lār.* Related to LEARN.]

lo tus (lō′təs), *n.* 1 any of various water lilies having large, often floating leaves and showy flowers, commonly represented in the deco-rative art of the Hindus and the Egyptians. 2 any of a genus of shrubby plants of the pea

lout

family, bearing red, pink, or white flowers. 3 in Greek legends: **a** a plant whose fruit was supposed to cause a dreamy and contented forgetfulness in those who ate it, and make them lose all desire to return home. **b** the fruit itself. Also, **lotos.** [< Latin < Greek *lōtos*]

lout (lout), *n.* an awkward, stupid fellow; boor. [probably < Scandinavian (Old Icelandic) *lūtr* stooping]

low (lō), *v.i., v.t.* make the sound of a cow; moo. —*n.* the sound a cow makes; mooing. [Old English *hlōwan*]

loz enge (loz′inj), *n.* 1 design or figure having four equal sides, two acute angles, and two obtuse angles; diamond; rhombus. 2 a small tablet of any shape used as medicine or candy. Cough drops are sometimes called lozenges. [< Old French *losenge*]

lu cent (lü′snt), *adj.* 1 bright or shining; luminous. 2 letting light through; translucent; lucid; clear. [< Latin *lucentem* < *lux, lucis* light] —**lu′cent ly,** *adv.*

lu di crous (lü′də krəs), *adj.* causing derisive laughter; amusingly absurd; ridiculous. [< Latin *ludicrus* < *ludus* sport] —**lu′di crous ly,** *adv.* —**lu′di crous ness,** *n.*

lu mi nous (lü′mə nəs), *adj.* 1 shining by its own light: *The sun and stars are luminous bodies.* 2 full of light; shining; bright. 3 easily understood; clear; enlightening. —**lu′mi nous ly,** *adv.* —**lu′mi nous ness,** *n.*

lunge (lunj), *n., v.,* **lunged, lung ing.** —*n.* any sudden forward movement, such as a thrust with a sword or other weapon. —*v.i.* move with a lunge; make a sudden forward movement; thrust. [< French *allonger,* originally, to lengthen] —**lung′er,** *n.*

lure (lür), *n., v.,* **lured, lur ing.** —*n.* 1 power of attracting or fascinating; charm; allure; attraction: *the lure of the sea.* 2 something that allures, entices, or tempts. 3 a decoy or bait, especially an artificial bait used in fishing. —*v.t.* 1 lead away or into something by arousing desire; allure; entice; tempt. 2 attract with a bait. [< Old French *leurre,* of Germanic origin] —**lur′er,** *n.*

lush (lush), *adj.* 1 tender and juicy; growing thick and green: *Lush grass grows along the river banks.* 2 characterized by abundant growth; producing abundantly. 3 luxurious. 4 rich in ornament; flowery. [Middle English *lache*] —**lush′ly,** *adv.* —**lush′ness,** *n.*

lus ter (lus′tər), *n.* 1 a bright shine on the surface; sheen: *the luster of pearls.* 2 brightness; radiance: *Her eyes lost their luster.* 3 fame; glory; brilliance: *The deeds of heroes add luster to a nation's history.* 4 a shiny, metallic, often iridescent surface on pottery or china. 5 lusterware. 6 the appearance of the surface of a mineral due to the reflection of light. Also, **lustre.** [< Middle French *lustre,* ultimately < Latin *lustrare* brighten] —**lus′ter less,** *adj.*

-ly¹, *suffix forming adverbs from adjectives.* 1 in a ___ manner: *Cheerfully = in a cheerful manner.* 2 in ___ ways or respects: *Financially = in financial respects.* 3 to a ___ degree or extent: *Greatly = to a great degree.* 4 in, to, or from a ___ direction: *Northwardly = to or from the north.* 5 in a ___ place: *Thirdly = in the third place.* 6 at a ___ time: *Recently = at a recent time.* [Old English *-līce* < *līc* -ly²]

-ly² *suffix forming adjectives from nouns.* 1 like a ___: *Ghostly = like a ghost.* 2 like

that of a ___; characteristic of a ___: *Brotherly = like that of a brother.* 3 suited to a ___; fit or proper for a ___: *Womanly = suited to a woman.* 4 of each or every ___; occurring once per ___: *Daily = of every day.* 5 being a ___; that is a ___: *Heavenly = that is a heaven.* [Old English *-līc* < *līc* body, form]

lyre (līr), *n.* an ancient stringed musical instrument somewhat like a small harp. [< Latin *lyra* < Greek]

lyr ic (lir′ik), *n.* 1 a short poem expressing personal emotion. A love poem, a patriotic song, a lament, and a hymn might all be lyrics. 2 Usually, **lyrics,** *pl.* the words for a song, especially a popular song. —*adj.* 1 having to do with lyric poems: *a lyric poet.* 2 characterized by a spontaneous expression of feeling. 3 of or suitable for singing. 4 (of a singing voice) light in volume and tender in character, and often used in the higher register. 5 of or for the lyre. [< Latin *lyricus* < Greek *lyrikos* of a lyre]

ma ca bre (mə kä′brə, mə kä′bər), *adj.* causing horror; gruesome; horrible; ghastly. [< French] —**ma ca′bre ly,** *adv.*

mail (māl), *n.* 1 a flexible armor made of metal rings or small loops of chain linked together, or of overlapping plates, for protecting the body against arrows, spears, etc. 2 protective covering. [< Old French *maille* < Latin *macula* a mesh in network]

Malacca cane, *n.* a light walking stick made of the stem of an East Indian rattan palm.

mal ad just ed (mal′ə jus′tid), *adj.* badly adjusted; not in a healthy relation with one's environment.

mal con tent (mal′kən tent′), *adj.* discontented; rebellious. —*n.* a discontented, rebellious person.

ma li cious (mə lish′əs), *adj.* 1 showing active ill will; wishing to hurt or make suffer; spiteful. 2 proceeding from malice: *malicious mischief.* —**ma li′cious ly,** *adv.* —**ma li′cious ness,** *n.*

mal nu tri tion (mal′nü trish′ən, mal′nyü trish′ən), *n.* a malnourished condition. Improper food can cause malnutrition.

mal prac tice (mal prak′tis), *n.* 1 criminal neglect or wrong treatment of a patient by a doctor. 2 misconduct in any official or professional position.

mal treat (mal trēt′), *v.t.* treat roughly or cruelly; abuse: *maltreat animals.* —**mal treat′ment,** *n.*

mam mal (mam′əl), *n.* any of a class of warm-blooded, vertebrate animals usually having hair, the females of which secrete milk from mammary glands to nourish their young. Human beings, horses, dogs, lions, bats, and whales are all mammals. [< New Latin *Mammalia,* ultimately < Latin *mamma* breast]

man gle (mang′gəl), *v.t.,* **-gled, -gling.** 1 cut or tear (the flesh) roughly; lacerate. 2 spoil; ruin. [< Anglo-French *mangler* < Old French *mahaignier* to maim] —**man′gler,** *n.*

man i fest (man′ə fest), *adj.* apparent to the eye or to the mind; plain; clear: *a manifest error.* —*v.t.* 1 show plainly; reveal; display. 2 put beyond doubt; prove. —*n.* list of cargo of a ship or aircraft. [< Latin *manifestus* palpable < *manus* hand + *-festus* (able to be) seized] —**man′i fest′ly,** *adv.*

marine biology (mə rēn′ bī ol′ə jē), *n.*

the scientific study of plant and animal life found in the sea.

ma son ry (mā′sn rē), *n., pl.* **-ries.** 1 wall, foundation, or part of a building built by a mason; stonework or brickwork. 2 trade or skill of a mason.

mas sa cre (mas′ə kər), *n., v.,* **-cred, -cring.** —*n.* the wholesale, pitiless slaughter of people or animals. —*v.t.* kill (many people or animals) needlessly or cruelly; slaughter in large numbers. [< Middle French, in Old French *macecle* shambles] —**mas sa crer** (mas′ə krər), *n.*

mas sive (mas′iv), *adj.* 1 forming a large mass; bulky and heavy; huge: *a massive rock.* 2 giving the impression of being large and broad: *a massive forehead.* 3 imposing; impressive. 4 in or by great numbers; extensive: *a massive assault.* 5 affecting a large area of bodily tissue: *a massive hemorrhage.* —**mas′sive ly,** *adv.* —**mas′sive ness,** *n.*

mast (mast), *n.* a long pole or spar of wood or metal rising from the keel of a vessel set upright on a ship to support the yards, sails, rigging, etc. [Old English *mæst*] —**mast′less,** *adj.* —**mast′like′,** *adj.*

ma ter i al ize (mə tir′ē ə līz), *v.,* **-ized, -iz ing.** —*v.i.* 1 become an actual fact; be realized: *Our plans did not materialize.* 2 appear in material or bodily form: *A spirit materialized from the smoke of the magician's fire.* —*v.t.* 1 give material form to: *The inventor materialized his ideas by building a model.* 2 cause to appear in material or bodily form. —**ma ter′i al i za′tion,** *n.*

maze (māz), *n.* 1 network of paths through which it is hard to find one's way; labyrinth. 2 state of confusion; muddled condition. [variant of *amaze*]

maz y (mā′zē), *adj.,* **maz i er, maz i est.** like a maze; intricate.

me an der (mē an′dər), *v.i.* 1 follow a winding course: *A brook meanders through the meadow.* 2 wander aimlessly: *We meandered through the park.* —*n.* 1 a winding course. 2 aimless wandering. 3 a looplike turn in a river or stream. [< Latin *maeandra* a winding course < Greek *Maiandros* (now, *Menderes*) a winding river in Asia Minor]

med ic (med′ik), *n.* INFORMAL. 1 physician. 2 a medical student. 3 member of a medical corps of the armed forces. [< Latin *medicus* physician]

med i ta tive (med′ə tā′tiv), *adj.* 1 fond of or given to meditating; thoughtful. 2 expressing meditation. —**med′i ta′tive ly,** *adv.*

mel an chol y (mel′ən kol′ē), *n., pl.* **-chol ies,** *adj.* —*n.* 1 condition of sadness and low spirits; gloominess; dejection. 2 sober thoughtfulness; pensiveness. —*adj.* 1 depressed in spirits; sad; gloomy. 2 causing sadness; depressing: *a melancholy scene.* 3 lamentable; deplorable: *a melancholy fact.* 4 soberly thoughtful; pensive. [< Greek *melancholia* < *melanos* black + *cholē* bile]

men ace (men′is), *n., v.,* **-aced, -ac ing.** —*n.* something that threatens; threat: *In dry weather forest fires are a menace.* —*v.t.* offer a menace to; threaten: *Floods menaced the valley with destruction.* —*v.i.* be threatening. [< Middle French < Latin *minaciae* (plural), ultimately < *minae* projecting points, threats] —**men′ac ing ly,** *adv.*

-ment, *suffix added to verbs to form nouns.* 1 act, process, or fact of ___ing: *Enjoyment = act of enjoying.* 2 condition of being ___ed: *Amazement = condition of being amazed.* 3 product or result of ___ing:

576

Pavement = product of paving. 4 means of or instrument for _____ing: *Inducement = means of inducing.* [< French < Latin *-mentum* result of]

mer maid (mèr′mād), *n.* 1 an imaginary sea maiden having the form of a fish from the waist down. 2 an expert woman swimmer. [< *mere* + *maid*]

met a mor pho sis (met′ə môr′fə sis), *n.,* *pl.* **-ses** (-sēz′). 1 a marked change in the form, and usually the habits, of an animal in its development after the embryonic stage. Tadpoles become frogs by metamorphosis; they lose their tails and grow legs. 2 change of form, structure, or substance by or as if by witchcraft; transformation. 3 form, shape, substance, etc., resulting from any such change. 4 a noticeable or complete change of character, appearance, circumstances, etc. [< Greek, ultimately < *meta-* after + *morphē* form]

me te or (mē′tē ər), *n.* mass of rock or metal that enters the earth's atmosphere from outer space with enormous speed; falling star; shooting star. Friction with air molecules in the atmosphere causes meteors to become so hot that they glow and usually burn up before reaching the earth's surface. [< Greek *meteoron* (thing) in the air < *meta-* after + *aeirein* to lift]

me ter[1] (mē′tər), *n.* 1 any kind of poetic rhythm; the arrangement of beats or accents in a line of poetry. 2 musical rhythm; the arrangement of beats in music as divided into parts or measures of a uniform length of time. Three-fourths meter is waltz time. Also, BRITISH **metre.** [< Old French *mètre* < Latin *metrum* measure < Greek *metron*]

me ter[2] (mē′tər), *n.* 1 device for measuring. 2 device that measures and records the amount of gas, water, electricity, etc., used. —*v.t., v.i.* measure or record with a meter. [< *mete*]

middy blouse, a loose blouse having a collar with a broad flap at the back, worn by sailors, children, and girls.

mim ic (mim′ik), **-icked, -ick ing,** *n.,* *adj.* —*v.t.* 1 make fun of by imitating. 2 copy closely; imitate; ape: *A parrot can mimic a person's voice.* 3 represent imitatively; simulate. 4 resemble closely in form, color, etc.: *Some insects mimic leaves.* —*n.* person or thing that mimics. —*adj.* 1 not real, but imitated or pretended for some purpose: *a mimic battle.* 2 imitative: *mimic gestures.*

mis-, *prefix.* 1 bad: *Misgovernment = bad government.* 2 badly: *Misbehave = behave badly.* 3 wrong: *Mispronunciation = wrong pronunciation.* 4 wrongly: *Misapply = apply wrongly.* [Old English or < Old French mes-]

mi ser (mī′zər), *n.* person who loves money for its own sake; one who lives poorly in order to save money and keep it. [< Latin, wretched]

molt (mōlt), *v.i.* shed the feathers, skin, hair, shell, antlers, etc., before a new growth. Birds, snakes, insects, etc., molt. —*v.t.* shed (feathers, skin, etc.): *We saw the snake molt its skin.* —*n.* act or process of molting. Also, **moult.** [Middle English *mouten* < Old English *mūtian* (as in *bemūtian* exchange for) < Latin *mutare* to change] —**molt′er,** *n.*

mo ly (mō′lē), *n., pl.* **mo lies.** (in Greek legends) an herb with a milk-white flower and a black root, having magic properties. [< Greek *mōly*]

mon goose or **mon goos** (mong′güs), *n., pl.* **-goos es.** any of several genera of slen-

der, carnivorous mammals of Asia and Africa, especially a species native to India, belonging to the same family as the civet and resembling a ferret. The Indian species has been introduced elsewhere to destroy rats and is noted for its ability to kill cobras and certain other poisonous snakes. [< Marathi (a language of western India) *maṅgūs*]

monk (mungk), *n.* man who gives up all worldly things and enters a monastery to live a life devoted to religious duties and contemplation. Monks live either in solitude as hermits or as members of a religious order and are bound by the vows of poverty, celibacy, and obedience to a superior. [Old English *munuc* < Late Latin *monachus* < Late Greek *monachos* < Greek *monos* alone]

mo not o ny (mə not′n ē), *n.* 1 sameness of tone or pitch. 2 lack of variety. 3 wearisome sameness.

moor (mùr), *v.t.* 1 put or keep (a ship, etc.) in place by means of ropes or chains fastened to the shore or to anchors. 2 fix firmly; secure. —*v.i.* 1 moor a ship. 2 be made secure by ropes, anchors, etc. [Middle English *moren*]

mo rass (mə ras′), *n.* 1 piece of low, soft, wet ground; swamp; marsh. 2 a difficult situation; puzzling mess. [< Dutch *moeras*]

mor bid (môr′bid), *adj.* 1 not wholesome; unhealthy: *A liking for horrors is morbid.* 2 caused by disease; characteristic of disease; diseased: *Cancer is a morbid growth.* 3 having to do with diseased parts: *morbid anatomy.* 4 horrible; gruesome; grisly: *the morbid details of a murder.* [< Latin *morbidus* < *morbus* disease] —**mor′bid ly,** *adv.* —**mor′bid ness,** *n.*

mor phine (môr′fēn), *n.* a bitter, white, crystalline narcotic drug obtained from opium, used in the form of its salts to relieve pain and induce sleep. [< French < *Morpheus* Morpheus]

mor sel (môr′səl), *n.* 1 a small portion of food; bite. 2 a small piece, quantity, or amount of anything; fragment; bit. [< Old French, diminutive of *mors* a bite, ultimately < Latin *mordere* to bite]

mor tar[1] (môr′tər), *n.* mixture of lime, cement, sand, and water, placed between bricks or stones to hold them together when it has dried and hardened. —*v.t.* plaster with mortar; fix with mortar. [< Old French *mortier* < Latin *mortarium* mortar[2]]

mor tar[2] (môr′tər), *n.* 1 bowl of porcelain, glass, or other very hard material, in which substances may be pounded to a powder with a pestle. 2 a very short cannon with a wide, unrifled barrel, used to fire shells at high angles over a short range. [Old English *mortere* < Latin *mortarium*]

mot ley (mot′lē), *adj., n., pl.* **-leys.** —*adj.* 1 made up of parts or kinds that are different or varied: *a motley crowd, a motley collection of butterflies, shells, and stamps.* 2 of different colors like a clown's suit. —*n.* 1 mixture of things that are different. 2 suit of more than one color worn by clowns: *Medieval jesters and fools wore motley.* 3 jester; fool. 4 a woolen fabric of mixed colors used for clothing in the 1300's to 1600's, especially in England. [Middle English *motteley*]

mus kel lunge (mus′kə lunj), *n., pl.* **-lunge.** a very large North American pike, valued as a food and game fish, but difficult to catch. [< Algonquian]

musk y (mus′kē), *adj.,* **musk i er, musk i est.** of or like musk; like that of musk: *a musky odor.* —**musk′i ness,** *n.*

mute (myüt), *adj., n.,* **mut ed, mut ing.**

—*adj.* 1 not making any sound; silent: *The little girl stood mute with embarrassment.* 2 unable to speak; dumb. 3 not pronounced; silent: *The "e" in "mute" is mute.* 4 without speech or sound: *a mute refusal of an offer, mute astonishment.* —*n.* person who cannot speak, usually because of deafness, loss of or damage to the tongue, etc. [< Latin *mutus*] —**mute′ly,** *adv.* —**mute′ness,** *n.*

mu ti nous (myüt′n əs), *adj.* 1 given to or engaged in mutiny; rebellious: *a mutinous crew.* 2 like or involving mutiny; characterized by mutiny: *a mutinous look.* 3 not controllable; unruly: *mutinous passions.* —**mu′-ti nous ly,** *adv.* —**mu′ti nous ness,** *n.*

mu ti ny (myüt′n ē), *n., pl.* **-nies,** *v.,* **-nied, -ny ing.** —*n.* open rebellion against lawful authority, especially by sailors or soldiers against their officers. —*v.i.* take part in a mutiny; rebel. [< obsolete *mutine* to revolt < Old French *mutiner* < *mutin* rebellious, ultimately < Latin *movere* to move]

nai ad (nā′ad, nī′ad), *n., pl.* **-ads, -a des** (-ə dēz′). 1 Also, **Naiad.** (in Greek and Roman myths) a nymph guarding a river, stream, or spring. 2 a girl swimmer. 3 an immature insect in one of a series of aquatic stages of development characteristic of dragonflies, mayflies, etc. Naiads somewhat resemble the adult form, but have gills.

na sal (nā′zəl), *adj.* 1 of, in, or from the nose: *nasal bones, a nasal voice.* 2 (in phonetics) requiring the nose passage to be open; spoken through the nose. *M, n,* and *ng* represent nasal sounds. —*n.* a nasal bone or part. [< Latin *nasus* nose] —**na′sal ly,** *adv.*

na ta to ri um (nā′tə tôr′ē əm, nā′tə tōr′ē-əm), *n., pl.* **-to ri ums, -to ri a** (-tôr′ē ə, -tōr′ē ə). a swimming pool, especially one in a gymnasium or other building.

neb u la (neb′yə lə), *n., pl.* **-lae** (-lē′), **-las.** a cloudlike cluster of stars or a hazy mass of dust particles and gases which occurs in interstellar space and which may be either dark or illuminated by surrounding stars. **Galactic nebulae** are clouds of gas and dust particles within our galaxy. **Extra-galactic nebulae** are galaxies outside the Milky Way. [Latin, mist, cloud]

ne go ti ate (ni gō′shē āt), *v.,* **-at ed, -at-ing.** —*v.i.* talk over and arrange terms; confer; consult: *The colonists negotiated for peace with the Indians.* —*v.t.* arrange for: *They finally negotiated a peace treaty.* [< Latin *negotiatum* engaged in business < *negotium* business < *neg-* not + *otium* ease] —**ne go′ti a′tor,** *n.*

ne go ti a tion (ni gō′shē ā′shən), *n.* a negotiating; arrangement.

-ness, *suffix added to adjectives to form nouns.* 1 quality or condition of being _____: *Preparedness = condition of being prepared.*

2 ____ action: ____ behavior: *Carefulness = careful action; careful behavior.* [Old English -*ness, -niss*]

neu ro sis (nů rō′sis, nyů rō′sis), *n., pl.* -**ses** (-sēz′). any of various mental or emotional disorders, less severe than a psychosis, characterized by depression, anxiety, abnormal fears, compulsive behavior, etc.; psychoneurosis.

neu rot ic (nů rot′ik, nyů rot′ik), *adj.* 1 having or appearing to have a neurosis. 2 of or having to do with a neurosis or neuroses. —*n.* a neurotic person. —**neu rot′i cal ly,** *adv.*

niche (nich), *n., v.,* **niched, nich ing.** —*n.* 1 recess or hollow in a wall for a statue, vase, etc.; nook. 2 a suitable place or position; place for which a person is suited. —*v.t.* place in a niche or similar recess. [< Middle French, ultimately < Latin *nidus* nest]

nigh (nī), *adv.* 1 near (in position, time, relationship, etc.). 2 nearly; almost. —*adj.* 1 near; close. 2 (of one of a team of horses) left; near. —*prep.* near. —*v.t., v.i.* draw near. [Old English *nēah*]

no ble (nō′bəl), *adj., v.,* -**bler, -blest,** *n.* —*adj.* 1 high and great by birth, rank, or title; aristocratic: *a noble family, noble blood.* 2 high and great in character; showing greatness of mind; good; worthy: *a noble knight, a noble deed.* 3 having excellent qualities; fine: *a noble poem, a noble animal.* 4 grand in appearance; splendid; magnificent: *a noble sight.* —*n.* person high and great by birth, rank, or title. [< Old French < Latin *nobilis* renowned, well-known < *gnoscere* to know] —**no′ble ness,** *n.*

no bly (nō′blē), *adv.* in a noble manner.

non-, *prefix.* not; not a; opposite of; lack of; failure of: *Nonessential = not essential. Nonresident = not a resident. Nonconformity = lack of conformity.* [< Latin < *non* not]

non com bat ant (non′kəm bat′nt, non-kom′bə tənt), *n.* 1 member of the armed forces who takes no part in combat, such as a surgeon, nurse, or chaplain. 2 person having civilian status in wartime. —*adj.* not taking part in combat; having civilian status.

nov el ty (nov′əl tē), *n., pl.* -**ties.** 1 novel character; newness: *After the novelty of washing dishes wore off, he did not want to do it any more.* 2 a new or unusual thing: *Staying up late was a novelty to the children.* 3 **novelties,** *pl.* small, unusual articles, such as toys, cheap jewelry, etc.

nov ice (nov′is), *n.* 1 one who is new to what he is doing; beginner. 2 person in the period of preparation before becoming a monk or a nun. [< Latin *novicius* < *novus* new]

ob scure (əb skyůr′), *adj.,* -**scur er, -scurest,** *v.,* -**scured, -scur ing.** —*adj.* 1 not clearly expressed; hard to understand: *an obscure passage in a book.* 2 not expressing meaning clearly: *an obscure style of writing.* 3 not well known; attracting no notice: *an obscure little village, an obscure poet, an obscure position in the government.* 4 not easily discovered; hidden: *an obscure path, an obscure meaning.* 5 not distinct; not clear: *an obscure form, obscure sounds, an obscure view.* 6 dark; dim: *an obscure corner.* 7 indefinite: *an obscure brown, an obscure*

vowel. —*v.t.* 1 hide from view; make obscure; dim; darken: *Clouds obscure the sun.* 2 make dim or vague to the understanding. [< Latin *obscurus*] —**ob′scu ra′tion,** *n.* —**ob scure′ly,** *adv.* —**ob scure′ness,** *n.* —**ob scur′er,** *n.*

ob se qui ous (əb sē′kwē əs), *adj.* polite or obedient from hope of gain or from fear; servile; fawning: *Obsequious courtiers greeted the king.* [< Latin *obsequiosus* < *obsequium* dutiful service < *ob-* after + *sequi* follow] —**ob se′qui ous ly,** *adv.* —**ob se′qui ous ness,** *n.*

o cean og ra phy (ō′shə nog′rə fē), *n.* science that deals with the oceans and seas, including marine life.

ode (ōd), *n.* a lyric poem, usually rhymed and sometimes in irregular meter, full of noble feeling expressed with dignity. It is often addressed to some person or thing. [< Late Latin < Greek *ōidē*, related to *aeidein* sing]

o pal (ō′pəl), *n.* a mineral somewhat like quartz, found in many varieties and colors, certain of which reflect light with peculiar rainbow play of colors and are valued as gems. Black opals show brilliant colored lights against a black background; milk opals are milky white with rather pale lights. [< Latin *opalus* < Greek *opallios* < Sanskrit *upala* gem]

o paque (ō pāk′), *adj.* 1 not letting light through; not transparent or translucent. 2 not conducting heat, sound, electricity, etc. 3 not shining; dark; dull. 4 hard to understand; obscure. 5 stupid. —*n.* something opaque. [< Latin *opacus* dark, shady] —**o paque′ly,** *adv.* —**o paque′ness,** *n.*

op pres sive (ə pres′iv), *adj.* 1 hard to bear; burdensome: *The intense heat was oppressive.* 2 harsh; unjust; tyrannical: *Oppressive measures were taken to crush the rebellion.* —**op pres′sive ly,** *adv.* —**op pres′sive ness,** *n.*

op ti mism (op′tə miz′əm), *n.* 1 tendency to look on the bright side of things. 2 belief that everything will turn out for the best. 3 doctrine that the existing world is the best of all possible worlds. [< French *optimisme* < Latin *optimus* best]

op tion (op′shən), *n.* 1 right or freedom of choice: *In your senior year you will have the option of taking Spanish, French, or German.* 2 act of choosing: *Where to travel should be left to each person's option.* 3 thing that is or can be chosen. [< Latin *optionem*, related to *optare* opt]

-or, *suffix forming nouns from verbs.* person or thing that ____s: *Governor = person who governs. Accelerator = thing that accelerates.*

o ra cle (ôr′ə kəl, or′ə kəl), *n.* 1 (in ancient Greece and Rome) an answer believed to be given by a god through a priest or priestess to some question. It often had a hidden meaning that was ambiguous or hard to understand. 2 place where the god was believed to give such answers. A famous oracle was at Delphi. 3 the priest, priestess, or other means by which the god's answer was believed to be given. 4 a very wise person. 5 something regarded as a very reliable and sure guide. 6 a very wise answer. [< Latin *oraculum* < *orare* speak formally]

or dain (ôr dān′), *v.t.* 1 establish as a law; order; fix; decide; appoint. 2 appoint or consecrate officially as a clergyman. 3 appoint as part of the order of the universe or of nature; destine. [< Old French *ordener* < Latin *ordinare* < *ordinem* order] —**or dain′er,** *n.*

-ous, *suffix forming adjectives from nouns.* 1 full of; having much; having: *Joyous = full of joy.* 2 characterized by: *Zealous = characterized by zeal.* 3 having the nature of: *Idolatrous = having the nature of an idolater.* 4 of or having to do with: *Monogamous = having to do with monogamy.* 5 like: *Thunderous = like thunder.* 6 committing or practicing: *Bigamous = practicing bigamy.* 7 inclined to: *Blasphemous = inclined to blasphemy.* [< Old French *-os, -us* < Latin *-osum*]

out crop (*n.* out′krop′; *v.* out krop′), *n., v.,* -**cropped, -crop ping.** —*n.* 1 a coming (of a rock, stratum, etc.) to the surface of the earth: *the outcrop of a vein of coal.* 2 part that comes to the surface: *The outcrop that we found proved to be very rich in gold.* —*v.i.* come to the surface; appear.

o ver lap (*v.* ō′vər lap′; *n.* ō′vər lap′), *v.,* -**lapped, -lap ping,** *n.* —*v.t.* 1 lap over; cover and extend beyond: *Shingles are laid to overlap each other.* 2 coincide partly with. —*v.i.* overlap another thing or each other: *The shingles overlap.* —*n.* 1 a lapping over. 2 part that overlaps.

o ver run (*v.* ō′vər run′; *n.* ō′vər run′), *v.,* -**ran** (-ran′), -**run, -run ning,** *n.* —*v.t.* 1 spread over and spoil or harm in some way, as weeds, vermin, disease, or invading troops do. 2 spread over; cover pleasingly: *Vines had overrun the wall.* 3 run or go beyond: *The speaker overran the time set for him. He overran third base and was tagged out.* —*n.* 1 an overrunning. 2 amount overrunning or carried over.

pa chi si (pə chē′zē), *n.* game somewhat like backgammon, originally from India, played on a cross-shaped board. [< Hindustani *pachīsī*]

pa ja mas (pə jä′məz, pə jam′əz), *n.pl.* 1 sleeping or lounging garments consisting of a jacket or blouse and loose trousers fastened at the waist. 2 loose trousers worn by Moslem men and women. Also, **pyjamas.** [< Hindustani *pājāmā* < Persian *pāe* leg + *jāmah* garment]

pall bear er (pôl′ber′ər, pôl′bar′ər), *n.* one of the men who walk with or carry the coffin at a funeral.

pal let (pal′it), *n.* bed of straw; small or poor bed. [< Old French *paillet* < *paille* straw < Latin *palea*]

pan de mo ni um (pan′də mō′nē əm), *n.* 1 place of wild disorder or lawless confusion. 2 wild uproar or lawlessness. 3 **Pandemonium, a** abode of all the demons; hell. **b** hell's capital. In Milton's *Paradise Lost,* the palace built by Satan as the central part of hell. [< Greek *pan-* + *daimōn* demon]

pa ral y sis (pə ral′ə sis), *n., pl.* -**ses** (-sēz′). 1 a lessening or loss of the power of motion or sensation in any part of the body. 2 condition of powerlessness or helpless inactivity; crippling: *The war caused a paralysis of trade.* [< Greek < *paralyein* be loosened < *para-*[1] + *lyein* loosen. Doublet of PALSY.]

parch (pärch), *v.t.* 1 dry by heating; roast slightly: *Corn is sometimes parched.* 2 make hot and dry or thirsty: *The fever parched her.* —*v.i.* become dry, hot, or thirsty: *I am parched with the heat.* [Middle English *parchen*]

Par chee si (pär chē′zē), *n.* trademark for a board game developed from pachisi.

pas sive (pas′iv), *adj.* 1 being acted on without itself acting; not acting in return: *a passive mind, a passive disposition.* 2 not resisting; yielding or submitting to the will of another; submissive: *the passive obedience of a slave.* [< Latin *passivus* < *pati* suffer] —**pas′sive ly,** *adv.* —**pas′sive ness,** *n.*

pearl y (pėr′lē), *adj.,* **pearl i er, pearl i est.** 1 like a pearl; having the color or luster of pearls: *pearly teeth.* 2 like mother-of-pearl, especially in color and luster; nacreous. 3 adorned with or containing many pearls.

ped i gree (ped′ə grē′), *n.* 1 list of ancestors of a person or animal. 2 line of descent; ancestry; lineage. 3 derivation, as from a source: *the pedigree of a word.* 4 distinguished or noble descent: *a man of pedigree.* [< Middle French *pie de grue* foot of crane (because a symbol resembling the toes of a bird was used in showing descent)]

peer (pir), *n.* 1 person of the same rank, ability, etc., as another; equal. 2 man belonging to the nobility, especially a British nobleman having the rank of duke, marquis, earl, count, viscount, or baron. [< Old French *per* < Latin *par* equal. Doublet of PAR.]

pelt (pelt), *v.t.* 1 hit with (objects, words, etc.) thrown one after another; attack or assail by throwing things at: *The children were pelting each other with snowballs. The attorney pelted the witness with angry questions.* 2 beat heavily or continuously upon: *Hail pelted the roof.* 3 throw; hurl: *The clouds pelted rain upon us.* —*v.i.* 1 beat heavily or continuously: *The rain came pelting down.* 2 go rapidly; hurry. —*n.* 1 a pelting. 2 speed: *The horse is coming at full pelt.* [origin uncertain] —**pelt′er,** *n.*

pen e trate (pen′ə trāt), *v.,* **-trat ed, -trat ing.** —*v.t.* 1 enter into or pass through: *The bullet penetrated this wall and two inches into the one beyond.* 2 pierce through: *Our eyes could not penetrate the darkness.* 3 soak or spread through; permeate: *The skunk's odor penetrated the whole house.* 4 see into or through; understand: *I could not penetrate the mystery.* 5 affect or impress very much. —*v.i.* pass through: *Even where the trees were thickest, the sunshine penetrated.* [< Latin *penetratum* gone through, pierced < *penitus* deep within]

pen sive (pen′siv), *adj.* 1 thoughtful in a serious or sad way. 2 melancholy. [< Old French *pensif* < *penser* think < Latin *pensare* ponder < *pendere* weigh] —**pen′sive ly,** *adv.* —**pen′sive ness,** *n.*

pe remp tor y (pə remp′tər ē, per′əmp tôr′ē, per′əmp tōr′ē), *adj.* 1 leaving no choice; decisive; final; absolute: *a peremptory decree.* 2 allowing no denial or refusal: *a peremptory command.* 3 imperious; dictatorial: *a peremptory professor.* [< Latin *peremptorius* that puts an end to, ultimately < *per-* to the end + *emere* to take] —**pe remp′tor i ly,** *adv.* —**pe remp′tor i ness,** *n.*

per func tor y (pər fungk′tər ē), *adj.* 1 done merely for the sake of getting rid of the duty; done from force of habit; mechanical; indifferent: *The little boy gave his face a perfunctory washing.* 2 acting in a perfunctory way: *The new nurse was perfunctory; he did not really care about his work.* [< Late Latin *perfunctorius* < Latin *per-* through + *fungi* execute] —**per func′tor i ly,** *adv.* —**per func′tor i ness,** *n.*

per il (per′əl), *n., v.,* **-iled, -il ing** or **-illed, -il ling.** —*n.* 1 chance of harm or loss; exposure to danger: *a time of great peril.* 2 cause of peril or danger: *Hidden rocks are a peril to ships.* —*v.t.* put in danger. [< Old French < Latin *periculum*]

per il ous (per′ə ləs), *adj.* full of peril; dangerous. —**per′il ous ly,** *adv.* —**per′il ous ness,** *n.*

per i scope (per′ə skōp), *n.* an optical instrument consisting of an arrangement of prisms or mirrors that reflect light rays down a vertical tube, used in a submarine, trench, etc., to obtain a view of the surface. —**per′i scope like′,** *adj.*

per plex (pər pleks′), *v.t.* 1 trouble with doubt; puzzle; bewilder. 2 make difficult to understand or settle; confuse. [< Latin *perplexus* confused < *per-* thoroughly + *plectere* intertwine] —**per plex′ed ly,** *adv.* —**per plex′ing ly,** *adv.*

per sist ent (pər sis′tənt, pər zis′tənt), *adj.* 1 not giving up, especially in the face of dislike, disapproval, or difficulties; persisting; persevering: *a persistent worker, a persistent beggar.* 2 going on; continuing; lasting: *a persistent headache that lasted for three days.* —**per sist′ent ly,** *adv.*

per tain (pər tān′), *v.i.* 1 belong or be connected as a part, possession, etc.: *We own the house and the land pertaining to it.* 2 have to do with; be related; refer: *documents pertaining to the case.* 3 be appropriate: *We had turkey and everything else that pertains to Thanksgiving.* [< Old French *partenir* < Latin *pertinere* reach through, connect < *per-* through + *tenere* to hold]

per vade (pər vād′), *v.t.,* **-vad ed, -vad ing.** go or spread throughout; be throughout: *The odor of pines pervades the air.* [< Latin *pervadere* < *per-* through + *vadere* go] —**per vad′er,** *n.*

per verse (pər vėrs′), *adj.* 1 contrary and willful; obstinately opposing what is wanted, reasonable, or required. 2 persistent in wrong. 3 morally bad; perverted; depraved. 4 not correct; wrong: *perverse reasoning.* [< Latin *perversum* turned away, perverted] —**per verse′ly,** *adv.* —**per verse′ness,** *n.*

pet u lant (pech′ə lənt), *adj.* likely to have little fits of bad temper; irritable over trifles; peevish. [< Latin *petulantem*] —**pet′u lant ly,** *adv.*

phlegm (flem), *n.* 1 the thick mucus discharged into the mouth and throat during a cold or other respiratory disease. 2 sluggish disposition or temperament; indifference. 3 coolness; calmness. [< Greek *phlegma* clammy humor (resulting from heat) < *phlegein* to burn]

pick et (pik′it), *n.* a pointed stake or peg placed upright to make a fence, to tie a horse to, etc. —*v.t.* enclose with pickets; fence. [< French *piquet,* diminutive of *pic* a pick] —**pick′et er,** *n.*

pi e ty (pī′ə tē), *n., pl.* **-ties.** 1 a being pious; reverence for God; devotion to religion; godliness; devoutness. 2 dutiful regard for one's parents. 3 a pious act, remark, belief, etc. [< Old French *piete* < Latin *pietatem* < *pius* pious. Doublet of PITY.]

pin to (pin′tō), *adj., n., pl.* **-tos.** —*adj.* spotted in two or more colors; pied. —*n.* a pinto horse. [< Spanish, painted, ultimately < Popular Latin *pinctus* < Latin *pictus*]

pitch (pich), *n.* 1 in music: the highness or lowness of a tone or sound, which depends upon the frequency of the vibrations producing it. The slower the rate of vibrations per second the lower the pitch. —*v.i.* 2 plunge with the bow rising and then falling: *The ship pitched about in the storm.* 3 slope downward; incline; dip.

hat, āge, fär; let, ēqual, tėrm;
it, īce; hot, ōpen, ôrder;
oil, out; cup, put, rüle;
ch, child; ng, long; sh, she;
th, thin; ᴛʜ, then; zh, measure;

ə represents *a* in about, *e* in taken,
i in pencil, *o* in lemon, *u* in circus.

< = from, derived from, taken from.

pi ton (pē′tän), *n.* a wedge that is driven into a rock surface for support. It often has an eye through which a rope can be passed.

plane (plān), *n., v.,* **planed, plan ing.** —*n.* a carpenter's tool with a blade for smoothing or shaping wood. —*v.t.* 1 smooth or level with a plane; use a plane on. 2 remove with a plane. [< Old French < Latin *plana* < *planare* make level < *planus* flat. Doublet of PIANO², PLAIN, PLAN.]

pluck (pluk), *v.t.* 1 pull off; pick: *pluck flowers in the garden.* 2 pull at; pull; tug; jerk: *pluck a person by the sleeve.* 3 pull on (the strings of a musical instrument). 4 pull off the feathers or hair from: *pluck a chicken.* 5 SLANG. rob; swindle; fleece. —*v.i.* 1 pull sharply or forcibly; tug (at): *She plucked at the loose threads of her coat.* 2 **pluck up,** get new courage; cheer up. —*n.* 1 act of picking or pulling. 2 courage; boldness; spirit. 3 heart, liver, and lungs of an animal killed for food. [Old English *pluccian*]

plum age (plü′mij), *n.* feathers of a bird: *A parrot has bright plumage.* [< Old French < *plume* plume]

pneu mo nia (nü mō′nyə, nü mō′nē ə; nyü mō′nyə, nyü mō′nē ə), *n.* 1 a bacterial or viral disease in which the lung becomes inflamed, often accompanied by chills, a pain in the chest, a hard, dry cough, and a high fever. 2 inflammation of the lung from irritants, such as chemicals, foreign particles, etc. [< Greek < *pneumōn* lung]

poign an cy (poi′nyən sē), *n.* a being poignant; sharpness; piercing quality.

poign ant (poi′nyənt), *adj.* 1 very painful; piercing: *poignant suffering.* 2 stimulating to the mind, feelings, or passions; keen; intense: *a subject of poignant interest.* 3 sharp, pungent, or piquant to the taste or smell: *poignant sauces.* [< Old French, present participle of *poindre* to prick < Latin *pungere*] —**poign′ant ly,** *adv.*

poise (poiz), *n., v.,* **poised, pois ing.** —*n.* 1 mental balance, composure, or self-possession: *She has perfect poise and never seems embarrassed.* 2 the way in which the body, head, etc., are held; carriage. 3 state of balance; equilibrium. —*v.t.* 1 balance: *poise yourself on your toes.* 2 hold or carry evenly or steadily: *The waiter poised the tray on his hand.* —*v.i.* 1 be balanced or held in equilibrium. 2 hang supported or suspended. 3 hover, as a bird in the air. [< Old French *pois, peis* < Popular Latin *pesum* < Latin *pensum* weight]

pol yp (pol′ip), *n.* 1 a small coelenterate attached at the base of its tubular body, with a mouth at the other end surrounded by fingerlike tentacles to gather in food, often growing in colonies, as hydras, corals, sea anemones, etc. 2 tumor or similar mass of enlarged tissue arising from a mucous or serous surface. [< Greek *polypous* < *poly-* + *pous* foot]

po man der (pə man′dər, pō′man dər), *n.* ball of mixed aromatic substances formerly carried for perfume or as a guard against infection. [< Old French *pome d'ambre* apple of amber]

port (pôrt, pōrt), *n.* 1 place where ships and boats can be sheltered from storms; harbor. 2 place where ships and boats can load and unload; city or town with a harbor. [Old English < Latin *portus*]

por tal (pôr′tl, pōr′tl), *n.* door, gate, or entrance, usually an imposing one. —*adj.* of or having to do with the portal vein. [< Medieval Latin *portale* < Latin *porta* gate]

post-, *prefix.* 1 after in time; later: *Postwar = after a war.* 2 after in space; behind: *Postnasal = behind the nasal cavity.* [< Latin]

post (pōst), *n.* 1 place where a soldier, policeman, etc., is stationed; place where one is supposed to be when on duty. 2 place where soldiers are stationed; military station; fort. 3 U.S. a local branch of a veterans' organization. 4 job or position: *the post of secretary, a diplomatic post.* 5 a trading post. —*v.t.* 1 station at a post at a particular point: *We posted guards at the door.* 2 make a deposit of: *post bail.* [< Middle French *poste* < Italian *posto* < Latin *positum* stationed, placed]

pox (poks), *n.* any disease characterized by eruption of pustules on the skin, such as chicken pox or smallpox. [variant of *pocks*, plural of *pock*]

prank (prangk), *n.* piece of mischief; playful trick: *On April Fools' Day people often play pranks on each other.* —*v.t.* dress in a showy way; adorn. [origin uncertain]

pre-, *prefix.* 1 before in time, rank, etc.: *Precambrian = before the Cambrian.* 2 before in position, space, etc.; in front of: *Premolar = in front of the molars.* [< Latin *prae-*, *pre-*]

pre cip i tate (*v.* pri sip′ə tāt; *adj., n.* pri sip′ə tit, pri sip′ə tāt), *v.*, **-tat ed, -tat ing,** *adj., n.* —*v.t.* 1 hasten the beginning of; bring about suddenly: *precipitate an argument.* 2 throw headlong; hurl: *precipitate a rock down a cliff, precipitate oneself into a struggle.* 3 separate (a substance) out from a solution as a solid. 4 condense (water vapor) from the air in the form of rain, dew, snow, etc. —*v.i.* 1 be deposited from solution as a solid. 2 be condensed as rain, dew, snow, etc. —*adj.* 1 very hurried; sudden: *A cool breeze caused a precipitate drop in the temperature.* 2 with great haste and force; plunging or rushing headlong; hasty; rash. —*n.* substance, usually crystalline, separated out from a solution as a solid. [< Latin *praecipitatum* thrown headlong < *praecipitem* headlong] —**pre cip′i tate ly,** *adv.* —**pre cip′i tate ness,** *n.* —**pre cip′i ta′tor,** *n.*

pre co cious (pri kō′shəs), *adj.* 1 developed earlier than usual in knowledge, skill, etc.: *This precocious child could read well at the age of four.* 2 developed too early; occurring before the natural time. [< Latin *praecocem < praecoquere* to mature or ripen early < *prae-* pre- + *coquere* ripen] —**pre co′cious ly,** *adv.* —**pre co′cious ness,** *n.*

pre des tine (prē des′tən), *v.t.*, **-tined, -tin ing.** determine or settle beforehand; foreordain.

pre lim i nar y (pri lim′ə ner′ē), *adj., n., pl.* **-nar ies.** —*adj.* coming before the main business; leading to something more important: *After the preliminary exercises of prayer and song, the speaker of the day gave an address.* —*n.* 1 a preliminary step; something preparatory. 2 a preliminary examination. 3 an athletic contest or match preceding the main event, especially in boxing or wrestling. [< New Latin *praeliminaris* < Latin *prae-* pre- + *limen* threshold] —**pre lim′i nar′i ly,** *adv.*

pre miere (pri mir′, prə myer′), *n., adj., v.,* **-miered, -mier ing.** —*n.* a first public performance: *the premiere of a new play.* —*adj.* premier. —*v.t.* give the first public performance or showing of (a play, movie, etc.). —*v.i.* 1 have the first public performance or showing: *The movie is premiering this month.* 2 perform publicly for the first time, especially as a star: *She premiered in London.* 3 appear for the first time: *The magazine is scheduled to premiere next fall.* [< French *première*]

pre sume (pri züm′), *v.*, **-sumed, -sum ing.** —*v.t.* 1 take for granted without proving; suppose: *The law presumes innocence until guilt is proved.* 2 take upon oneself; venture; dare: *May I presume to tell you you are wrong* — ' 1 take an unfair advantage: *Don't presume on his good nature by borrowing from him every week.* 2 act with improper boldness; take liberties. [< Latin *praesumere* take for granted < *prae-* pre- + *sumere* take] —**pre sum′er,** *n.* —**pre sum′ing ly,** *adv.*

pre vail (pri vāl′), *v.i.* 1 exist in many places; be in general use: *The custom of exchanging gifts at Christmas still prevails.* 2 be the most usual or strongest: *Sadness prevailed in our minds.* 3 be the stronger; win the victory; succeed: *prevail against an enemy. Reason prevailed over emotion.* 4 be effective. 5 **prevail on, prevail upon,** or **prevail with,** persuade. [< Latin *praevalere < prae-* pre- + *valere* have power]

pri me val (prī mē′vəl), *adj.* 1 of or having to do with the first age or ages, especially of the world: *In its primeval state the earth was without any forms of life.* 2 ancient; primeval forests untouched by the ax. [< Latin *primaevus* early in life < *primus* first + *aevum* age] —**pri me′val ly,** *adv.*

prism (priz′əm), *n.* 1 a solid figure whose bases or ends have the same size and shape and are parallel to one another, and each of whose sides is a parallelogram. 2 a transparent body of this form, often of glass and usually with triangular ends, used for separating white light passing through it into its spectrum or for reflecting beams of light. [< Greek *prisma* something sawed off, prism < *priein* to saw]

pris mat ic (priz mat′ik), *adj.* 1 of or like a prism. 2 formed by a transparent prism. 3 varied in color; brilliant. —**pris mat′i cal ly,** *adv.*

priv et (priv′it), *n.* any of several shrubs much used for hedges. Some are evergreen. [origin uncertain]

priv y (priv′ē), *adj., n., pl.* **priv ies.** —*adj.* 1 private. 2 ARCHAIC. secret; hidden. 3 **privy to,** having secret or private knowledge of. —*n.* a small outhouse used as a toilet. [< Old French *prive* < Latin *privatum.* Doublet of PRIVATE.]

pro-, *prefix.* 1 before; preceding; prior to, as in *prologue.* 2 in front of; anterior, as in *prothorax, proscenium.* [< Greek]

probe (prōb), *v.*, **probed, prob ing,** *n.* —*v.t.* 1 search into; examine thoroughly; investigate: *I probed my memory for her name.* 2 examine with a probe. —*v.i.* search; penetrate: *probe into the causes of a crime.* —*n.* 1 a thorough examination; investigation. 2 investigation, usually by a legislative body, in an effort to discover evidences of law violation. [< Late Latin *proba* proof < Latin *probare* prove < *probus* good. Doublet of PROOF.] —**prob′er,** *n.* —**prob′ing ly,** *adv.*

pro ce dure (prə sē′jər), *n.* 1 way of proceeding; method of doing things: *What is your procedure in making bread?* 2 the customary manners or ways of conducting business: *parliamentary procedure, legal procedure.*

prod (prod), *v.*, **prod ded, prod ding,** *n.* —*v.t.* 1 poke or jab with something pointed: *prod an animal with a stick.* 2 stir up; urge on: *The lateness of the hour prodded me to finish quickly.* —*n.* 1 poke; thrust. 2 a sharp-pointed stick; goad. 3 words, actions, or feelings that prod. [origin uncertain] —**prod′der,** *n.*

pro fuse (prə fyüs′), *adj.* 1 very abundant: *profuse thanks.* 2 spending or giving freely; lavish; extravagant. [< Latin *profusum* poured forth < *pro-* forth + *fundere* pour] —**pro fuse′ly,** *adv.* —**pro fuse′ness,** *n.*

pro fu sion (prə fyü′zhən), *n.* 1 great abundance. 2 extravagance; lavishness.

pro jec tile (prə jek′təl), *n.* any object that is thrown, hurled, or shot, such as a stone or bullet. —*adj.* 1 capable of being thrown, hurled, or shot: *projectile weapons.* 2 forcing forward; impelling: *a projectile force.*

proph e cy (prof′ə sē), *n., pl.* **-cies.** 1 a telling what will happen; foretelling future events. 2 thing told about the future. 3 a divinely inspired utterance, revelation, writing, etc.

pro phet ic (prə fet′ik), *adj.* 1 belonging to a prophet; such as a prophet has: *prophetic power.* 2 containing prophecy: *a prophetic saying.* 3 giving warning of what is to happen; foretelling: *Thunder is often prophetic of showers.* —**pro phet′i cal ly,** *adv.*

prov i dence (prov′ə dəns), *n.* 1 God's care and help. 2 **Providence,** God. 3 instance of God's care and help. 4 a being provident; prudence.

pro voc a tive (prə vok′ə tiv), *adj.* 1 irritating; vexing. 2 tending or serving to call forth action, thought, laughter, anger, etc.: *a provocative remark.* —*n.* something that rouses or irritates. —**pro voc′a tive ly,** *adv.* —**pro voc′a tive ness,** *n.*

prow (prou), *n.* 1 the front part of a ship or boat; bow. 2 the projecting front of anything: *the prow of an aircraft.* [< Middle French *proue* < Italian *prua* < Latin *prora* < Greek *prōira*]

prox im i ty (prok sim′ə tē), *n.* nearness; closeness.

pru dence (prüd′ns), *n.* 1 wise thought before acting; good judgment. 2 good management; economy.

psy cho sis (sī kō′sis), *n., pl.* **-ses** (-sēz′). any severe form of mental disorder, which may also be associated with physical disease, and which produces deep and far-reaching disruption of normal behavior and social functioning.

psy chot ic (sī kot′ik, si kot′ik), *adj.* 1 having a psychosis. 2 of, having to do with, or caused by a psychosis. —*n.* a psychotic person. —**psy chot′i cal ly,** *adv.*

puce (pyüs), *n.* a purplish brown. —*adj.* purplish-brown. [< French]

punc tu al i ty (pungk/chü al/ə tē), *n.* a being on time; promptness.

pur chase (pėr/chəs), *v.,* **-chased, -chas ing,** *n.* —*v.t.* 1 get by paying a price; buy: *purchase a new car.* 2 get in return for something: *purchase safety at the cost of happiness.* 3 hoist, haul, or draw by the aid of some mechanical device. —*n.* 1 act of buying. 2 thing bought. 3 a firm hold to help move something or to keep from slipping: *Wind the rope twice around the tree to get a better purchase.* 4 device for obtaining such a hold. [< Anglo-French *purchacer* pursue < Old French *pur-* forth + *chacier* to chase] —**pur/chas a ble,** *adj.* —**pur/chas er,** *n.*

pur ga to ry (pėr/gə tôr/ē, pėr/gə tōr/ē), *n., pl.* **-ries.** 1 (in Roman Catholic belief) a temporary condition or place in which the souls of those who have died penitent are purified from venial sin or the effects of sin by punishment. 2 any condition or place of temporary suffering or punishment. [< Medieval Latin *purgatorium,* originally, purging < Latin *purgare.*]

purl (pėrl), *v.i.* 1 flow with rippling motions and a murmuring sound: *A shallow brook purls.* 2 pass with a sound like this. —*n.* 1 a purling motion or sound. 2 act of purling. [perhaps < Scandinavian (Norwegian) *purla* to ripple]

pur pose (pėr/pəs), *n., v.,* **-posed, -pos ing.** —*n.* 1 something one has in mind to get or do; aim; intention. 2 object or end for which a thing is made, done, used, etc. 3 **on purpose,** with a purpose; not by accident; intentionally. 4 **to good purpose,** with good results. 5 **to little purpose** or **to no purpose,** with few or no results. 6 **to the purpose,** to the point; relevant; pertinent. —*v.t., v.i.* plan; aim; intend. [< Old French *pourpos* < *pourposer* propose < *pour-* forth + *poser* to put, pose]

pur pose ful (pėr/pəs fəl), *adj.* having a purpose. —**pur/pose ful ly,** *adv.* —**pur/pose ful ness,** *n.*

pu tre fy (pyü/trə fī), *v.t., v.i.,* **-fied, -fy ing.** break down or cause to break down plant or animal matter by the action of bacteria and fungi, producing foul-smelling gases; decay; rot: *putrefied meat.* [< Middle French *putrefier* < Latin *putrifieri* < *puter* rotten + *fieri* become]

quaint (kwānt), *adj.* strange or odd in an interesting, pleasing, or amusing way: *Old photographs seem quaint to us today.* [< Old French *cointe* pretty, clever < Latin *cognitum* known] —**quaint/ly,** *adv.* —**quaint/ness,** *n.*

quea sy (kwē/zē), *adj.,* **-si er, -si est.** 1 inclined to nausea; easily upset: *a queasy stomach.* 2 tending to unsettle the stomach. 3 uneasy; uncomfortable. 4 squeamish; fastidious. [origin uncertain] —**quea/si ly,** *adv.* —**quea/si ness,** *n.*

quell (kwel), *v.t.* 1 put down (disorder, rebellion, etc.): *quell a riot.* 2 put an end to; overcome: *quell one's fears.* [Old English *cwellan* to kill]

quiv er (kwiv/ər), *n.* 1 case to hold arrows. 2 supply of arrows in such a case. [< Old French *cuivre*]

rail (rāl), *v.i.* complain bitterly; use violent and reproachful language: *rail at one's hard*

luck. [< Middle French *railler* to mock, ridicule, ultimately < Late Latin *ragere* to bray, brawl] —**rail/er,** *n.*

ral ly (ral/ē), *v.,* **-lied, -ly ing,** *n., pl.* **-lies.** —*v.t.* 1 bring together, especially to get in order again: *The commander was able to rally the fleeing troops.* 2 pull together; revive: *We rallied all our energy for one last effort.* —*v.i.* 1 come together in a body for a common purpose or action. 2 come to help a person, party, or cause: *She rallied to the side of her injured friend.* —*n.* 1 a rallying; recovery. 2 a mass meeting or assembly for a common purpose or action: *a political rally.* [< Middle French *rallier* < *re-* again + *allier* to ally]

ram bunc tious (ram bungk/shəs), *adj.* INFORMAL. 1 wild and uncontrollable; unruly. 2 noisy and violent; boisterous. [alteration of *robustious* < *robust*] —**rambunc/tious ly,** *adv.* —**ram bunc/tious ness,** *n.*

ram pant (ram/pənt), *adj.* 1 growing without any check: *The vines ran rampant over the fence.* 2 passing beyond restraint or usual limits; unchecked: *Anarchy was rampant after the dictator died.* 3 angry; excited; violent. 4 (in heraldry) standing up on the hind legs. [< Old French, ramping] —**ram/pant ly,** *adv.*

ram part (ram/pärt), *n.* 1 a wide bank of earth, often with a wall on top as a fortification, built around a fort for defense. 2 anything that defends; defense; protection. [< Middle French *rempart* < *remparer* fortify]

ran cid (ran/sid), *adj.* 1 stale; spoiled: *rancid butter.* 2 tasting or smelling like stale fat or butter: *rancid odor.* [< Latin *rancidus* < *rancere* be rank] —**ran/cid ly,** *adv.* —**ran/cid ness,** *n.*

rapt (rapt), *adj.* 1 lost in delight. 2 so busy thinking of or enjoying one thing that one does not know what else is happening. 3 showing a rapt condition; caused by a rapt condition: *a rapt smile.* [< Latin *raptum* seized] —**rapt/ly,** *adv.* —**rapt/ness,** *n.*

rar i ty (rer/ə tē, rar/ə tē), *n., pl.* **-ties.** 1 something rare: *A man over a hundred years old is a rarity.* 2 fewness; scarcity. 3 lack of density; thinness.

rav en ous (rav/ə nəs), *adj.* 1 very hungry. 2 greedy. 3 rapacious. —**rav/en ous ly,** *adv.* —**rav/en ous ness,** *n.*

ra vine (rə vēn/), *n.* a long, deep, narrow gorge eroded by running water. [< French, violent rush]

raw hide (rô/hīd/), *n., v.,* **-hid ed, -hid ing.** —*n.* 1 the untanned skin of cattle. 2 rope or whip made of this. —*v.t.* whip with a rawhide.

re-, *prefix.* 1 again; anew; once more: *Reappear = appear again.* 2 back: *Repay = pay back.* Also, sometimes before vowels, **red-.** [< Latin]

re buke (ri byük/), *v.,* **-buked, -buk ing,** *n.* —*v.t.* express disapproval of; reprove. —*n.* expression of disapproval; scolding. [< Anglo-French *rebuker* < Old French *rebuchier* < *re-* back + *buchier* to strike] —**re buk/er,** *n.* —**re buk/ing ly,** *adv.*

re count (ri kount/), *v.t.* tell in detail; give an account of: *He recounted all the happenings of the day.* [< Middle French *reconter* < *re-* + *conter* relate, count]

re crim i na tion (ri krim/ə nā/shən), *n.* an accusing in return; counter accusation.

re dou ble (rē dub/əl), *v.,* **-bled, -bling.** —*v.t.* 1 double again. 2 increase greatly; double: *When he saw land ahead, the swimmer redoubled his speed.* 3 (in games) to

hat, āge, fär; let, ēqual, tėrm;
it, īce; hot, ōpen, ôrder;
oil, out; cup, put, rüle;
ch, child; ng, long; sh, she;
th, thin; ᴛʜ, then; zh, measure;

ə represents *a* in about, *e* in taken, *i* in pencil, *o* in lemon, *u* in circus.

< = from, derived from, taken from.

double (an opponent's double). —*v.i.* 1 double back: *The fox redoubled on his trail to escape the hunters.* 2 be doubled.

re es tab lish or **re-es tab lish** (rē/ə stab/lish), *v.t.* establish again; restore. —**re/es tab/lish ment, re/-es tab/lish ment,** *n.*

re lent (ri lent/), *v.i.* become less harsh or cruel; be more tender and merciful. [ultimately < Latin *re-* again + *lentus* slow]

re luc tant (ri luk/tənt), *adj.* 1 showing unwillingness; unwilling. 2 slow to act because unwilling: *be reluctant to leave.* [< Latin *reluctantem* struggling against < *re-* back + *luctari* to struggle] —**re luc/tant ly,** *adv.*

re mark (ri märk/), *v.t.* 1 say in a few words; state; comment. 2 notice; observe. —*v.i.* make a remark; comment. —*n.* 1 something said in a few words; short statement; comment. 2 act of noticing; observation. [< French *remarquer* < *re-* again + *marquer* to mark]

re me di al (ri mē/dē əl), *adj.* tending to relieve or cure; remedying; helping. —**re me/di al ly,** *adv.*

rem i nis cence (rem/ə nis/ns), *n.* 1 a remembering; recalling past persons, events, etc. 2 Often, **reminiscences,** *pl.* account of something remembered; recollection. 3 thing that makes one remember or think of something else. [< Latin *reminiscentia* < *reminisci* remember < *re-* again + *mens* mind]

re pent (ri pent/), *v.i.* feel sorry for having done wrong and seek forgiveness: *The sinner repented.* —*v.t.* feel sorry for; regret: *repent one's choice.* [< Old French *repentir,* ultimately < Latin *re-* repeatedly + *paenitere* cause to regret] —**re pent/er,** *n.*

rep er toire (rep/ər twär, rep/ər twôr), *n.* the list of plays, operas, parts, pieces, etc., that a company, an actor, a musician, or a singer is prepared to perform. [< French *répertoire* < Late Latin *repertorium*]

rep e ti tion (rep/ə tish/ən), *n.* 1 a repeating; doing or saying again: *Repetition helps learning.* 2 thing repeated.

re pet i tive (ri pet/ə tiv), *adj.* of or characterized by repetition. —**re pet/i tive ly,** *adv.* —**re pet/i tive ness,** *n.*

re proach (ri prōch/), *n.* 1 blame or censure. 2 a cause of blame or disgrace; discredit. 3 object of blame, censure, or disapproval. 4 expression of blame, censure, or disapproval. —*v.t.* 1 blame or censure; upbraid. 2 disgrace; shame. [< Middle French *reproche* < *reprocher* < Popular Latin *repropiare* lay at the door of, ultimately < Latin *re-* again + *prope* near] —**re proach/a ble,** *adj.* —**re proach/er,** *n.* —**re proach/ing ly,** *adv.* —**re proach/less,** *adj.*

re proach ful (ri prōch/fəl), *adj.* full of reproach; expressing reproach. —**re proach/ful ly,** *adv.* —**re proach/ful ness,** *n.*

re pug nance (ri pug/nəns), *n.* strong dislike, distaste, or aversion.

req ui site (rek′wə zit), *adj.* required by circumstances; needed; necessary: *the qualities requisite for a leader.* —*n.* thing needed; requirement. [< Latin *requisitum* < *re-* again + *quaerere* ask] —**req′ui site ly**, *adv.* —**req′ui site ness**, *n.*

res o lute (rez′ə lüt), *adj.* 1 having a fixed resolve; determined; firm. 2 constant in pursuing a purpose; bold. [< Latin *resolutum* resolved] —**res′o lute′ly**, *adv.* —**res′o lute′ness**, *n.*

re sound (ri zound′), *v.i.* 1 give back sound; echo. 2 sound loudly. 3 be filled with sound. 4 be much talked about. —*v.t.* 1 give back (sound); echo. 2 repeat loudly; celebrate.

re sume (ri züm′), *v.,* **-sumed, -sum ing.** —*v.t.* 1 begin again; go on: *Resume reading where we left off.* 2 get or take again: *Those standing may resume their seats.* —*v.i.* begin again; continue. [< Latin *resumere* < *re-* again + *sumere* take up] —**re sum′a ble**, *adj.*

res ur rect (rez′ə rekt′), *v.t.* 1 raise from the dead; bring back to life. 2 bring back to sight, use, etc.: *resurrect an old custom.* [back formation < resurrection]

re tal i ate (ri tal′ē āt), *v.i.,* **-at ed, -at ing.** pay back wrong, injury, etc.; return like for like, usually to return evil for evil: *If we insult them, they will retaliate.* [< Latin *retaliatum* paid back] —**re tal′i a′tion**, *n.*

re tract (ri trakt′), *v.t.* 1 draw back or in: *The kitten retracted her claws when I petted her.* 2 withdraw; take back: *retract an offer.* [< Latin *retractum* drawn back < *re-* + *trahere* to draw] —**re tract′a ble**, *adj.*

re trac tor (ri trak′tər), *n.* 1 person or thing that draws back something. 2 muscle that retracts an organ, protruded part, etc. 3 a surgical instrument for drawing back the edges of a wound.

re treat (ri trēt′), *v.i.* go back; move or draw back; withdraw: *The enemy retreated before the advance of our troops.* —*n.* 1 act of going back or withdrawing; withdrawal: *an orderly retreat.* 2 signal for retreat: *The drums beat a retreat.* 3 signal on a bugle or drum, given at sunset during the lowering of the flag. 4 a safe, quiet place; place of rest or refuge. 5 **beat a retreat,** run away; retreat. [< Old French *retraite* retreat < *retraire* withdraw < Latin *retrahere* < *re-* + *trahere* to draw]

retro-, *prefix.* backward; back; behind, as in *retrocede.* [< Latin < *retro* back]

rev el (rev′əl), *v.,* **-eled, -el ing** or **-elled, -el ling.** —*v.i.* 1 take great pleasure *(in): The children revel in country life.* 2 make merry. —*n.* a noisy good time; merrymaking. [< Old French *reveler* be disorderly, make merry < Latin *rebellare.* Doublet of REBEL.] —**rev′el er, rev′el ler,** *n.*

rev e la tion (rev′ə lā′shən), *n.* 1 act of making known. 2 the thing made known: *Her true nature was a revelation to me.* 3 God's disclosure of Himself and of His will to His creatures. 4 **Revelation,** the last book of the New Testament, supposed to have been written by the apostle John. [< Latin *revelationem* < *revelare* reveal]

re ver ber ate (ri vėr′bə rāt′), *v.,* **-rat ed, -rat ing.** —*v.i.* 1 echo back: *His voice reverberates from the high ceiling.* 2 be cast back; be reflected a number of times, as light or heat. —*v.t.* 1 reecho (a sound or noise). 2 cast back; reflect (light or heat). [< Latin *reverberatum* beaten back < *re-* back + *verber* a blow] —**re ver′be ra′tion**, *n.*

re vive (ri vīv′), *v.,* **-vived, -viv ing.** —*v.t.* 1 bring back to life or consciousness: *revive a half-drowned person.* 2 bring back to a fresh, lively condition. 3 make fresh; restore; refresh: *Hot coffee revived the cold, tired man.* 4 bring back to notice, use, fashion, memory, activity, etc.: *revive an old song.* —*v.i.* 1 come back to life or consciousness. 2 come back to a fresh, lively condition: *Flowers revive in water.* 3 become fresh. 4 come back to notice, use, fashion, memory, activity, etc. [< Latin *revivere* < *re-* again + *vivere* to live] —**re viv′er,** *n.*

re weave (rē wēv′), *v.t.,* **re wove, re weaving.** to weave over again.

rife (rīf), *adj.* 1 happening often; common; numerous; widespread. 2 full; abounding: *The city was rife with rumors of political corruption.* [Old English *rīfe*] —**rife′ly,** *adv.*

ri fle (rī′fəl), *n., v.,* **-fled, -fling.** —*n.* 1 gun with spiral grooves in its long barrel which spin or rotate the bullet as it is fired. A rifle is usually fired from the shoulder. 2 **rifles,** *pl.* a body of soldiers armed with rifles; riflemen. —*v.t.* 1 cut spiral grooves in (a gun barrel). 2 search and rob; ransack and rob. 3 take away; steal. 4 strip bare: *The boys rifled the apple tree.* [< Old French *rifler* to scratch; of Germanic origin] —**ri′fler,** *n.*

rill (ril), *n.* a tiny stream; little brook. [< Dutch *ril* groove, furrow]

rit u al (rich′ü əl), *n.* 1 form or system of rites. The rites of baptism, marriage, and burial are parts of the ritual of most churches. 2 a prescribed order of performing a ceremony or rite. Secret societies have a ritual for initiating new members. 3 book containing rites or ceremonies. 4 the carrying out of rites. —*adj.* of or having to do with rites or rituals; done as a rite: *a ritual dance, ritual laws.* —**rit′u al ly,** *adv.*

riv et (riv′it), *n.* a metal bolt having a head at one end, the other end being passed through holes in the things to be joined together and then hammered into another head. Rivets fasten heavy steel beams together. —*v.t.* 1 fasten with a rivet or rivets. 2 flatten (the end of a bolt) so as to form a head. 3 fasten firmly; fix firmly: *Their eyes were riveted on the speaker.* 4 command and hold (one's attention, interest, etc.): *The new design of the engine riveted our curiosity.* [< Old French < *river* to fix, fasten] —**riv′et er,** *n.*

rois ter (roi′stər), *v.i.* be boisterous; revel noisily; swagger. [< Old French *ruistre* rude < Latin *rusticus* rustic]

rouse (rouz), *v.,* **roused, rous ing,** *n.* —*v.t.* 1 wake up: *I was roused by the ring of the telephone.* 2 stir up: *The dogs roused a deer from the bushes.* 3 excite: *be roused to anger by an insult.* —*v.i.* become active; rise; wake. —*n.* a rousing. [Middle English *rowsen* shake the feathers] —**rous′er,** *n.*

rout (rout), *v.t.* 1 dig (out); get by searching. 2 put (out); force (out): *be routed out of bed at five o'clock.* 3 root with the snout as pigs do. 4 hollow out; scoop out; gouge. —*v.i.* 1 dig with the snout. 2 poke; search; rummage.

row el (rou′əl), *n., v.,* **-eled, -el ing** or **-elled, -el ling.** —*n.* a small wheel with sharp points, attached to the end of a spur. —*v.t.* spur (a horse); use a rowel on. [< Old French *roel, rouelle,* diminutive of *roue* wheel]

ruf fi an (ruf′ē ən), *n.* a rough, brutal, or cruel person; bully; hoodlum. —*adj.* rough; brutal; cruel. [< Middle French < Italian *ruffiano* pander]

ru in a tion (rü′ə nā′shən), *n.* ruin; destruction; downfall.

ru mor (rü′mər), *n.* 1 a story or statement talked of as news without any proof that it is true. 2 vague, general talk, not based upon definite knowledge: *Rumor has it that the new girl went to school in France.* —*v.t.* tell or spread by rumor. [< Latin]

sab o tage (sab′ə täzh), *n., v.,* **-taged, -tag ing.** —*n.* 1 damage done to work, tools, machinery, etc., by workmen as an attack or threat against an employer. 2 such damage done by civilians of a conquered nation to injure the conquering forces. 3 damage done by enemy agents or sympathizers in an attempt to slow down a nation's war effort. —*v.t.* damage or destroy by sabotage. [< French < *saboter* to bungle, walk noisily < *sabot*]

sa chet (sa shā′, sash′ā), *n.* 1 a small bag or pad containing perfumed powder. 2 perfumed powder. [< French, diminutive of *sac* sack]

sack (sak), *v.t.* plunder (a captured city); loot and despoil; pillage. —*n.* a plundering of a captured city. [< Middle French *(mettre à) sac* (put to the) sack < Italian *sacco* sack < Latin *saccus*] —**sack′er,** *n.*

sage (sāj), *adj.,* **sag er, sag est.** —*adj.* 1 showing wisdom or good judgment: *a sage reply.* 2 wise: *a sage adviser.* 3 wise-looking; grave; solemn: *Owls are sage birds.* —*n.* a very wise man. [< Old French, ultimately < Latin *sapere* be wise] —**sage′ly,** *adv.* —**sage′ness,** *n.*

sanc tion (sangk′shən), *n.* 1 permission with authority; support; approval: *We have the sanction of the recreation department to play ball in this park.* 2 solemn ratification or confirmation. 3 in law: **a** provision of a law enacting a penalty for disobedience to it or a reward for obedience. **b** the penalty or reward. 4 action by several nations toward another, such as a blockade, economic restrictions, etc., intended to force it to obey international law. 5 consideration that leads one to obey a rule of conduct. 6 binding force. —*v.t.* 1 authorize; approve; allow: *Her conscience does not sanction stealing.* 2 confirm. [< Latin *sanctionem* < *sancire* ordain] —**sanc′tion er,** *n.*

sanc tu ar y (sangk′chü er′ē), *n., pl.* **-ar ies.** 1 a sacred place. A church is a sanctuary. 2 the part of a church around the altar. 3 the most sacred part of any place of worship. 4 place of refuge or protection: *a wildlife sanctuary.* 5 refuge or protection: *The cabin provided sanctuary from the rain.*

sas sa fras (sas′ə fras), *n.* 1 a slender eastern North American tree of the same family as the laurel, having fragrant, yellow flowers, bluish-black fruit, and soft, light wood. 2 the aromatic dried bark of its root, used in medicine and to flavor candy, soft drinks, etc. [< Spanish *sasafrás*]

saun ter (sôn′tər, sän′tər), *v.i.* walk along slowly and happily; stroll: *saunter in the park.* —*n.* 1 a leisurely or careless gait. 2 a stroll. [origin uncertain] —**saun′ter er,** *n.*

sa vor (sā′vər), *n.* 1 a taste or smell: *The soup has a savor of onion.* 2 a distinctive quality; noticeable trace: *There is a savor of conceit in what she says.* —*v.t.* 1 enjoy the savor of; perceive or appreciate by taste or smell: *We savored the soup.* 2 give flavor to; season. 3 show traces of the presence or influence of: *Bad manners savor a bad education.* —*v.i.* 1 taste or smell *(of)*: *That sauce savors of lemon.* 2 have the quality or nature *(of)*: *a request that savors of a command.* Also, BRITISH **savour.** [< Old French < Latin *sapor,* related to *sapere* to taste, be wise] —**sa′vor er,** *n.* —**sa′vor less,** *adj.*

scape goat (skāp′gōt′), *n.* person or thing made to bear the blame for the mistakes or sins of others. The ancient Jewish high priests used to lay the sins of the people on a goat (called the scapegoat) which was then driven out into the wilderness. [< *scape,* variant of *escape* + *goat*]

scorn ful (skôrn′fəl), *adj.* showing contempt; full of scorn; mocking. —**scorn′ful ly,** *adv.* —**scorn′ful ness,** *n.*

scour (skour), *v.t.* 1 move quickly over: *They scoured the country round about for the lost child.* 2 look into every part of; search: *scour one's memory for a forgotten date.* —*v.i.* go rapidly in search or pursuit. [probably < Scandinavian (Old Icelandic) *skura* rush violently]

scowl (skoul), *v.i.* 1 look angry or sullen by lowering the eyebrows; frown. 2 have a gloomy or threatening aspect. —*v.t.* 1 affect by scowling. 2 express with a scowl. —*n.* an angry, sullen look; frown. [Middle English *skoulen*] —**scowl′er,** *n.*

scram (skram), *v.i.,* **scrammed, scramming.** SLANG. go at once. [short for *scramble*]

scud (skud), *v.,* **scud ded, scud ding,** *n.* —*v.i.* 1 run or move swiftly: *Clouds scudded across the sky driven by the high wind.* 2 (of a boat, etc.) run before a storm with little or no sail set. —*n.* 1 a scudding. 2 clouds or spray driven by the wind. [perhaps < Scandinavian (Danish) *skyde* shoot, glide]

scur vy (skėr′vē), *n., adj.,* **-vi er, -vi est.** —*n.* disease caused by a lack of vitamin C in the diet, characterized by swollen and bleeding gums, extreme weakness, livid spots on the skin, and prostration. Scurvy used to be common among sailors when they had little to eat except bread and salt meat. —*adj.* mean; contemptible; base: *a scurvy fellow, a scurvy trick.* [< *scurf*] —**scur′vi ly,** *adv.* —**scur′vi ness,** *n.*

scut tle (skut′l), *v.,* **-tled, -tling,** *n.* —*v.i.* run with quick, hurried steps; scamper; scurry. —*n.* a short, hurried run. [variant of earlier *scuddle,* frequentative of *scud*] —**scut′tler,** *n.*

scythe (sīTH), *n., v.,* **scythed, scyth ing.** —*n.* a long, thin, slightly curved blade on a long handle, for cutting grass, etc. —*v.t.* cut or mow with a scythe. [Old English *sithe;* spelling influenced by Latin *scindere* to cut]

se clud ed (si klü′did), *adj.* shut off from others; undisturbed: *a secluded cabin in the woods.* —**se clud′ed ly,** *adv.* —**se clud′ed ness,** *n.*

semi-, *prefix.* 1 half: *Semicircle = half circle.* 2 partly; incompletely: *Semicivilized = partly civilized.* 3 twice. Semi____ly means in each half of a ____, or twice in a ____: *Semiannually = every half year, or twice a year.* [< Latin]

→ Words starting with **semi-** are not usually hyphenated except before proper names (*semi-Christian*) or words beginning with *i* (*semi-invalid*).

sen su ous (sen′shü əs), *adj.* 1 of or derived from the senses; having an effect on the senses; perceived by the senses: *a sensuous*

love of color. 2 enjoying the pleasures of the senses. —**sen′su ous ly,** *adv.* —**sen′su ous ness,** *n.*

se ren i ty (sə ren′ə tē), *n., pl.* **-ties.** 1 peace and quiet; calmness. 2 clearness; brightness. 3 **Serenity,** a title of honor given to reigning princes and other dignitaries.

serge (sėrj), *n.* kind of fabric having diagonal lines or ridges on its surface. Worsted serge is used for coats and suits. Silk serge is used for linings. [< Old French *sarge* < Latin *serica (vestis)* silken (garment) < Greek *sērikē* < *Sēres* the Chinese]

sev er (sev′ər), *v.t.* 1 cut apart; cut off: *sever a rope.* 2 break off: *The two countries severed friendly relations.* —*v.i.* part; divide; separate: *The rope severed and the swing fell down.* [< Old French *sevrer,* ultimately < Latin *separare* to separate] —**sev′er a ble,** *adj.*

shab by (shab′ē), *adj.,* **-bi er, -bi est.** 1 much worn: *This old suit looks shabby.* 2 wearing old or much worn clothes. 3 poor or neglected; run-down: *a shabby old house.* 4 not generous; mean; unfair: *a shabby way to treat an old friend.* [< obsolete *shab* scab, Old English *sceabb*] —**shab′bi ly,** *adv.* —**shab′bi ness,** *n.*

sham ble (sham′bəl), *v.,* **-bled, -bling,** *n.* —*v.i.* walk awkwardly or unsteadily: *shamble across the room.* —*n.* a shambling walk. [probably special use of *shamble,* singular of obsolete *shambles* benches; with reference to the straddling legs of a bench]

sham poo (sham pü′), *v., n., pl.* **-poos.** —*v.t.* wash (the hair, a rug, etc.) with a soapy or oily preparation. —*n.* 1 a washing of the hair, a rug, etc. 2 preparation used for shampooing. [< Hindustani *chāmpō,* literally, press!] —**sham poo′er,** *n.*

share crop per (sher′krop′ər, shar′krop′ər), *n.* person who farms land for the owner in return for part of the crops.

sheath (shēth), *n., pl.* **sheaths** (shēTHz, shēths). 1 case or covering for the blade of a sword, knife, etc. 2 any similar covering, especially on an animal or plant. 3 a narrow, tight-fitting dress with straight lines. [Old English *scēath*]

sheathe (shēTH), *v.t.,* **sheathed, sheathing.** 1 put (a sword, etc.) into a sheath. 2 enclose in a case or covering: *a mummy sheathed in linen, doors sheathed in metal.* —**sheath′er,** *n.*

shift less (shift′lis), *adj.* lazy; inefficient. —**shift′ less ly,** *adv.* —**shift′less ness,** *n.*

shim my (shim′ē), *n., pl.* **-mies,** *v.,* **-mied, -my ing.** —*n.* 1 an unusual shaking or vibration: *a dangerous shimmy of a ladder.* 2 a jazz dance with much shaking of the body, popular in the 1920's. —*v.i.* 1 shake; vibrate: *The front wheels of the car shimmied.* 2 dance the shimmy. [variant of *chemise* (taken as plural)]

ship mate (ship′māt′), *n.* a fellow sailor on a ship.

shoal (shōl), *n.* 1 a large number; crowd: *a shoal of fish, a shoal of tourists.* —*v.i.* form into a shoal; crowd together. [perhaps Old English *scolu* host (of people), school of fish]

shoat (shōt), *n.* a young pig that no longer suckles. Also, **shote.** [origin uncertain]

short wave (shôrt′wāv′), *n., v.t., v.i.,* **-waved, -wav ing.** —*n.* a radio wave having a wavelength of 60 meters or less. —*v.t., v.i.* transmit by shortwaves: *The President's speech was shortwaved overseas.*

shrap nel (shrap′nəl), *n.* 1 shell filled with fragments of metal and powder, set to ex-

hat, āge, fär; let, ēqual, tėrm;
it, īce; hot, ōpen, ôrder;
oil, out; cup, pùt, rüle;
ch, child; ng, long; sh, she;
th, thin; ᴛʜ, then; zh, measure;

ə represents *a* in about, *e* in taken,
i in pencil, *o* in lemon, *u* in circus.

< = from, derived from, taken from.

plode in midair and scatter the fragments over a wide area. 2 fragments scattered by such a shell. [< Henry *Shrapnel,* 1761-1842, British army officer who invented it]

shroud (shroud), *n.* 1 cloth or garment in which a dead person is wrapped or dressed for burial. 2 something that covers, conceals, or veils: *The fog was a shroud over the city.* 3 Usually, **shrouds,** *pl.* rope from a mast to the side of a ship. Shrouds help support the mast. 4 one of the lines attached to the canopy of a parachute. —*v.t.* 1 wrap or dress for burial. 2 cover; conceal; veil: *Their plans are shrouded in secrecy.* [Old English *scrūd*]

siege (sēj), *n., v.,* **sieged, sieg ing.** —*n.* 1 the surrounding of a fortified place by enemy forces trying to capture it; a besieging or a being besieged: *The Japanese laid siege to Corregidor.* 2 any long or persistent effort to overcome resistance; any long-continued attack: *a siege of illness.* 3 **lay siege to,** a besiege. b attempt to win or get by long and persistent effort. —*v.t.* besiege. [< Old French, seat, siege, ultimately < Latin *sedere* sit]

sim u late (sim′yə lāt), *v.t.,* **-lat ed, -lat ing.** 1 put on a false appearance of; pretend; feign: *simulate interest.* 2 act like; look like; imitate: *Certain insects simulate flowers or leaves.* [< Latin *simulatum* simulated < *similis* like] —**sim′u la′tor,** *n.*

si mul ta ne ous (sī′məl tā′nē əs, sim′əl tā′nē əs), *adj.* existing, done, or happening at the same time: *The two simultaneous shots sounded like one.* [< Medieval Latin *simultaneus* simulated < Latin *similis* like; confused in sense with Latin *simul* at the same time] —**si′mul ta′ne ous ly,** *adv.* —**si′mul ta′ne ous ness,** *n.*

sire (sīr), *n., v.,* **sired, sir ing.** —*n.* 1 a male ancestor. 2 male parent; father: *Lightning was the sire of the racehorse Danger.* 3 title of respect used formerly to a great noble and now to a king. —*v.t.* be the father of. [< Old French < Latin *senior* older. Doublet of SENIOR.]

skep ti cal (skep′tə kəl), *adj.* 1 of or like a skeptic; inclined to doubt; not believing easily. 2 questioning the truth of theories or apparent facts. Also, **sceptical.** —**skep′ti cal ly,** *adv.*

skir mish (skėr′mish), *n.* 1 a brief fight between small groups of soldiers. 2 a slight conflict, argument, contest, etc. —*v.i.* take part in a skirmish. [< Old French *eskirmiss-,* a form of *eskirmir,* originally, ward off; of Germanic origin] —**skir′mish er,** *n.*

sledge ham mer (slej′ham′ər), *n.* a large, heavy hammer, usually swung with both hands. —*v.t.* hit with, or as if with, a sledgehammer. —*adj.* powerful; crushing.

slug gish (slug′ish), *adj.* 1 slow-moving; not active; lacking energy or vigor: *a sluggish mind.* 2 lazy; idle. 3 moving slowly; having little motion. A sluggish river has very little current. **—slug′gish ly,** adv. **—slug′-gish ness,** n.

sluice (slüs), n., v., **sluiced, sluic ing. —n.**
1 structure with a gate or gates for holding back or controlling the water of a canal, river, or lake. 2 gate that holds back or controls the flow of water. When the water behind a dam gets too high, the sluices are opened. 3 the water held back or controlled by such a gate. 4 a means of controlling the flow or passage of anything: *War opens the sluices of hatred and bloodshed.* 5 channel for carrying off overflow or surplus water. **—v.t.** 1 let out or draw off (water, etc.) by opening a sluice. 2 flush or cleanse with a rush of water; pour or throw water over. **—v.i.** flow or pour in a stream; rush: *Water sluiced down the channel.* [< Old French *escluse* < Late Latin *exclusa* barrier to shut out water < Latin *excludere* shut out]

slump (slump), v.i. 1 drop heavily; fall suddenly: *The boy's feet slumped repeatedly through the melting ice.* 2 move, walk, sit, etc., in a drooping manner; slouch: *The bored students slumped in their seats.* 3 fall off; decline: *The stock market slumped.* **—n.** 1 a heavy or sudden fall; collapse. 2 a great or sudden decline in prices, activity, performance, etc. [perhaps imitative]

smite (smīt), v., **smote, smit ten** or **smit, smit ing. —v.t.** 1 give a hard blow to (a person, etc.) with the hand, a stick, or the like; strike. 2 give or strike (a blow, stroke, etc.). 3 strike with a weapon, etc., so as to cause serious injury or death. 4 attack with a sudden pain, disease, etc.: *a city smitten with pestilence. His conscience smote him.* 5 impress suddenly with a strong feeling, sentiment, etc.: *smitten with curiosity.* 6 punish severely; chasten. **—v.i.** 1 deliver a blow or blows, a stroke, etc., with or as with a stick, weapon, etc.; strike. 2 come with force (upon): *The sound of a blacksmith's hammer smote upon their ears.* [Old English *smītan*] **—smit′er,** n.

smith (smith), n. 1 worker in metal, especially iron. 2 blacksmith. [Old English]

sol emn (sol′əm), adj. 1 of a serious, grave, or earnest character: *a solemn face.* 2 causing serious or grave thoughts: *The organ played solemn music.* 3 done with form and ceremony: *a solemn procession.* 4 connected with religion; sacred. 5 gloomy; dark; somber in color. [< Latin *sollemnis*] **—sol′emn ly,** adv. **—sol′emn ness,** n.

so lic i tous (sə lis′ə təs), adj. 1 showing care or concern; anxious; concerned: *Parents are solicitous for their children's progress in school.* 2 desirous; eager: *solicitous to please.* [< Latin *sollicitus* < *sollus* all + *ciere* arouse] **—so lic′i tous ly,** adv. **—so-lic′i tous ness,** n.

sol i tar y (sol′ə ter′ē), adj., n., pl. **-tar ies.** **—adj.** 1 alone or single; only: *A solitary rider was seen in the distance.* 2 without companions; away from people; lonely: *lead a solitary life. The house is in a solitary spot miles from a town.* 3 (in zoology) living alone, rather than in colonies: *a solitary bee.* 4 (in botany) growing separately; not forming clusters. **—n.** person living alone, away from people. [< Latin *solitarius* < *solus* alone. Doublet of SOLITAIRE.] **—sol′i tar′i ly,** adv. **—sol′i tar′i ness,** n.

som ber or **som bre** (som′bər), adj.

1 having deep shadows; dark; gloomy: *A cloudy winter day is somber.* 2 melancholy; dismal: *His losses made him very somber.* [< French *sombre*] **—som′ber ly, som′-bre ly,** adv. **—som′ber ness, som′bre-ness,** n.

so na ta (sə nä′tə), n. piece of music, for one or two instruments, having three or four movements in contrasted rhythms but related keys. [< Italian, literally, sounded < Latin *sonare* to sound]

sor cer er (sôr′sər ər), n. person who practices sorcery; wizard; magician.

sor cer ess (sôr′sər is), n. woman who practices sorcery; witch.

sor cer y (sôr′sər ē), n., pl. **-cer ies.** magic performed with the supposed aid of evil spirits; witchcraft. [< Old French *sorcerie,* ultimately < Latin *sors* chance, lot]

souse (sous), v., **soused, sous ing,** n. **—v.t., v.i.** 1 plunge into liquid; soak in a liquid. 2 soak in vinegar, brine, etc.; pickle. 3 SLANG. make or become drunk. **—n.** 1 a plunging into a liquid; drenching. 2 liquid used for pickling. 3 something soaked or kept in pickle, especially the head, ears, and feet of a pig. 4 SLANG. drunkard. [ultimately < Old French *sous* pickled pork; of Germanic origin]

sov er eign (sov′rən), n. 1 supreme ruler; king or queen; monarch. 2 person, group, or nation having supreme control or dominion; master: *sovereign of the seas.* 3 a British gold coin, worth 20 shillings, or one pound. **—adj.** 1 having the rank or power of a sovereign. 2 greatest in rank or power. 3 independent of the control of other governments. 4 above all others; supreme; greatest: *Character is of sovereign importance.* 5 very excellent or powerful. [< Old French *soverain,* ultimately < Latin *super* over] **—sov′er eign ly,** adv.

Spanish moss, a mosslike, epiphytic plant of the same family as the pineapple, growing on the branches of certain trees, from which it hangs in gray streamers. It is found in the southern United States and tropical America.

spar (spär), n., v., **sparred, spar ring. —n.** 1 a stout pole used to support or extend the sails of a ship; mast, yard, gaff, boom, etc., of a ship. 2 the main horizontal support of an airplane wing. **—v.t.** provide (a ship) with spars. [Middle English *sparre* rafter]

spark (spärk), n. 1 a gay, showy young man; dandy. 2 beau; lover. **—v.t., v.i.** INFORMAL. court; woo. [perhaps < Scandinavian (Old Icelandic) *sparkr* lively] **—spark′er,** n.

spasm (spaz′əm), n. 1 a sudden, abnormal, involuntary contraction of a muscle or muscles. 2 any sudden, brief fit or spell of unusual energy or activity. [< Greek *spasmos* < *span* draw up, tear away]

spat[1] (spat), n., v., **spat ted, spat ting. —n.** 1 a slight quarrel; tiff. 2 a light blow; slap. **—v.i.** INFORMAL. quarrel slightly or briefly. **—v.t.** slap lightly. [perhaps imitative]

spat[2] (spat), v. a pt. and a pp. of **spit.**

spat[3] (spat), n. Usually, **spats,** pl. a short gaiter worn over the instep, reaching just above the ankle. [short for *spatterdash*]

spat[4] (spat), n., v., **spat ted, spat ting. —n.** 1 the spawn of oysters or certain other shellfish. 2 a young oyster. **—v.i.** (of oysters and certain other shellfish) spawn. [origin uncertain]

spec i men (spes′ə mən), n. 1 one of a group or class taken to show what the others are like; sample: *She collects specimens of all kinds of rocks.* 2 INFORMAL. a human being; person. [< Latin < *specere* to view]

spec u late (spek′yə lāt), v.i., **-lat ed, -lat-ing.** 1 think carefully; reflect; meditate; consider: *The philosopher speculated about time and space.* 2 guess; conjecture. [< Latin *speculatum* observed, viewed < *specula* watchtower < *specere* to view]

spe le o lo gist (spē′lē ol′ə jist), n. an expert in speleology.

spe le o lo gy (spē′lē ol′ə jē), n. the scientific study of caves. [< Greek *spēlaion* cave]

spe lunk er (spi lung′kər), n. person who explores and maps caves as a hobby. [< Latin *spelunca* cave < Greek *spēlaion*]

spend thrift (spend′thrift′), n. person who spends money extravagantly or wastefully. **—adj.** wastefully extravagant.

spir it (spir′it), n. Often, **spirits,** pl. a strong alcoholic liquor obtained by distilling, as whiskey, brandy, gin, etc.

spir it ed (spir′ə tid), adj. full of energy and spirit; lively; dashing. **—spir′it ed ly,** adv. **—spir′it ed ness,** n.

splay (splā), v.t. 1 spread out; expand; extend. 2 make slanting; bevel. **—v.i.** 1 have or lie in a slanting direction; slope. 2 spread out; flare. **—adj.** 1 wide and flat; turned outward. 2 awkward; clumsy. **—n.** 1 a spread; flare. 2 surface which makes an oblique angle with another, as the beveled jamb of a window or door; a slanting surface. [Middle English *splayen,* short for *displayen* display]

spoil (spoil), n. 1 Often, **spoils,** pl. things taken by force; things won; booty; loot: *The soldiers carried the spoils back to their own land.* 2 **spoils,** pl. government offices and positions filled by the political party that has won an election. 3 an object of plundering; prey. [< Old French *espoillier,* ultimately < Latin *spolium* booty, spoil] **—spoil′a ble,** adj.

sprat (sprat), n., pl. **sprats** or **sprat.** 1 a small herring of the Atlantic coast of Europe. 2 any of certain similar herrings. [Old English *sprott*]

sprint (sprint), v.i. run at full speed, especially for a short distance. **—n.** a race or any short spell of running, rowing, etc., at top speed. [probably < Scandinavian (Old Icelandic) *spretta*] **—sprint′er,** n.

spume (spyüm), n., v., **spumed, spum ing. —n.** frothy matter; foam; froth. **—v.i.** foam or froth. [< Latin *spuma*]

spurn (spėrn), v.t. 1 refuse with scorn; scorn: *spurn a bribe, spurn an offer of friendship.* 2 strike with the foot; kick away. **—v.i.** oppose with scorn: *spurn at restraint.* **—n.** 1 disdainful rejection; contemptuous treatment. 2 a kick. [Old English *spurnan*] **—spurn′er,** n.

squan der (skwon′dər), v.t. spend foolishly; waste: *squander one's money in gambling.* [origin uncertain] **—squan′der er,** n.

stac ca to (stə kä′tō), adj. 1 (in music) with breaks between the successive tones; disconnected; detached. 2 abrupt: *a staccato manner.* **—adv.** in a staccato manner. [< Italian, literally, detached]

stam pede (stam pēd′), n., v., **-ped ed, -ped ing. —n.** 1 a sudden scattering or headlong flight of a frightened herd of cattle, horses, etc. 2 any headlong flight of a large group. 3 a general rush: *a stampede to newly discovered gold fields.* **—v.i.** 1 scatter or flee in a stampede. 2 make a general rush. **—v.t.** cause to stampede. [< Mexican Spanish *estampida* < Spanish *estampar* to stamp]

star board (stär′bərd, stär′bôrd, or stär′bōrd), n. the right side of a ship, when facing forward. —*adj.* on, at, or of the right side of a ship. —*v.t., v.i.* turn (the helm) to the right side. [Old English *stēorbord* the side from which a vessel was steered < *stēor* steering paddle + *bord* side (of a ship)]

stay (stā), *n., v.,* **stayed, stay ing.** —*n.* 1 one of the strong ropes, often of wire, by which the mast of a ship is held in position. 2 any rope or chain attached to something to steady it. —*v.t.* support or secure with stays. —*v.i.* (of a ship) change to the other tack. [Old English *stæg*]

stealth y (stel′thē), *adj.,* **stealth i er, stealth i est.** done in a secret manner; secret; sly: *The cat crept in a stealthy way toward the bird.* —**stealth′i ly,** *adv.* —**stealth′i ness,** *n.*

steel (stēl), *n.* 1 an alloy of iron and varying amounts of carbon (always less than two percent, the amount in cast iron, but more than the amount in wrought iron). Steel has greater hardness and flexibility than iron and hence is used for tools and machinery. 2 something made from steel; a sword or a piece of steel for making sparks; a rod of steel for sharpening knives. 3 steellike hardness or strength: *nerves of steel.* —*adj.* 1 made of steel. 2 resembling steel in color, hardness, etc. 3 of or having to do with the production of steel. —*v.t.* 1 point, edge, or cover with steel. 2 make hard or strong like steel: *steel oneself against possible failure.* [Old English *stēle*] —**steel′less,** *adj.* —**steel′like′,** *adj.*

sten cil (sten′səl), *n., v.,* **-ciled, -cil ing** or **-cilled, -cil ling.** —*n.* 1 a thin sheet of metal, paper, cardboard, etc., having letters or designs cut through it. When it is laid on a surface and ink or color is applied, these letters or designs appear on the surface. 2 the letters or designs so made. —*v.t.* 1 mark or paint with a stencil: *The curtains have a stenciled border.* 2 produce (letters or designs) by means of a stencil. [< Old French *estanceler* to ornament with colors, ultimately < Latin *scintilla* spark]

stet son hat (stet′sən), *n.* a high-crowned felt hat with a broad brim.

sti fle (stī′fəl), *v.,* **-fled, -fling.** —*v.t.* 1 stop the breath of; smother: *The smoke stifled the firemen.* 2 keep back; suppress; stop: *stifle a cry, stifle a yawn, stifle business activity, stifle a rebellion.* —*v.i.* 1 be unable to breathe freely: *I am stifling in this hot room.* 2 die or become unconscious by being unable to breathe. [Middle English *stuflen, stiflen* < *stuffen* to stuff, stifle]

stile (stīl), *n.* 1 step or steps for getting over a fence or wall. 2 turnstile. [Old English *stigel,* related to *stīgan* climb]

still ness (stil′nis), *n.* 1 absence of noise; silence. 2 absence of motion; calm.

stock (stok), *n.* part used as a support or handle; part to which other parts are attached: *the wooden stock of a rifle.*

stooge (stüj), *n., v.,* **stooged, stoog ing.** —*n.* INFORMAL. 1 person on the stage who asks questions of a comedian and is the butt of the comedian's jokes. 2 person who follows and flatters another; hanger-on. —*v.i.* be or act as a stooge *(for): stooge for a comedian.* [origin uncertain]

stow (stō), *v.t.* 1 put away to be stored; pack: *The cargo was stowed in the ship's hold.* 2 pack things closely in; fill by packing: *stow a pantry with cans of food.* 3 SLANG. stop. 4 have room for; hold. —*v.i.* **stow away,** hide on a ship, airplane, etc., to get a free passage or to escape secretly. [Old English

stōw a place] —**stow′er,** *n.*

strait (strāt), *n.* 1 a narrow channel connecting two larger bodies of water. 2 **straits,** *pl.* difficulty; need; distress: *be in desperate straits for money.* —*adj.* ARCHAIC. 1 narrow; limited; confining. 2 strict. [< Old French *estreit* < Latin *strictum* drawn tight. Doublet of STRICT.] —**strait′ly,** *adv.* —**strait′ness,** *n.*

strick en (strik′ən), *adj.* 1 hit, wounded, or affected by (a weapon, disease, trouble, sorrow, etc.): *a stricken deer, a city stricken by fire.* 2 **stricken in years,** old. —*v.* a pp. of **strike.**

stri dent (strīd′nt), *adj.* making or having a harsh sound; creaking; grating; shrill. [< Latin *stridentem*] —**stri′dent ly,** *adv.*

stu pe fac tion (stü′pə fak′shən, styü′pə fak′shən), *n.* 1 a dazed or senseless condition; stupor. 2 overwhelming amazement, shock, etc.

sty (stī), *n., pl.* **sties.** 1 pen for pigs. 2 any filthy or disgusting place. [Old English *stig* a building]

styl ize (stī′līz), *v.t., v.i.,* **-ized, -iz ing.** make or design according to a particular or conventional style. —**styl′i za′tion,** *n.* —**styl′iz er,** *n.*

sua vi ty (swä′və tē, swav′ə tē), *n., pl.* **-ties.** smoothly agreeable quality or behavior; smooth politeness; blandness.

sub-, *prefix.* 1 under; below: *Subnormal = below normal.* 2 down; further; again: *Subdivide = divide again.* 3 near; nearly: *Subtropical = nearly tropical.* 4 lower; subordinate: *Subcommittee = a lower or subordinate committee.* 5 resulting from further division: *Subsection = section resulting from further division of something.* 6 slightly; somewhat: *Subacid = slightly acid.* [< Latin *sub* under, beneath]

sub merge (səb mėrj′), *v.,* **-merged, -merg ing.** —*v.t.* 1 put under water; cover with water: *land submerged by a flood.* 2 cover; bury: *His talent was submerged by his shyness.* —*v.i.* 1 sink under water; go below the surface: *The submarine submerged.* 2 sink out of sight. [< Latin *submergere* < *sub-* under + *mergere* to plunge]

sub stan tial (səb stan′shəl), *adj.* 1 having substance; material; real; actual: *People and things are substantial; dreams and ghosts are not.* 2 strong; firm; solid: *The house is substantial enough to last a hundred years.* 3 large; important; ample: *make a substantial improvement in health.* 4 providing ample or abundant nourishment: *Eat a substantial breakfast.* 5 in the main; in essentials: *The stories told by the two children were in substantial agreement.* 6 well-to-do; wealthy. —**sub stan′tial ly,** *adv.*

sul fa nil a mide (sul′fə nil′ə mīd, sul′fə nil′ə mid), *n.* a white, crystalline substance used as the basis for most of the sulfa drugs. *Formula:* $C_6H_8N_2O_2S$. Also, **sulphanilamide.**

sul len (sul′ən), *adj.* 1 silent because of bad humor or anger: *The sullen child refused to answer my question.* 2 showing bad humor or anger. 3 gloomy; dismal: *The sullen skies threatened rain.* [Middle English *soleine,* ultimately < Latin *solus* alone] —**sul′len ly,** *adv.* —**sul′len ness,** *n.*

sul try (sul′trē), *adj.,* **-tri er, -tri est.** 1 hot, close, and moist: *We expect sultry weather during July.* 2 hot or fiery: *a sultry sun, sultry glances.* [< obsolete *sulter* (verb) swelter; related to *swelter*] —**sul′tri ly,** *adv.* —**sul′tri ness,** *n.*

hat, āge, fär; let, ēqual, tėrm;
it, īce; hot, ōpen, ôrder;
oil, out; cup, pút, rüle;
ch, child; ng, long; sh, she;
th, thin; ᴛʜ, then; zh, measure;

ə represents *a* in about, *e* in taken,
i in pencil, *o* in lemon, *u* in circus.

< = from, derived from, taken from.

super-, *prefix.* 1 over; above: *Superimpose = impose over or above.* 2 besides; further: *Superadd = add besides or further.* 3 in high proportion; to excess; exceedingly: *Superabundant = abundant to excess.* 4 surpassing: *Supernatural = surpassing the natural.* [< Latin *super* over, above]

su perb (sù pėrb′), *adj.* 1 grand and stately; majestic: *Mountain scenery is superb.* 2 rich; elegant: *a superb dinner.* 3 very fine; first-rate; excellent: *a superb performance.* [< Latin *superbus* < *super* above] —**su perb′ly,** *adv.* —**su perb′ness,** *n.*

sup ple (sup′əl), *adj.,* **-pler, -plest,** *v.,* **-pled, -pling.** —*adj.* 1 bending or folding easily: *a supple birch tree, supple leather.* 2 moving easily or nimbly: *a supple dancer.* 3 readily adaptable to different ideas, circumstances, people, etc.; yielding: *a supple mind.* —*v.t., v.i.* make or grow supple. [< Old French *souple* < Latin *supplex* submissive < *supplicare* bend down, supplicate] —**sup′ply,** *adv.* —**sup′ple ness,** *n.*

sup pli ant (sup′lē ənt), *adj.* asking humbly and earnestly: *He sent a suppliant message for help.* —*n.* person who asks humbly and earnestly: *She knelt as a suppliant at the altar.* [< Middle French, present participle of *supplier* supplicate] —**sup′pli ant ly,** *adv.*

sup pli cant (sup′lə kənt), *adj., n.* suppliant. —**sup′pli cant ly,** *adv.*

sup press (sə pres′), *v.t.* 1 put an end to; stop by force; put down: *suppress a rebellion.* 2 keep in; hold back; keep from appearing: *She suppressed a yawn. Each nation suppressed news that was not favorable to it.* 3 subdue (a feeling, etc.): *suppressed desires.* 4 check the flow of; stop: *suppress bleeding.* 5 keep secret; refrain from disclosing or divulging: *suppress the truth.* [< Latin *suppressum* pressed down < *sub-* down + *premere* to press] —**sup press′er, sup pres′sor,** *n.*

surge (sėrj), *v.,* **surged, surg ing,** *n.* —*v.i.* 1 rise and fall; move like waves: *A great wave surged over us. The crowd surged through the streets.* 2 rise or swell (up) violently or excitedly, as feelings, thoughts, etc. —*n.* 1 a swelling wave; sweep or rush of waves. 2 something like a wave: *A surge of anger swept over him.* [ultimately < Latin *surgere* rise < *sub-* up + *regere* to reach]

sur round (sə round′), *v.t.* 1 shut in on all sides; extend around: *A high fence surrounds the field.* 2 form an enclosure around; encircle: *They surrounded the invalid with every comfort.* —*n.* border or edging nearly surrounding a central piece: *the plastic surround of the television screen.* [< Anglo-French *surounder* surpass < Late Latin *superundare* overflow < Latin *super-* over + *unda* wave]

su sur rus (sù sėr′əs), *n.* a rustling or whispering sound.

su ture (sü′chər), *n., v.,* **-tured, -tur ing.** —*n.* 1 the sewing together or joining of two surfaces, especially the edges of a cut or wound. 2 seam formed in sewing up a wound. 3 one of the stitches or fastenings used. 4 the material used, as gut, linen, or silk. —*v.t.* unite by suture or as if by a suture. [< Latin *sutura* < *suere* to sew]

swell (swel), a long, unbroken wave, or waves: *The boat rocked in the swell.*

swoon (swün), *v.i.* 1 faint: *swoon at the sight of blood.* 2 fade or die away gradually. —*n.* a faint. [ultimately < Old English *geswōgen* in a swoon] —**swoon′ing ly,** *adv.*

tack (tak), *n.* 1 in nautical use: **a** a zigzag course against the wind. **b** the direction in which a ship moves in regard to the direction of the wind and the position of her sails. On port tack, a ship is close-hauled with the wind on her left. **c** one of the movements in a zigzag course. **d** act of zigzagging; turn from one direction to the next. 2 in nautical use: **a** a rope to hold in place the outer lower corner of some sails. **b** corner to which such a rope is fastened.

taint (tānt), *n.* 1 a stain or spot; trace of decay, corruption, or disgrace. 2 a cause of any such condition; contaminating or corrupting influence. —*v.t.* give a taint to; spoil, corrupt, or contaminate. —*v.i.* become tainted; decay. [< Old French *teint*, past participle of *teindre* to dye < Latin *tingere*] —**taint′less,** *adj.*

tat ter (tat′ər), *n.* 1 a torn piece; rag: *After the storm the flag hung in tatters upon the mast.* 2 **tatters,** *pl.* torn or ragged clothing. —*v.t.* tear or wear to pieces; make ragged. —*v.i.* be or become tattered. [< Scandinavian (Old Icelandic) *tǫtturr* rag]

taunt (tônt, tänt), *v.t.* 1 jeer at; mock; reproach; deride. 2 get or drive by taunts; provoke: *taunt someone into taking a dare.* —*n.* a bitter or insulting remark; mocking; jeering. [origin uncertain] —**taunt′er,** *n.* —**taunt′ing ly,** *adv.*

taut (tôt), *adj.* 1 tightly drawn; tense: *a taut rope.* 2 in neat condition; tidy: *a taut ship.* [Middle English *tought*] —**taut′ly,** *adv.* —**taut′ness,** *n.*

taut en (tôt′n), *v.t., v.i.* make or become taut; tighten.

tel e cast (tel′ə kast′), *v.,* -cast or -cast-ed, -cast ing, *n.* —*v.t., v.i.* broadcast by television. —*n.* a television broadcast. —**tel′e cast′er,** *n.*

tem per a ment (tem′pər ə mənt), *n.* 1 a person's nature or disposition: *a nervous temperament.* 2 an easily irritated, sensitive nature. An artist, singer, or actress often has temperament.

ten sion (ten′shən), *n.* 1 a stretching. 2 a stretched condition: *The tension of the bow gives speed to the arrow.* 3 mental or nervous strain: *A mother feels tension when her baby is sick.* 4 a strained condition: *political tension.* —*v.t.* make tense; tighten; draw out. [< Latin *tensionem* < *tendere* to stretch] —**ten′sion less,** *adj.*

ten si ty (ten′sə tē), *n.* tense quality or condition.

ten ta cle (ten′tə kəl), *n.* 1 one of the long, slender, flexible growths, usually occurring on the head or around the mouth of an animal, used to touch, hold, or move. 2 a sensitive, hairlike growth on a plant. [< New Latin *tentaculum* < Latin *tentare* to try]

ten ta tive (ten′tə tiv), *adj.* 1 done as a trial or experiment; experimental: *a tentative plan.* 2 hesitating: *a tentative laugh.* [< Medieval Latin *tentativus* < Latin *tentare* to try] —**ten′ta tive ly,** *adv.* —**ten′ta tive ness,** *n.*

tern (tėrn), *n.* any of a family of sea birds of the same order as the gulls but with a more slender body and bill and usually a long, forked tail. [< Scandinavian (Danish) *terne*]

ter rain (te rān′, ter′ān), *n.* tract of land, especially considered with respect to its extent and natural features in relation to its use in warfare. [< French, ultimately < Latin *terra* earth, land]

teth er (teᴛʜ′ər), *n.* 1 rope or chain for fastening an animal so that it can graze or move only within a certain limit. 2 **at the end of one's tether,** at the end of one's resources or endurance. —*v.t.* fasten or confine with or as with a tether. [< Scandinavian (Old Icelandic) *tjōthr*]

ther a py (ther′ə pē), *n., pl.* -pies. treatment of diseases or disorders. [< Greek *therapeia* < *therapeuein* to cure, treat < *theraps* attendant]

thick et (thik′it), *n.* 1 shrubs, bushes, or small trees growing close together; copse; brake. 2 a thick, dense mass; jumble.

throb (throb), *v.,* **throbbed, throb bing,** *n.* —*v.i.* 1 beat rapidly or strongly; pulsate; palpitate: *The long climb up the hill made her heart throb.* 2 beat steadily. —*n.* 1 a rapid or strong beat: *a throb of pain.* 2 a steady beat: *the throb of a pulse.* [Middle English *throbben*] —**throb′bing ly,** *adv.*

throng (thrông, throng), *n.* 1 a crowd; multitude. 2 a pressing or crowding; crowded condition. —*v.t.* crowd; fill with a crowd: *The people thronged the theater to see the new movie.* —*v.i.* come together in a crowd; go or press in large numbers. [Old English (ge)thrang]

ti dings (tī′dingz), *n.pl.* news; information: *joyful tidings.* [Old English *tīdung* < *tīdan* happen]

tim or ous (tim′ər əs), *adj.* 1 easily frightened; timid. 2 characterized by or indicating fear. [< Latin *timor* fear < *timere* to fear] —**tim′or ous ly,** *adv.* —**tim′or ous ness,** *n.*

-tion, *suffix* added to verbs to form nouns. 1 act or process of ___ing: *Addition = act or process of adding.* 2 condition of being ___ed: *Exhaustion = condition of being exhausted.* 3 result of ___ing: *Reflection = result of reflecting.* [< Latin *-tionem*]

tip sy (tip′sē), *adj.,* -si er, -si est. 1 tipping easily; unsteady; tilted. 2 somewhat intoxicated, but not thoroughly drunk. —**tip′si ly,** *adv.* —**tip′si ness,** *n.*

toil (toil), *n.* hard work; labor: *succeed after years of toil.* —*v.i.* 1 work hard. 2 move with difficulty, pain, or weariness: *They toiled up the steep mountain.* [< Old French *toeillier* drag about < Latin *tudiculare* stir up < *tudicula* olive press < *tudes* mallet] —**toil′er,** *n.*

tol er ant (tol′ər ənt), *adj.* 1 willing to let other people do as they think best; willing to endure beliefs and actions of which one does not approve: *The founders of the colony of Rhode Island were tolerant toward all religious beliefs.* 2 able to endure or resist the action of a drug, poison, etc. —**tol′er ant ly,** *adv.*

tor por (tôr′pər), *n.* 1 torpid condition or quality; apathy; lethargy. 2 absence or suspension of movement or feeling, as of a hibernating animal. [< Latin < *torpere* be numb]

tor tu ous (tôr′chü əs), *adj.* 1 full of twists, turns, or bends; twisting; winding; crooked: *We found the river's course very tortuous.* 2 mentally or morally crooked; not straightforward: *tortuous reasoning.* [< Latin *tortuosus,* ultimately < *torquere* to twist] —**tor′tu ous ly,** *adv.* —**tor′tu ous ness,** *n.*

tor ture (tôr′chər), *n., v.,* -tured, -tur ing. —*n.* 1 act or fact of inflicting very severe pain, especially in hatred or revenge, as a means of extortion, or to force a person to confess to or give evidence about a crime. 2 very severe pain. 3 cause of very severe pain. —*v.t.* 1 cause very severe pain to. 2 twist the meaning of. 3 twist or force out of its natural form: *Winds tortured the trees.* [< Late Latin *tortura* < Latin *torquere* to twist] —**tor′tur er,** *n.*

tor tur ous (tôr′chər əs), *adj.* full of, involving, or causing torture. —**tor′tur ous ly,** *adv.*

trace (trās), *n.* 1 either of two straps, ropes, or chains by which an animal pulls a wagon, carriage, etc. 2 **kick over the traces,** throw off controls or restraints; become unruly. [< Old French *traiz,* plural of *trait* < Latin *tractus* a drawing out < *trahere* to drag]

trac ta ble (trak′tə bəl), *adj.* 1 easily managed or controlled; easy to deal with; docile: *Dogs are more tractable than mules.* 2 easily handled or worked; malleable: *Copper and gold are tractable.* [< Latin *tractabilis* < *tractare* to handle] —**trac′ta ble ness,** *n.* —**trac′ta bly,** *adv.*

tran quil (trang′kwəl), *adj.,* -quil er, -quil est or -quil ler, -quil lest. free from agitation or disturbance; calm; peaceful; quiet. [< Latin *tranquillus*] —**tran′quil ly,** *adv.* —**tran′quil ness,** *n.*

trans-, *prefix.* 1 across; over; through, as in *transcontinental, transmit.* 2 on the other side of; beyond, as in *transatlantic.* 3 to a different place, condition, etc., as in *transmigration, transform.* [< Latin *trans* across]

trans ac tion (tran zak′shən, tran sak′-shən), *n.* 1 act or process of transacting: *She attends to the transaction of important matters herself.* 2 piece of business: *A record was kept of the firm's latest transaction.* 3 **transactions,** *pl.* record of what was done at the meetings of a society, club, etc.

trans fix (tran sfiks′), *v.t.* 1 pierce through: *The hunter transfixed the lion with a spear.* 2 fasten or fix by piercing through with something pointed; impale. 3 make motionless or helpless (with amazement, terror, grief, etc.). —**trans fix′ion,** *n.*

trans lu cent (tran slü′snt, tranz lü′snt), *adj.* letting light through without being transparent: *Frosted glass is translucent.* [< Latin *translucentem* < *trans-* through + *lucere* to shine] —**trans lu′cent ly,** *adv.*

trans mute (tran smyüt′, tranz myüt′), *v.,* -mut ed, -mut ing. change from one nature, substance, or form into another: *We can transmute water power into electrical power.* [< Latin *transmutare* < *trans-* thoroughly + *mutare* to change] —**trans mut′er,** *n.*

tran spire (tran spīr′), *v.i.,* -spired, -spir ing. 1 take place; happen; occur: *I heard later what transpired at the meeting.* 2 leak out; become known. [< Middle French *transpirer* < Latin *trans-* through + *spirare* breathe]

trav erse (*v.* trav′ərs, trə vėrs′; *n., adj.* trav′ərs), *v.,* -ersed, -ers ing, *n., adj.* —*v.t.* 1 pass across, over, or through: *We traversed* the desert. 2 go to and fro over or along (a place, etc.); cross. 3 ski or climb diagonally across. —*n.* 1 act of traversing. 2 something put or lying across; transverse. 3 a sideways motion of a ship, part in a machine, mountain climbers, etc. 4 the zigzag course taken by a ship because of contrary winds or currents. 5 obstacle; hindrance; opposition. —*adj.* lying, passing, or extending across; cross; transverse. [< Old French *traverser* < Late Latin *transversare* < Latin *transversum* transverse.] —**trav′ers a ble,** *adj.* —**trav′ers er,** *n.*

tra vois (trə voi′), *n.*, *pl.* **-vois.** vehicle without wheels used by Great Plains Indians, consisting of two shafts or poles joined by a platform or net for holding the load. [< Canadian French]

tread (tred), *v.*, **trod, trod den** or **trod, tread ing,** *n.* —*v.i.* 1 set the foot down; walk; step: *tread through the meadow.* 2 step heavily; trample: *Don't tread on the flower beds.* —*v.t.* set the feet on; walk on or through; step on: *tread the streets.*

trel lis (trel′is), *n.* frame of light strips of wood or metal crossing one another with open spaces in between; lattice, especially one supporting growing vines. —*v.t.* 1 furnish with a trellis. 2 support or train (vines, etc.) on a trellis. 3 cross or interweave as in a trellis. [< Old French *trelis,* ultimately < Latin *trilix* triple-twilled < *tri-* three + *licium* thread]

trem u lous (trem′yə ləs), *adj.* 1 trembling; quivering: *a voice tremulous with sobs.* 2 timid; fearful. 3 that wavers; shaky: *tremulous writing.* [< Latin *tremulus* < *tremere* to tremble] —**trem′u lous ly,** *adv.* —**trem′u lous ness,** *n.*

trill (tril), *v.t.*, *v.i.* 1 sing, play, sound, or speak with a tremulous, vibrating sound. 2 (in music) sing or play with a trill. 3 (in phonetics) pronounce with a trill. —*n.* 1 act or sound of trilling. 2 a quick alternation of two musical notes either a tone or a half tone apart. 3 in phonetics: **a** a rapid vibration of the lips, the tip of the tongue, or the uvula. **b** sound produced by such a vibration. Spanish *rr* is a trill. [< Italian *trillare*]

trough (trôf, trof), *n.* 1 a narrow, open, boxlike container for holding food or water, especially for farm stock or other animals. 2 something shaped like this: *The baker uses a trough for kneading dough.* 3 a channel for carrying water; gutter. 4 a long hollow between two ridges, especially the hollow between two waves or two hills. 5 (in meteorology) a long, narrow area of relatively low barometric pressure. [Old English *trog*] —**trough′like′,** *adj.*

tu mult (tü′mult, tyü′mult), *n.* 1 noise or uproar; commotion: *the tumult of the storm.* 2 a violent disturbance or disorder: *The cry of "Fire!" caused a tumult in the theater.* 3 a violent disturbance of mind or feeling; confusion or excitement. [< Latin *tumultus*]

tu nic (tü′nik, tyü′nik), *n.* 1 garment like a shirt or gown, usually reaching to the knees, worn by men and women in ancient Greece and Rome. 2 any garment like this. 3 a woman's garment, usually belted, extending below the waist or over the skirt. 4 a short, close-fitting coat worn by soldiers, policemen, etc. [< Latin *tunica*]

tur bu lence (tėr′byə ləns), *n.* 1 turbulent condition; disorder; tumult; commotion. 2 an eddying motion of the atmosphere interrupting the flow of wind.

twang (twang), *n.* 1 a sharp, ringing sound:

The bow made a twang when I shot the arrow. 2 a sharp, nasal tone: *the twang of a Yankee farmer.* —*v.t.* 1 make a sharp, ringing sound. 2 play, pluck, shoot, etc., with a twang. 3 speak (words, etc.) with a sharp, nasal tone. —*v.i.* 1 make a sharp, ringing sound: *The banjos twanged.* 2 speak with a sharp, nasal tone. [imitative]

tweak (twēk), *v.t.*, *v.i.* seize and pull with a sharp jerk and twist: *tweak a person's ear.* —*n.* a sharp pull and twist. [Old English *twiccian* to pluck]

-ty¹, *suffix added to numbers.* ____ tens; ____ times ten: *Seventy = seven tens, or seven times ten.* [Old English *-tig*]

-ty², *suffix added to adjectives to form nouns.* quality, condition, or fact of being ____: *Safety = condition or quality of being safe.* Also, **-ity.** [< Old French *-te, -tet* < Latin *-tas, -tatem*]

tyr an ny (tir′ə nē), *n.*, *pl.* **-nies.** 1 cruel or unjust use of power. 2 a tyrannical act. 3 government, position, rule, or term of office of a tyrant or absolute ruler. 4 state ruled by a tyrant.

un-¹, *prefix.* not ____; the opposite of ____: *Unequal = not equal; the opposite of equal. Unchanged = not changed. Unjust = not just.* [Old English]

un-², *prefix.* do the opposite of ____; do what will reverse the act: *Unfasten = do the opposite of fasten. Uncover = do the opposite of cover.* [Old English *un-, on-*]

➤ *un-* is used freely to form verbs expressing the reversal of the action of the verb.

unceasing (un sēs′ing), *adj.* not stopping; not coming to an end.

un con cerned (un′kən sėrnd′), *adj.* not concerned; not interested; free from care or anxiety; indifferent. —**un′con cern′ed ly,** *adv.* —**un′con cern′ed ness,** *n.*

un der mine (un′dər mīn′, un′dər mīn′), *v.t.*, **-mined, -min ing.** 1 make a passage or hole under; dig under: *undermine a foundation.* 2 wear away the foundations of: *a cliff undermined by waves.* 3 weaken by secret or unfair means: *undermine a person's reputation by scandal.* 4 weaken or destroy gradually: *Many severe colds had undermined her health.* —**un′der min′er,** *n.*

un du late (*v.* un′jə lāt′; *adj.* un′jə lit, un′jə lāt; un′dyə lit, un′dyə lāt), *v.*, **-lat ed, -lat ing.** —*v.i.* 1 move in waves: *undulating water.* 2 have a wavy form or surface: *undulating hair, an undulating prairie.* —*v.t.* 1 cause to move in waves. 2 give a wavy form or surface to. —*adj.* wavy. [< Latin *undulatus* wavy < *unda* wave]

un eas y (un ē′zē), *adj.*, **-eas i er, -eas i est.** 1 restless; disturbed; anxious: *an uneasy sleep, be uneasy about a decision.* 2 not comfortable. 3 not easy in manner; awkward. —**un eas′i ly,** *adv.* —**un eas′i ness,** *n.*

un furl (un fėrl′), *v.t.*, *v.i.* spread out; shake out; unfold: *unfurl a sail. The flag unfurled.*

un hal lowed (un hal′ōd), *adj.* 1 not made holy; not sacred. 2 wicked; sinful; evil.

u ni corn (yü′nə kôrn), *n.* an imaginary animal like a horse, but having a single long horn in the middle of its forehead, the hind legs of an antelope, and the tail of a lion. [< Latin *unicornis* < *unus* one + *cornu* horn]

u ni son (yü′nə sən, yü′nə zən), *n.* 1 harmonious combination or union; agreement:

hat, āge, fär; let, ēqual, tėrm;
it, īce; hot, ōpen, ôrder;
oil, out; cup, pút, rüle;
ch, child; ng, long; sh, she;
th, thin; ‡H, then; zh, measure;

ə represents *a* in about, *e* in taken, *i* in pencil, *o* in lemon, *u* in circus.

< = from, derived from, taken from.

The feet of marching soldiers move in unison. They spoke in unison. 2 identity in pitch of two or more sounds, tones, etc. 3 combination of tones, melodies, etc., at the same pitch, as performed by different voices or instruments. [< Medieval Latin *unisonus* sounding the same < Latin *unus* one + *sonus* sound]

un kempt (un kempt′), *adj.* 1 not combed: *unkempt hair.* 2 not properly cared for; neglected; untidy. [< *un-¹* + Old English *cembed* combed]

un prec e dent ed (un pres′ə den′tid), *adj.* having no precedent; never done before; never known before: *an event unprecedented in history.* —**un prec′e dent′ed ly,** *adv.*

un rul y (un rü′lē), *adj.* hard to rule or control; not manageable; disorderly: *an unruly horse, an unruly child.* —**un rul′i ness,** *n.*

un scathed (un skā‡Hd′), *adj.* not harmed; uninjured.

un wit ting (un wit′ing), *adj.* not knowing; unaware; unconscious; unintentional. —**un wit′ting ly,** *adv.*

up surge (up′sėrj′), *n.*, *v.*, **-surged, -surging.** —*n.* a rising upward; rise; upturn. —*v.i.* surge upward.

val iant (val′yənt), *adj.* having or showing courage; brave; courageous: *a valiant soldier, a valiant deed.* —*n.* a brave or courageous person. [< Old French *vaillant,* present participle of *valoir* be strong < Latin *valere*] —**val′iant ly,** *adv.* —**val′iant ness,** *n.*

va lid i ty (və lid′ə tē), *n.*, *pl.* **-ties.** 1 truth or soundness: *the validity of an argument.* 2 legal soundness or force; being legally binding. 3 effectiveness.

va por (vā′pər), *n.* 1 moisture in the air that can be seen, such as steam, fog, mist, etc.

va por ous (vā′pər əs), *adj.* 1 full of vapor; misty. 2 like vapor. 3 soon passing; worthless. —**va′por ous ly,** *adv.* —**va′por ous ness,** *n.*

vast (vast), *adj.* very great; immense: *Texas and Alaska cover vast territories. A billion dollars is a vast amount.* —*n.* an immense space. [< Latin *vastus*] —**vast′ly,** *adv.* —**vast′ness,** *n.*

veer (vir), *v.i.* change in direction; shift; turn: *The wind veered to the south. The talk veered to ghosts.* —*v.t.* change the direction of: *We veered our boat.* —*n.* a change of direction; shift; turn. [< Middle French *virer*] —**veer′ing ly,** *adv.*

ven er a ble (ven′ər ə bəl), *adj.* 1 worthy of reverence; deserving respect because of age, character, or importance: *a venerable priest, venerable customs.* 2 designating an archdeacon of the Anglican Church (used as a title of respect). 3 (in the Roman Catholic Church) designating a person recognized as having attained a degree of virtue but not yet recognized as beatified or canonized. —**ven′-er a bly,** *adv.*

ven e ra tion (ven′ə rā′shən), *n.* 1 a feeling of deep respect; reverence: *veneration for learning.* 2 act of venerating: *veneration of one's ancestors.* 3 condition of being venerated.

ve ran da or **ve ran dah** (və ran′də), *n.* a large porch or gallery along one or more sides of a house. [< Hindustani *varandā*]

ver min (vėr′mən), *n. pl.* or *sing.* 1 small animals that are troublesome or destructive. Fleas, lice, bedbugs, rats, and mice are vermin. 2 animals or birds that destroy game, poultry, etc. 3 very unpleasant or vile person or persons. [< Old French < Latin *vermis* worm]

ves tige (ves′tij), *n.* 1 a slight remnant; trace; mark: *Ghost stories are vestiges of a former widespread belief in ghosts.* 2 (in biology) a part, organ, etc., that is no longer fully developed or useful but performed a definite function in an earlier stage of the existence of the same organism or in lower preceding organisms. 3 RARE. footprint or track. [< French < Latin *vestigium* footprint]

vig il (vij′əl), *n.* 1 a staying awake for some purpose; a watching; watch: *All night the mother kept vigil over the sick child.* 2 a night spent in prayer. 3 **vigils,** *pl.* devotions, prayers, services, etc., on the night before a religious festival. 4 the day and night before a solemn religious festival. [< Latin *vigilia* < *vigil* watchful]

vig or ous (vig′ər əs), *adj.* full of vigor; strong and active; energetic; forceful: *wage a vigorous war against disease.* —**vig′-or ous ly,** *adv.* —**vig′or ous ness,** *n.*

vile (vīl), *adj.,* **vil er, vil est.** 1 very bad: *vile weather.* 2 foul; disgusting; obnoxious: *a vile smell.* 3 evil; low; immoral: *vile habits.* 4 poor; mean; lowly: *the vile tasks of the kitchen.* 5 of little worth or account; trifling. [< Latin *vilis* cheap] —**vile′ly,** *adv.* —**vile′ness,** *n.*

vir tu al (vėr′chü əl), *adj.* being something in effect, though not so in name; for all practical purposes; actual; real: *The battle was won with so great a loss of soldiers that it was a virtual defeat.* —**vir′tu al ly,** *adv.*

vir tu o so (vėr′chü ō′sō), *n., pl.* **-sos, -si** (-sē), *adj.* —*n.* 1 person skilled in the techniques of an art, especially in playing a musical instrument. 2 person who has a cultivated appreciation of artistic excellence; connoisseur. 3 student or collector of objects of art, curios, antiquities, etc. —*adj.* showing the artistic qualities and skills of a virtuoso. [< Italian, learned, virtuous]

vi tal (vī′tl), *adj.* 1 of or having to do with life: *Growth and decay are vital processes.* 2 necessary to life: *Eating is a vital function. The heart is a vital organ.* 3 very necessary; very important; essential: *a vital question. Drainage of the nearby swamp was considered vital to the welfare of the community.* 4 causing death, failure, or ruin: *a vital wound, a vital blow to an industry.* 5 full of life and spirit; lively. —*n.* **vitals,** *pl.* **a** parts or organs necessary to life. The brain, heart, lungs, and stomach are vitals. **b** essential parts or features of anything; essentials. [< Latin *vitalis* < *vita* life] —**vi′tal ly,** *adv.*

vix en (vik′sən), *n.* 1 a female fox. 2 a bad-tempered or quarrelsome woman. [Old English *fyxen* < *fox* fox]

vol un tar y (vol′ən ter′ē), *adj., n., pl.* **-tar ies.** —*adj.* 1 done, made, given, etc., of one's own free will; not forced or compelled: *a voluntary contribution.* 2 acting of one's own free will or choice: *voluntary workers.* 3 able to act of one's own free will: *People are voluntary agents.* 4 deliberately intended; done on purpose: *voluntary manslaughter.* 5 controlled by the will: *Talking is voluntary; breathing is only partly so.* —*n.* anything done, made, given, etc., of one's own free will. [< Latin *voluntarius* < *voluntatem* will < *vol-,* stem of *velle* to wish]

vor tex (vôr′teks), *n., pl.* **-tex es** or **-ti ces.** 1 a whirling mass of water, etc., that sucks everything near it toward its center; whirlpool. 2 a violent whirl of air; cyclone; whirlwind. 3 whirl of activity or other situation from which it is hard to escape: *The two nations were unwillingly drawn into the vortex of war.* [< Latin, variant of *vertex.*]

vul gar (vul′gər), *adj.* 1 showing a lack of good breeding, manners, taste, etc.; not refined; coarse; low. 2 of the common people. 3 current or prevalent among people; popular; general: *vulgar prejudices.* 4 in common use; common; ordinary. —*n.* **the vulgar,** the common people. [< Latin *vulgaris* < *vulgus* common people] —**vul′gar ly,** *adv.* —**vul′gar ness,** *n.*

wa ger (wā′jər), *v.t., v.i.* make a bet; bet; gamble. —*n.* 1 something staked on an uncertain event. 2 act of betting; bet. [< Anglo-French *wageure* < Old North French *wage* pledge, wage] —**wa′ger er,** *n.*

war ble (wôr′bəl), *v.,* **-bled, -bling.** —*v.i.* 1 sing with trills, quavers, or melodious turns: *Birds warbled in the trees.* 2 make a sound like that of a bird warbling: *The brook warbled over its rocky bed.* —*v.t.* 1 sing (a song, musical notes, etc.) with trills, quavers, or melodious turns. 2 express in or as if in song. —*n.* 1 a melodious song with trills, quavers, etc. 2 any sound like warbling. 3 act of warbling. [< Old North French *werbler* < *werble* melody; of Germanic origin]

ward room (wôrd′rüm′, wôrd′rùm′), *n.* the living and eating quarters for all the commissioned officers on a warship except the commanding officer.

ware¹ (wer, war), *n.* 1 Usually, **wares,** *pl.* a manufactured thing; article for sale: *The peddler sold his wares cheap.* 2 kind of manufactured thing or article for sale; goods (now chiefly in compounds): *tinware.* 3 pottery; earthenware: *porcelain ware. Delft is a blue-and-white ware.* [Old English *waru*]

ware² (wer, war), *adj., v.,* **wared, war ing.** ARCHAIC. —*adj.* aware. —*v.t., v.i.* look out (for); beware (of). [Old English *wǽr*]

warp (wôrp), *v.t.* 1 bend or twist out of shape: *Age had warped and cracked the floor boards.* 2 mislead; pervert: *Prejudice warps our judgment.* 3 move (a ship, etc.) by ropes fastened to something fixed. 4 arrange (threads or yarn) so as to form a warp. —*v.i.* 1 become bent or twisted out of shape: *The floor has warped so that it is not level.* 2 be misled or perverted. 3 (of a ship) be moved by warping. —*n.* 1 a bend or twist, as in wood that has dried unevenly. 2 distortion of judgment; mental twist; bias. 3 rope fixed at one end and pulled upon to move a ship.

4 the threads running lengthwise in a fabric. The warp is crossed by the woof. [Old English *weorpan* to throw] —**warp′er,** *n.*

war y (wer′ē, war′ē), *adj.,* **war i er, war i est.** 1 on one's guard against danger, deception, etc.: *a wary fox.* 2 cautious or careful: *give wary answers to a stranger's questions.* 3 **wary of,** cautious or careful about: *be wary of driving in heavy traffic.* [< *ware²*]

weft (weft), *n.* 1 the threads running from side to side across a fabric; woof. 2 something woven or spun, as a web. [Old English *weft* < *wefan* to weave]

well (wel), —*v.i.* spring, rise, or gush: *Water wells from a spring beneath the rock.* —*v.t.* send gushing up or pouring forth. [Old English *welle,* stem of *weallan* to boil]

well-ground ed (wel′groun′did), *adj.* 1 based on good grounds; well-founded. 2 thoroughly instructed in the fundamental principles of a subject.

whee dle (hwē′dl), *v.,* **-dled, -dling.** —*v.t.* 1 persuade by flattery, smooth words, caresses, etc.; coax: *The children wheedled their parents into letting them go to the picnic.* 2 get by wheedling: *They finally wheedled the secret out of him.* —*v.i.* use soft, flattering words. [Old English *wǽdlian* beg] —**whee′dler,** *n.* —**whee′dling ly,** *adv.*

whence (hwens), *adv.* 1 from what place; from where: *Whence do you come?* 2 from what place, source, or cause; from what: *Whence has he so much wisdom?* 3 from which: *Let them return to the country whence they came.* —*conj.* from what place, source, or cause: *She told whence she came.* [Middle English *whennes* < Old English *hwanone*]

whet (hwet), *v.,* **whet ted, whet ting,** *n.* —*v.t.* 1 sharpen by rubbing: *whet a knife.* 2 make keen or eager; stimulate: *The smell of food whetted my appetite.* —*n.* 1 act of whetting. 2 something that whets. 3 appetizer. [Old English *hwettan*]

whim si cal (hwim′zə kəl), *adj.* 1 full of whims; having many odd notions or fancies; capricious: *a whimsical person.* 2 of or like a whim or whims; odd; fanciful: *a whimsical expression.* —**whim′si cal ly,** *adv.* —**whim′si cal ness,** *n.*

wield (wēld), *v.t.* hold and use; manage; control: *wield a hammer. A writer wields the pen. The people wield the power in a democracy.* [Old English *wieldan*] —**wield′er,** *n.*

wil y (wī′lē), *adj.,* **wil i er, wil i est.** using wiles or subtle tricks to deceive; crafty; cunning; sly: *a wily thief, a wily fox.* [Middle English *wil* wile; a trick to deceive] —**wil′ly,** *adv.*

wince (wins), *v.,* **winced, winc ing,** *n.* —*v.i.* draw back suddenly; flinch slightly: *I winced when the dentist's drill touched my tooth.* —*n.* act of wincing. [< variant of Old French *guencir;* of Germanic origin]

wist ful (wist′fəl), *adj.* longing; yearning: *A child stood looking with wistful eyes at the toys in the window.* [< obsolete *wist* attentive (< *wistly* intently, of uncertain origin) + *-ful*] —**wist′ful ly,** *adv.* —**wist′ful ness,** *n.*

with er (wiᴛʜ′ər), *v.i., v.t.* 1 lose or cause to lose freshness, vigor, etc.; dry up; shrivel: *The grass withered in the hot sun. Age had withered the old woman's face.* 2 feel or cause to feel ashamed or confused: *wither at the thought of a public rebuke, be withered by a scornful look.* [Middle English *wideren,* variant of *wederen* to weather]

with ers (wiᴛʜ′ərz), *n.pl.* the highest part of a horse's or other animal's back, between the shoulder blades. [origin uncertain] wolf (wùlf), *n., pl.* wolves, *v.* —*n.* 1 either of two species of carnivorous wild mammals of the dog family, with a long muzzle, high, pointed ears, and a bushy tail. Wolves usually hunt in packs and are sometimes destructive to livestock. 2 any of several similar mammals. 3 a cruel, greedy person. 4 SLANG. man who flirts with or tries to entice women. 5 **cry wolf,** give a false alarm. 6 **keep the wolf from the door,** keep safe from hunger or poverty. 7 **wolf in sheep's clothing,** person who hides harmful intentions or an evil character beneath an innocent or friendly exterior. —*v.t.* eat greedily: *The starving man wolfed down the food.* [Old English *wulf*] —**wolf′like′,** *adj.*

won der ment (wun′dər mənt), *n.* 1 wonder; surprise. 2 object of wonder.

won drous (wun′drəs), *adj.* wonderful. —*adv.* wonderfully. —**won′drous ly,** *adv.* —**won′drous ness,** *n.*

wraith (rāth), *n.* 1 ghost of a person seen before or soon after his death. 2 specter; ghost. [origin uncertain]

wrench (rench), *n.* 1 a violent twist or twisting pull: *The knob broke off when he gave it a sudden wrench.* 2 injury caused by twisting. 3 grief; pain: *It was a wrench to leave the old home.* 4 distortion of the original or proper meaning, interpretation, etc. 5 tool for turning nuts, bolts, etc. —*v.t.* 1 twist or pull violently: *The policeman wrenched the gun out of the man's hand.* 2 injure by twisting: *She wrenched her back*

in falling from the horse. 3 distress or pain greatly. 4 twist the meaning of. —*v.i.* pull or tug at something with a twist or turn. [Old English *wrencan* to twist]

wretch (rech), *n.* 1 a very unfortunate or unhappy person. 2 a very bad person. [Old English *wrecca* exile]

writhe (rīFH), *v.,* **writhed, writh ing.** —*v.i.* 1 twist and turn; twist about: *writhe with pain. The snake writhed along the branch.* 2 suffer mentally; be very uncomfortable. —*v.t.* twist or bend (something). [Old English *wrīthan*]

wroth (rôth, roth), *adj.* angry. [Old English *wrāth*]

wrought (rôt), *v.* ARCHAIC. a pt. and a pp. of **work.** —*adj.* 1 made: *The gate was wrought with great skill.* 2 formed with care; not rough or crude. 3 manufactured or treated; not in a raw state. 4 (of metals or metalwork) formed by hammering.

-y¹, *suffix forming adjectives chiefly from nouns.* 1 full of ____: *Bumpy = full of bumps.* 2 containing ____: *Salty = containing salt.* 3 having ____: *Cloudy = having clouds.* 4 characterized by ____: *Funny = characterized by fun.* 5 somewhat ____: *Chilly = somewhat chill.* 6 inclined to ____: *Sleepy = inclined to sleep.* 7 resembling or suggesting ____: *Sugary = resembling sugar.* 8 In certain words, such as *paly, steepy, stilly,*

yaw

hat, āge, fär; let, ēqual, tėrm; it, īce; hot, ōpen, ôrder; oil, out; cup, pùt, rüle; ch, child; ng, long; sh, she; th, thin; ᴛʜ, then; zh, measure;

ə represents *a* in about, *e* in taken, *i* in pencil, *o* in lemon, *u* in circus.

< = from, derived from, taken from.

vasty, the addition of *y* does not change the meaning. [Old English *-ig*]

-y², *suffix forming nouns from other nouns.* 1 small ____: *Dolly = a small doll.* 2 dear ____: *Daddy = dear dad.* [Middle English]

-y³, *suffix forming nouns from adjectives, nouns, and verbs.* 1 ____ condition or quality: *Jealousy = a jealous condition or quality.* 2 condition or quality of being ____: *Victory = condition or quality of being a victor.* 3 act or activity of ____ing: *Delivery = act of delivering.* [< Old French *-ie* < Latin *-ia* < Greek]

yaw (yô), *v.i.* 1 turn from a straight course; go unsteadily. 2 (of an aircraft) turn from a straight course by a motion about its vertical axis. —*n.* movement from a straight course. [origin uncertain]

589

Index of Extensions:

Reading: 113, 356, 412.
Speaking: 71, 137, 185, 232, 356, 365, 395, 401, 458,
              462, 489, 491, 495.
Writing: 8, 28, 37, 108, 162, 165, 174, 195, 205, 356,
              367, 381, 387, 441, 442, 453, 454, 459, 479,
              480, 497, 525.

Index of Vocabulary Exercises:

Context: 9, 59, 108, 162, 185, 215, 260, 292, 365, 443,
                479.
Structure: 23, 59, 152, 162, 260, 271, 320, 395, 426,
                489.
Pronunciation: 28, 59, 162, 174, 260, 395, 495.
Dictionary: 28, 59, 79, 93, 162, 260, 292, 320, 342, 379,
                395, 443, 455, 495.

Index of Authors and Titles

Adams, Franklin P.; *The Rich Man*, 543
Adventures of Ulysses, The, 276
after any sunset, 463
Ancient Gesture, An, 357
Anderson, Sherwood; *Stolen Day*, 60
Annixter, Paul; *Last Cover*, 72
Apparently with No Surprise, 457
Apprentice, The (excerpt), 536
Asimov, Isaac; *Key Item*, 428

Bagnold, Enid; from *National Velvet*, 532
Bahe, Liz Sohappy; *Farewell*, 464
Baroque Marble, The, 128
Beauty Is Truth, 168
Beetle Bemused, 551
Being Somebody, 224
Between Two Cultures (Notes and Comments), 167
Birdman, The, 19

Boles, Paul Darcy; *A Few Notes About the Arabian Oryx*, 468
Broken Sky, 544
Bruce, Mary Celinia; *after any sunset*, 463
Buck, Pearl S.; *The Old Demon*, 262
Builders, The, 442
Business, 437

Campers at Kitty Hawk, The, 216
Carnegie Hero Fund, The (Notes and Comments), 206
Carroll, Ellison; *Teacher, Teacher*, 498
Carroll, Lewis; *Jabberwocky*, 366
Caught in a Grip of Stone, 196
Chipmunk's Day, The, 459
Ciardi, John; *Speed Adjustments*, 10
Circuit, The, 12
Clifton, Lucille; *in the inner city*, 175
Cole, William; *What Could It Be?*, 534

Conjurer's Revenge, The, 122
Contraption, The, 438
Crawford, Shirley; *The River Took My Sister*, 490
Cruz, Victor Hernández; *Business*, 437
Cullen, Countee; *Under the Mistletoe*, 449
Cummings, E. E.; *old age sticks*, 29; *who knows if the moon's*, 447

Demon of the Gibbet, The, 440
Dickinson, Emily; *I'm Nobody*, 138; *Apparently with No Surprise*, 457
Dos Passos, John; *The Campers at Kitty Hawk*, 216

Eliot, T. S.; *Macavity: The Mystery Cat*, 380

Emergency at Sea (Notes and Comments), 260
English Borrowings from Greek (Notes and Comments), 332
Enright, Elizabeth; *Nancy,* 140
Evslin, Bernard; *The Adventures of Ulysses,* 276

Fallen Angel, The, 402
Farewell, 464
Few Notes About the Arabian Oryx, A, 468
Fisher, Dorothy Canfield; from *The Apprentice,* 536
For an Old Man, 559
Forecast, The, 454
Foreign Student, 538
Fox and the Grapes, The, 80
Francis, Robert; *While I Slept,* 481
Frost, Robert; *The Pasture,* 458; *A Time to Talk,* 497

Gentleman of Río en Medio, 492
Get That Straight, 390
Gift, The, 38
Giovanni, Nikki; *Kidnap Poem,* 434
Glanville, Brian; *Win or Lose,* 114
Glossary of Jabberwocky Terms (Notes and Comments), 367
Goldstone, Herbert; *Virtuoso,* 396
Guest, Anna; *Beauty Is Truth,* 168

Haircut, A, 110
Hardison, O. B., Jr.; *To a Dead Goldfish,* 436
Harriet Tubman (excerpt), 207
Hay, Sara Henderson; *The Builders,* 442
Holman, Felice; *Who Am I?,* 491
Hugo, Leon; *My Father and the Hippopotamus,* 482
Hummingbird That Lived Through Winter, The, 527
Hundredth Dove, The, 362
Hunger, 153
Hunt, Evelyn Tooley; *Mama Is a Sunrise,* 480
Hunter, Evan; *The Fallen Angel,* 402
Hunter, The, 435

I Am Through, 496
Identity, 186
If Dolphins Could Talk, What Would They Say? (Notes and Comments), 109
I Know That Feeling, 450
I'll Give You Law, 24
I'm Nobody, 138
in the inner city, 175
It Doesn't Have to Rhyme (Notes and

Comments), 444
It Says a Lot in a Little (Notes and Comments), 456

Jabberwocky, 366
Jaffe, Dan; *The Forecast,* 454
Jarrell, Randall; *The Chipmunk's Day,* 459
Jiménez, Francisco; *The Circuit,* 12; *The Story Behind the Story* (Notes and Comments), 17
Johnson, Dorothy; *A Time of Greatness,* 81

Kantor, MacKinlay; *A Man Who Had No Eyes,* 68
Key Item, 428
Kidnap Poem, 434
Kipling, Rudyard; *Rikki-tikki-tavi,* 368; *The White Seal's Lullaby,* 552

Last Cover, 72
Leacock, Stephen; *The Conjurer's Revenge,* 122
Let Me Hear You Whisper, 96
Lister, R. P.; *Beetle Bemused,* 551
Longfellow, Henry Wadsworth; from *The Wreck of the Hesperus,* 552
Loud Sneer for Our Feathered Friends, A, 157

Macavity: The Mystery Cat, 380
Mama Is a Sunrise, 480
Man Who Had No Eyes, A, 68
Markowitz, Jack; *Caught in a Grip of Stone,* 196
McKenney, Ruth; *A Loud Sneer for Our Feathered Friends,* 157
McLaren, Floris Clark; *For an Old Man,* 559
Merriam, Eve; *Metaphor,* 544; *Simile: Willow and Ginko,* 555
Metaphor, 544
Millay, Edna St. Vincent; *An Ancient Gesture,* 357
Minnie Morse, 550
Mirror of Ice, 30
Momaday, N. Scott; *Trees and Evening Sky,* 553
Monreal, David Nava; *Woodpeckers in Summer Frolic,* 460
Monsters Are Due on Maple Street, The, 413
Moore, Marianne; *The Fox and the Grapes,* 80
Mori, Toshio; *Say It with Flowers,* 2
Morrison, Lillian; *The Sidewalk Racer,* 18
Moving Camp Too Far, 166

Munro, H. H. (Saki); *The Storyteller,* 382
Murray, Pauli; *Words,* 448
My Father and the Hippopotamus, 482
My True Name, 176

Nakata, I. S.; *A Haircut,* 110
Nancy, 140
Nash, Ogden; *The Hunter,* 435; from *To a Small Boy Standing on My Shoes While I Am Wearing Them,* 560
National Velvet (excerpt), 532
Noboa, Julio, Jr.; *Identity,* 186
Nobody's Better Off Dead, 272
Nomad Harvesters, The, 188
Northsun, Nila; *Moving Camp Too Far,* 166

O'Brien, Fitz-James; *The Demon of the Gibbet,* 440
old age sticks, 29
Old Demon, The, 262
Ortiz, Simon; *I Know That Feeling,* 450

Parker, Dorothy; *Penelope,* 359
Parmenter, Ross; *Rain,* 461
Pasture, The, 458
Penelope, 359
Petry, Ann; from *Harriet Tubman,* 207
Pharmacist's Mate, The, 233
Picon, Molly; *I'll Give You Law,* 24
Portrait, 451
Proulx, E. A.; *The Baroque Marble,* 128

Questions Put to a Playwright (Notes and Comments), 427

Rain, 461
Reynolds, Quentin; *Nobody's Better Off Dead,* 272
Rich Man, The, 543
Rikki-tikki-tavi, 368
River Took My Sister, The, 490
Robinson, Barbara B.; *Foreign Student,* 538
Rodgers, Carolyn; *Portrait,* 451
Roll of Thunder, Hear My Cry (excerpt), 540
Rutsala, Vern; *Visits,* 445

Sabin, Francene; *Being Somebody,* 224
Saki (see **Munro, H. H.**)
Sandburg, Carl; *Street Window,* 452; *Broken Sky,* 544

Sandoz, Mari; *The Birdman*, 19
Sarah Cynthia Sylvia Stout Would Not Take the Garbage Out, 163
Saroyan, William; *The Hummingbird That Lived Through Winter*, 527
Say It with Flowers, 2
Schisgall, Oscar; *Take Over, Bos'n*, 546
Schulberg, Budd; *The Pharmacist's Mate*, 233
Sedillo, Juan A. A.; *Gentleman of Río en Medio*, 492
Serling, Rod; *The Monsters Are Due on Maple Street*, 413
Sidewalk Racer, The, 18
Silverstein, Shel; *Sarah Cynthia Sylvia Stout Would Not Take the Garbage Out*, 163; *Where the Sidewalk Ends*, 388
Simile: Willow and Ginkgo, 555
Song of the Sky Loom, 462
Speed Adjustments, 10
Starbird, Kaye; *Minnie Morse*, 550
Steinbeck, John; *The Gift*, 38
Stephens, James; *Washed in Silver*, 542
Stevenson, Robert Louis; from *The Wind*, 535
Stolen Day, 60
Story Behind the Story, The (Notes and Comments), 17
Storyteller, The, 382
Strange Owl; *Where the Girl Saved Her Brother*, 192
Street Window, 452
Swenson, May; *The Contraption*, 438

Take Over, Bos'n, 546
Taylor, Mildred; from *Roll of Thunder, Hear My Cry*, 540
Teacher, Teacher, 498
Tewa Indian; *Song of the Sky Loom*, 462
Time of Greatness, A, 81
Time to Talk, A, 497
To a Dead Goldfish, 436
To a Small Boy Standing on My Shoes While I Am Wearing Them (excerpt), 560
Too "Modern" for Her Time (Notes and Comments), 139
Trai, Nguyen; *I Am Through*, 496
Trees and Evening Sky, 553
Two Songs, 94

Ulibarri, Sabine; *Get That Straight*, 390
Uncovering the Real Troy (Notes and Comments), 284
Under the Mistletoe, 449
Uvavnuk; *Two Songs*, 94

Virtuoso, 396
Visits, 445

Washed in Silver, 542
Welch, Marie de L.; *The Nomad Harvesters*, 188
Weller, George; *Emergency at Sea* (Notes and Comments), 260
What Could It Be?, 534
Where the Girl Saved Her Brother, 192
Where the Sidewalk Ends, 388
While I Slept, 481
White Seal's Lullaby, The, 552
Who Am I?, 491
who knows if the moon's, 447
Wind, The (excerpt), 535
Win or Lose, 114
Woodpeckers in Summer Frolic, 460
Words, 448
Wreck of the Hesperus, The (excerpt), 552
Wright, Gary; *Mirror of Ice*, 30
Wright, Richard; *Hunger*, 153

Yep, Laurence; *My True Name*, 176
Yolen, Jane; *The Hundredth Dove*, 362
You're Imagining Things (Notes and Comments), 389

Zindel, Paul; *Let Me Hear You Whisper*, 96